MAN AND THE ENVIRONMENT

An Introduction to
Human Ecology and Evolution

MAN AND THE ENVIRONMENT

An Introduction to Human Ecology and Evolution

Arthur S. Boughey
Department of Population and Environmental Biology
University of California, Irvine

THE MACMILLAN COMPANY · NEW YORK
COLLIER-MACMILLAN LIMITED · LONDON

Printed in the United States of America

THE MACMILLAN COMPANY
866 THIRD AVENUE, NEW YORK, NEW YORK 10022

COLLIER-MACMILLAN CANADA, LTD., TORONTO, ONTARIO

Library of Congress catalog card number: 77–126185

First Printing

Preface

Human ecology is a young and yet an old science. As with all disciplines which are generated from the union of several older traditions, the earliest publications were mostly anthologies. Increasing numbers of such volumes are now appearing. They contain contributions gleaned from an extensive coverage of both specialist and general works and well illustrate the still diffuse nature of studies in human ecology. Some will therefore consider the preparation of a comprehensive text on human ecology by a single author at the present time presumptuous. Nevertheless, spontaneous but parallel developments in the social sciences, engineering, and biology demand that the effort to integrate the new science of human ecology be made.

These developments can be summarized as follows. First, the social scientists have turned from the introspection and qualitative theorizing which long dominated their thought to an emphasis on quantitative studies of populations and communities. Second, engineers, who generally regard themselves as a "service" group, have always understood that although many of the present environmental crises can be provided with engineering solutions, they must seek elsewhere for decisions on economic policies and political issues. Third, medical biologists have tended to emphasize the morphology, biochemistry, physiology, and behavior of the individual, while nonmedical biologists passed into a phase of experimental investigation which usually proscribed the use of *Homo sapiens* as an experimental animal. All biologists, whatever their particular specialty, have now realized the need to set aside, for the time being at least, studies on other organisms and concentrate on human populations.

Although these converging interests of the social, biological, and medical sciences, together with engineering, represent largely independent incursions into human ecology, it is apparent that they must meet on some common ground. The rational focus for these varied interests is on the fundamental ecological concept of the *ecosystem*. Societies of *Homo sapiens*, however affluent and sophisticated, are tied inescapably to the micro- and macroecosystems of this planet. They are subject to the same ecological laws that govern the performance and behavior of the other populations included within these ecosystems. The perilous situation of all contemporary ecosystems provides the only present pretext for the single-handed preparation of a unified text on human ecology.

The dilemma confronting the author of such a work has been very eloquently expressed by Gordon Orians in rationalizing his single-handed survey of the whole discipline of biology. He presents the philosophy of what Konrad Lorenz has termed the "aha" experience, which epitomizes what is basically the only valid *raison d'être* for the university professor. The "aha" situation arises when a previously disordered sequence of circumstances is suddenly perceived as falling into a logical relationship. It has to be invoked in each one of us separately. The experienced pedagogue can set the scene that will trigger the response, but cannot impose it.

A text such as this, therefore, contains material extracted—with due permission and acknowledgment—from original sources. It is designed to set the scene for Lorenz's "aha" response. An appropriate simile is the "closed" and "open" call system described in these pages. A presentation of facts as such, however accurate and up to date, is forever a "closed" system. Further stimulation is required before these uncoordinated facts come to be arranged into integrated sets of *new* facts, which thereby converts this previously closed system to an *open* one. Such an *open* system will go far beyond these pages if this text succeeds in triggering a response to relationships beyond those to which attention has actually been drawn.

This work is designed for use as an introductory text in human ecology or as a supplement for related courses. Preferably, the reader should have some basic understanding of elementary biology from either a high school or a college course experience. Key references are provided for further reading in the bibliographical material at the end of each chapter, and a glossary explains the usage of such expressions as are readily definable. The appendices contain information too exhaustive to incorporate in the text.

In order to emphasize the distinction between much that has to be speculation in this text and what is currently accepted theory, the specialist references are rather extensive. Nevertheless, they should not be taken as an exhaustive coverage of particular aspects of human ecology. Often only the most recent of a series of publications can be cited. More complete bibliographical lists are to be found in recent readings collections.

An introductory text must have some coherent and developing story. To me, and I hope to the reader, this ecological account of the origins and final emergence of our urban technocracy is fascinating, and it is very relevant. It is high time that we looked critically and dispassionately at ourselves, our nature, and our behavior as it has come to us from the past, at our present relations with our environment and with one another, and at our future prospects for survival in the universe which we are now with a few first hesitant steps finally beginning to explore.

A. S. B.

Contents

Introduction 1

The term *human ecology* is not yet so well understood and established in contemporary idiom that it requires no explanation or definition. Various alternative terms, usually involving the words "population" and "environment," are still current, and their use tends to cause some confusion. The discipline of ecology itself—the study of populations and communities relative to one another and to their environment—has only recently emerged as a distinct science. It is sometimes alternatively and even more simply and briefly described as the study of ecosystems. From any such basic definition of the parental science it is possible to interpolate and define human ecology as the study of the development and interactions of human societies with one another and with their environment.

THE PURPOSE OF HUMAN ECOLOGY

Traditionally, human ecology has been defined and approached in a slightly different manner. Human societies have amassed, particularly over the last few millennia, a unique, complex, and immense store of rituals. Two groups within our culture, the humanists and the social scientists, have over the years emerged as specialists, the one to record, the other to study these rituals. These groups have gradually become even further specialized, and others have appeared in such areas as the health sciences, engineering, agriculture, forestry, and the earth sciences. The concerns of the latter are with technical applications of cultural rituals to human societies, or, in terms which will be explained later, with the production of artifacts based on mentifact developments.

Insofar as the ecologist relates to these various groups in his studies of human populations, it is with particular reference to the evolution of human form and behavior, and to the use and abuse of the resources of the ecosystems which our cultures have learned to exploit.

To this holistic concept of the scope of human ecology has been added an urgent demand for examination of this inexorable process of resource exploitation. Within the past 20 years it has become apparent that we have produced too many people, too many pollutants, too much waste, too many poisons, too much stress. At the same time we have too little food, shelter, education, health, and understanding. We are squandering our global resources of fossil fuels, mineral ores, productive lands, wildlife, air, water, landscape, wilderness, and biotic diversity. Disaster looms on every horizon, both for our own population and for the ecosystems we occupy.

Ecological studies on the early history of our ancestral societies show that we were not always so wantonly destructive of natural systems. As will be discussed later, the evidence available to us from fossil forms, such as it is, and from comparative studies of contemporary but presumably ancient rituals, suggests the previous existence of regulatory feedback mechanisms which prevented our overexploitation of irreplaceable resources.

The study of human ecology, as it is most commonly understood by ecologists, therefore includes both a backward view of these early ecosystems in which human forms played an integral but less destructive role, and a forward look necessitating an urgent consideration of the catastrophic effects of this latest human intrusion into contemporary environments.

We still have much to learn about ourselves. We are beginning to trace our primate origins and relate these to our biochemical reactions and behavioral patterns. Yet we have hardly begun to understand how far we are still conditioned by primate behavior, or to what extent our species has been subjected to group selection favoring social as opposed to individual survival. We must also consider the degree to which we still need social identity, social hierarchies, competition, and continuing selective adaptation.

Shepard (1967), in a critical review of current progress in human ecology, quotes an appropriate passage from Chase (1949): "The difference between primitive and civilized mentality is not absolute, there is no chasm between them . . . we live in the same world as the savages. Our deepest experience, needs, and aspirations are the same, as surely as the crucial biological and psychic transitions occur in the life of every human being and force culture to take account of them in aesthetic forms." Shepard nevertheless takes a somewhat restricted view of human ecology, which he considers will never be more than a troika discipline comprising individual physiological studies, general landscape and ecosystem ecology, and exploratory investigations of human nature as a feedback system. The approach followed in this text goes appreciably further and attempts to achieve both a wider and a deeper role for human ecology, while recognizing that Chase's dictum concerning the primitive and the savage still holds true.

Our power is now absolute. We are the only animal species possessed of a cultural apparatus which enables us to escape from the confines of one unique ecological niche, and indeed even from the bounds of this planet. Cultural control of ourselves and our microenvironment permits us to adjust readily to the special requirements of any ecological niche. There is thus no living heterotroph with which we could not compete. We have already annihilated or drastically reduced in number and dispersal area many carnivores, both large and small; we have similarly eliminated many autotrophs.

The latest environmental crises are not always the result of such direct or indirect competitive interaction; The pathways of interference are sometimes more tenuous, not always completely clarified. Human society has become so complex that the short-term gains of one group may be allowed to override the long-term necessity for all which is not even perceived, let alone taken into consideration (Holling, 1969).

Human ecology cannot *resolve* such problems. A text such as this can only attempt to outline them, explore their possible origins, and indicate the causal relationships which may provide a more complete understanding of the technical problems for which solutions must rapidly be found, if we and our descendants are to continue to survive on this planet.

Only with the development of the ecosystem concept in ecology was it realized that populations, communities, and ecosystems had to be studied together, the so-called *holistic approach* (Smuts, 1926). Fortunately this realization was soon followed by an appreciation that the techniques of systems analysis could be applied to such studies. Previously the experimental ecologist carefully isolated one population, factor, or interaction while he manipulated it and held everything else steady (Figure 1–4). But it is now clear that unmanipulated populations, communities, and ecosystems can be investigated, provided their operation is broken down into very simple steps, reproducible by iterative logical procedures in computer simulation models. How one leading proponent of such a systems approach represents this schematically is shown in Figure 1–1.

The more ecosystems came to be studied with this holistic approach, the more ecologists realized that the effect of human occupation was all-pervasive (Odum, 1969). There was no population, community, or ecosystem left on earth completely independent of the effects of human cultural behavior. Now this influence has begun to spread beyond the globe to our planetary system and even to the universe itself.

This text is therefore a generalized and basic account which attempts to explain the complementary development of human populations and the earth's ecosystems, the interaction between them, the current state of imbalance which has become suddenly manifest through many disturbing environmental occurrences, and the courses of action which remain open to us if ultimate disaster is to be avoided.

Many human societies are again populated by a majority of young people, as all have been in their initial growth stages. In a world which

Plate 1. *An undisturbed ecosystem* in the Wasatch Mountains of Utah. Occasional fires interacting with other environmental factors produce a mosaic of communities dominated by coniferous trees, deciduous trees, and sagebrush. Light grazing of this unfenced range by cattle does not radically change the steady-state relationship of these communities.

boasts of democracy, the part this youth is allowed to play, and the extent of total resources to which young people are presently permitted access, can only be described as limited (Mead, 1969). If human society has any meaning at all, it is to ensure the persistence under more favorable conditions of each new generation. Despite this, it is always contemporary youth who have to bear the brunt of society's mistakes and failures; it is they who must take actions we ourselves were not prepared to take.

The rallying cry of "law and order" sometimes has been disparaged as the resort of the "haves" when dealing with the "have nots," the old when confronting the young. We must have peace if our society is to remedy in time its many defects; but it has to be an acceptable peace, the result of an agreed allocation of the earth's power and resources, not the adjudication

Plate 2. *Insertion of a homestead* into the type of ecosystem illustrated in Plate 1 causes only local disturbance to its communities. The meadows along the valley bottoms by the stream are mown for hay, the winter feed of the beef cattle. Electricity or oil is not used for heating because of the relative cheapness and availability of timber.

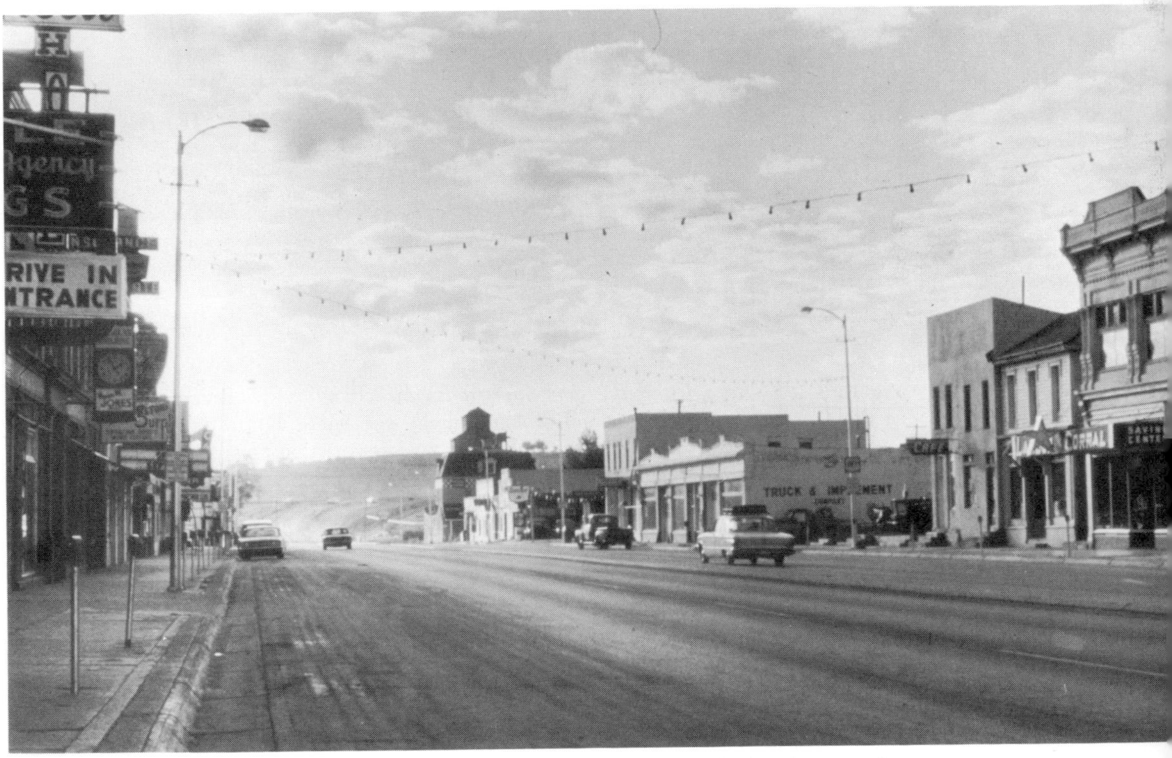

Plate 3. *Main Street, U.S.A.* The urban ecosystem is usually completely alien to the communities of the natural ecosystems of the region. Although this small town in Wyoming lies close to the site of the homestead illustrated in Plate 2, its communities and its microenvironments are almost entirely different.

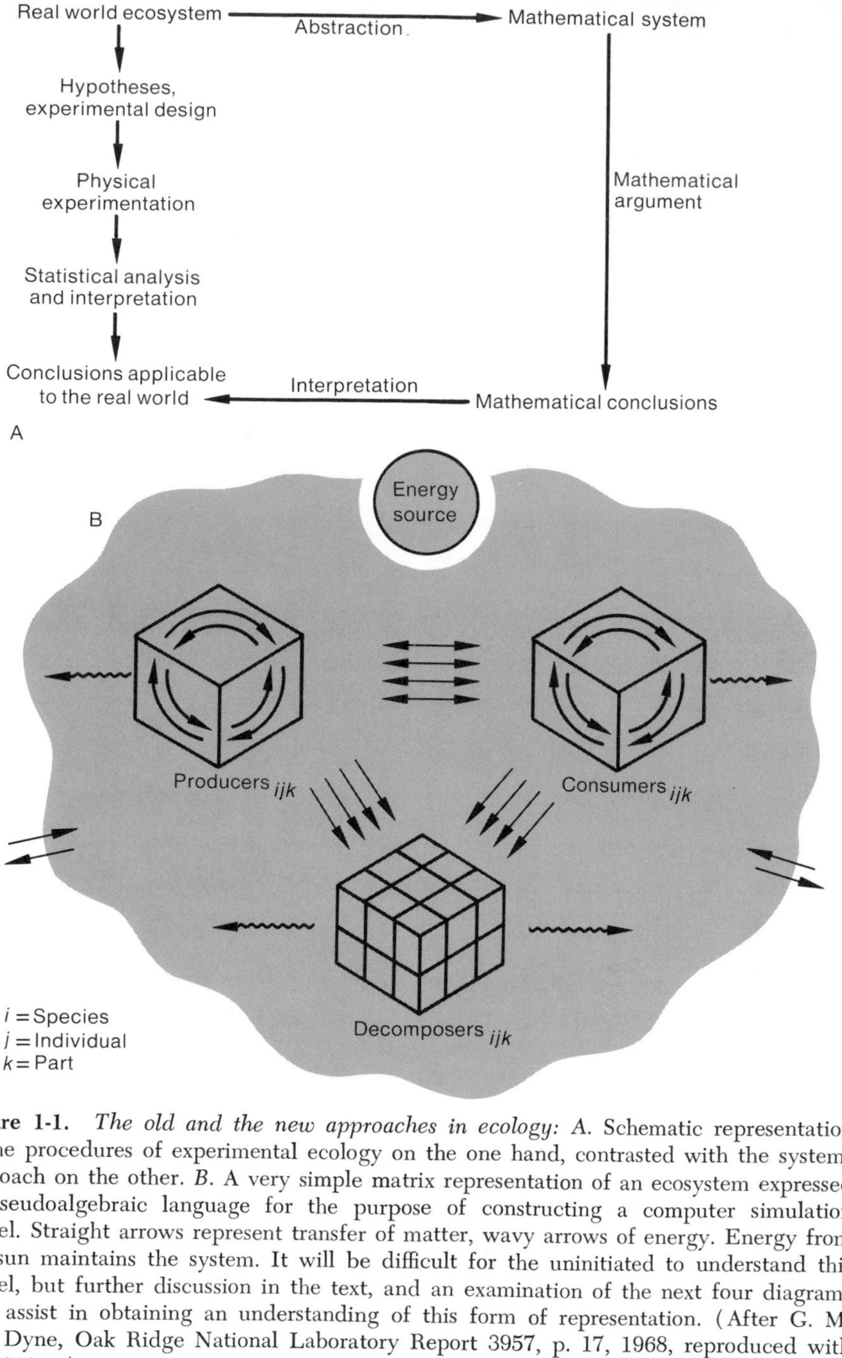

Figure 1-1. *The old and the new approaches in ecology: A.* Schematic representation of the procedures of experimental ecology on the one hand, contrasted with the systems approach on the other. *B.* A very simple matrix representation of an ecosystem expressed in pseudoalgebraic language for the purpose of constructing a computer simulation model. Straight arrows represent transfer of matter, wavy arrows of energy. Energy from the sun maintains the system. It will be difficult for the uninitiated to understand this model, but further discussion in the text, and an examination of the next four diagrams may assist in obtaining an understanding of this form of representation. (After G. M. Van Dyne, Oak Ridge National Laboratory Report 3957, p. 17, 1968, reproduced with permission.)

of a past generation as to what may be secured from life by another. A move to restore this ecological imbalance has recently been taken in Britain, where the legal age for obtaining one's majority has been reduced to 18 years. Such proposals have not been so favorably received this side of the Atlantic.

Many human ecologists today find themselves trapped by their own reflections into passing moral judgments which trespass onto the confines of other disciplines, in this instance philosophy and political science. This will also be apparent from many of the references which are provided at the end of every chapter in this text. Human ecologists have, for the time being at least, had to become prophets—if not jeremiahs and prophets of doom, at least prophets of dire disaster—unless specific political decisions are made to legislate against particular eventualities. These ecological prophets are exasperated by an unwillingness to listen on the part of much of our society. The glossy magazines are full of the good life and advertisements for swimming pools, second homes, dune buggies, camping trailers, sports tackle, and world cruises. The press features articles on the four-day week and the use of greater leisure. A college education for all is forecast before many decades have passed. "Leisure Worlds" and similar retirement communities set eligibility for senior citizenship at 52 years of age or even less, little more than 20 years out of graduate school.

The activist human ecologist striving to establish some prerequisites for the achievement of these utopias tends to be brushed aside by vested interests and lobbyist concerns of one faction or another. When he seeks government support or action, he is confronted by a formidable array of diversification in administrative responsibilities. The list of organizations tabulated in Appendix I indicates the range of departments a human ecologist might consider as possibly involved in such an issue as the destruction of a natural ecosystem like an estuary.

It has been noted in the preface that a basic knowledge of biology is assumed for the purposes of this text, and this would include some ecology. However, in view of the central importance of the *ecosystem concept* in human ecology, it appears advisable to review briefly its salient features.

THE ECOSYSTEM CONCEPT

Living organisms on this planet do not exist under natural conditions in physical and biological isolation. There is an interplay both between the various populations themselves, and with the physical and chemical components of the environment. The functional system which results from this interplay is known as an *ecosystem.* In terms of energetics, i.e., energy transfer, the ecosystem is a living complex of interlocking processes characterized by many cause-effect pathways. This complex of interactions provides feedback mechanisms which modify the rate of growth and development of the population of living organisms involved. The feedback mechanisms tend always to produce a steady state or *homeostasis* in the system as a whole.

There are therefore two basic elements in a given ecosystem, the living or *biotic* one and a nonliving or *abiotic* one. Our whole planet may be regarded as a single ecosystem; its biotic components are the living populations of plants, animals, and microbes. These are sometimes described as forming the *biosphere.* By contrast, the abiotic components are the atmosphere, the oxygen, carbon dioxide, water vapor and other gases and suspended particles of the air, together with the various geological, chemical, and physical features of sea and land which comprise the totality of habitats on this globe—the *ecosphere* (Cole, 1958).

Although we can regard the ecosphere of our planet as a single ecosystem, and for some purposes it is most convenient to do so—as when considering atmospheric or water pollution—for many other purposes it is preferable to imagine a considerably less all-embracing unit. At the opposite extreme, a single rain puddle can be regarded as an ecosystem, one which could indeed be vital in particular studies on human ecology. For example, among the populations of such a microecosystem could develop larval stages of a vector of a disease with a high incidence in adjoining human populations.

Whatever size is taken for an ecosystem, the decision is always based on convenience. The ecosystem is a *concept* applied to a somewhat arbitrary series of functions of the world about us. This is not in fact made up of an interlocked mosaic of ecosystems with clearly defined borders, awaiting only a scientific determination of their precise limits. We may be able to recognize certain topographical boundaries like rivers, mountain ranges, or oceans, or some physical barrier such as a thermocline, cultivation clearing, or fire burn as providing a discrete outline to an ecosystem which we are describing. However we must not ignore the fact that there is a continuous gradation throughout the world, rather than a jigsaw pattern of naturally defined units.

Ecosystem Organization

An ecosystem, as we define it, must contain the following elements:

1. Abiotic environment
2. Population of autotrophic and/or heterotrophic organisms
3. Energy output and utilization
4. Nutrient input and/or cycling

In Figure 1–2 these elements are related to one another schematically. A majority of naturally occurring ecosystems utilize solar radiation as their energy source; these are autotrophic or autotroph-based ecosystems. An energy input in the form of solar radiation is not, however, an essential feature of a self-perpetuating ecosystem. More especially in complex ecosystems there are various subsidiary ecosystems which utilize energy obtained from organic matter, for example, the system which develops on cow dung in a pasture. The deep layers of the sea provide another example, for they receive no radiant energy. A pond in an evergreen forest may receive very little sunlight, deriving its energy from forest detritus which blows or falls into it. Such decomposer, heterotrophic, or detritus-based ecosystems

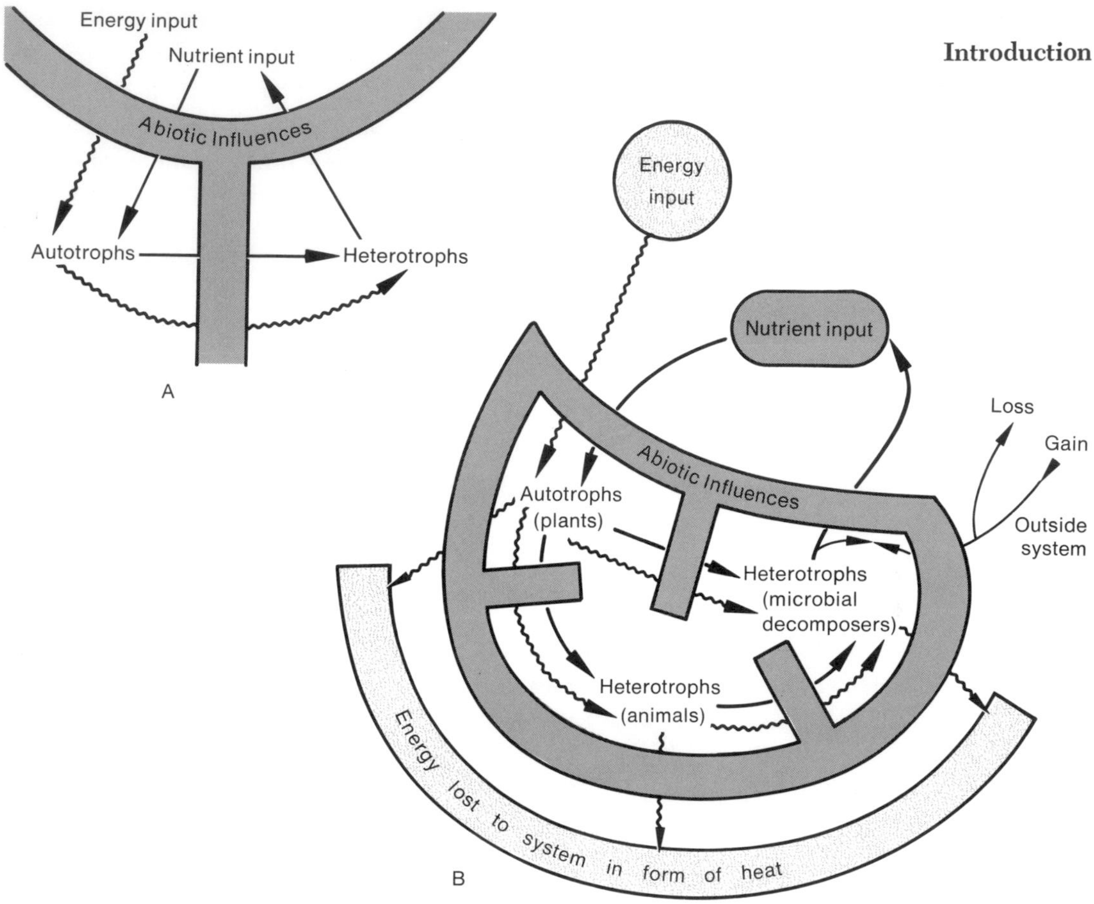

Figure 1-2. *Representations of ecosystem fundamentals: A.* The flow of energy and nutrients between the biotic and abiotic components of a schematic elemental self-sustaining ecosystem. This oversimplifies any real system by ignoring *biotic* influences on living populations and by disregarding energy and nutrient exchanges across the external boundaries of the system. *B.* A slightly more complicated schematic ecosystem allows for external energy and nutrient exchange, but still takes no account of biotic influences. These latter are especially vital when considering, first, population size regulation, second, evolutionary relationships.

are supplied with chemical energy obtained from the "rain" of organic matter which continuously falls or settles from the outside.

In the case of the autotrophic ecosystems which utilize radiant solar energy, this energy is absorbed into the ecosystem and transformed by the group of organisms collectively known as *producers.* In natural ecosystems these are represented mainly by green plants. When the ecosystem is self-perpetuating, the autotrophs or producers must be associated with another element, the heterotrophic *reducers* or *decomposers.* These will break down the organic production or *biomass* of the consumer populations and will *recycle* back into the system nutrients necessary for the growth of the producers. The decomposers are normally various *saprobes,* that is microbial populations generally specifically related to some particular reaction in the total process of organic decomposition.

Another heterotrophic element is also present in most ecosystems, namely, the *consumers,* which remove a portion of the biomass built up by the activities of the producers. These are usually animal populations. In a mature or climax situation it is believed that ten times as much energy is circulating through the subsidiary decomposer ecosystems as through the producer-consumer pathways.

The consumers themselves are generally a complex system of *primary consumers* or herbivores, and *secondary consumers* or carnivores. The latter are commonly divided into primary carnivores, with secondary carnivores feeding on these, and sometimes third- and even fourth-level carnivores. The last consumer level of an ecosystem comprises the *top carnivores.* Each of these consumer levels, together with those represented by producer and decomposer populations, is known as a *trophic level* (Figure 1–3).

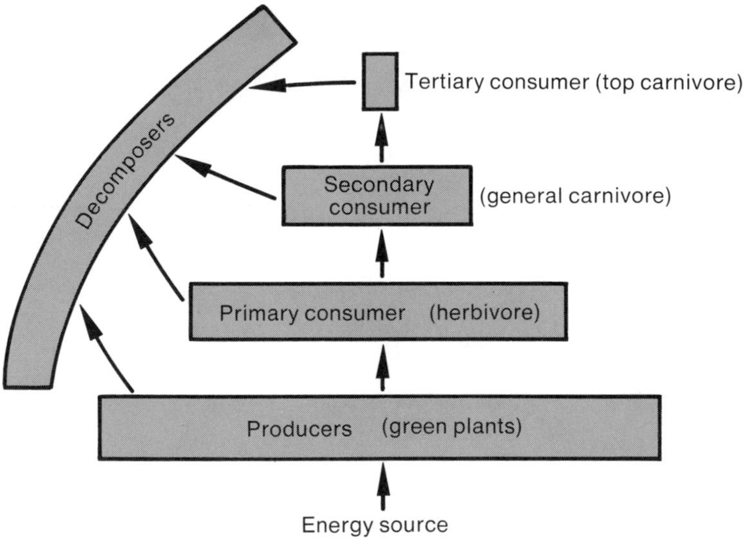

Figure 1-3. *Diagram of an Eltonian pyramid* named after Charles Elton, a British ecologist who first conceived this way of expressing the relationship between the several *trophic levels* of an ecosystem. Conventionally this pyramid scheme is used to model specific aspects of an ecosystem such as energy relations, as in this case, numbers of organisms, size of organisms, or biomass of organisms, thus contrasting with a more general model of the type shown in Figure 1-2. See text for further explanations.

The whole biological history of the earth, from the origin of life, which dates back perhaps 3½ billion years, to the contemporary world, is the story of the evolution, diversification, and elaboration of ecosystems which have varied continuously in time and space. Evolutionary processes have operated especially on two particular types of interfaces in these developing ecosystems. One kind of interface is formed by competing populations at the same trophic level, a competition which leads either to extinction or diversification. The second kind is produced by interactions between the organisms in different trophic levels. This concerns populations at a particular trophic level which are used as food, and those at the next highest trophic level consuming the food. In particular it involves such relationships as the predator-prey interaction. While evolution also occurs at this second type of interface, extinction is much less frequent.

For approximately one thousandth of all biological time, the presence of our human populations has exerted additional selection pressures on ecological relationships without our consciously understanding or reflecting upon the ultimate results of such pressures.

Information Accumulation

Evolutionary development in response to selection pressures from several sources has continuously fed information into the world's ecosystems; this information has been stored in the ecosystems and has directed their further elaboration. Indeed, instead of looking at evolution as a process in which adaptations are continuously occurring in response to changing features of the living and the physical environment, we can regard it as a continuing accumulation of biological information within ecosystems.

As evolution proceeds, this information is sometimes inadequate to allow particular populations to adapt to environmental change, whether natural or man-made. Segments of this accumulated information are therefore lost with the ensuing biological extinction. As we shall see later, one feature of the modern world which greatly disturbs ecologists is the increasing loss of information, as we lose stability in ecosystems because of human interference with their feedback mechanisms. The direct or indirect consequence of inserting ourselves at particular trophic levels is to destroy much of the diversity which has resulted from millions of years of biological variation and adaptation.

Energy Flow

The energy flow between the various trophic levels of an ecosystem is controlled by a number of factors, some physical, others biological. The laws of thermodynamics determine that there are some losses during energy transfer owing to its conversion to heat energy and subsequent dispersal into the environment. Considerable losses of energy are involved in the metabolic process of respiration which the consumer levels usually further increase because of the locomotor activity of the animals involved. Various calculations suggest that only some 10 per cent of the energy absorbed by one trophic level can be transmitted to the next higher trophic level in an ecosystem.

The energy pyramid in an ecosystem therefore soon reaches an apex.

This severely limits the number of successive trophic levels which can be accommodated in a given ecosystem, and explains the conventional representation of the Eltonian pyramid illustrated in Figure 1-3. As a consequence of this inevitable energy transfer loss, terrestrial ecosystems rarely have more than two to four levels of secondary consumers. Moreover, the higher up the trophic level at which we insert our human population, the less energy will be available. The herbivorous vegetarian will be able to extract ten times more energy from a given ecosystem than the carnivorous beef eater, the salmon fancier will have access only to one tenth or even one hundredth of the energy available to the clam lover (Figure 1-4). Study of these various energy transfers involves the investigation of what is termed *productivity.*

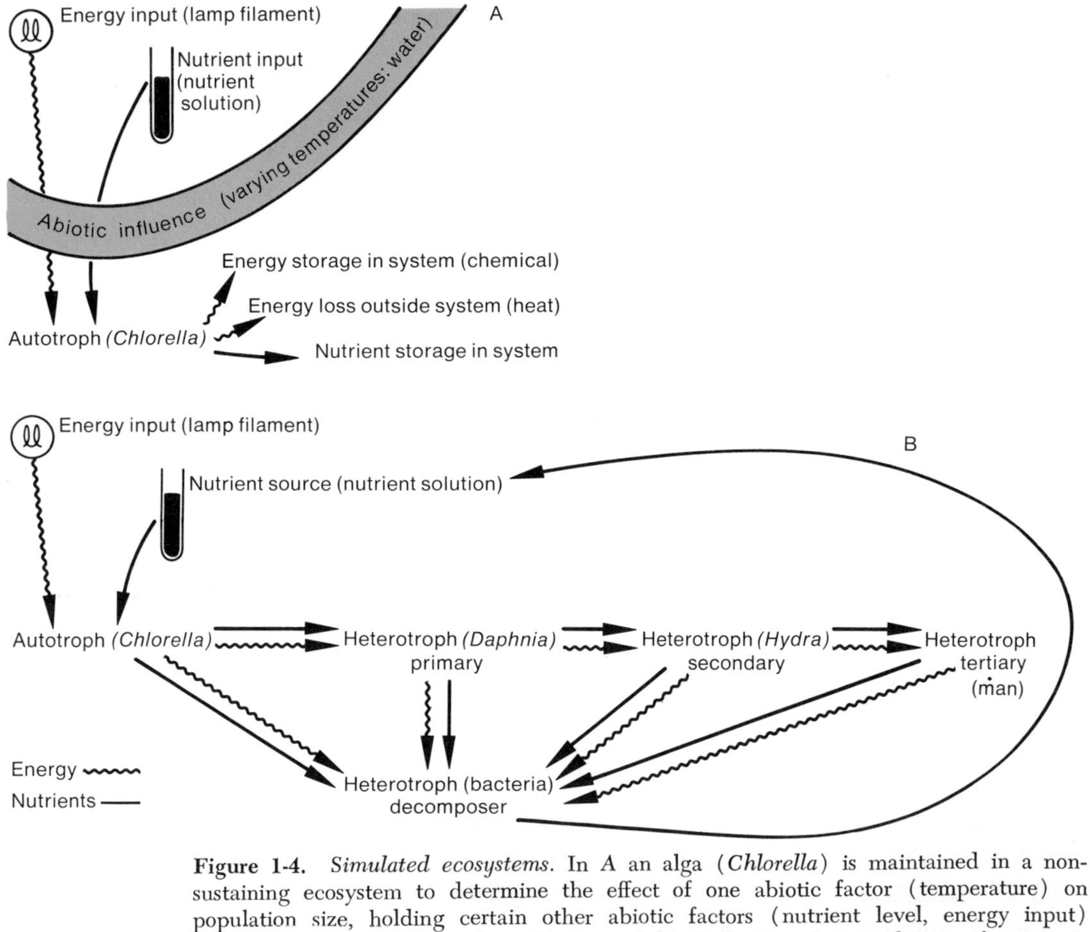

Figure 1-4. *Simulated ecosystems.* In *A* an alga (*Chlorella*) is maintained in a non-sustaining ecosystem to determine the effect of one abiotic factor (temperature) on population size, holding certain other abiotic factors (nutrient level, energy input) constant, while ignoring other abiotic and biotic factors (accumulation of autotoxic substances). *B* is a model of a self-sustaining experimental ecosystem which could be used to study two variables, the effect of varying the population density of the producer organisms, and the effect of varying the rate of predation by a tertiary consumer. As in *A*, some relationships are still ignored, for example, the possible effects of autotoxic substances and energy loss or gain outside the system.

PRODUCTIVITY

Although the word productivity is employed for what is generally acknowledged to be one of the most fundamental properties of all ecosystems, there is still no precise definition of this term. It is also difficult to measure accurately experimentally.

Developing from a consideration of the energetics of an ecosystem, productivity can be regarded as a *rate,* expressed as the heat energy (calories) produced per unit area (one square meter) per unit time (one year). This is the *gross productivity,* and it results entirely from the photosynthetic activities of the producer organisms, which are finite, thus setting an absolute limit on the total biotic population of the world ecosystem. Also, the producers will utilize some of the gross productivity in respiration processes. When losses from producer respiration are deducted from the gross productivity, *net productivity* is the result.

Another way of measuring productivity is to regard it not as a rate, but a *yield,* and when conceived in this way it is usually called *production.* The yield of an agricultural field in bushels of corn per acre is an expression of *biomass production.*

These ways of looking at productivity are all concerned with what is called *primary* productivity, that which results from the energy-fixing activity of the producer trophic level. The amount of energy contained in other trophic levels is known as *secondary productivity.* Since it involves only about one tenth of the total energy content of net primary productivity, in terms of gross primary productivity it can be largely ignored. It is not, however, insignificant in respect to the consumer trophic levels in an ecosystem. It varies with another aspect of ecosystem structure—community composition.

Communities

The biotic element of an ecosystem is divisible into a number of populations which normally show some interaction. These populations can be at the same trophic level, in which case the populations tend to be competing for the same resources. Or they may be at different trophic levels, with one group using the other as a food resource. In either case the assembly of interrelated populations is known as a *community.*

ECOLOGICAL SUCCESSION

When a given ecosystem is analyzed in terms of its community representation, it is rarely found to be completely stable. More usually it is apparently composed of a mosaic of communities, each of which replaces another in an orderly and predictable sequence. These sequential community changes comprise *ecological succession,* a process associated with an increase in species diversity and in the total standing crop. There is, as a consequence of the last circumstance, an increase in respiration which results in a decrease in net productivity.

The earliest stages of succession, the *pioneer communities,* are therefore characterized by a high level of net primary productivity. When the situation has become stabilized and there is no further succession, the *climax* has been reached. At this time respiration and other energy losses at all trophic levels exactly balance the caloric value of the energy fixed by the producer trophic level. There is no further succession unless some change occurs in the biotic or abiotic elements of the ecosystem. Such climax communities are clearly of little use to human societies, as there is no net productivity to be exploited. It is primarily into the pioneer communities with their high net productivities that human societies have entered.

Ecologists at one time were greatly concerned with successional relationships of communities and with the recognition and definition of climaxes. A greater emphasis on ecosystem energetics has now tended to diminish the significance of such studies.

In the world of today we must go out of our way to find examples of *primary succession,* an uninterrupted succession of seral communities beginning with the invasion of a virgin habitat by pioneer communities and culminating in a stable climax community. Nor are we certain of the real stability of many of the communities once thought to be climaxes. Quite often it is clear that some abiotic factor, such as the occurrence of wildfires, or a biotic one such as animal grazing, has temporarily halted succession and holds the seral communities in a delicately balanced steady state.

Moreover, succession is usually of a secondary, not a primary type, starting from abandoned farmland, a clear-felled forest, or some other such partially colonized substrate rather than from a virgin habitat. In addition, although there is an undeniable increase in species diversity as one community succeeds another in the process of ecological succession, some ecosystems appear to contain feedback mechanisms which ensures a maximum diversity by producing a steady-state pattern of seral stages. It has been shown, for example by Boughey (1963), that a maximum range of game animals in certain African preserves is obtained from such mosaics, rather than from uniform climax communities. In very much the same way, in the Pacific Southwest of the United States, the chaparral ecosystems become less diversified if periodic burns are totally excluded. Under "natural" conditions chaparral is a mosaic of successional stages of recovery from lightning-set wildfires.

Such consideration of ecosystem relationships will be discussed further in other sections of this text. One of the important concepts introduced will be interpretation of the various levels of human societies as a successional series.

Succession in Geological Time

Ecological succession can thus be regarded as a concept arising from a consideration of the energetics of contemporary ecosystems, but there are other ways of looking at this phenomenon. One is to regard succession as an increase in *information content* of the ecosystem. Regarded from this standpoint, there can be no such community stage as a "climax," because information content is open-ended; potentially at least it must continuously increase with the passage of time. The populations within a community maintain a store of variation, which is continuously interacting with biotic and abiotic elements of the ecosystem to effect further *adaptation,* and therefore further *evolution.* Each evolutionary step increases the information store of the community and represents further *niche diversification* within it. Our own populations have uniquely acquired the ability to adapt to niche diversification by cultural evolution. This permits us to utilize the information store of the ecosystem and of our own culture and so modify our techniques that we can adjust culturally, or behaviorally, while retaining the same biological form and structure.

We have changed comparatively little in either form or physiology over 3 or 4 million years, despite the passing of 100,000 or more human generations. Culturally this time interval has taken us from a unique omnivorous niche to where we can at will either insert ourselves into or control any ecological niche. This ability has already been noted, and we will refer to it again a number of times. Meanwhile one last aspect of the ecosystem concept should be briefly reviewed, *ecosystem structure.*

ECOSYSTEM STRUCTURE

Within each ecosystem there is usually a definable system of *food webs* in which particular populations of organisms at each trophic level are bound to one another in a consumer-consumed relationship.

Food Webs

These food webs are elaborations of simple food chains which embody the consumer-consumed relationships. Food chains, resulting from a simple association between two or more populations at successive trophic levels (Figure 1-3), most frequently represent situations encountered under experimental laboratory conditions (Figure 1-4). They may also fit the case of some agriculture, horticulture, and forestry circumstances where the cultivator endeavors to create a synthetic ecosystem in which competition from noneconomic populations at each trophic level is avoided by restricting the food webs to those species being economically exploited. Examples would include an alfalfa-cow-man ecosystem, or a wheat-man ecosystem

(Figure 1-5). Such synthetic ecosystems represent the ultimate in the destruction of community diversity in which human populations can engage.

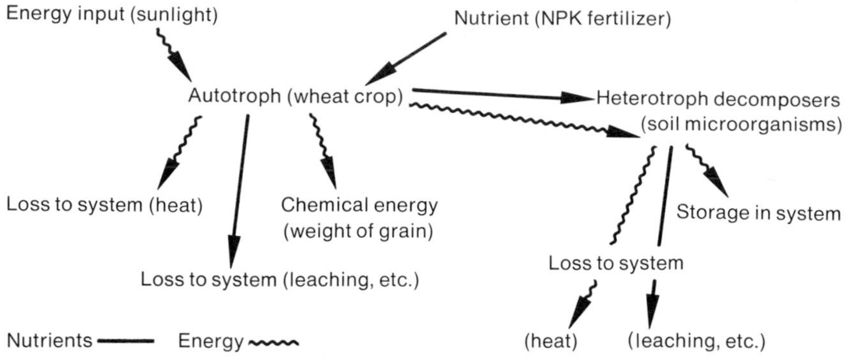

Figure 1-5. *Model of a simple agricultural ecosystem,* where customarily experimental information is restricted to such items as the nutrient input (artificial nitrogen-phosphorus-potassium fertilizers) in relation to yield of grain harvested. Although this model includes other interactions, for example, the storage of nutrients in the soil, these are often largely disregarded. Failure to take into account what nutrients are lost to the system as shown in this model has led to one of our present environmental crises, as will be seen later when water pollution is discussed. This model entirely ignores the abiotic factors that will influence energy transfer in this system.

In destroying this diversity, together with the energy pathways which regulated the relationships between organisms at various trophic levels, and most of the information content, we have unfortunately also eliminated many other features of the ecosystem, including possibly the mechanisms which governed our own population size. This is the most serious but by no means the only consequence of our increasing dominance of the various world ecosystems; nor is it the only disastrous consequence. There are, unhappily, many others.

Waste Products

One of these consequences is the uncontrollable accumulation of wastes which human populations deposit at a far greater rate than the microbial populations of the decomposer trophic level can contain. Partly this is the result of the huge biomass of wastes which we now form, but often it results from presentation of wastes in the form of synthetic substances new to populations of decomposer organisms.

Given sufficient evolutionary time, decomposer organisms will usually adapt to the utilization of virtually any kind of chemical substance, the principle of *microbial infallibility* (Alexander, 1964). We are now depositing many new materials which simply accumulate, because no decomposer organisms have yet adapted to break them down and circulate the nutrient elements back into our ecosystems. Quite often we also insert actual toxic substances into this recycling process at one trophic level or another. This interferes with and even stops the process of nutrient cycling, and actually kills individual organisms in populations at higher trophic levels, where *selective concentration* causes accumulation of these poisons beyond the tolerance levels of the particular organisms. Unfortunately also, the capacity of biogeochemical cycling diminishes as we pass backward through an ecosystem to earlier successional ecological stages (Bormann and Likens, 1970). The heaviest nutrient losses to the outside through failure of the recycling processes occur in just those early successional stages which are the favored sites for human occupation. This may still further lower the nutrient status of particular ecosystems.

As for ourselves, we have become an exceedingly complex animal, and the biological information which has been incorporated into our genetic system is correspondingly vast. There sometimes appears to be only a very tenuous connection between these basic principles of ecosystem structure and function and the behavior exhibited by our populations and their individual members. Nevertheless, there is no reason to doubt that is is from these basic principles that all human behavior stems, as the quotation from Chase indicated. In succeeding chapters we shall attempt to follow the development of some of these behavioral patterns, and the manner in which accumulating cultural information has been applied to the adaptation of techniques permitting our exploitation of energy sources available in natural ecosystems. All too frequently we have either remained ignorant of the consequences of this application, or we have deliberately ignored them. In either case, our actions have brought us close to the brink of disaster as far as the continuing survival of our species is concerned.

Bibliography

REFERENCES

Alexander, M. "Biochemical ecology of soil microorganisms," *Ann. Rev. Microbiol.*, **18**: 217–52, 1964.

Bormann, F. H., and Likens, G. E. "The nutrient cycles of an ecosystem," *Scientific American*, **223**(4): 92–101, 1970.

Boughey, A. S. "Interaction between animals, vegetation, and fire in Southern Rhodesia," *Ohio J. Sci.*, **63** (5), 193–209, 1963.

Chase, R. *Quest for Myth*, Baton Rouge: Louisiana State University Press, 1949.

Cole, L. C. "The ecosphere," *Scientific American*, **198**(4): 83–92, 1958.

Holling, C. S. "Stability in ecological and social systems," in *Diversity and Stability in Ecological Systems,* Woodwell, G. M., and Smith, H. H. (eds.), Brookhaven Symposia in Biology No. 22, 1969, pp. 128–41.

Mead, M. "The generation gap," *Science,* **164**(No. 3876): leader, April 11, 1969.

Odum, E. P. "The strategy of ecosystem development," *Science,* **164:** 262–70, 1969.

Shepard, P. "Whatever happened to human ecology?" *Bioscience,* **17:** 901–11, 1967.

Smuts, J. C. *Holism and Evolution,* New York: Macmillan, 1926.

Van Dyne, G. M. "Ecosystems, systems ecology, and systems ecologists," *Oak Ridge National Lab. Rep.,* **3957:** 1–31, 1966.

FURTHER READINGS

Boughey, A. S. *The Ecology of Populations,* New York: Macmillan, 1968.

Hutchinson, G. E. "The Biosphere," *Scientific American,* **223**(3): 44–53, 1970.

Turner, F. B. (ed.) "Energy flow and ecological systems," *American Zoologist,* **8:** 10–69, 1968.

Watt, K. E. F. *Ecology and Resource Management,* New York: McGraw-Hill, 1968.

Whittaker, R. H. *Communities and Ecosystems,* New York: Macmillan, 1970.

The Earliest Stages of Hominid Evolution

2

Any study of human ecology must first relate the surviving species of our genus in time and space to the other biological populations and the ecosystem environments with which it has evolved. From such considerations it is already possible to identify many factors which have provided the selection pressures which led—through response and adaptation to the emergence of *Homo sapiens* as a distinct species population. The later stages of the evolution of our species have been characterized more especially by *cultural speciation,* adaptations in *behavioral* as contrasted with *physical* traits. One particular behavioral feature, an enormous capacity for social learning, has led to the assembly of vast information stores in the form of *ritual.* The accumulation of ritual has become so great that we tend sometimes to ignore its behavioral origin and imagine that it has an independent existence. It is little more than a hundred years since the true relationship between ritual and human behavior was first perceived, less than a decade that we have generally been able dispassionately to examine our own evolution without castigating ourselves as materialists. The change of attitude has resulted partly from increasing evidence demonstrating our evolutionary relationships, but also because physical concepts of the universe are coming increasingly to be based on stochastic rather than deterministic models. This has added an element of chance to materialistic processes and removed one of the previous main sources of philosophic objections to this evolutionary approach.

ORIGIN OF LIFE ON EARTH

The earth is now believed to be approximately 5 billion years old, and living matter is thought to have originated somewhere between 4 and 3½ billion years ago (Echlin, 1969). There are indications that photosynthetic autotrophs (green plants) have existed for more than 3 billion years;

heterotrophs (animals and decomposers) may not have appeared until the beginning of the Cambrian period, half a billion years ago. It is thus possible to consider that for about a half billion years there have been self-sustaining ecosystems composed of producer (plant), consumer (animal), and reducer (microbe) trophic level populations and a nutrient recycling system. These ecosystems have been characterized by an ever-extending diversity, as adaptation in response to selection pressures has led to further niche diversification of their component populations, and to an increased net primary productivity, making possible a greater structural complexity. Thus the fossil record shows a general evolutionary progression of animal dominants in these increasingly complex ecosystems, as fishes, amphibians, reptiles, mammals, and finally man succeed one another in geological time.

CYCLIC OROGENIES

This process of ecosystem adaptation and diversification has not always evolved at a continuous and steady pace, but appears to have proceeded by a series of quantum advances, associated usually with massive extinctions of species populations. It seems also to have been associated with geological cataclysms, first extensively discussed by Brooks (1926), which occur cyclically at intervals of approximately 250 million years (Figure 2-1). These cataclysms are preceded by a period of mountain-building (orogeny) and volcanic activity (volcanism), followed by a series of ice ages. For a minimum period of 4 or 5 million years during such cataclysms, the climates and topography at the earth's surface become considerably modified, as do sea levels. At times temperatures are generally lower, rainfall is heavier, and topography of the land varies in altitude from sea level to 10,000 m or more. Following these cyclic orogenies, erosion slowly wears down the mountain masses and warmer climates melt the polar ice caps. The sea level, which has lowered some 100 m or so because of the freezing of vast amounts of water at the poles, returns to its previous height. Land again becomes, for much of the remaining 250-million-year intervals, flat, monotonous, surrounded by marine bays and covered with shallow fresh-water lakes.

Although we are still only beginning to relate these geologic and climatic events to ecosystem evolution, it appears possible that quantum advances in biological development may have been associated with them. It is a comparatively simple matter to correlate the biological changes and the

Figure 2-1. *Cyclic cataclysms in the history of the earth* showing the temperature fluctuations which are estimated to have occurred during the last three cataclysms at about 500, 250, and 5 million years BP. The time scales are successively lengthened, so that the geological intervals they represent increase from the Paleozoic to the Cenozoic to Recent time. The climatic regime the Earth presently enjoys is one of the temporary cool periods during otherwise long uninterrupted hot intervals. (Reproduced by permission of the publisher from C. E. P. Brooks in *The Compendium of Meteorology,* Boston, Mass.: American Meteorology Society, 1951, p. 1017.)

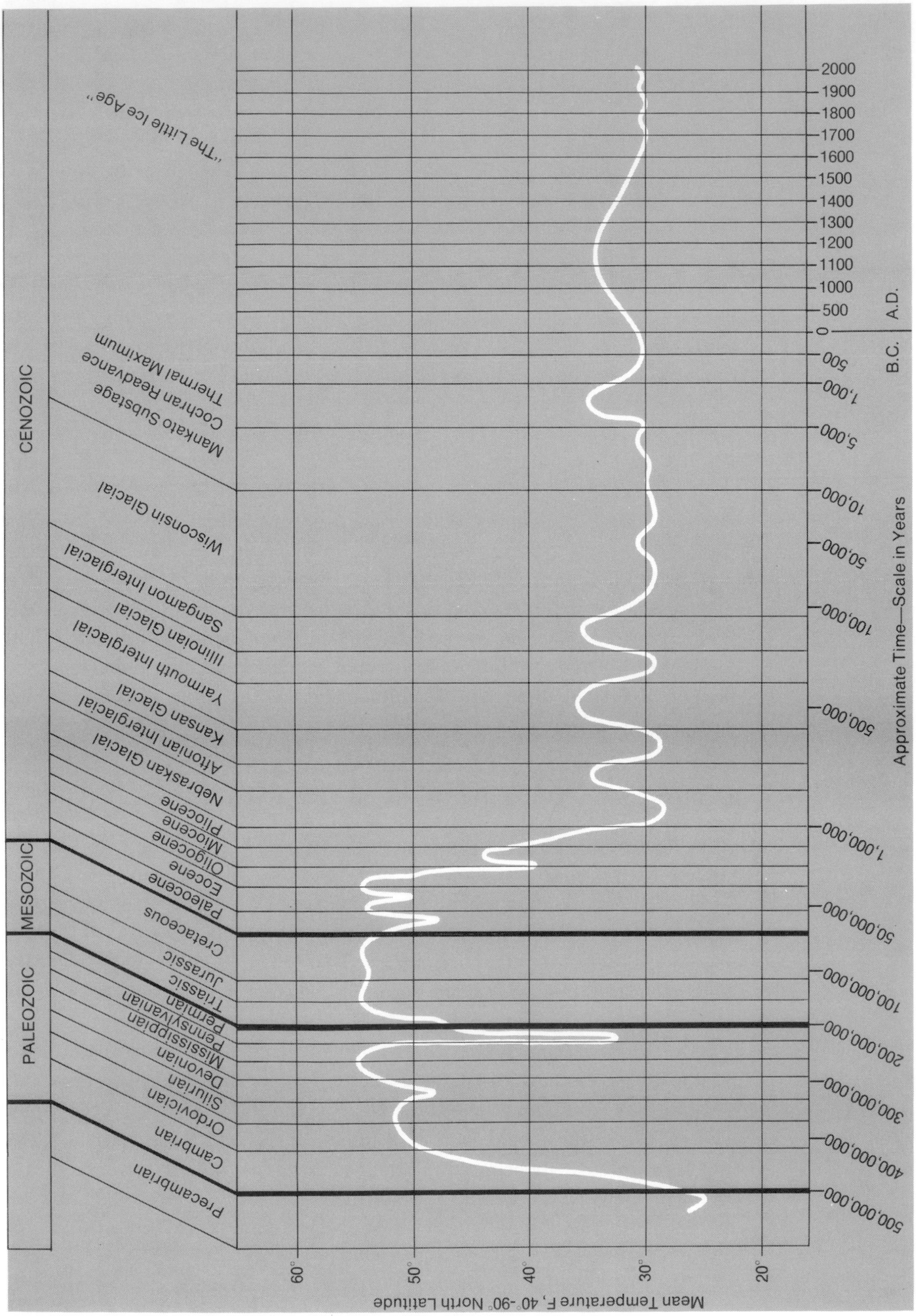
CENOZOIC
MESOZOIC
PALEOZOIC
"The Little Ice Age"
Mankato Substage
Cochran Readvance
Thermal Maximum
Wisconsin Glacial
Sangamon Interglacial
Illinoian Glacial
Yarmouth Interglacial
Kansan Glacial
Aftonian Interglacial
Nebraskan Glacial
Pliocene
Miocene
Oligocene
Eocene
Paleocene
Cretaceous
Jurassic
Triassic
Permian
Pennsylvanian
Mississippian
Devonian
Silurian
Ordovician
Cambrian
Precambrian
2000
1900
1800
1700
1600
1500
1400
1300
1200
1100
1000
500
0
A.D.
B.C.
500
1,000
5,000
10,000
50,000
100,000
500,000
1,000,000
50,000,000
100,000,000
200,000,000
300,000,000
400,000,000
500,000,000
Approximate Time—Scale in Years
60°
50°
40°
30°
20°
Mean Temperature F, 40°-90° North Latitude

geology of the Pleistocene ice ages, which began between 1 and 2 million years ago and ended, if indeed they have yet done so, perhaps 10,000 years ago. When, however, we look at the penultimate cataclysm which occurred approximately 250 million years ago, in the Permo-Carboniferous periods toward the close of the Mesozoic, there is much less surviving biological and geological evidence, although some still remains (Tavener-Smith, 1955). For example, in southern Africa it is possible to find rocks which have only recently been uncovered from overlying morainic material by erosion, bearing the characteristic scratches made when a glacier moves boulders across the face of a smoothed rock surface. Such scratches from the Pleistocene ice ages are a very familiar and characteristic feature of any glaciated region of North America and the north temperate zone as a whole.

Ice ages such as those that occurred in the Permo-Carboniferous and the Pleistocene must have had profound effects on the contemporaneous ecosystems. Many of the animal consumers would become extinct, unable to adapt sufficiently rapidly either genetically or phenotypically to the changed conditions. Plant (producers) species would be removed from vast areas where their genetic plasticity was insufficient to permit the evolution of forms suitable for the new conditions. During periods of glacial recession, virgin morainic soils would afford a rich habitat for any surviving pioneer plant species which could invade them. New plant communities with dominants of quite different life forms would have the opportunity to develop at first in these virgin habitats without the limits imposed by the continuous cropping of herbivore populations.

EVOLUTION OF TROPICAL RAIN FOREST

Speculating as to what may have occurred at such times of climatic amelioration, it may be supposed that following the close of the Permo-Carboniferous glaciation, about 230 million years ago, one of the new forms of plants with the potential to exploit pioneering situations was the group we now call *flowering plants* (Boughey, 1957). The unique possession of the propagule known as a *seed,* with a highly efficient water-conducting tissue, the *vessels,* and a reproductive system which gave full opportunity for genetic *variation,* contributed to this newly evolved group of plants a far greater ability to adapt to changing circumstances than had been possessed by producers in any earlier ecosystems. By the onset of the period which geologists term the Cretaceous, 120 million years ago, the success of these new forms was demonstrated in their ubiquitous spread throughout the warmer regions of the world. They formed tropical rain forests not entirely dissimilar in structure and composition from the moist forests of the humid tropics of today (Seward, 1931).

In a rather similar maneuver, the typical reptilian forms of the late Paleozoic (Permian) came to be associated in the Early Mesozoic (Jurassic) with mammallike reptiles, and especially a group known as therapsids. These were carnivorous forms, but their teeth appear to have been modified to permit cutting food into small pieces before swallowing, rather than gulping it down in large chunks and then having a long digestive period. Other changes in the vertebrae, limbs, and feet departed from the reptilian plan and approached mammalian forms.

During the Jurassic many reptilian groups became extinct, and by the Cretaceous, mammals of a somewhat opossumlike appearance had begun to assume their place as dominants of the tropical forest ecosystems. These were fur-covered homoiotherms (warm-blooded) contrasting with the naked skinned poikilothermous (no constant temperature regulation) reptiles.

Diversity of Form and Structure

The evolution of multistoried tree communities presented a range of aerial habitats which had never previously been available on the earth's surface (Figure 2-2). This unique diversity was fully exploited by one particular group of animals, which had been simultaneously exhibiting niche diversification in the flowering plant rain forest ecosystem. These were the *primates.*

Figure 2-2. *Tropical rain forest structure.* This schematic profile shows the three-layer stratification which typifies African tropical forest but is not so characteristic of that of other equatorial regions.

Just as flowering plants had shown specialized features which enabled them to form multistoried forest communities over vast areas of the earth's surface, so the primates also possessed unique features which allowed them to adapt more readily to differentiating habitats and to evolve with them

Primate Characteristics

Some eight groups of features characterize primates but are not constant features of every primate. All of them are, however, relevant to a survey of human evolution because, to a greater or lesser degree, they are characteristic of our own biological organization.

1. MANUAL GRASPING CAPABILITIES

Manual grasping results partly from the substitution of flat nails for claws on the digits of the four limbs, which retain the original pentadactylism of early mammals (five digits, articulating on two bones, relating to

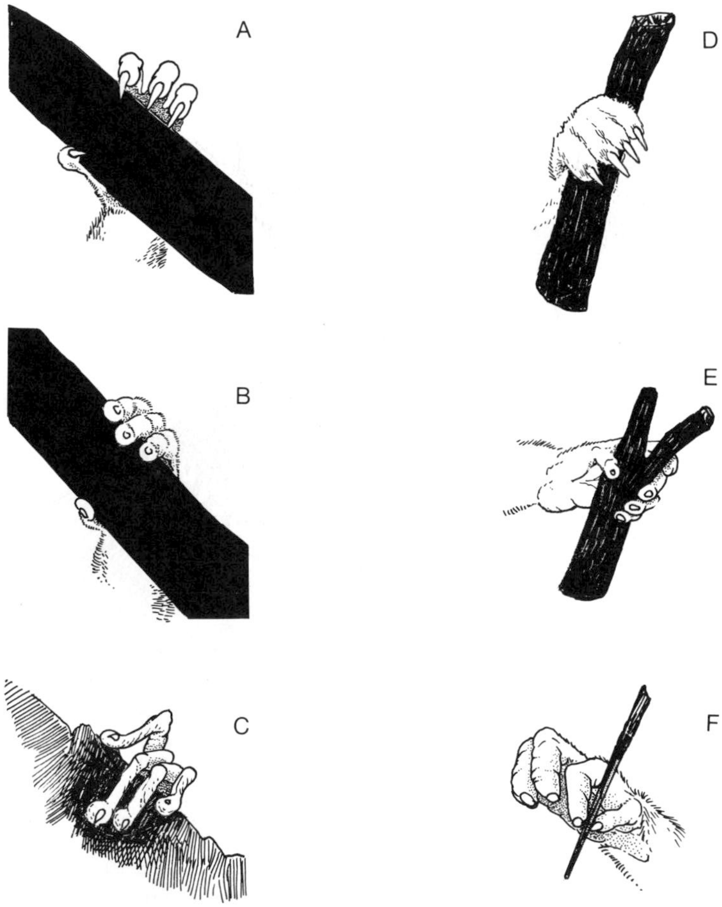

Figure 2-5. *Evolution of primate grasping abilities in hand of forelimb. A.* Tree shrew (*Tupaia*), little more than a multiple grappling hook. *B.* Loris (*Loris*), a very strong grip. *C.* Tarsier (*Tarsius*), a jumper with disclike swellings at end of "fingers" to assist grasping. *D.* Marmoset (*Callithrix*), fingers all operate in the same plane, "hand" a clasping structure only. *E.* Macaque (*Macaco*), opposable "thumb," clutching capacity very extensive. *F.* Chimpanzee (*Pan troglodytes*), also an extensive clutching capacity, but reduced compared with macaque because of shorter "thumb." (Based on a drawing in Eimerl and DeVore, 1965.)

one bone attached to the skeletal frame). Associated with this grasping capability (Bishop, 1964) is a greater tactile sensitivity of the lower surfaces of the digits and an ability to articulate these, especially the two largest (finger and thumb, big and first toe, Figure 2-5).

The retention of the clavicle (collar bone) further enhanced the maneuverability of the manual grasping equipment.

2. EMPHASIS OF VISUAL SENSE

The development of visual sense appears to be a corollary of the previous characteristic, for small objects could be grasped and held up for visual examination instead of being smelled or touched *in situ*. There was also a need to see less movable objects, which could be climbed on or over. All primates have binocular vision; possibly all diurnal species have some form of color vision, but this has not yet been fully determined.

3. ELABORATION OF THE CEREBRAL CORTEX

The elaboration of the cerebral cortex was required by the increased need for rapid and extensive eye-limb coordination centers. Together with the reduction in the size of the snout, made possibly by reduction of the olfactory in favor of the visual sense, and the frontal position of the eyes required for binocular vision, this gave a characteristic shape to the cranium (brain case) not encountered in any nonprimate group.

4. LENGTHENING OF GESTATION PERIOD

A longer gestation period is associated with a further elaboration of the uterus and placental structures, developing presumably as a response to the increased complexity of the cerebral cortex and optical equipment, which necessitated a longer prenatal period of development (Table 2-1).

5. PROLONGED INFANCY

A prolonged infancy provides for a lengthened interval before sexual maturity during which development of mental and physical equipment can be completed. More important, perhaps, the long period of infancy affords the opportunity during play periods to perfect under parental supervision many of the brain-limb instruction maneuvers essential for adult survival. Moreover, the prolonged intimate relationship between parent and offspring provides the opportunity for an increased transmission of behavior learned by imitation. This is an infinitely less hazardous way of acquiring behavioral patterns than individual trial and error.

6. COMPARATIVE LONGEVITY

Comparative longevity is associated possibly with the long infancy, which would be wasted without a reasonably extended potential breeding life. Longevity is perhaps also linked to the marked tendency toward single births. This could be a response to the considerable hazards of arboreal

Table 2-1 ***Gestation Periods in Selected Mammals*** The length of the gestation period is correlated with the size of the embryo at birth, but in all the examples cited below, the body size of the primate is much smaller by comparison with that of other mammals with similar gestation periods. In other words, the gestation period for primates is far longer than would be expected on the basis of their size alone.

SPECIES	*LENGTH OF GESTATION (Days)*
Virginia opossum (*Didelphis viginiana*)	12
Golden hamster (*Mesocricetus auratus*)	16
Mouse (*Mus musculus*)	20
Rat (*Rattus norvegicus*)	22
Rabbit (*Oryctolagus cuniculus*)	31
Weasel (*Mustela nivalis*)	35
Gray squirrel (*Sciurus vulgaris*)	40
Tree shrew (*Tupaia* sp.)	46–50
Cat (*Felis maniculata*)	63
Guinea pig (*Cavia cobaya*)	67
Lion (*Panthera leo*)	110
Lemur (*Lemur catta*)	120–140
Spider monkey (*Ateles paniscus*)	139
Marmoset (*Callimico jacchus*)	140–150
Sheep (*Ovis aries*)	150
Langur (*Presbytis entellus*)	170–190
Chacma baboon (*Papio ursinus*)	180–190
Brown bear (*Ursus americanus*)	210
Gibbon (*Hylobates lar*)	210
Hippo (*Hippotamus amphibius*)	240
Chimpanzee (*Pan troglodytes*)	216–260
Orangutan (*Pongo pygmaeus*)	220–270
Porpoise (*Phocaena phocaena*)	220–270
Cow (*Bos taurus*)	278
Man (*Homo sapiens*)	280
Gorilla (*Gorilla gorilla*)	250–290
Horse (*Equus caballus*)	340
Sperm whale (*Physeter catadon*)	365
Giraffe (*Giraffa camelopardalis*)	450
Elephant (*Elephas maximus*)	660

life which are increased considerably if attention must be divided between more than one offspring.

7. SOCIALITY

Sociality is observable obviously only in *living* primates but by inference it was general also in fossil forms and more developed and complex than in any other animal group. Perhaps this resulted from the vastly increased ability to observe and react to visual stimuli; it also provided a further opportunity for juveniles to learn.

8. CUSP PATTERN

The molar teeth of primates retain a simple cusp pattern characteristic of the more primitive mammals (Figure 2-6).

Adaptive Radiation in Primates

The adaptive radiation which primates exhibit appears to have resulted from their locomotor adaptations for climbing. Such adaptations to an arboreal life are the only distinguishing features which all primates have in common. These adaptations, as indicated above, include a lengthening of the digits to permit clasping, substitution of nails for claws, emphasis on vision with a corresponding reduction in the sense of smell and size of the

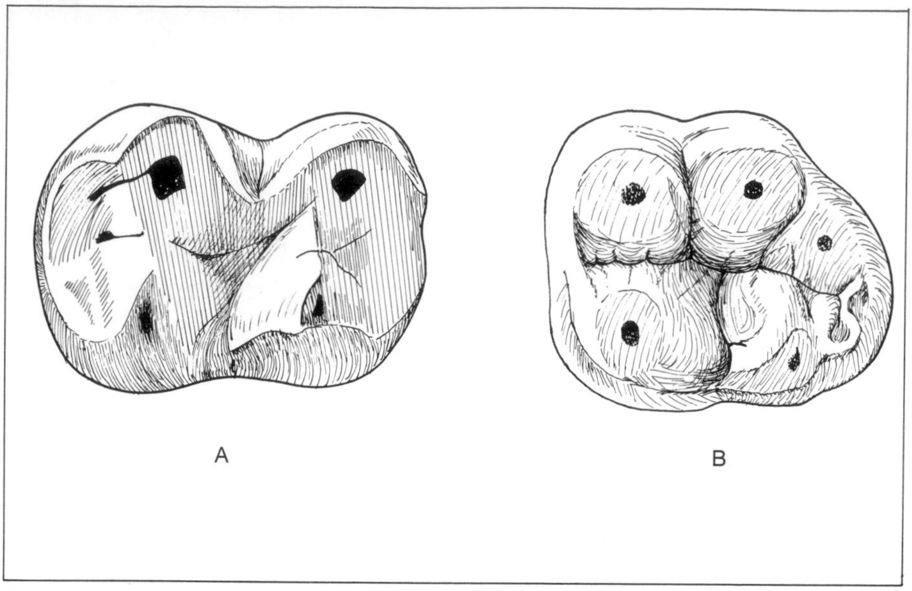

Figure 2-6. *Molar cusp patterns* distinguish the Old World monkeys (Cercopithecoidea) from the hominoids (Hominoidea). The crowns of the Old World monkeys have *four* cusps in two pairs, a ridge joining each of the paired cusps (*A*). In hominoids (*B*) there are *five* cusps, and a Y-shaped depression in the crown separates one cusp from the two pairs either side of it. This last pattern is not found in any fossil form occurring before the Miocene about 25 million years ago.

snout, and consumption of soft food which permits a reduction in the size of the teeth. The insectivore digestive systems were capable of coping with an omnivorous diet, which could range from any form of vegetable matter except cellulose and lignin, to animal proteins.

The unspecialized limb structure enables primates to use their extremities as climbing, clasping, and feeding organs. From a lateral position, the eyes became frontal, thus providing for the development of stereoscopic vision. This would be of very high selective value in a multistoried forest community where leaping from one branch to another required precise judgment as to distance and the penalty of any misjudgment was immediate death or severe damage. Rather similarly, the hazards to the young inherent in an arboreal life generally reduced the number of offspring produced at a birth to one. This had become associated with a period of parental care after birth which also could be utilized for instruction in acquired behavioral characteristics (Figure 2-7). Perhaps frequently associated with this behavioral instruction would be a social structure of both a genetic and socially learned form. Wynne-Edwards (1963) discusses how such a social system might evolve.

Social Life of Primates

It is only in the past few years that we have begun to understand, as a result of experimentation in the laboratory and observation in the field, the

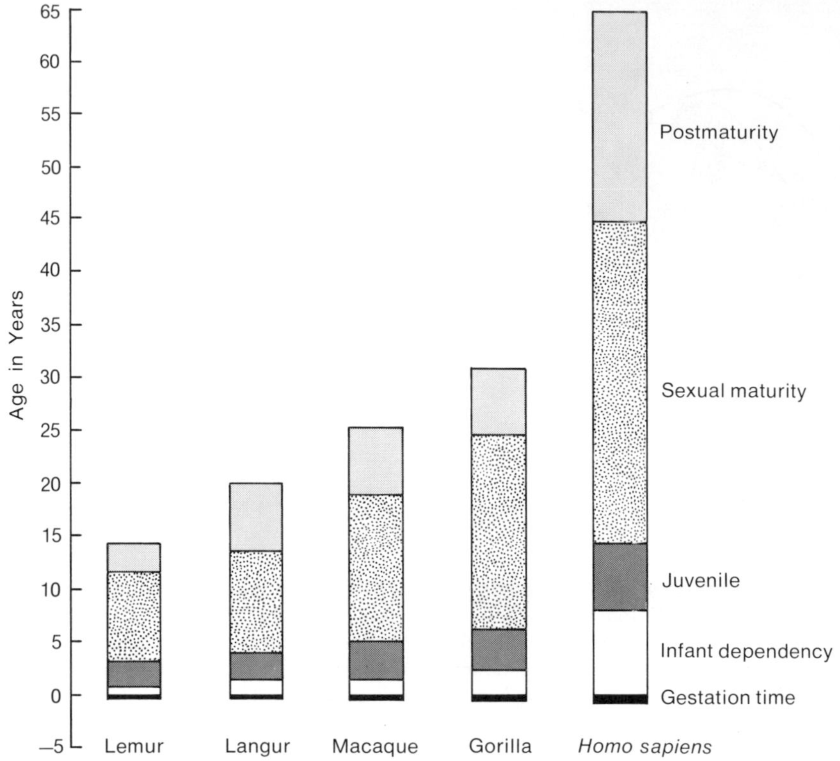

Figure 2-7. *Primate evolution* essentially features cultural evolution. Selection has favored variants with a larger brain, whose development necessitates a longer gestation period, an extension of the time for infant dependency, and of the play years when the juvenile is perfecting adult movements and coordinating central nervous system-muscular activity. The lemur is lowest in the evolutionary scales shown here, man the highest. Although taking twice as long to reach sexual maturity as the gorilla, the period each *H. sapiens* female is potentially fertile is also twice as long.

social life of primates, and particularly of monkeys and apes. In the United States, for example, there are now eleven primate centers where primate behavioral studies are being carried out. This research is revealing with increasing authority the significance of early experience in determining the adult primate responses, and field observations are reinforcing the conclusions from such experimental observations. Understanding the behavioral patterns and social life of primates is crucial to human ecology, where direct experimental evidence is scanty, because experimentation on ourselves is necessarily limited.

Early Primates

Early primates, commonly known as the *prosimians,* and including tarsiers, lorises, and lemurs, were extensively distributed over both the Old and New Worlds in the Paleocene, apparently attaining a maximum dispersal and radiation in the Eocene, after which the majority passed to extinction. No primate, indeed no small mammal fossils are known from the African

Eocene, but from fossil remains elsewhere it is apparent that during this period three further groups evolved, two of them forming respectively the Old World and New World "monkeys." These two groups were always independent, populations of each remaining in distinct continents. The third group which evolved included the apes. Their evolution was associated with the perfection of binocular and color vision and a consequent major advance in arboreal locomotor activity which permitted the transfer of exploratory and feeding functions from the snout to the forelimbs. One of the more common general classifications of these various primates is shown in Table 2-2.

Brachiation

Associated with this transfer of function is the evolution in the apes of a new locomotor procedure known as *brachiation.* This is a swinging arm-

Table 2-2 Classification and Relationships Within the Primate Order The figure after the common name of a group indicates the number of living genera it is usually considered to contain.

SUBORDER	*INFRAORDER*	*SUPERFAMILY*	*FAMILY*
Prosimii (prosimians)			
	Tupaiiformes (Tree shrews, 4)		
	Tarsiiformes (Tarsiers, 1)		
	Lorisformes (Lorises, 5)		
	Lemuriformes (Lemurs, 9)		
Anthropoidea (monkeys and apes)			
		Ceboidea (New World or Platyrrhine monkeys, 13)	
		Cercopithecoidea (Old World or Catarrhine monkeys, 13)	
		Hominoidea (Hominoids)	
			Pongidae (Pongids or apes, 5)
			Hominidae (Hominids, 1)

over-arm motion such as may best be observed in modern gibbons. Brachiation required a change from a *pronograde*, or horizontal body position, to an *orthograde* (upright) posture, which in turn resulted in changes in the muscular attachment of the internal organs, the breathing muscles, rib case, and so forth. While several groups of monkeys can occasionally brachiate, this mode of locomotion associated with an orthograde posture is characteristic of apes. It is typified in the surviving groups of these forms, the gibbons and simiangs (Southeast Asia), orangutan (Borneo), chimpanzee (Africa), and gorilla (Africa). The last three, sometimes known collectively as the *great apes*, are also capable of extensive bipedal progression; this is the preferred locomotor procedure for the last modern anthropoid group, man.

Dentition

Old World anthropoids, that is, monkeys, apes, and man, are characterized by an identical dental formula. Proceeding on each side from front to rear each jaw has two incisors, a canine, two premolars, and three molars, conventionally written as:

$$\frac{2:1:2:3}{2:1:2:3} = 32$$

This permanent dentition is preceded by a juvenile deciduous form expressed by the formula:

$$\frac{2:1:2}{2:1:2} = 20$$

A summary of the variation in the permanent dental formula found in primates is provided in Table 2-3. It can be seen that the number and form of permanent primate teeth vary little between one group and another, but there is a general tendency toward a small reduction in number, usually by the loss of a pair of incisors or premolars. Once a particular pair of teeth has been lost in an evolutionary sense, it cannot be replaced by the same teeth. Therefore, in examining any evolutionary relationships, the number of teeth in a postulated ancestral form *must* be the same as or larger than that in the form whose ancestry is being traced.

Cusp Patterns

The morphology of mammalian teeth has been investigated in great detail. Many aspects of the general shape, roots, and crown are constant within a group, and evolutionary relationships can be reliably determined from them. One such pattern relates to the *cusps*, the portions of the crowns which project beyond the general surface. As illustrated in Figure 2-6, this cusp pattern can be used to distinguish hominoids from other primates.

Table 2-3 ***Primate Dentition*** Traditionally, the form of the permanent primate dentition is expressed in a *dental formula.* This enumerates for one side the teeth in the upper (above) and lower jaws (below), starting with the number of incisors, and continuing successively with the number of canines, premolars, and molars. As this selection of dental formulae shows, primates exhibit remarkably little variation in the general plan of their dentition. Only the aye-aye, a highly specialized lemur, shows a major departure from the basic pattern.

For detailed comparative studies it would be necessary to take into account also the deciduous dentition or "milk teeth."

PRIMATE GROUP	*FORMULA*	*TOTAL NUMBER OF TEETH*
Prosimians		
Tupaiiformes (Tree shrews)	2.1.3.3. / 3.1.3.3.	38
Tarsiiformes (Tarsiers)	2.1.3.3. / 1.1.3.3.	34
Lorisiformes (Lorises)	2.1.3.3. / 2.1.3.3.	36
Lemuriformes (Lemurs)		
Lemuridae (Diurnal lemurs)	2.1.3.3. / 2.1.3.3.	36
Lepilemur (Sportive lemur)	0.1.3.3. / 2.1.3.3.	32
Indridae (Indris)	2.1.2.3. / 1.1.2.3.	30
Daubentonioidea (Aye-aye)	1.0.1.3. / 1.0.0.3.	18
Anthropoids		
Ceboidea	2.1.3.3. / 2.1.3.3.	36
	or	
	2.1.3.2. / 2.1.3.2.	32
Cercopithecoidea	2.1.2.3. / 2.1.2.3.	32
Pongids (Gorilla)	2.1.2.3. / 2.1.2.3.	32
Hominids (*Homo sapiens*)	2.1.2.3. / 2.1.2.3.	32

Coevolution

In the early Cenozoic we therefore find increasing evidence of a parallel evolution between the developing plant structures of tropical ecosystems and the primate groups which are adaptively radiating within them. The arboreal life to which all these forms adapted exerted strong selection pressures for those adaptations conferring a greater awareness of this essentially three-dimensional, complex, and physically hazardous environment. The most significant evolutionary trend is a progressive development of the brain, associated with nervous and muscular mechanisms which operated rapidly and precisely, yet with versatility. This involved enlargement of that portion known as the *cerebral cortex,* which is associated with sensory representation, i.e., with visual interpretation and association.

APPEARANCE OF GRASSLANDS

As the Cenozoic proceeded, the general onset of aridity which appeared progressively after each periodic ice age series (Bond, 1962) began to affect the evolutionary trends exhibited by the plants and animals of the rain forest. On the margins of the multistoried forest communities, arid periods would favor, instead of trees and shrubs, smaller plants which could survive the dry winter season in a dormant condition either as some form of underground food-reserve storage organ or as persisting seeds. These *geophytic perennials* and *annual herbs* when growing together in large stretches constituted an entirely different type of community from forest, one which we now usually place under the general ecological term of *grassland.*

As the Tertiary period advanced, grassland began to appear not only on forest margins but also in the drier interior sections of the tropical rain forests throughout the area that they covered. It is this second "ecological" type of grassland which was probably of far greater significance in hominid evolution than the "geographically" marginal type. The drier climates would have a considerable rainfall during six or seven months of the year, whereas the other months would be dry and relatively rainless. River valleys, which under the previous more continuously well-watered regimes would have supported trees able to survive water-logging, would be colonized by new types of plants. These would have to be capable of withstanding the water-logged condition of the valley soil during the rainy season, but equally capable of sustaining the drought conditions of the dry season. Even in modern times, few tree groups have evolved which are capable of this, species of the genus *Syzygium* being a notable exception. For the most part it was annual herbs and perennial geophytes which evolved into this new niche and formed the seasonally flooded valley grasslands which many workers believe are the main natural grasslands of undisturbed tropical African habitats. (Figure 2-8).

Grassland Pioneers

These evolving tropical grassland ecosystems provided an entirely new habitat for animal species, and it may be surmised that they were first occupied by some of the more mobile animal forms—insects, for example. Among the more successful of such colonizing animal groups appears to have been the terrestrial stock of a group already mentioned, the *rodents.* Their

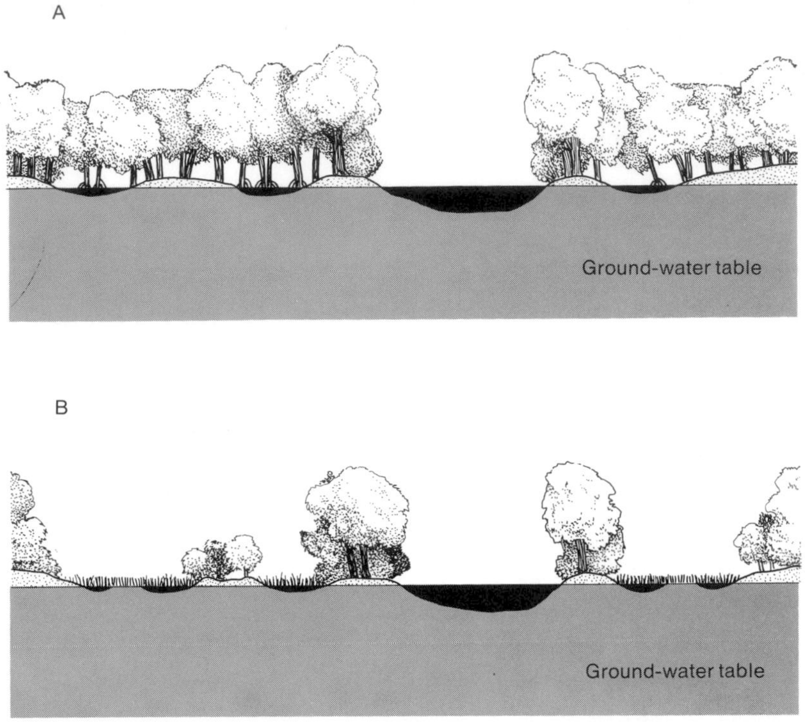

Figure 2-8. *Evolution of savanna grassland in the African tropics during the Mesozoic.* In *A*, the Late Paleozoic, a well-distributed rainfall of some 1500 mm per annum maintained a water table in the flood plain bordering the rivers at about or above soil level. This section of the *catena* supported *periodically inundated* forest, with tree dominants adapted (by stilt roots, etc.) to saturated soils. There are no grasslands. In *B*, total rainfall may still be as high as 1500 mm per annum but there is a prolonged *dry season* during which the water table is considerably lowered in the flood plain. The tree species able to survive the saturated soils of the rainy season cannot withstand the lowering of the water table in the dry season. New life forms, grasses and other herbaceous plants, evolve to occupy this new habitat.

potent capacity for adaptive radiation into these early grasslands is attributed to their immense reproductive abilities. It is significant that many modern rodent species are either entirely insectivorous, entirely seed-eating, or, if they are mainly vegetarian, supplement their diet with insects. The genetic flexibility of the rapidly evolving primate stock would permit them also to colonize these new grassland habitats, and it is not surprising that in the geological record soon after the appearance of grasslands we begin to find primate fossils in such areas.

EARLY APES

The most extensive series of fossil primates associated with these Tertiary grasslands has been found in equatorial regions of Africa, and especially in Uganda (Leakey, 1943, MacInnes, 1943). These fossils dated to the Miocene period, which lasted from 25 to 12 million years ago, and have been placed in the aggregate genus *Proconsul*. The selection of this name by its authors is said (Harrison and Montagna, 1969) to have been due to a resemblance between the teeth and jaws of these fossil creatures and those of a chimpanzee at one time living in the London zoological gardens who was named "Consul."

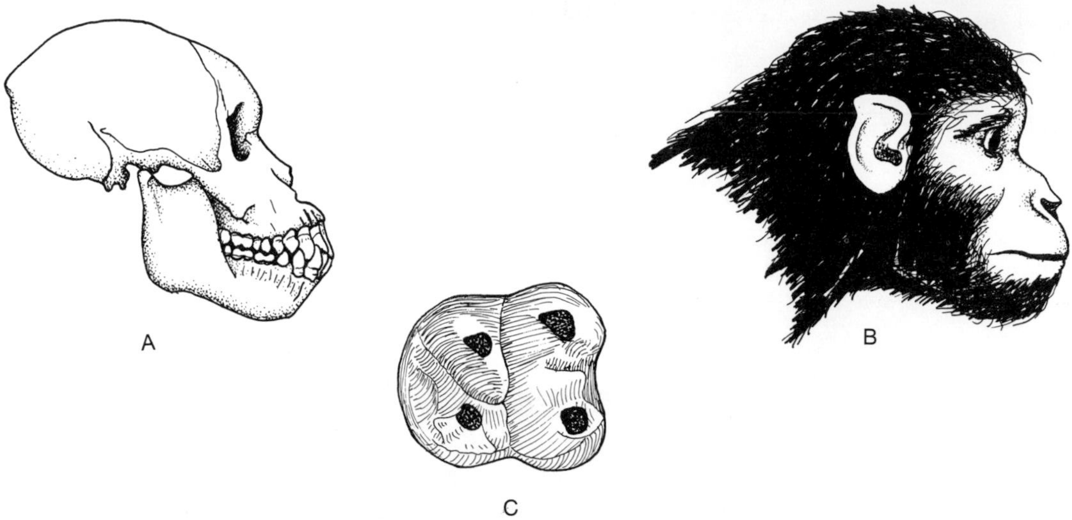

Figure 2-9. *Various features of Proconsul. A.* Composite drawing of the skull. *B.* Reconstruction of the head showing the receding forehead, small nose, and prognathous face. *C.* Upper molar showing characteristic monkey cusp pattern (see Figure 2-6). The mixture of monkey and ape characters suggests *Proconsul* resembles the common ancestor of both. Probably also it is not separable taxonomically from forms placed in the genus *Dryopithecus*.

Proconsul

Proconsul is not classifiable as an Old World monkey because of its brain size, dentition, and skeletal features (Figures 2-9). Nor is *Proconsul* clearly identifiable as an ape or hominid form. It is therefore often considered to have represented a stage of primate evolution before the ape stock (pongids) differentiated from the human one (hominids).

Definition of Terms

The use of some classificatory terms at this stage is unavoidable. The term *primates* is capitalized when it refers to the zoological *order* of Primates; when referring to most of this group in general, but not using the term in a taxonomic sense, it is uncapitalized.

Pongidae is the *family,* including living and fossil great apes, whose most obvious but not most significant characteristic is that they are tailless. Such forms are often termed *pongids* here; pongid may also be used as an adjective.

All human species in the genus *Homo,* and all "subhuman" forms are placed in the family Hominidae, commonly termed the *hominids.* This term also may be used as an adjective. Hominidae and Pongidae can be combined in a superfamily Hominoidea, the hominoids, and this noun and its derived adjective are occasionally used here. The terms subhominoid, or protohominoid, are sometimes applied to forms like *Proconsul* but are not used in this text. Some authorities place *Proconsul* in a pongid subfamily Dryopithecinae, which includes a number of Miocene-Pliocene fossil apes of which about 550 fossil specimens are known. Table 2-2 shows a generalized version of the taxonomic relationship and classification of these various primate forms. For technical reasons relating to the skills associated with particular disciplinary training, hominids, which are primarily Pleistocene forms, have been investigated by anthropologists and anatomists, whereas prehominids such as Dryopithecinae, which are essentially Tertiary forms, have been studied by vertebrate paleontologists. This has not been an inflexible dichotomy, but it has dispersed papers over several professional journals, and produced a slightly different approach. Unfortunately the Pleistocene specialists have suffered from taxonomic oversplitting, so that some 30 genera and many species of hominids have been named and described. This oversubdivision has resulted especially from the fragmentary nature of most osteological material, the difficulty of dating it, and the relative absence of knowledge concerning breeding barriers in populations known only from fossils.

Tool-Using Capacity

The anatomical and mental attributes exhibited by all living apes, especially the relative freedom of movement of their forelimbs, indicate that all members of this group shared the limited capacity for *tool-using* which behaviorists have been able to demonstrate in the modern great apes. There is every reason to suppose that *Proconsul,* together with the other ape forms whose variation attained its zenith in the Miocene, possessed this limited tool-using ability.

BEHAVIORAL PATTERNS

It is difficult enough to relate the behavior of living primates to human behavior, and to draw conclusions about possible analogous and homologous relationships (Haldane, 1956). When we are dealing with an exclusively fossil group such as the genus *Proconsul* represents, comparative evidence is circumstantial indeed. Nevertheless in such groups of fossil primates, behavioral patterns must have been of extreme importance in evolutionary development; speculation has to be made on whatever circumstantial evidence is available. Among living forms there is always a strong resemblance discernible between human behavior and that of the other primates whether observations have been obtained in the field or in the laboratory (Figure 2-10). Phenomena such as mother-baby recognition, play periods, and weaning trauma appear to be constant features of all the primate groups, and it is very easy for these patterns to become part of anthropocentric arguments if care is not taken to avoid doing so.

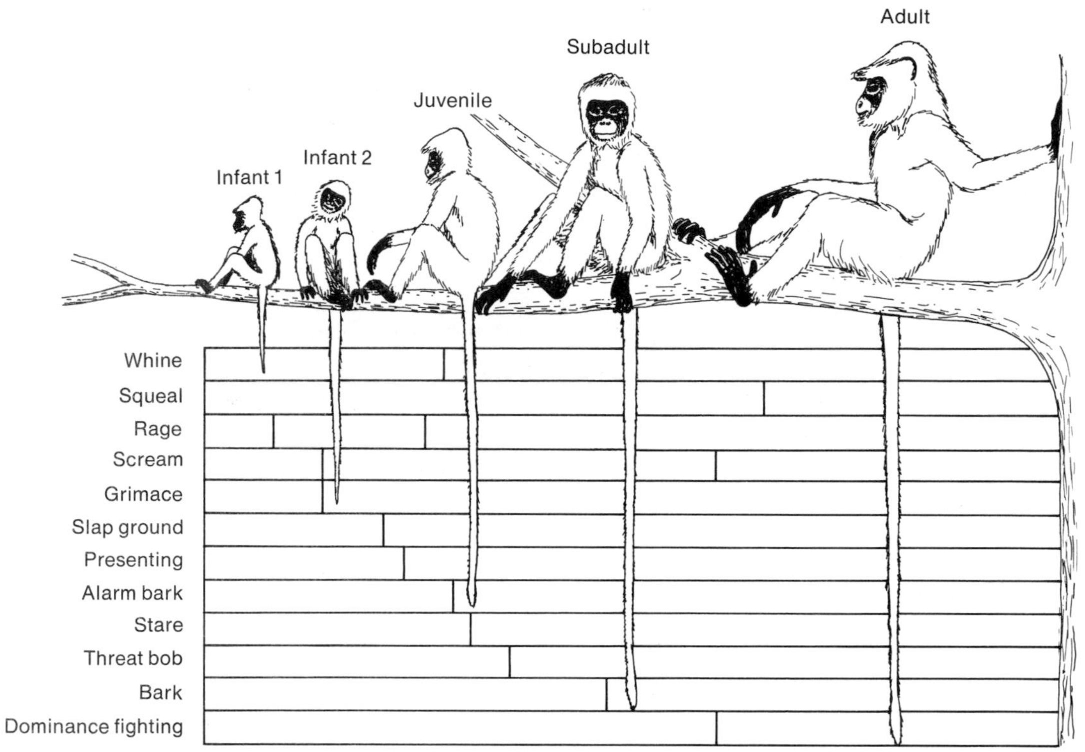

Figure 2-10. *Social communication in langur monkeys* and its development. The social communication system in langurs, explored by P. Jay, includes *calls,* such as the alert bark which would provide information for animals out of sight. The grimace by contrast is an effective signal only to animals in direct visual range. A terrestrial social primate form might tend to extend the latter type of communication, an arboreal troop whose members' field of view soon becomes obscured by trees might elaborate the call system. (Adapted from P. Jay, 1965.)

There appears to be universal agreement that major features of vertebrate social behavior—including gregariousness, social communication, territoriality, dominance hierarchy, sexuality, parental care, and social play—also characterize primate behavior. In outlining this and illustrating it with an account of rhesus monkeys (*Macaca mulatta*) Altmann (1962) emphasizes that as a result of affinities among members of a group and aggression toward individuals outside the group, primates live in discrete and highly stable social units. The implications of this will be referred to later as hominid evolution and human diversity are considered.

Social Life of Arboreal Primates

Working on langur monkeys in India, Jay (1963) has described the social life of an Old World monkey troop. She lived in the territories of four different langur troops and was able, after two years of familiarization with their members, to predict much of their behavior. She observed a dominance hierarchy of males in each troop and a somewhat less pronounced hierarchy among females, to which individual females engaged in raising a young infant did not conform. A newborn infant was an object of curiosity to the females in the troop, who gathered round the mother to inspect it and take turns holding it.

The growing infant rode about by clutching its mother's front. It stayed close to her at all times, performing the same actions she did and learned by imitation. As it became more competent at walking, the infant tended to wander away from its mother and play with others of its age group.

This social mixing is apparently necessary in order for the young langur to develop a well-adjusted personality. Harlow and Harlow (1962) were able to demonstrate experimentally the need for such social interaction in young animals. They discovered that if monkeys were raised in isolation and not allowed to play, even if they were within sight of other members, they became neurotic and then psychotic. They could not subsequently make any kind of social contact, nor were the males ever able to copulate. It therefore appeared first that maternal interest and care were required during raising if young females were to become in their turn competent mothers, and, second, that periods of play with other infants were necessary for the proper development of social behavioral patterns, even of sexual behavior.

After weaning at about 15 months, langur juveniles associated in one of two groups according to sex. The female juveniles got to hold and sometimes look after infants of other females for a time. The males indulged in increasingly vigorous competitive play, during which their adult hierarchical position became established (Altmann, 1962).

A langur troop is essentially an *arboreal* population. Although individuals are completely accustomed to movement on the ground, this never takes them more than a few paces from a tree. When danger threatens it is a case of *chacun pour soi*. Mothers snatch up their babies, and every member of the troop leaps for the nearest tree. Males have very little to do with babies and juveniles in the troop, and there has been no adaptation of social behavior in response to group selection for such interests. The situation is very different in a terrestrial primate species population.

Social Life of Terrestrial Primates

The work on the langur monkey illustrates some of the behavioral patterns of an essentially *arboreal primate* species. The behavior of *ter-*

Figure 2-11. *An African chacma baboon* (PAPIO URSINUS) *troop moving out across its feeding ground.* The dominant clique of dogs (*A*) at the center protects the females with nursing young (*B*); younger males take point (*C*). Individual dog baboons (*D*, *E*) high up in the dominance hierarchy squire individual females in the final stages of estrus (*F*, *G*) or bring up the rear (*H*); juveniles cavort on the flanks (*K*, *L*). If threatened, the dominant pair of dogs (*A*) will come right out of the center and attack, with the primary intention of driving off, rather than killing, the predator, which is usually a leopard. See text for further explanation. (Based partly on a drawing by DeVore, I, 1965.)

restrial primates provides a marked contrast and may therefore indicate more appropriately the nature of *Proconsul* behavior. Studies have been made of several baboon species, in particular the Asiatic macaques and African species such as chacma's baboon (Figure 2-11). The characteristic and common feature of all such terrestrial social primate species is an individual *aggressive* temperament (Washburn and De Vore, 1961). This is not something which is exhibited as a behavioral response invoked by particular environmental stimuli but is an integral part of the individual animal's personality. It is exhibited not only in the manner in which the troop is constantly ready to defend itself and its individual members against a predator, but also in the fierceness and the insistence with which the dominance hierarchy is maintained (Figure 2-12).

Dominance

The normal mode of behavior within a macaque or baboon troop is peaceful, but it is maintained only because it is enforced by the dominant animals (Hall, 1962). These have not only a specific function in defending the group against external aggression, but a parallel function in policing the troop to prevent internal strife.

Internally, however, it is a threat of force rather than the use of it which

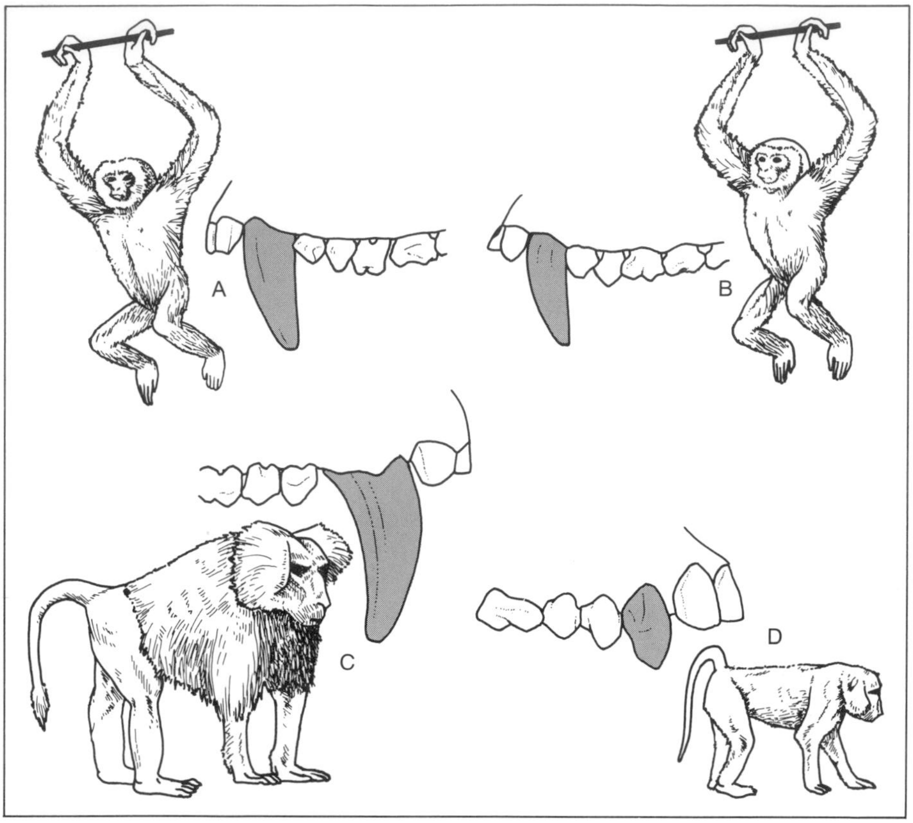

Figure 2-12. *Group selection for defense.* Male gibbons (*Hyalobates*), as illustrated in *A*, show little difference in body size and dentition from females, as shown in *B*; defense against predators in such social *arboreal* primates is usually on an individual basis. In a terrestrial social primate such as the baboon (*Papio*) the male (*C*) is much larger and stronger than the female (*D*) with the canines especially developed as very effective tearing and piercing weapons. This adaptation of the dog baboon favors the survival of the troop as well as the individual male, and therefore provides an example of group selection. (Based partly on a drawing in Eimerl and DeVore, 1965.)

is normally employed to maintain order. In macaques, for example, a "threat thermometer" has been formulated (Figure 2-13). Starting with the mildest form of threat, a stare, it rises through an open-mouthed glare to "bobbing," which is the most extreme form of threat short of actual physical contact. Supplementing these threats are subsidiary behavioral performances, the drawing back of the ears, grunts, forward steps, slapping the ground, and a number of other ritual procedures and actions.

If dominance is accepted by the individual being threatened, there are various forms of submissive gestures which signal acceptance. Among them are looking away, crouching close to the ground, actual flight, abandoning food, offers of grooming, and permitting symbolic mounting.

The dominance system in baboons and macaques is further complicated by the fact that, unlike dominance in other social animals such as birds and certain other mammals, there appears to be a system of dominance by a

Figure 2-13. *The "threat thermometer" in macaques* (*Macaco*). The lowest level threat is *staring* (*A*), followed by an open-mouthed *glare* (*B*). The most extreme threat not involving physical contact is *bobbing* (*C*). (Based partly on a drawing in Eimerl and DeVore, 1965.)

clique rather than by individual members (Figure 2-14). This may be because aggression is so strongly developed in these terrestrial primates that it would be impossible for one individual to maintain dominance in the face of such strong rivalries. Moreover, individual dominance would pose a survival problem for a troop subject to predation and attack; it is likely that the troop would be disorganized at least long enough for serious damage to be done to it if the one top individual were suddenly incapacitated. If, on the other hand, dominance is shared by a small establishment, it is not so exposed to the possibility of this catastrophe.

The female hierarchy is not so clearly established in baboons as is the male one. This is partly related to the cyclic hierarchical situation imposed by the reproductive cycle through which the female passes periodically. As long as the female has an infant with her in close attendance, she remains, as it were, outside the female dominance hierarchy. Likewise, a female in estrus is also in a special hierarchical category.

Hereditary Dominance Cliques

Nevertheless, one effect of even this loose hierarchical structure in the female population of a troop is a hereditary position for offspring in the

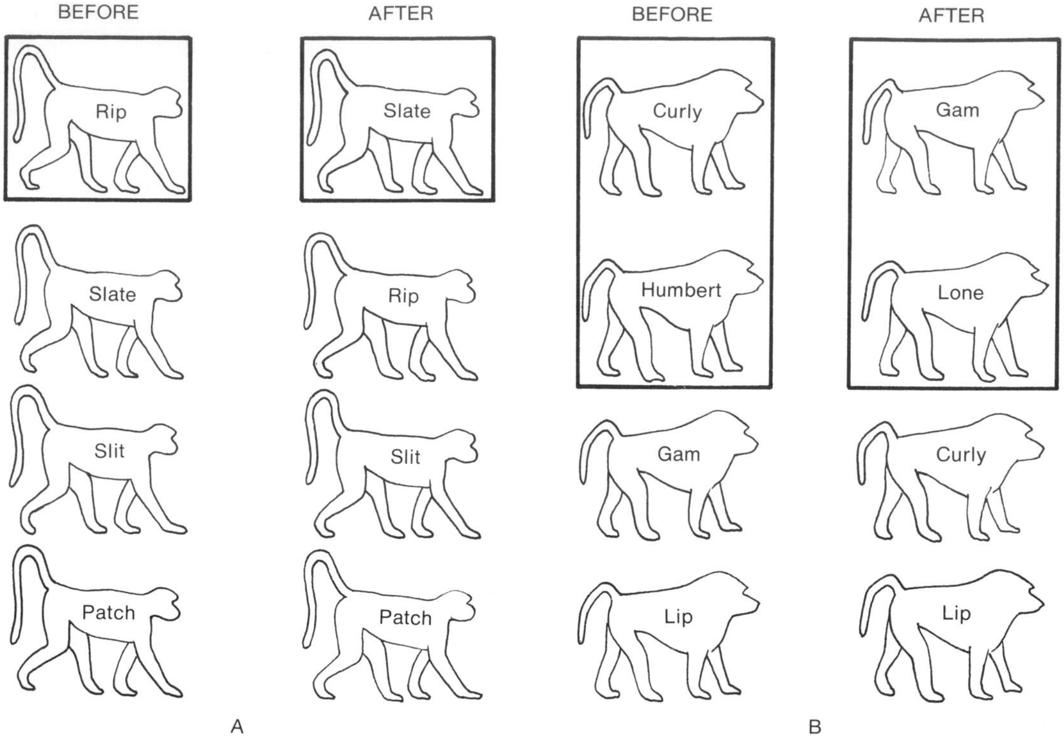

Figure 2-14. *Dominance cliques.* A langur troop observed by P. Jay had the simple individual dominance hierarchy illustrated in *A*. The animals to which she gave the names indicated exchanged positions when Slate browbeat Rip into surrendering dominance to him. In a macaque troop, as reported by Imanishi, two males, Curly and Humbert, combined to form a dominance clique (*B*). When Humbert disappeared, Gam formed a clique with a male Lone from outside the troop, and the two displaced Curly at the head of the dominance hierarchy. (Based partly on a drawing in Eimerl and DeVore, 1965.)

troop hierarchy. A male offspring born to a dominant female is less continuously harassed by the bickering and squabbling of the females, and will be more serene and arrogant, likely to occupy a high place in the order when adult. The male offspring of a female in the lowest hierarchical cluster will be pushed around as an infant and in adulthood is more likely to retain a similarly low place in the male hierarchical order. This hereditary acquisition of hierarchical status may result in a clique of siblings, associated with nephews and nieces, coming to monopolize the uppermost hierarchical positions—a primate example of nepotism.

It is tempting to read anthropomorphic analogies into this behavior on the part of baboon and other terrestrial primate troops. It is equally dangerous to argue from these behavioral patterns to the probable behavior of fossil apes such as *Proconsul.* It is possible that any similarities in either case are due entirely to coincidence or a common response to selection pressures which evoke rather similar adaptations, in the same manner that ecological equivalents can be developed with apparently similar morphological adaptations.

The same argument applies in even greater force to the behavior of infants —and in particular to the significance of single as opposed to multiple births—and the unique feature of the grip which the infant, using all four limbs, maintains on its mother's hair, either on her back or on her front. This behavior could be a matter of a common response to a similar need in any arboreal population.

Clasping

The question of clasping has also been the subject of experimental investigation. Harlow and Harlow (1962) report a number of experiments on surrogate "mothers." In one of these half the surrogates had bare wire bodies, whereas similar structures were covered with terry cloth for the other half. They further developed this variation by providing a milk supply in one half of the terry cloth-covered surrogates. To these various surrogates the Harlows introduced newborn macaque babies. By far the strongest attraction was found to lie in the terry cloth, rather than in the milk, and the infants spent considerable periods huddled up against the surrogates provided with this cloth, whether or not there was also a milk supply. In this and other experiments the Harlows were able to demonstrate that the infant macaque's primary need was for the security provided by contact with its mother's body. Without this the infant would be frightened by any strange objects, but if he could return to his cloth-covered surrogate, he would eventually overcome his fear of anything new and proceed to investigate it.

Evolution of Group Activities

There is one further major difference between an arboreal and a terrestrial primate in the significance of the clinging action of infants. Although both groups tend to seek refuge in trees, the time which the arboreal species will spend in them is usually a longer portion of the day. The effect of a single moment's slackening of the grip of the infant on its mother will usually be fatal, and the clinging relationship develops uniquely between the mother and her offspring. In terrestrial groups, which will only resort momentarily to trees to escape danger, and to pass the night, a continuous and persistent clinging is not such a vital necessity, and this protective mother-child relationship is extended to any member of the troop, including the males. If an infant is threatened on the ground by some predator, any animal in the troop will remove it to safety.

There is a reasonable supposition that the essentially terrestrial *Proconsul* forms exhibited behavioral patterns not very dissimilar from those reported for baboons. To what extent these patterns were transmitted to hominids will be further discussed in another section.

As to the question of communication, Hockett and Ascher (1964) speculate that at the level of *Proconsul* this was probably by means of a *call system* quite similar to that of modern gibbons (Carpenter, 1940). They argue that the gibbon call system has evolved little beyond the *Proconsul* stage, while in other anthropoids, where the call system appears less complex, there are more subtle means of variance. It seems possible, however, that the gibbon call system evolved to meet the needs of an arboreal social group whose members were normally unable to *see* one another. In a terrestrial social group, individual members would not usually be out of sight, and visual communication could have lessened the value of an advanced call system.

EVOLUTION OF *PROCONSUL*

The origins of *Proconsul* are not clear, but some fragmentary remains have been found of interesting primates in the Fayoum oasis in upper Egypt (Simons, 1964), which date from the Oligocene Epoch. From the anatomical structure of the forelimbs of some of these fossils, it is concluded that they may have been early brachiating forms. Like all apes they were tailless.

The location of such fossil forms so far north in Africa may appear strange. However, somewhat scanty remains in the form of macrofossils suggest that in mid-Tertiary times a tropical rain forest-type vegetation extended this far beyond the Tropic of Cancer, reaching to the shore of the Mediterranean which was then, because of marine transgression, located much further south than now. It might be expected that the ancestors of ground apes would be the rapidly evolving group of brachiating apes, and that terrestrial adaptations would occur in precisely such marginal forest habitats where interplay between the increasingly arid climate and the adaptation of more fit plant types would take place, and where grassland ecosystems were developing for the first time.

Characteristics of *Proconsul*

From the skeletal structure of the foot and leg, and the form of the pelvic girdle, it is surmised that *Proconsul* could stand approximately upright and would be able to shamble along at least for a time in this position (Figure 2–9). The assumption of an upright habit was not yet fully facilitated by these skeletal adaptations, and probably for an appreciable amount of the time the various *Proconsul* forms would run on all fours in a manner similar to a modern chimpanzee.

The dentition of *Proconsul* in all its forms includes massive canine teeth, which implies that this genus of ground apes probably had not yet assumed the extensive use of artifacts as defensive tools, but, like its brachiating arboreal ancestors defended itself by biting. Studies on the origin of tool-using employ the decreasing size of the canines as evidence for the substitution of artifacts in defense instead of teeth, and therefore the development of tool-using and later tool-making species. The significance of the bipedal habit also lies in its indication of this tool-using ability. An upright posture is a disadvantage in terms of running speed, but it frees the arms to use and carry tools. The structure of the hand, and in particular the arrangements for the opposition of the thumb and fingers, also have some bearing on tool use and tool making.

Proconsul was not a single species of ground ape. At least two forms are known to have occurred which we can demonstrate by lumping the larger skeletons which have been found into one species and the smaller ones into another. It is probable that these early ground apes, even if they originated from a single common ancestor, diversified rapidly in the new valley grassland habitat. On such slender evidence as the skeletal remains, which is all we have today, it is difficult to make any conclusions about the behavioral patterns of these first ground apes. It can, however, be conjectured that they were social animals associated in troops, and with a nucleated territoriality. That is to say, the territory was not defended at its boundaries, as is the case with many birds, but each group was centered upon a particular area, with commonly overlapping use of marginal portions.

Some support for the proposition that *Proconsul* was a social animal may be deduced from the prosimians of Madagascar. This large island became separated from the African mainland at some time in the early Cenozoic not yet precisely determined. Its separation may have been completed by the Miocene, because no primate form higher than a prosimian has ever been present, while these are still extensively represented by a total of fifteen living species of lemur. Of these, six are nocturnal and solitary, but all the other nine species are not only diurnal, but are also social animals (Petter, 1962). This social behavior in surviving diurnal prosimians, as well as in monkey-grade primates, suggests it is unlikely the diurnal *Proconsul* was an evolutionary exception.

Pigmentation in *Proconsul*

Because of the dense hairy coat which *Proconsul* species supposedly possessed, they would have had to forage in the grasslands in the early morning and late afternoon, passing the night and the heat of the day in the forest margins, probably roosting in trees at night as do the modern chimpanzees, gorillas, and baboons. They would have been diurnal animals with little or no night vision. Because of the comparatively low light intensity beneath the canopy of the forests which their ancestors had occupied, they would not at first have been heavily pigmented. Probably one of the earliest adaptations to a terrestrial life in forest clearings was to develop a heavy pigmentation in the naked parts of the skin, especially the face, to prevent overproduction of vitamin D when they ventured into grassland habitats. The same kind of pigmentation is seen in modern tropical apes, which similarly are exposed to full sunlight in forest clearings. This issue will be returned to later.

Predation

With the possible exception of occasional attacks by leopardlike animals which may have evolved by this time, and by large snakes, the arboreal ancestors of *Proconsul* would have suffered little predation. As Simons (1963) notes, some genera of carnivores, including the big cats (*Panthera*), are known from late Miocene–early Pliocene deposits (10–15 million years BP). On the grasslands there would likewise be no immediate evolution of a predator sufficiently strong and courageous to brave the bites from the large canines of the dominant male members of a *Proconsul* troop. The many rodent species there would be far easier prey for any predator. Again, the island of Madagascar may support this contention, for the prosimian populations there have no predators apart from snakes. Grasslands do not appear to have been part of the original landscape of Madagascar either, and neither are antelope, bovine, or equine species found there. Perhaps the big cat predators of the African mainland did not evolve until the larger herbivorous herd animals became established on grassland and savanna.

Diet of *Proconsul*

The general nature of the diet in the grassland ecosystem would probably be little different in form for terrestrial primates from that in the forest. It might have consisted of insects and underground storage organs of plants, varied with edible fruits at particular times of year. Obviously some forest foods would continue to be used. As herbivorous animals, large and small, adapted to the grassland habitat, *Proconsul* may also have scavenged dead animals, or even chased and caught smaller ones, particularly rodents. This chasing activity could have had considerable evolutionary significance, as will be discussed later.

Distribution of *Proconsul*

Although this composite group of ground apes which is placed in the genus *Proconsul* must have been common and extensively distributed in some parts of tropical Africa throughout the Miocene, no representatives of it are known from any other part of the world, nor have any related forms yet been found in the succeeding epochs of the Tertiary or the Pliocene. There is therefore a gap of some 20 million years before further and more recent forms of ground apes are known to have occurred; only in the past several years have scientists begun to fill this gap.

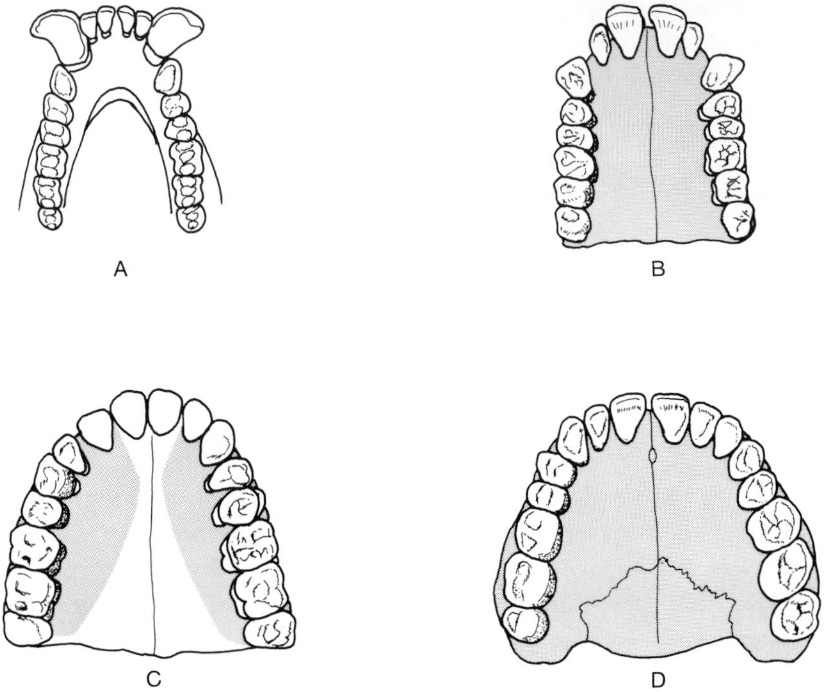

Figure 2-15. *Comparison of dentition of* RAMAPITHECUS *with that of other anthropoids. A.* Capuchin (*Cebus*). *B. Orangutan* (*Pongo*). *C. Ramapithecus. D.* Man. All are scaled so as to reduce to the same length. The U-shaped arc in the capuchin and orangutan contrast distinctly with the curved arc of *Ramapithecus* and man. Simons considers this as supporting the contention that *Ramapithecus* is the oldest ancestral hominid known and a distinct genus from *Proconsul.* The lack of conspicuous canines suggests one of three possibilities: *Ramapithecus* was essentially an arboreal form, it lacked troop dominance hierarchies, or it was able to defend itself with artifacts. See text for further explanation.

Simons (1963) suggests that the restriction of *Proconsul* to Africa may have been the consequence of taxonomic proliferation of dryopithecine genera and may be more apparent than real. He notes that from sites in Europe, Africa, and Asia which are considered to have had a relatively warm climate in the Miocene, many fossil "ape" genera have been described. He believes that all these could be reduced to at most four genera, *Dryopithecus, Sivapithecus, Proconsul,* and *Ramapithecus.* A species of the last genus, *R. brevirostris* from the early Pliocene of the Siwalik hills of India, has dental features remarkably similar to the Pleistocene australopithecines to be discussed in Chapter 3 (Figure 2–15). Leakey (1962) has described a contemporaneous East African specimen, *Kenyapithecus wickeri,* which in Simons' opinion is not significantly different from forms described under *Ramapithecus.*

SEPARATION OF PONGID AND HOMINID LINES

Although fossil remains from the Pliocene are rare, an elegant method of approaching such a time gap in a phylogenetic progression has been described by Sarich and Wilson (1967) using immunological cross reactions. This method is based on the clear structural relationship between proteins and genes, and the supposition that quantitative comparative studies of protein structure will aid in clarifying the genetic relationship.

Sarich and Wilson have demonstrated that albumin evolution in primates is a very regular process, and that lineages of equal time depth show similar degrees of change in their albumins. Therefore, the degrees of change exhibited would appear to be a function of time. Through a mathematical relationship between an index of dissimilarity determined by immunological methods, they fix the time of divergence of two species of primates.

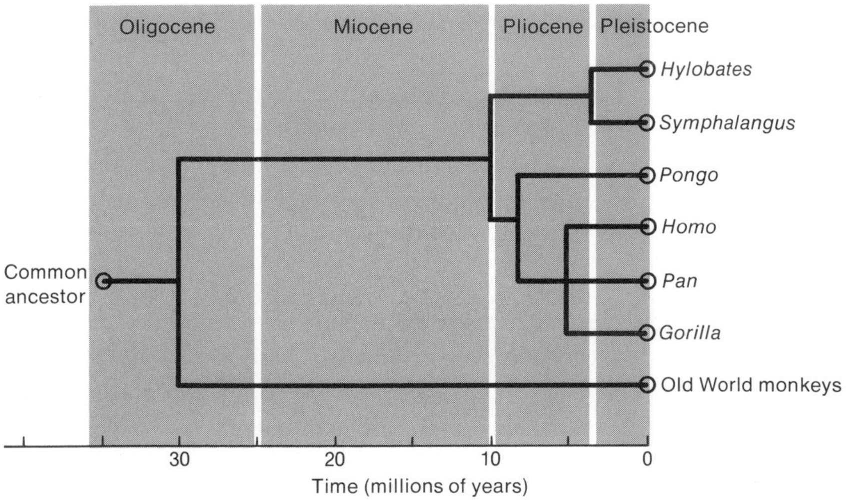

Figure 2-16. *The time of divergence of pongid and hominid stocks* as estimated using immunological data from contemporary anthropoid groups. Sarich and Wilson (1967) suggest a date of 5 million years BP for this separation, but as seen from their diagram, they place this event in the early part of the Pliocene. Revised calculations of Pliocene dates could therefore modify this time estimate. (Reproduced with the permission of the authors and publisher from V. M. Sarich and A. C. Wilson, *Science,* **158**:1201, 1967. Copyright 1967 by the American Association for the Advancement of Science.)

The results of such an examination are shown in Figure 2–16, in which it can be seen that Old World monkeys and an undifferentiated hominid-pongid stock shared a common ancestor in the Oligocene. This is consistent with the supposition that populations referred to the genus *Proconsul* represent terrestrial forms of a group of arboreal apes which became highly successful in the Oligocene owing to the development of the locomotor-feeding adaptation of *brachiation.*

The albumins of the gorilla, chimpanzee, and man were considered to be equidistantly related. The three genera into which these forms are presently placed, *Gorilla, Pan,* and *Homo,* are thought to have separated in the late Pliocene, whereas the orangutan (*Pongo*) diverged from this anthropoid group in the early Pliocene; the gibbons and simiangs did so at the very beginning of the Pliocene, only finally branching into individual genera (*Hylobates* and *Synbalangus*) at the close of the Pleistocene.

These biochemical investigations, which can be further substantiated by an examination of other amino acid sequences of proteins, clearly have interesting applications in confirming deductions from fossil remains, and in providing hypotheses of phylogenetic relationships even if fossils are lacking. In the particular instance of the origin of the genus *Homo,* they appear to substantiate the general time scale for evolution of the earliest members of this genus from a prosimian primate stock during the early Tertiary.

The next chapter describes the appearance of the genus *Homo* and the relationship and evolution of its presently known forms. *Proconsul* is the last of the identified fossil forms to show a mixture of hominid and pongid characteristics. Later anthropoid ape fossils are considered to represent groups which have clearly evolved into populations referable either to the genus *Homo* or to one of the various great ape genera.

Features which the first terrestrial anthropoid apes, as represented by *Proconsul,* have contributed to our own morphology, physiology, and behavior, and which have therefore persisted for some 25 million years, may be summarized as:

1. A pentadactyl limb structure, with hind limbs modified for bipedal movement, together with an orthograde body position
2. A clavicle, permitting extensive movement of the forelimbs, and opposable thumbs, both facilitating tool-using
3. A diurnal habit, associated with stereoscopic color vision and a drastic reduction in olfactory capabilities, associated with increased conceptual brain development
4. Single births, with long gestation and infancy periods, the latter relating to learning through play and imitation
5. A social grouping with dominance hierarchies, inherited dominance cliques, and a communication system
6. Selection for social characters such as group identity and defense, infant protection, and group occupation of a nucleated territory
7. Development of pigmentation on exposed body surfaces to prevent overproduction of vitamin D
8. An omnivorous diet, associated with a dentition of identical dental formula, but with canines in *Homo* not projecting beyond the level of the other teeth

As far as morphological and physiological adaptation is concerned, ecological evolution in *Proconsul* has almost reached the point where any further development has to be regarded as producing only minor changes. The dominant emphasis hereafter is on cultural adaptation.

Bibliography

REFERENCES

Altman, S. A. "Social behavior of anthropoid primates: analysis of recent concepts," in E. L. Bliss (ed.), *Roots of Behavior,* New York: Harper, 1952, pp. 277–85.

Bishop, A. "Use of the hand in lower primates," in J. Buettner-Janusch (ed.), *Evolutionary and Genetic Biology of Primates,* Vol. 2, New York: Academic Press, 1964, p. 133.

Bond, G. *Past Climates of Central Africa,* London: Oxford University Press, 1962.

Boughey, A. S. *The Origin of the African Flora,* London: Oxford University Press, 1957.

Brooks, C. E. P. *Climate Through the Ages,* New York: Coleman, 1926.

Brooks, C. E. P. "Geological and historical aspects of climate change," in *Compendium of Meterology,* Boston: Malone, pp. 1004–1018, 1951.

Carpenter, C. R. "A field study in Siam of the behavior and social relations of the gibbon," Comparative Psychology Monographs No. 16, 1940 (republished in C. R. Carpenter, *Naturalistic Behavior of Non-Human Primates,* University Park, Penn.: Pennsylvania State University Press, 1944).

Corner, E. J. H. "The durian theory or the origin of the modern tree," *Ann. Bot.,* **13:** 367–417, 1949.

Echlin, P. "The origins of plants," *New Scientist,* **42:** 286–89, 1969.

Haldane, J. B. S. "The argument from animals to men: an examination of its value in anthropology," Huxley Memorial Lecture, *J. Roy. Anthrop. Inst.,* **86:** 1–14, 1956.

Hall, K. R. L. "The sexual, agonistic and derived social behavior patterns of the wild chacma baboon *Papio ursinus,*" *Proc. Zool. Soc. London,* **139:** 131, 1962.

Harlow, H. F., and Harlow, M. K. "Social deprivation in monkeys," *Scientific American,* **207**(5): 136–46, 1962.

Harrison, R. L., and Montagna, W. *Man,* New York: Appleton-Century-Crofts, 1969.

Hockett, C. F., and Ascher, R. "The human revolution," *Curr. Anthrop.,* **5**(3): 135–68, 1964.

Jay, P. "Aspects of material behavior among langurs," *Ann. N.Y. Acad. Sci.,* **102:** 468, 1963.

Jay, P. "The common langur of North India," in J. DeVore (ed.), *Primate Behavior,* New York: Holt, Rinehart and Winston, pp. 197–249, 1965.

Leakey, L. S. B. "A Miocene anthropoid mandible from Rusinga, Kenya," *Nature,* **152:** 319, 1943.

Leakey, L. S. B. "A new lower Pliocene fossil primate from Kenya," *Ann. Mag. Nat. Hist.,* **4:** 689, 1962.

Macinnes, D. G. "Notes on the East African Miocene primates," *J. E. African and Uganda Nat. Hist. Soc.,* **17:** 141–81, 1943.

Petter, J. J. "L'ecologie et l'ethologie des lemuriens Malgaches," *Memoires du Museum d'Histoire Naturelle,* t27, fasc. 1, Paris, 1962.

Sarich, V. M., and Wilson, A. C. "Immunological time scale for hominid evolution," *Science,* **158:** 1200–1203, 1967.

Seward, A. C. *Plant Life Through the Ages,* Cambridge: Cambridge University Press, 1931 .

Simons, E. L. "Some fallacies in the study of hominid phylogeny," *Science,* **141:** 879–89, 1963.

Simons, E. L. "The early relatives of man," *Scientific American,* **211**(1): 50–62, 1964.

Simons, E. L. "The earliest apes," *Scientific American,* **217**(6): 28–35, 1967.

Tavener-Smith, R. "Glacial phenomena in the lower Karroo rocks of the Kandabure coal area, Zambesi Valley," *Rec. Geol. Surv. Northern Rhodesia,* 19–22, 1955.

Washburn, S. L., and DeVore, I. "The social life of baboons," *Scientific American,* **204**(6): 62–71, 1961.

Wynne-Edwards, V. C. "Intergroup selection in the evolution of social systems," *Nature,* **200:** 623, 1963.

FURTHER READINGS

Campbell, B. G. *Human Evolution,* Chicago: Aldine, 1966.

Colbert, E. H. "The ancestors of mammals," *Scientific American,* **180**(3): 40–43, 1949.

Davis, P. R. "Hominid fossils from Bed I Olduvai: a tibia and fibula," *Nature,* **201:** 967–68, 1964.

Davis, P. R., and Napier, J. "A reconstruction of the skull of *Proconsul africanus* (R.S. 51)," *Folia Primat.,* **1:** 20–28, 1963.

Day, M. *Guide to Fossil Man,* London: Cassel, 1965.

Eimerl, S., and DeVore, I. *The Primates,* New York: Time-Life, 1965.

Emiliani, C. "Ancient temperatures," *Scientific American,* **198**(2): 54–62, 1958.

Goodman, M. "Immunochemistry of the primates and primate evolution," *Ann. N.Y. Acad. Sci.,* **102:** 219, 1962.

Le Gros Clark, W. E. *The Fossil Evidence for Human Evolution,* 2nd ed., Chicago: University of Chicago Press, 1964.

Napier, J. R., and Davis, P. R. *The Forelimb Skeleton and Associated Remains of Proconsul africanus,* London: British Museum (Nat. Hist.), 1959.

Napier, J. R., and Napier, P. H. *Handbook of Living Primates,* New York: Academic Press, 1966.

Newell, N. D. "Crises in the history of life," *Scientific American,* **208**(2): 76–92, 1963.

Oakley, K. P. "Dating the emergence of man," *Advancement of Science,* **18**: 415–26, 1962.

Pilbeam, D. "Gigantopithecus and the origins of Hominidae," *Nature,* **225**: 516–19, 1970.

Rheingold, H. L. (ed.) *Maternal Behavior in Mammals,* New York: Wiley, 1963.

Rosenblum, L. A., and Cooper, R. W. (eds.) *The Squirrel Monkey,* New York: Academic Press, 1968.

Schultz, A. H. "Some factors influencing the social life of primates in general and early man in particular," in S. L. Washburn (ed.), *Social Life of Early Man,* Chicago: Aldine, 1961, pp. 58–90.

Simons, E. L. "On the mandible of *Ramapithecus,*" *Proc. Nat. Acad. Sci. U.S.A.,* **51**: 528–36, 1964.

Tattersall, I. "More on the ecology of North Indian Ramapithecus," *Nature,* **224**: 821–22, 1969.

Tobias, P. V. "Early man in East Africa," *Science,* **149**: 22–23, 1965.

Van Valen, L., and Sloan, R. E. "The earliest primates," *Science,* **150**: 743–45, 1965.

Wilson, A. T. "Origin of ice ages: an ice shelf theory for pleistocene glaciation," *Nature,* **201**: 147–49, 1964.

Wood, A. E. "Eocene radiation and phylogeny of the rodents," *Evolution,* **13**: 354–61, 1959.

Pleistocene Hominids

3

Chapter 2 considered the coevolution of plants and animals in the late Mesozoic and early Cenozoic through adaptive radiation in both the primates and the flowering plants of the evolving tropical rain forest ecosystem. Increasing aridity led to the development in this ecosystem of valley grasslands, on which there evolved pongid and hominid forms, differentiating from a common anthropoid stock. Despite the long geologic interval which has since elapsed, certain characteristics of the early pongid-hominid stock, as represented by *Proconsul,* appear to be identifiable in our own contemporary species. This chapter considers the evolution of Pleistocene hominids, and their continuing divergence and differentiation, which resulted in the development of further human features.

THE PLIOCENE-PLEISTOCENE BOUNDARY

The duration of the Pliocene epoch has not yet been determined. The Miocene is believed to have ended some 12 to 13 million years ago, and the Pleistocene until comparatively recently was thought to have begun about 1 million years ago. However, a growing consensus now places the Pliocene-Pleistocene boundary at somewhere from 3½ to 4 million years ago. As this postdating has not generally affected the time estimates of the onset of glaciations, the interval of the Pleistocene which preceded the ice ages, generally known as the Villafranchian, has become greatly extended. The situation is further confused by the fact that "Villafranchian" is sometimes applied to the last epoch of the Pliocene.

The Villafranchian

The Villafranchian is essentially a stratigraphically defined geological interval recognized by the contemporary occurrence of the remains of the four genera *Equus* (horse), *Elephas* (elephant), *Camelus* (camel), and *Bison* (bison). As these genera are believed to have originated in the New World and subsequently to have spread from there to the Old, their occurrence in Eurasia implies some continuity of the Bering land bridge, and therefore a significant alteration of the relative levels of sea and land in that region.

The periods of continuity between Eurasia and North America appear to have become successively shorter as the Cenozoic progressed, and the opportunities for transcontinental migration accordingly became more restricted. After the last of the four genera to evolve, *Elephas*, had migrated, there was apparently no major faunal movement across this Bering land bridge apart from that of *Homo* himself.

Many authorities now consider that the start of the Villafranchian, and therefore of the Pleistocene period, can be dated from the time when *Elephas* is first noted in Old World deposits. This time has yet to be confirmed by potassium-argon dating, but it appears likely that when this is done, it will be somewhere around 4 million BP (Table 3-1).

Table 3-1 ***Estimated Chronological Range of Principal Hominid Grades*** There is still some uncertainty as to the precise dating of these geological periods, which is really of no overriding concern. As seen from this table, there is even more uncertainty of the precise dates of appearance and extinction of particular hominid "grades."

Period	*Grade*	*Approximate Life Span of "Grade" or Species*
Holocene 0–30,000 BP	*Homo sapiens*	40,000 years
Pleistocene 30,000–4 million BP	*erectus-sapiens* (2 million to 40,000 BP)	? 2,000,000 years
	Homo erectus (4 million to 2 million BP)	? 2,000,000 years
	Paranthropus species } *Homo africanus* (? continuing from late Pliocene, relicts persisting perhaps to about 1 million BP) ↓	3,000,000 years
Pliocene 4 million to 12–13 million BP	(? found in late Pliocene)	
	(continuity into early Pliocene) ↑	
Miocene	*Ramapithecus* (late Miocene)	? 5,000,000 years
	Proconsul (middle Miocene)	? 5,000,000 years

Dating Techniques

In addition to the radiometric measurement of age by the potassium-argon method, which utilizes the estimated decay rate of the radioactive isotope of potassium, K-40, to form argon (described in Appendix II), there is now another dating method for this period employing an analysis of deep-sea sediments. This is based on the circumstance that climatic fluctuations are reflected in the planktonic composition of these sediments. If changes in the sediments can be correlated with a number of independently established dates, an absolute time sequence of sediments can be produced. Using such comparatively new methods of dating, which are further described in Appendix II, the time of the first glaciation, which ended the Villafranchian, the Günz, is now placed at 1½ million years ago.

Tropical Time Sequences

The somewhat indefinite time schedule in the Pleistocene is further confused when one turns to the tropics, and correlations with tropical African sequences are still very incomplete (Table 3-2). It is therefore somewhat difficult to integrate into a time sequence the next series of early Pleistocene fossils to be discovered, which are for convenience now commonly lumped together under the general term of *Australopithecines*. This word means "southern apes" and implies no special relationships with either pongid (ape) or hominid (human) lines.

Table 3-2 ***Correlations Between Regional Climatic Sequences in the Pleistocene*** These are still uncertain. The original basal sequence which referred to glaciations in the Swiss Alps, now must be correlated with nonalpine occurrences in temperate North America and Eurasia, and with wet and dry periods in the tropics. Correlations and absolute dating shown here for the several wet and dry episodes in African Pleistocene prehistory are still largely conjectural.

Pluvial-Sequences in Tropical Eastern Africa	*Glacial Intervals in Swiss Alps*	*Approximate Absolute Datings in 1000 Years* BP
Dry phase	Interstadial	10
Gamblian pluvial	Würm	70
Dry phase	Interstadial	
Kanjeran pluvial	Riss	300
Dry phase	Interstadial	
Kamasian pluvial	Mindel	500
Dry phase	Interstadial	
Kageran pluvial	Günz	750

AUSTRALOPITHECINES

The first of the Australopithecines to be correctly so designated was found at Tuang, in what is now Botswana. It was the skull of a juvenile animal aged about six years and was described by a professor of anatomy, R. A.

Dart. With the amazing combination of skill and intuition characteristic of the various workers who have been associated with such hominid finds, Dart immediately recognized in this six-year-old skull a form of ape entirely different from any previously discovered in early Pleistocene deposits, and he named it *Australopithecus africanus* (Dart, 1925). It is the first of a group, found especially in the Transvaal Province of South Africa, which will probably come to be known as *Homo africanus,* although the nomenclature in such hominid lines is excessively confused at the present time (Simons *et al.,* 1969). Indeed, it seems cavalier to engage in taxonomic lumping and so briefly to sweep away the arguments arising from the

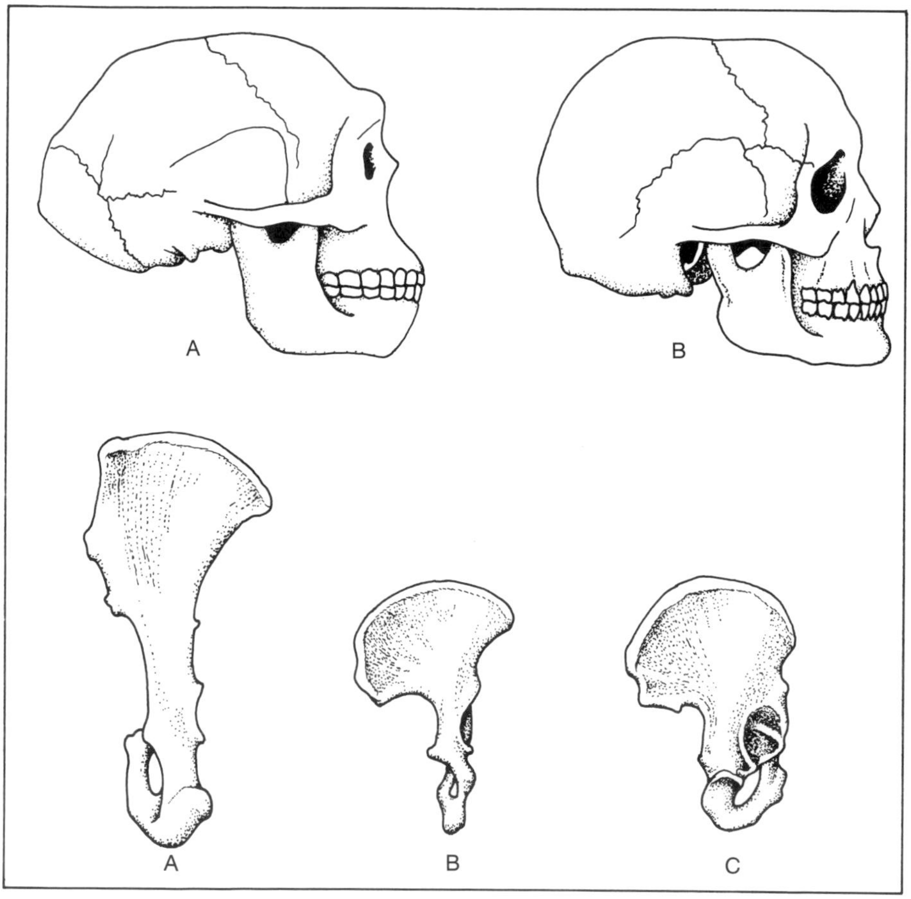

Figure 3-1. *The skull and pelvis of Homo africanus* reconstructed and drawn from a number of fragmental skeletal remains. Above, skull of *H. africanus* (*A*) compared with that of *H. sapiens* (*B*). Below, half pelvis of *H. africanus* (*B*) compared with that of a gorilla (*A*) and *H. sapiens* (*C*). This hominid form has been variously referred to as *Australopithecus transvaalensis, Homo transvaalensis,* and a number of other epithets. Its cranial capacity exceeded that of any known contemporary or fossil pongid and overlapped that of contemporary man, so that it is now generally placed in the genus *Homo.* Although an extensive tool-user, conclusive evidence of tool manufacture is lacking, and for the purposes of this text, tool-using forms such as this are all placed under this one species. Fossil remains have been found over a wide area of tropical Africa, and variously dated from about 4 million to some ½ million years BP.

patient, scholarly, and skilled work devoted to each of these still rare hominid finds, as well exemplified in a review by Simons (1968). However, some simplified theme must be identified.

Homo africanus

Subsequent findings of skulls and skeletons of mature animals reveal that the hominids included within this aggregate species, which appear to have been extensively distributed in Southern Africa from 600,000 or 700,000 years ago to not later than 250,000 years BP, were about one half or one third the size of present-day Americans. Their weight is estimated to have varied from about 60 to 120 lb. They had pronounced bony ridges above their eyes and jaws which were massive in relation to the size of their skulls. Although these last two features would appear to suggest their placement in the pongid line, their brains were significantly and substantially larger than those of modern apes in comparison to their size; estimates of cranial capacity vary from 600 to 900 cm^3. On this basis alone they are best regarded as hominids.

Examination of *H. africanus* skulls shows that the spinal cord enters the bottom rather than the back of the skull (Figue 3-1). The head was thus carried erect and this hominid walked upright, as was confirmed when a complete humanlike half pelvis was discovered in 1947 (Figure 3-1). Coupled with a strong reduction of the canines which, while still large, scarcely projected beyond the incisors, this led to the deduction that *H. africanus* was an extensive tool-user (Figure 3-2).

The Earliest Occurrence of *H. africanus*

Although many of the earlier australopithecine finds were estimated to be in the region of half a million years old, some remains at Olduvai gorge

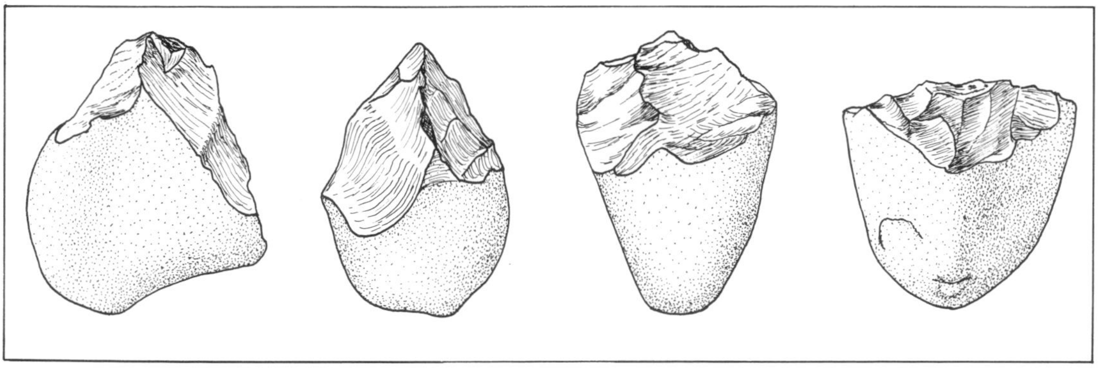

Figure 3-2. *Pebble tools* were primitive tools which could have been manufactured artifacts made and used by *Homo africanus,* or accidentally fractured pebbles which were merely selected when needed. Pebbles such as this have been found in various African localities in association with remains of several *Homo* species, and also with those of *Paranthropus.* One-quarter natural size.

were dated between 1.75 and 2.5 million years BP. Excavations in 1967 and 1968 by F. Clark Howell and his Chicago University group in the Omo valley of Ethiopia (Howell, 1969), reported on prior to this by R. Leakey (1968), suggest that australopithecines of both an *H. africanus* and *Paranthropus* type (see below) existed about 4 million years BP. Although the full significance of this postdating of australopithecine appearance relative to the also postdated revised estimates of the commencement of the Pleistocene have not been assessed, the broad hypotheses of australopithecine relationships discussed here seem valid.

OLDUVAI DISCOVERIES—*HOMO HABILIS*

After the Transvaal finds, and before the recent Ethiopian ones, discoveries were made elsewhere in Africa of early Pleistocene hominids. The most extensive were those unearthed in the Olduvai gorge in northern Tanzania beginning with *Zinjanthropus boisei* in 1959 by L. S. B. Leakey, his wife, and his colleagues. Some of these were estimated to be even older than the Transvaal material, a potassium-argon date on one giving an age of nearly 2 million years. Unlike the South African material, the remains were extensively and undeniably associated with pebble tools, and gradually it was realized that they fell into two fairly distinct groups.

To state very simply what is coming to be a generally accepted pattern for these varied finds, on the one hand is a hominid group of smaller body size but with proportionally larger brains and less pronounced jaws and brow ridges, which are generally classified as one or another species of the genus *Homo,* creatures with an omnivorous diet. On the other hand is a

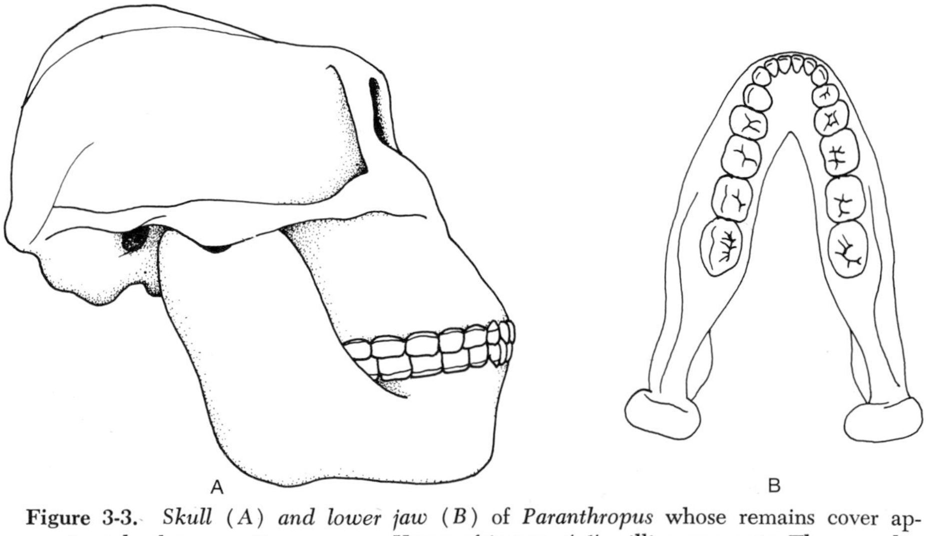

Figure 3-3. *Skull (A) and lower jaw (B)* of *Paranthropus* whose remains cover approximately the same time span as *Homo africanus,* 4–½ million years BP. They are distributed more widely over the Old World, however, reaching from tropical Africa to as far east as Central China and into Indonesia.

second hominid group with a larger body and more massive skull, with proportionally a rather lower brain capacity, and a largely vegetarian diet; this group is placed in the genus *Paranthropus* (Figure 3-3). The dentition of *Paranthropus* shows wear on the crowns of the molar teeth, which indicates that these creatures could *chew*, a distinction from modern pongids.

Pebble Tools

In 1959 Mrs. Leakey found fragments of a skull, subsequently allocated to *Zinjanthropus boisei*, lying on a working floor for the manufacture of pebble tools. This is cited as the first acceptable proof of what archeologists call a paleolithic or early stone-age culture associated with any Australopithecine. In 1960 less crude pebble tools were found associated with another type of Australopithecine, which, because of this greater tool-making ability, Dr. Leakey named *Homo habilis*. From essentially tool-using, and perhaps occasionally tool-making *Homo africanus*, a cultural ritual of extensive tool manufacture had now been clearly established with *Homo habilis*. It can thus be said that the evolution of human societies began in Africa in the early Pleistocene, approximately 2 million years ago. Perhaps further work and more finds over the next few years will double this estimate.

ASIAN AUSTRALOPITHECINES

The crude pebble tools which provide evidence of the earliest forms of human culture have now been sequentially arranged from artifacts discovered at Olduvai, and the culture has been termed *Oldowan*. The adaptive success of even the crudest of these tools, coupled with anatomical adaptions freeing the forelimbs for their manufacture, transport, and use—and perhaps associated with the development of other behavioral traits such as speech—is evidenced by their extensive occurrence from the Mediterranean coast to the Cape of Good Hope. Later and less crude forms are found even more extensively in many of the tropical and subtropical regions of the Old World. Australopithecine remains also have been discovered there.

Peking Man

Some of these finds were made at the same time, a few even previously to that of the African forms, but they were mostly too scattered to permit the construction of any substantial hypothesis before the African story had been partially pieced together. The best-known of these forms is "Peking man."

In 1927 several "human" teeth were discovered in a cave near the town of Choukoutien, about 30 miles southwest of Peiping, or Peking as it was

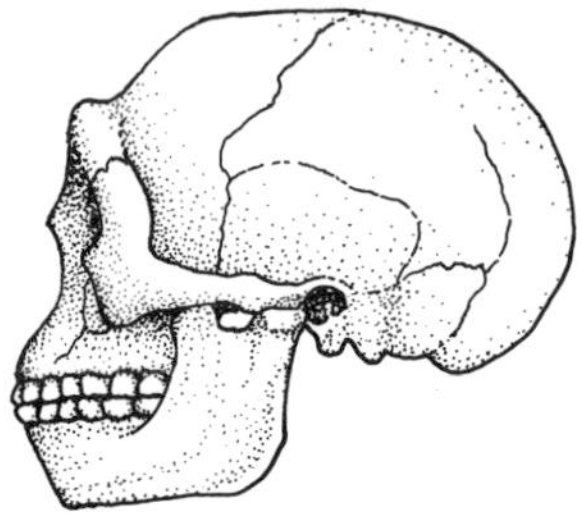

Figure 3-4. *Skull of the earliest form of Peking Man.* Although later material from the same deposits seems to belong definitely to *Homo erectus,* the earliest remains from the Choukoutien series can probably be considered as referrable to *Paranthropus.* They are tentatively dated to about 600,000 BP.

then generally called. Davidson Black, a Canadian anatomist at the Peking Union Medical College, after studying one of these teeth, stated that it belonged to a human species which he named *Sinanthropus pekinensis* (Figure 3-4). Excavations over the next 10 years in this same area not only revealed a rich series of fossil hominid remains, but also hearths with which were associated butchered and roasted animals. These various forms were painstakingly and accurately described and illustrated by a German refugee, Franz Weidenreich. This was fortunate, because virtually all the original fossil material crated for transport to the United States for safer storage disappeared at the time of Pearl Harbor and has never been recovered. This circumstance was almost as disastrous as the experience of J. T. Robinson in South Africa, who, returning to begin a new season's excavations, discovered that the cave limestone he was working for hominid remains had been sold to a toothpaste manufacturer.

Java Man

Many years before the work in China, in 1890, a Dutch anatomist, Eugene Dubois, inspired by reading *The Descent of Man* (Darwin, 1871), had searched for and found the first remains of what came to be called Java man. Dubois recognized the hominid nature of his finds and placed them in a new species, *Pithecanthropus erectus* (erect ape-man). The significance of his finds was lost because European "authorities" attacked Dubois' ideas so heatedly that he retreated into silence for 30 years. When he finally emerged again it is said he had lost his nerve and described his fossils as representing a new form of gibbon.

EUROPEAN AUSTRALOPITHECINES

It appears that this split-pebble culture, which hominids adopted toward the close of the Lower Pleistocene and which persisted for more than 600,000 years (Clark, 1963), conferred a great ecological advantage and led to extensive hominid dispersal over the Old World. Such a wide distribution is not common among animals, but it was achieved by other carnivores, for example *Panthera* (lion) and very large herbivores such as *Elephas* (elephant). Some idea of the distribution of this hominid phase may be obtained from the map of pebble-tool occurrence (Figure 3-2).

To date no hominid remains in Europe have been clearly related to the pebble-tool culture encountered there, but one fragmentary find has received attention which history may consider beyond proportion to its significance. In 1907 a hominid lower jaw was found in a sand pit in the village of Mauer, close to Heidelberg in West Germany. It was associated with an extensive megafauna including elephant, rhinoceros, horse, saber-toothed tiger, hippopotamus, and giant beaver. Even without modern methods of radiometric dating, this permitted the placing of the find in the interglacial interval between the Mindel (second) and Riss (third) glaciations of the Middle Pleistocene. A new species of *Homo, H. heidelbergensis,* was defined by O. Schoetensack at Heidelberg University on the basis of characteristics exhibited by his jaw. Such forms are now placed in *Homo erectus,* discussed in the next chapter, which deals with the later stages of human evolution.

TROPHIC DISPLACEMENT

From the fragmentary evidence of the scattered African remains discussed here, it would appear that over a wide geographical area of central and southern Africa, as in certain other regions of the Old World, various hominid species first assigned by their discoverers to many genera, but here reduced to either *Paranthropus* or *Homo,* were sympatric (Figures 3-5 and 3-6). It is supposed that there was competition between some of these coexisting hominid species because their upright habit, their tool using, their occupation of a similar ecological habitat (valley grasslands scattered in wooded or forested landscapes), their omnivorous diet, and probably troop behavioral patterns, would bring them into competition. Whenever this occurs, ecologists have observed that there must be *character displacement* if both species are to survive. That is to say, where sympatry develops there has to be modification of a particular character or characters which causes further niche diversification between the competing species. These then come to occupy slightly different ecological niches, and the species populations are thus able to avoid direct and annihilating competition.

In the case of *Homo* and *Paranthropus,* if the sweeping assumption is made that all these early Pleistocene hominids can be allocated to one genus or the other, a recent theory has suggested that *trophic displacement* or a behavioral diversification occurred (Schaffer, 1968). Whereas the species of both genera originally had an omnivorous diet, members of the genus *Homo* became more specialized in tool using, and eventually tool manufacture. They used this greater technology to maintain their omnivo-

Figure 3-5. *Paranthropus male and female.* The stature is upright and locomotion bipedal, teeth large, causing prognathy, but canines not exceeding the length of the other teeth, brains about the size of a modern gorilla. Total weight was probably about an average 140 lb in mature males, somewhat less in females; skin color black. Time period about 2 million years BP, distribution, Old World tropics. (Based on Matternes, 1965.)

rous diet and remained essentially secondary consumers (Figure 3–7). Species of the genus *Paranthropus* became increasingly and eventually exclusively vegetarian, *i.e.*, primary consumers, and did not greatly extend whatever tool using ability they possessed.

Put in slightly different terms, there was at first a jack-of-all-trades (*Homo africanus*) who was tool using and omnivorous. This jack came to be sympatric, i.e., he coexisted with a somewhat similar jack of different origin (*Paranthropus*). The latter was therefore forced by competition to adopt an exclusively vegetarian diet, becoming *P. robustus,* while the first became a tool maker and accentuated the carnivorous element of his diet (*H. habilis*). This hominid jack then evolved into a specialized tool-making carnivore (*H. erectus*), while *Paranthropus,* with competition thus reduced, tended to revert toward the original behavior of the *Paranthropus* jack.

The Aggression Theory

A rival theory explaining the origin of forms attributable to the genus *Homo* must be mentioned; it was presented by Ardrey (1961) after review-

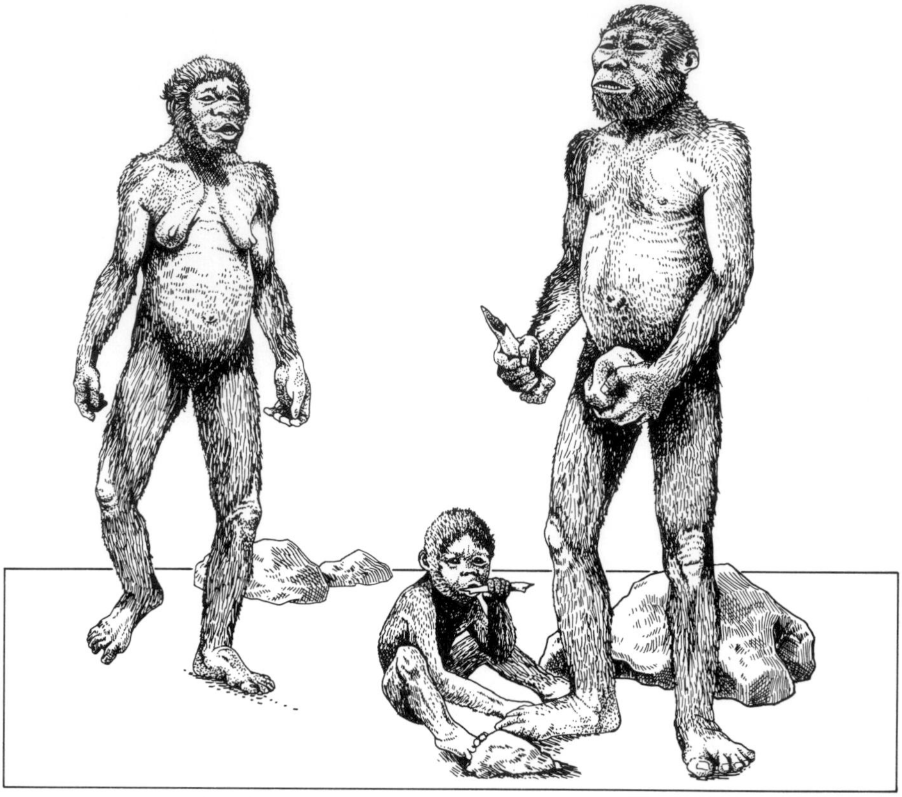

Figure 3-6. *Australopithecus africanus* male, female, and infant, contemporary and sympatric with *Paranthropus* illustrated in Figure 3-5. Similar upright stature and bipedalism, black skin pigment, hairiness, prognathy and large teeth, but with less massive jaws and slighter stature, averaging about 100 lb. Tool-using; shown here bashing bones with stones so as to permit extraction of bone marrow, but little different from *Paranthropus* in this respect. Time period the same, about 2 million BP, distribution also Old World. (Based on Matternes, 1965.)

ing the work of R. A. Dart. This theory is based on the discovery by Dart in South Africa of many fossil baboon skulls, 42 in fact, which had been battered in, with holes which fitted the indentations which could be made by the distal end of the femur of a small antelope. Ardrey and Dart maintained that such femurs were present in significantly larger proportions than they should have been if they were not used as weapons in this way. They presented the thesis that cultural behavior attributable to the genus *Homo* evolved when australopithecines discovered how to use a tool to destroy other sympatric animals, and especially other and competing anthropoid species. Thus, they claimed, originated the aggressive behavioral feature which has since characterized all hominid evolution. Ardrey (1966) subsequently amended this theory by incorporating it into a *territorial* concept.

Whether the emergence of *H. erectus* resulted from trophic displacement, the development of aggressive or territorial behavior, or some combination of these several features, it would have been impossible unless associated with the development of speech and language.

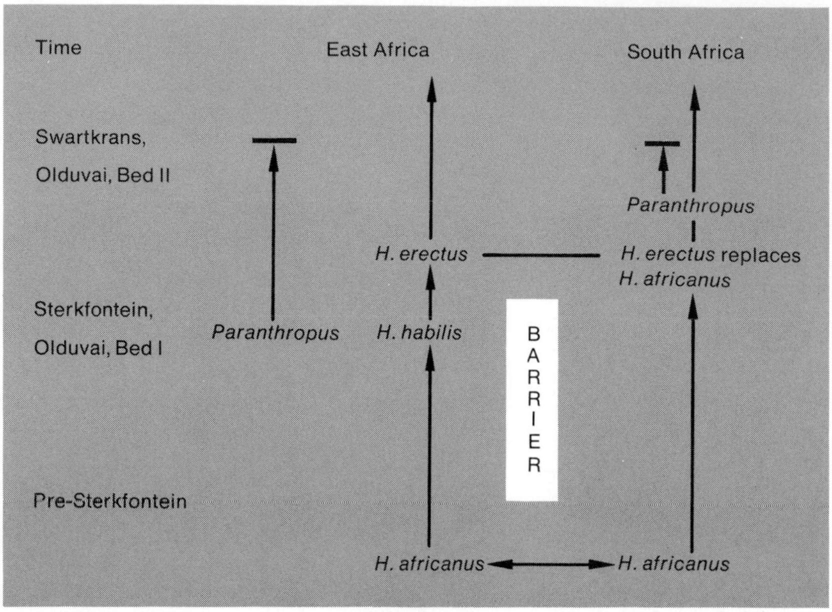

Figure 3-7. *Trophic displacement in the genus Homo* illustrating the time sequence and stratigraphical relationships of the several lower Pleistocene species of *Homo*. This is one of several possible schemes which can be prepared to fit the still scanty information on these early human forms; see text for further information. (Reproduced with modifications by permission of the publisher from W. M. Schaffer, *American Naturalist,* **102:** 928, 1968.)

EVOLUTION OF LANGUAGE

Hockett and Ascher (1964) have described how the evolution of language may have developed from a call system such as it seems reasonable to suppose persisted from the *Proconsul* grade through *Homo africanus* and *H. habilis.* They presume that many generations of chattering in an increasingly elaborate call system increased the sensitivity of the vocal tract. This greater sensitivity eventually made possible the insertion of minor variations within the sequence matrix of the call system. It became necessary to listen for these variations and it was no longer possible to identify a message completely from the opening cadences of the call. In this way true language developed from within a call system, still retaining features such as intensity, pitch, and variation.

The basic similarities of all modern languages Hockett and Ascher argue, is evidence of their common origin. They believe language originated but once, about 2 million years ago, and the increase in cranial capacity in hominids which is observed from then until about 40,000 years ago, is associated with the gradual elaboration of language and other cultural features.

An interesting observation made by Schultz (1961) is that the development of language provided for continuing selection of a sense of hearing.

This was necessary not for the detection of *external* sounds, the approach of possible predators, but to sense *social* sounds emitted by other members of the band. The sense of smell, having no such selective advantage, continuously declined from prosimian grades, although the custom of rubbing noses still practiced among some human groups may be a ritual survival of this vestigial sense.

Significance of Language

There is great significance in the creation of language in the early hominids, and its gradual development and perfection as a precise means of communication in the various forms of *Homo erectus*. Perhaps because of the immense archeological effort devoted to the study of artifacts, the effects of the evolution and use of various types of tools has been somewhat overemphasized. Such expressions as "man the tool maker" constantly underline this latter aspect of human behavioral evolution, and there is little or no reference to "man the language user."

It is possible today to recognize between five and ten thousand different languages (Greenberg, 1969), the actual number depending on the distinctions made between a language and a dialect. Whatever this total, all known modern languages and dialects are exceedingly complex, and none could be labeled "primitive." All are structured to impart accurate information on the past, the present, and the future. This is in direct contrast with the evolution of tool manufacture, where even in the contemporary world examples may still be found of paleolithic, mesolithic, and neolithic peoples.

Language unfortunately leaves no trace of its existence unless it is transcribed in a written form, but it seems likely that in early hominids the development of languages was an essential precursor of social evolution and the more material aspects of cultural evolution such as tool making. To illustrate this probability rather bluntly, in modern society a deaf and dumb child is as much handicapped in acquiring social learning as a blind child. Until the invention of written forms of language, we learned by listening and asking questions. This is still the basic form of instruction followed in our schools.

Historical Linguistics

The first modern studies of languages took the form of what is called *historical* or *comparative linguistics*. Developed toward the middle of the nineteenth century, they explored the relationship between languages by identification of *loan words*, together with phonetic evolution and divergence. Loan words are those that are transferred from one language to another. This is done more especially by bilingual individuals whose parents spoke different languages, but also by travelers, traders, and invaders.

Studies on comparative linguistics were able to trace modern languages back some two or three thousand years, relating them to the common sources from which they derived, and sometimes identifying the base languages, but usually hypothesizing the existence of a common language no longer spoken.

Because the discipline was studied especially by European scholars, the first language family to be thus explored was the Indo-European group, including ancient languages such as Hittite, which is extinct, and Sanskrit, which is known in written form only. Others are Persian, Greek, Italic dialects which survive in the Romance languages, the Celtic languages, and the Germanic and various Slavic languages as well as the Semitic, Aramaic, Arabic, and Ethiopian group. To illustrate how certain features are common to all these languages, the word for "mother" essentially has an "m" sound as the French *mère*, Spanish *madre*, German *mutter*, Latin *mater*, Arabic *um*, and so forth.

Language Transmission

It must be remembered, however, that language is a ritual of human behavior. Like all rituals, it has to be learned, and between one individual and another this learning process is imperfect. Language also becomes modified in use so that it is always changing from generation to generation. There is no such thing as *correct speech* or *correct language;* there is only *contemporary speech* and *contemporary language*. Meanings, words, pronunciation, and form change continuously.

Until written languages were developed some two or three thousand years ago, these modifications were not recorded. Since they have been recorded, it has become apparent how rapidly languages change. Biblical English now appears formal and stilted, the language of Chaucer is alien even to individuals whose mother tongue is English. Classical Arabic as expressed in the writings of the Koran employs many words no longer used in, for example, colloquial Egyptian or Palestinian.

Modern communications have generally hastened the rate of loan word introduction into many languages. They have also greatly stressed a limited number of widely used languages. What appears likely to happen within the next few centuries is the emergence of three or four languages—say, Russian, Spanish, English, Mandarin—as world tongues with which all scholars will be familiar. Other languages will probably gradually disappear, except in illiterate pockets of the world, either through disuse or from being swamped with loan words.

The Origin of Speech

An excellent presentation of the origin of speech is given by C. F. Hockett (1960), and much of his account is incorporated in this section.

Hockett suggests that in order to investigate the origin of speech and language, it is necessary to study the basic design features of all communication systems whether they relate to humans, animals, or machines. Using this approach, it is possible to postulate the methods of communication of ancestral hominids, and the evolutionary steps by which their communication system developed into language in successive hominid stages. The thirteen design features of any communication system which Hockett identifies are:

1. Vocal-auditory channels
2. Broadcast, transmission, and directional reception
3. Rapid fading transitoriness
4. Interchangeability
5. Total feedback
6. Specialization
7. Semanticity
8. Arbitrariness
9. Discreteness
10. Displacement
11. Productivity
12. Traditional transmission
13. Duality of patterning

The first five of these design features are common to the communication systems of all land mammals. Use of the *vocal-auditory* channel, for example, leaves the limbs free for other activities, thereby contrasting with the "bee dance," described by von Frisch which requires the whole body. The second feature, *broadcast transmission,* means that the communication can be picked up by any auditory system within range. The *rapid fading* of the signal contrasts, for example, with the mapping out of a territory with excreta or some persistent glandular secretion. *Interchangeability* differs, for example, from communication during courtship displays, where the male can only transmit male signals and receive female transmissions, and vice versa. In rather the same way, *feedback* also differs from such communications as courtship displays, because the transmitter can listen to what he is transmitting, whereas the animal performing a courtship display is unable to view his actions.

To these five design features a *call system,* such as that found in primates like gibbons, adds three other features. The first of these is *specialization,* use of the transmission as a signal triggering a particular feeling. *Semanticity* still further defines this triggering and restricts it to a particular range of feelings; an example is a gibbon danger call. Call systems also show *arbitrariness* in that the sounds have no obligatory relation to the feeling which is being triggered. This contrasts with the bee dance, in which the movements are faster if the source of nectar is close, slower if it is farther away.

Discreteness, which is a feature of call systems as well as of language, refers to the use of a discontinuous rather than a continuous series of sounds. In the bee dance, the variation of signals is continuous rather than discrete. A given signal in call systems and languages does not merge continuously into another one, but is always discrete from it; if the signal is not made clearly it may be confusing and depend on the discretion of the receiver to interpret in one way or the other.

Early hominids, or protohominids as they are sometimes described, appear to have incorporated these nine features in a call system such as is now exemplified by modern gibbons. The problem of the origin of speech can therefore be defined as the determination of how and when the remaining four features of language were inserted into or superimposed on such a hominid call system.

Blending

The feature labeled productivity distinguishes what linguists call a *closed* system from an *open* one. Hockett and Ascher (1964) describe how *blending* can convert the former to the latter. They postulate the representation of acoustic contours of two calls, for example, by representing them with a series of letters ABCD for one call and EFGH for another. ABCD might mean "food is here" while EFGH conveys "danger is coming." The calls are so familiar that hearing only a portion can lead to a correct interpretation.

An early hominid encountering both food and danger might then stumble on a blending of these calls, using the first part of the one and the last part of the other in the form ABGH. Should this new call become established in use, then both the two old calls and the new one will have become *composite.* That is, in ABCD the first part AB comes to mean "food," and the second part CD to convey "no danger": in the second call EFGH, EF says "no food," and GH communicates "danger."

Open Systems

If, as Hockett and Ascher suppose, the original closed call system had ten calls, when each of these blended once with each of the others, there would be a total of 100 calls. The system is still a closed one, but each of the 100 calls now has two parts, some of which recur in other calls. This is the basis for building composite signals, and the essential feature of an open system which transforms it from a call system into a language. Once this openness has been achieved, the characteristic known as productivity—with its great potentiality—has been added. This potentiality cannot, however, be completely realized without some form of *traditional transmission.*

This pattern of learning may be observed in children, who are believed initially to acquire language in the form of a closed system. The child first appears to learn whole sentences as inflexible units; only later does he perceive the blending possibilities of these sentences and begin to develop the productivity of the language. This is also the basis of the modern method of foreign language teaching employed in schools. Foreign languages are now taught first through conversation, which provides the framework of whole sentences in the form of a closed system. As familiarity with the language proceeds, these set sentences are blended with others to provide a more refined and open communication system in the language.

Selection Pressures

Much stress is placed on the strong selective pressures for manipulative skills in hominids which provided for more efficient and more effective tool making and tool using. It is possible that a comparable or even greater selection pressure developed for the characteristics of traditional transmission and productivity in speech. Genotypes which produced phenotypes eager to acquire by traditional transmission the full language insofar as it had been developed, and which were innovative in increasing its productivity, must have been more "fit" than phenotypes not displaying these characteristics. They therefore would have been subject to strong positive selection pressures.

Duality of Patterning

The *duality of patterning* features of language is necessitated by the small number of discontinuous sounds available for language construction, or the building of *morphemes,* which is the linguist's term for words. To illustrate this, the meaningless sounds "n," "t," and "e," can be arranged in two ways in English to make meaningful morphemes, as "net," and "ten." Combinations of four or more sounds can be made into even larger numbers of morphemes.

Call systems do not have this language characteristic. Nor do they have the last feature, *displacement,* which can trigger communication of events and objects in a different space or time. This is, however, a feature of some other known language communication systems, for example, the bee dance.

Language Sophistication

Through the 3 or 4 million years of development of *Homo erectus* it may be imagined that these four features of *displacement, productivity, duality of patterning,* and *traditional transmission* were developing and refining an open communication system in the form of what we know as speech or language, from a closed call system. The uniqueness of the genus *Homo* and its final evolutionary development is thus not solely related to progress in the manufacture and manipulation of tools. This by itself would probably have been insufficient to permit the rise of hominids appreciably beyond the pongid stage, if no better method of communication has been devised than a closed call system, even if supplemented with a sophisticated range of grimaces (Figures 3-8). The adaptive acquisition of an effective language permitted the development, storage, and transmission of ritualistic behavior and so provided for human cultural evolution.

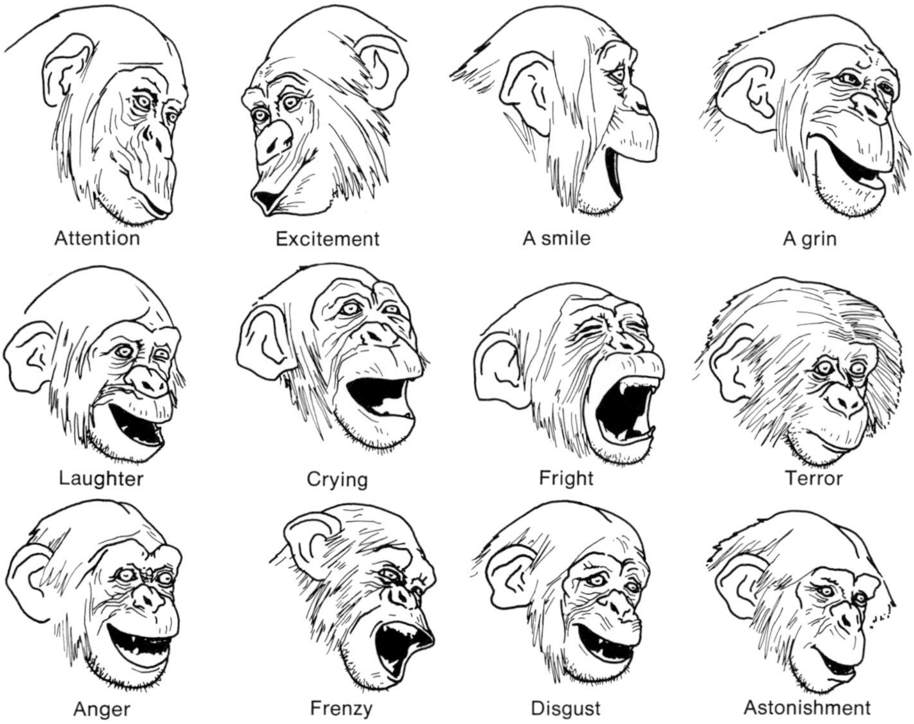

Figure 3-8. *Facial expressions of young chimpanzees.* Before the evolution of an effective language, an intricate series of facial expressions probably evolved among early hominid grades, more sophisticated than that of chimpanzees illustrated here, but basically similar.

The use of such facial expressions was of significance in mother-infant relationships even after language was perfected and may also have caused the change from dorsal to the ventral copulation which probably characterized all hominids. (Based on Kohts, 1935.)

The previously noted absence of an *elementary* form of language in any living human group suggests that speech patterns had achieved a great sophistication in all populations of *Homo erectus* by middle Pleistocene times at the latest. Further quantum cultural evolution in the form of permanent settlements permitted the more considerable specialization of activity which is evident in modern industrial societies, and which could not have been achieved without an effective communication system.

Simultaneous with the perfection of speech and language in evolving Pleistocene hominids, other variations must have been occurring; one of the more important of these would have been the degree of skin pigmentation.

Variations in the skin color presently found in human groups has occasionally led to much speculation as to its causative factors. The most plausible explanation for the diversity in this characteristic has been given by W. F. Loomis (1967), who believes that different types of skin color are adaptations to maximize ultraviolet light penetration in high latitudes, and minimize it in low ones (Figure 3-9).

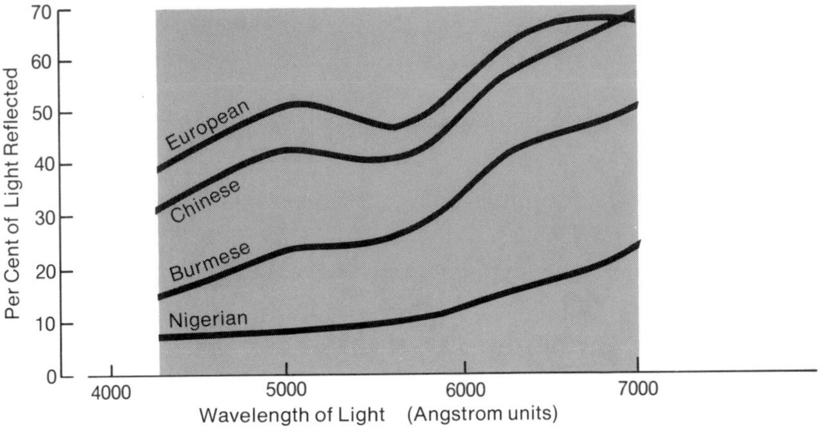

Figure 3-9. *Skin reflectance* as measured using a reflectance spectrophotometer and expressed for a range of light wavelengths in *A,* caucasoid (European); *B,* mongoloid (Chinese); *C,* mongoloid (Burmese); *D,* negroid (Nigerian) skins. The steep rise in reflectance with longer wavelengths in *A, B,* and *C* is due to reflectance from hemoglobin in subcutaneous blood vessels. (Modified from E. J. Clegg, *The Study of Man,* New York: American Elsevier, 1968, p. 76; reproduced with permission of the original publisher, The English Universities Press, London.)

A world map of the extent of pigmentation among major groups of aborigine peoples before the onset of the current waves of migration in the last few centuries, shows a marked correlation between skin pigmentation and equatorial latitudes. The reversible summer pigmentation and keratinization known as sun tan is seen by Loomis as a means of maintaining a physiologically constant rate of vitamin D synthesis despite the great seasonal variation in the ultraviolet radiation experienced in high latitudes.

Vitamin D

The principal function of vitamin D in human metabolism is considered to be the regulation of calcium absorption from the intestine, and control of the rate of deposition of inorganic minerals in unossified bone. This vitamin, sometimes known as the "sunshine vitamin," is produced in the skin, where very short ultraviolet radiation of wavelengths from 290 to 320 $m\mu$ transform the provitamin 7-dehydrochol-esterol into vitamin D.

This vitamin cannot be obtained in significant quantity in the more usual human diets. In high latitudes it is not present in any foodstuffs in winter;

elsewhere it occurs principally in the liver of bony fishes, most familiarly as cod liver oil.

Absence of vitamin D synthesis for any significantly long period causes the disease known as *rickets.* In modern societies sufficient quantity of the vitamin to permit normal bone calcification is obtained through artificial fortification of milk and other foods.

Hypervitaminosis D

While too little vitamin D causes the typical rickets symptoms of bow-legs, knock-knees, and twisted spines, especially in infants, amounts of vitamin D in excess of 2.5 mg per day result in symptoms of what is called *hypervitaminosis D.* In this pathological condition arising from an excess of vitamin D in the body, the levels of both calcium and phosphorus in the blood are raised. The condition is fatal once it affects the kidneys and kidney stones have developed.

Apparently human metabolic processes have no ability to regulate the amount of vitamin D in the bloodstream or to selectively secrete this substance to obtain the physiological regulation of its concentration in the body. Loomis and workers before him have proposed that the rate of vitamin D synthesis in the stratum granulosum of the skin is regulated by pigmentation and keratinization of the overlying stratum corneum. This controls the amount of solar ultraviolet radiation penetrating the outer layers of the skin and therefore determines the amount of vitamin D synthesized in the underlying region.

Experimental Evidence on Ultraviolet Reflectance

Loomis quotes the work of Beckmeier who in 1958 estimated that 1 cm^2 of white skin could synthesize up to 18 IU (international units) of vitamin D in three hours. This rate would provide a sufficient daily dose of vitamin D for Northern European infants who daily have no more than their faces exposed to "some fresh air and sunshine." Loomis proceeds to a calculation which shows that such an unpigmented individual would synthesize in six hours in the tropics up to 800,000 IU of vitamin D, eight times the amount sufficient to produce hypervitaminosis D.

Loomis quotes various experiments which have been made on detached human skin which demonstrate that the degree of blackness as measured by skin reflectance is inversely proportional to the amount of ultraviolet radiation transmitted. It has further been shown that the common mutation for albinism in black human groups produces an individual whose skin ultraviolet transmission is within the range of that of the skin of non-pigmented groups.

From the various figures which are available, it is apparent that if only the face of a Negro infant is exposed in a high latitude winter climate, too little vitamin D is synthesized to meet his physiological requirement. It is therefore not surprising that evidence from medical experience finds Negroes the most susceptible of all peoples to rickets. These observations are now becoming theoretical in view of the general availability and use of cod liver oil to supplement vitamin D deficiencies in the diet.

The data available explain why Negroes living on the equator synthesize 5 to 10 per cent vitamin D as compared with unpigmented individuals under these same conditions, and why Negroes living in tropical climates do not suffer from kidney stones and other signs of overcalcification. Not all workers accept this explanation of skin pigmentation; some place a greater emphasis on negative correlations which have been demonstrated between pigment intensity and the susceptibility to skin cancer (Blum, 1961).

Origin of Depigmented Groups

Loomis proceeds to extend his observations and theories to account for the origin of white skin. He considers that because of their beginnings, early hominids were probably both deeply pigmented and fur-covered. (This is the supposition made in the previous chapter in discussing the movement of primates from a forest to a savanna environment.) He supposes that the northward migratory expansion of early hominids would have been halted somewhere near the Mediterranean because of the increasing tendency of infants to develop the bent legs and twisted spines of ricket deformities. This factor would also limit the penetration of fully pigmented hominids to about latitude 40° S. The one exception to this rule is found in the Eskimo and Aleut peoples, who are moderately pigmented despite their occurrence in extremely high latitudes. Loomis accounts for this anomaly on the basis of the essentially fish oil and meat diet of these groups, which contains an adequate but not excessive dose of vitamin D.

As melanin granules (which are black or brown) and yellowish kerato-hyaline granules (which produce nails) both reduce the amount of ultra-violet penetration and are controlled by polygenic systems, it may be supposed that any gene mutation in these systems would produce a pheno-type with a somewhat lighter skin, which if inherited would permit still further permanent penetration of high latitudes. Thus, by slow increases in gene frequencies of such depigmented mutants, there would gradually evolve peoples with a demelanized and dekeratinized skin of maximum transparency who were capable of living in the highest latitudes without suffering from underproduction of vitamin D in their skins.

MORPHOLOGICAL EVOLUTION

So far we have been concerned mainly with the behavioral (language), physiological (melanin production), and cultural evolution of Pleistocene hominids, but the morphological evolution is also of interest, more par-

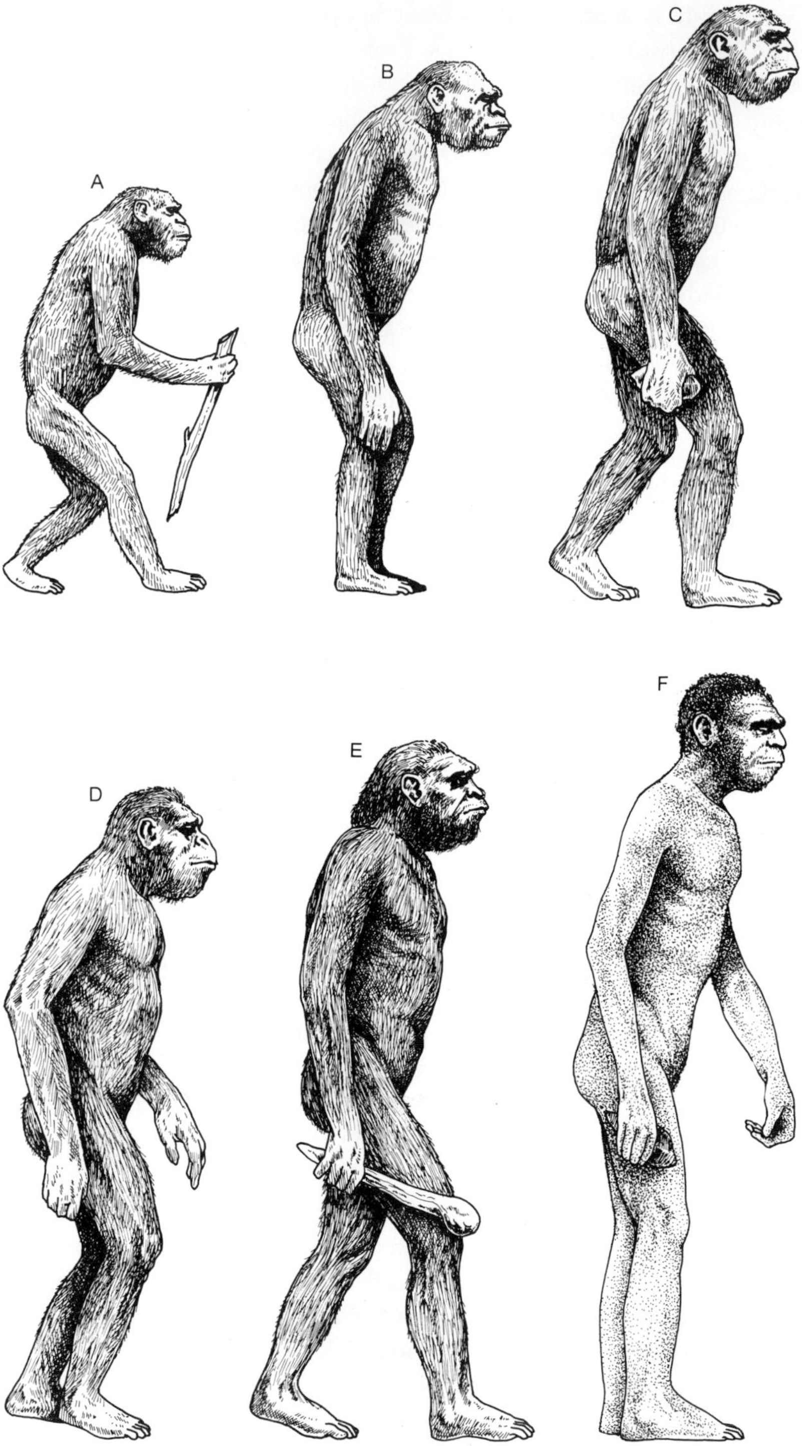

Figure 3-10. *Conjectural reconstruction of stages in the evolution of Pleistocene hominids* all found in tropical Africa. *A. Proconsul* circa 20 million BP. *B. Ramapithecus* circa 15 million BP. *C. Homo africanus* circa 1.8 million BP. *D. Paranthropus* circa 1.7 million BP. *E. Homo habilis* circa 1.5 million BP. *F. Homo erectus* circa 1 million BP. (Based partly on Clark Howell, 1965.)

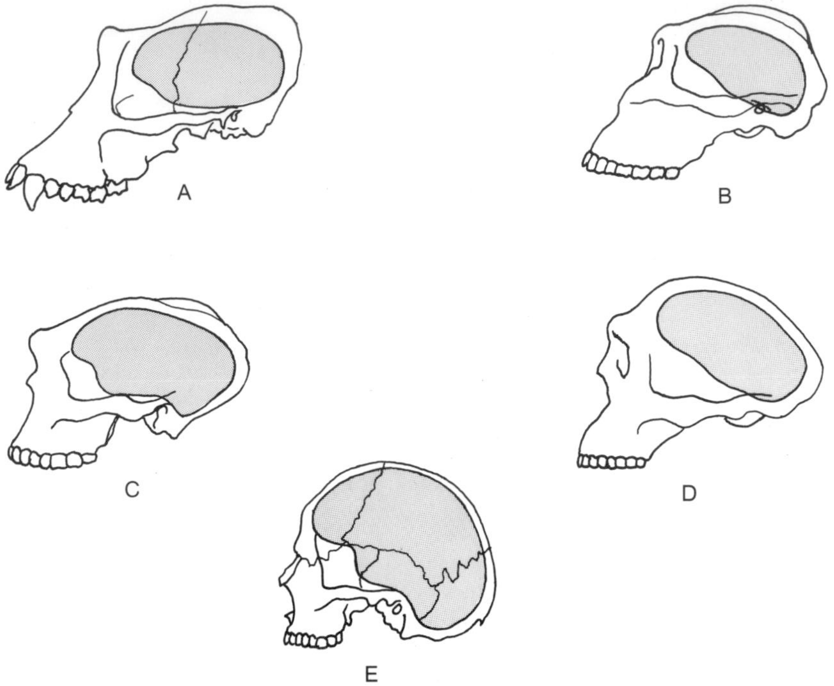

Figure 3-11. *Evolution of the skull, dentition, and brain in anthropoids. A.* Gorilla (*Gorilla gorilla*). *B. Paranthropus. C. Homo africanus* grade. *D. Homo erectus* grade. *E.* Contemporary man (*Homo sapiens*). In all the hominids the teeth, although still varying in size, have crowns attaining a common level, and tend to become smaller. The brain case and brain enlarge proportionally, and the sagittal crest disappears as the jaws are reduced. Simultaneously prognathy is also reduced.

ticularly as the changes which took place represented the last major morphological adaptations to occur in any *Homo* grade.

The series of conjectural reconstructions of the body form in Figure 3-10 illustrate the comparatively small change in morphology which occurred during the Pleistocene. The Miocene mold, as shown by forms such as *Proconsul* and *Ramapithecus,* remained largely the same.

The most significant changes occur in the skull (Figure 3-11). The massive jaws, large teeth, and brow ridges of Miocene hominids are reduced, while the cranial capacity is increased. This produces a change in the head's center of gravity and permits a reduction in the size of both the nuchal (neck) and temporal (lower jaw) muscles (Figure 3-12).

These changes in the balance of the head are associated with a completely upright stature attained by final adaptations of the locomotor apparatus. The pelvis broadens to provide a greater attachment surface for the muscles which provide forward movement. The effect of this broadening is to shorten the ilium and bring close together the articulation points of the leg, the *sacral articulation,* and the *acetabulum* (Figure 3-13). From this comes a bipedal striding walk unique among animals and a behavioral characteristic of the genus *Homo.* The morphological adaptation to bi-

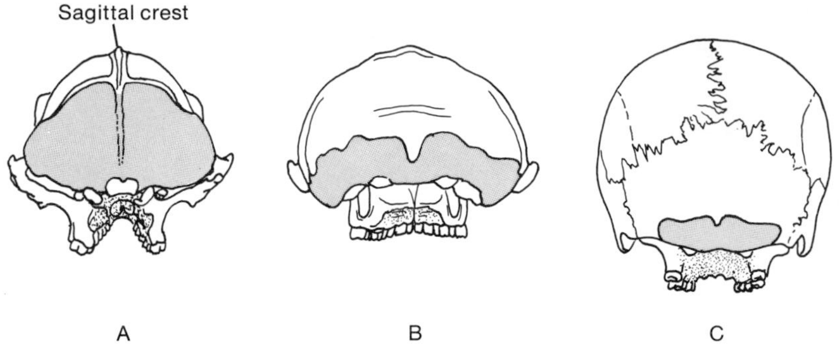

Figure 3-12. *Occipital view of some anthropoid skulls showing how the neck muscles* (the nuchal musculature) became reduced during *africanus-erectus-sapiens* evolution as the center of gravity of the head moved nearer the point where the head pivots on the occipital condyles with the top of the spine. This change developed from reductions in the at-first massive jaws and teeth, the thickness of orbital ridges and of the facial bones in general, through the adoption of a more upright carriage made possible by other relatively minor skeletal changes. The size of the nuchal muscles as judged by their area of attachment indicated here by stippling on the skulls of (*A*) gorilla (*Pan gorilla*), an orthograde primate whose spine still enters from the back of the skull. (*B*) *Homo erectus* grade. *C. H. sapiens* grade. This provides evidence for archeologists and anthropologists as to the nature of the rest of the head, its muscles, and the posture of hominid and pongid forms. The sagittal crest, to which are attached the temporal muscles supporting the lower jaws, furnishes evidence of this same kind.

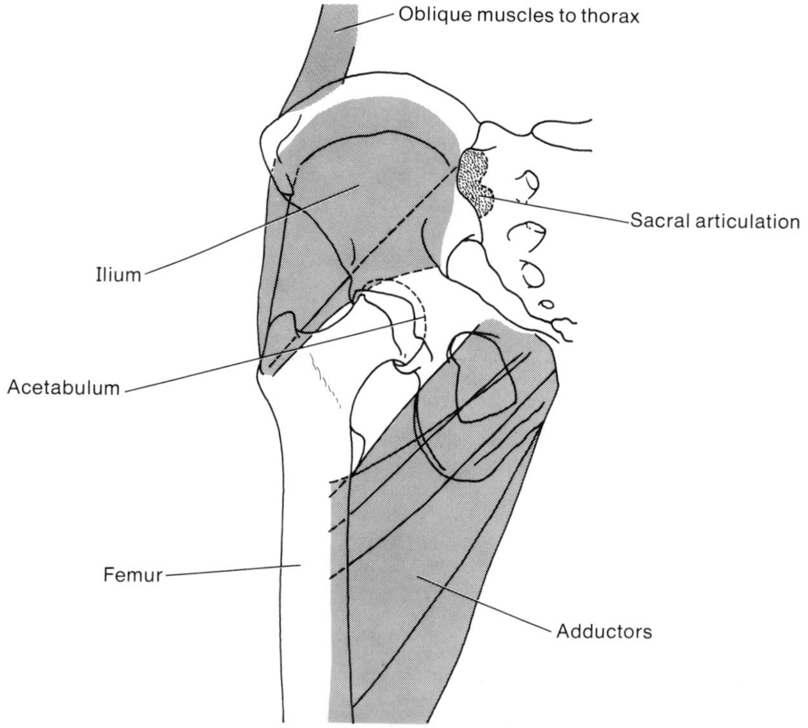

Figure 3-13. *The principal thigh muscles controlling lateral movement* in man (*Homo sapiens*) where all the weight is borne on one leg at a time at each step, the abductor muscles (upper shaded area) pulling the body forward in this action and the adductors balancing it.

pedalism was probably completed, apart from some minor modifications, by the beginning of the Pleistocene 4 million years ago (Figure 3-14).

The forelimb of hominids underwent even less change (Figure 3-15). The *scapula* by which each forelimb is attached to the thorax is very little modified in all primates. The *clavicle,* which permits a freer maneuverability of the forelimb, also is scarcely modified in all anthropoids. With all such skeletal structures, as described in Appendix III, a vast store of information on minutiae has been accumulated by long and careful study and measurement. The bones, through their articulations, origins of muscular attachments, and blood and nerve supplies, provide a great wealth of factual information which supports speculation on other morphological, physiological, behavioral, and cultural features. It is probable that only in the

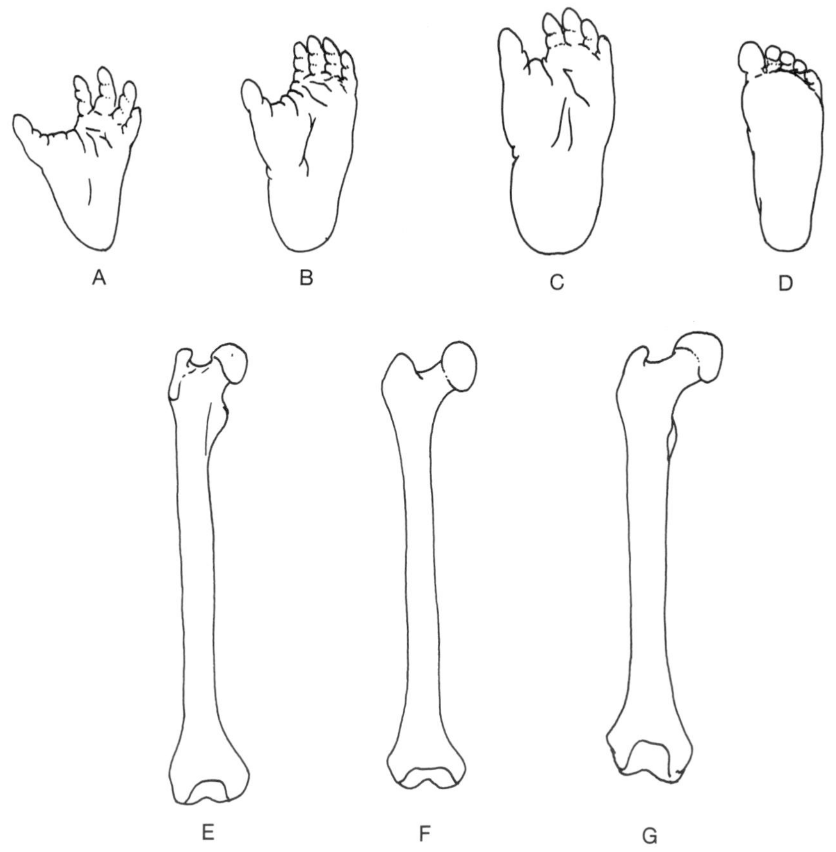

Figure 3-14. *Evolution of locomotory equipment* in hominids has involved only minor changes over the past 15–20 million years once bipedalism replaced brachiation. Above: The outline of the feet of *A,* the chimpanzee (*Pan troglodytes*); *B,* the lowland gorilla (*Gorilla gorilla*); *C,* the mountain gorilla (*Gorilla beringei*); *D,* contemporary man (*Homo sapiens*). Below: The leg bone (femur) of *E, Proconsul; F,* lowland gorilla; *G,* modern man drawn to the same size and therefore not to the same scale. (Reproduced in part by permission of the publisher from D. J. Morton, *The Human Foot,* New York: Columbia University Press, 1964, p. 41.)

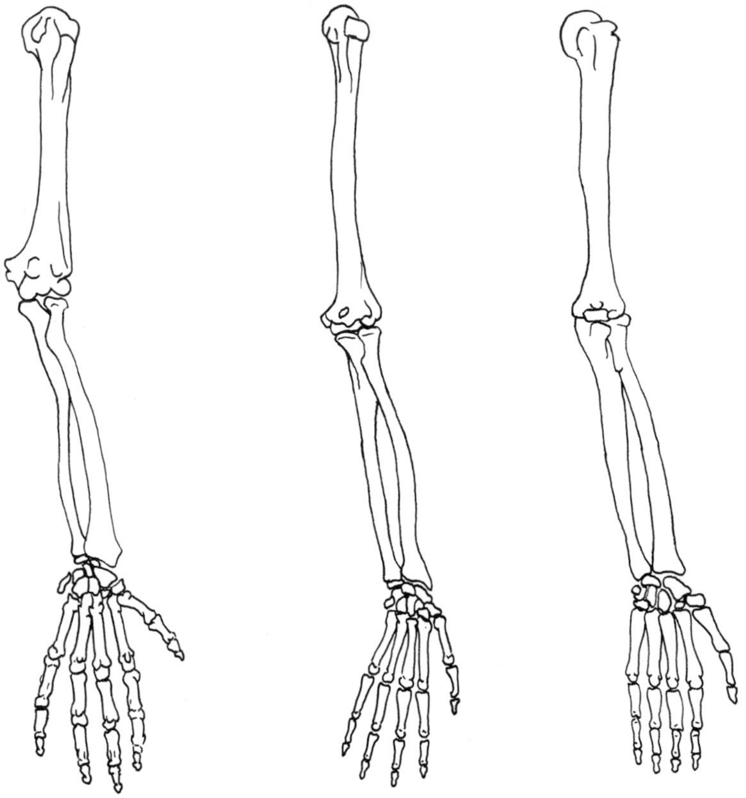

Figure 3-15. *Evolution of the forelimb* in hominids involved very little skeletal adaptation over the past 15–20 million years, once bipedalism had replaced brachiation as the commoner mode of locomotion. The forelimb skeleton of *A, Proconsul; B,* chimpanzee (*Pan troglodytes*); *C,* contemporary man (*Homo sapiens*); drawn so as to appear the same length, shows very little variation. Evolution, which has proceeded from a clumsy tool-user such as *Proconsul* to form such an exquisitely delicate performer as the violinist Yehudi Menuhin, has scarcely involved the basic skeleton structure while enormously refining the sensory perception and the muscular coordination. (Reprinted by permission of Quadrangle Books, Inc., from *The Antecedents of Man* by W. E. Le Gros Clark, copyright © 1959 by Edinburgh University Press, p. 216.)

science of human anatomy is so much information extracted from so little material.

MENTAL CAPACITY

Some contemporary experimental work is available in support of certain deductions as to mental capacity of hominids made from morphological observations. Various experiments have been conducted to determine the reasoning powers of monkeys, no species of which even begins to approach the cranial capacity of an australopithecine. The most ambitious of these studies, reported by Weinstein tested the monkey's ability to identify both similarities and differences. Nine objects of different shapes and colors were placed on a tray. The monkey being tested was handed one of these as a symbol and had to select others which resembled it. Thus a triangle required all *red* objects to be selected, a circle, *blue*. The ability of the test monkeys to perform the necessary symbolic association revealed a relatively high power of reasoning.

Comparison between such performances at the monkey grade and those of contemporary man permits a crude correlation between hominid cranial reasoning capacity and probable mental ability. On this basis a reasoning capacity, but *not* a cultural knowledge, as high as that of contemporary man had probably been developed in hominids by 2 million years BP, for some cranial capacities of *Homo erectus* from that period overlap those given for modern man.

The further evolution of *Homo erectus* and the reasons why it must be considered the direct ancestor of *H. sapiens*—or the changes occurring as the *erectus* grade evolved into the *sapiens grade*—are considered in the next chapter.

The earliest stages of the *H. erectus* grade, which could well have originated some 4 million years ago, may be considered to have contributed the following characteristics over and beyond those given in the previous chapter as persisting from Miocene-Pliocene times, which have further evolved in *H. erectus* and persisted into the *H. sapiens* grade:

1. Completely bipedal habit
2. Enlarged brain
3. Geographical variations in degree of pigmentation
4. Reduced canines
5. Speech and language
6. Tool-making dexterity
7. Social division of labor
8. Extended infant and juvenile dependence

It must be emphasized that with the appearance of the *H. erectus* grade in Pleistocene hominids much of the observable human *morphological* evolution had been achieved. Of the above list, only the first four features are morphological; the rest are behavioral. Further evolution was more concerned with behavioral than physiological characteristics.

Bibliography

REFERENCES

Ardrey, R. *African Genesis,* New York: Delta, 1961.

Ardrey, R. *The Territorial Imperative,* New York: Delta, 1966.

Blum, H. F. "Does the melanin pigment of human skin have adaptive value?" *Quart. Rev. Biol.,* **36**: 50–63, 1961.

Clark, J. D. "The evolution of culture in Africa," *American Naturalist,* **97**: 15–28, 1963.

Dart, R. "Australopithecus africanus: the man-ape of South Africa," *Nature,* **115**: 195, 1925.

Greenberg, J. H. "Language universals: a research frontier," *Science,* **166**: 473–78, 1969.

Hockett, C. F. "The origin of speech," *Scientific American,* **203**(3): 88–96, 1960.

Hockett, C. F., and Ascher, R. "The human revolution," *Current Anthropology,* **5**: 135–68, 1964.

Howell, F. C. "Remains of Hominidae from Pliocene/Pleistocene formations in the lower Omo Basin, Ethiopia," *Nature,* **223**: 1234–39, 1969.

Leakey, R. E. F. "Early *Homo sapiens* from the Omo River Region of Southwest Ethiopia," *Nature,* **222**: 1132–38, 1969.

Loomis, W. F. "Skin-pigment regulation of vitamin-D biosynthesis in man," *Science,* **157**: 501–506, 1967.

Schaffer, W. M. "Character displacement and the evolution of the Hominidae," *American Naturalist,* **102**: 559–71, 1968.

Schultz, A. H. "Some factors influencing the social life of primates in general and early man in particular," in S. L. Washburn (ed.), *Social Life of Early Man,* Chicago: Aldine, 1961, pp. 58–90.

Simons, E. L. "Assessment of a fossil hominid," *Science,* **160**: 672–75, 1968.

Simons, E. L., Pilbeam, D., and Ettel, P. C. "Controversial taxonomy of fossil hominids," *Science,* **166**: 258–59, 1969.

FURTHER READINGS

Altman, S. A. "Social behavior of anthropoid primates: analysis of recent concepts," in E. L. Bliss, *Roots of Behavior,* New York: Harper, 1962, pp. 277–85.

Biegert, J. *Volarhaut der Hände und Füsse Handbuch der Primatenkunde* II/1 Lieferung 3, Basel and New York: S. Karger, 1961.

Bishop, W. W., and Clark, J. D. (eds.) *Background to Evolution in Africa,* Chicago: University of Chicago Press, 1969.

Campbell, B. G. *Human Evolution,* Chicago: Aldine, 1967.

Carpenter, C. R. "A field study of the behavior and social relations of the gibbon," Comparative Psychology Monographs No. 16, 1940 (republished in C. R. Carpenter, *Naturalistic Behavior of Nonhuman Primates,* University Park, Penn.: Pennsylvania State University Press, 1964).

Caspari, E. "Selective forces in the evolution of man," *American Naturalist,* **97**: 5–14, 1963.

Clark, J. D. "Human ecology during Pleistocene and later times in Africa south of the Sahara," *Current Anthropology,* **1**: 307–24, 1960.

Emden, J. M. "Natural selection and human behavior," *J. Theoret. Biol.,* **12**: 410–18, 1966.

Goodall, J. M. "My life among wild chimpanzees," *National Geographic Magazine,* **124**: 272–308, 1963.

Goodall, J. M. "Tool-using and aimed throwing in a community of free-living chimpanzees," *Nature,* **201**: 1264, 1964.

Harrisson, B. *Orang-utan,* London: Collins, 1962.

Kurth, G. (ed.) *Evolution and Hominisation,* 2nd ed. Stuttgart: Fischer, 1968.

Morton, D. J. *The Human Foot,* New York: Hafner, 1964.

Oakley, K. P. "Dating the emergence of man," *Advancement of Science,* **18**: 415–26, 1962.

Payne, M. M. "Family in search of prehistoric man," *National Geographic Magazine,* **127**: 194–231, 1965.

Reynolds, V. *Budongo, an African Forest and Its Chimpanzees,* New York: Natural History Press, 1965.

Schaller, G. B. *The Year of the Gorilla,* Chicago: University of Chicago Press, 1964.

Spuhler, J. N. (ed.) *The Evolution of Man's Capacity for Culture,* Detroit: Wayne State University Press, 1961.

Washburn, S. L. (ed.) *The Social Life of Early Man,* Viking Fund Publications in Anthropology No. 31, Chicago: Aldine, 1961.

Washburn, S. L., and Jay, P. C. (eds.) *Perspectives in Human Evolution,* New York: Holt, Rinehart & Winston, 1968.

Homo Erectus 4

With the emergence of *Homo erectus* the long story of man's evolution is almost over in time, but regarding achievement, it is only just beginning. It took perhaps 1½ billion years for life to evolve on this planet, and another 3 billion years before animals appeared. Almost a further half billion years passed before primates developed, but then after only a further 57 million years forms referable to the genus *Homo* are to be found. From the first known culture (Oldowan) to that of the second, *H. erectus* (Chelles-Acheul), there is an interval of a mere half million years, which is approximately the time which elapsed before the Industrial Revolution. From that point quantum advances in human culture proceed very rapidly, through the "atomic age" to the "computer era." The progress of cultural evolution so accelerates that from time intervals recorded in billions of years we are reduced to expressing the passage of time first in centuries and then in months.

Therein lies the uniqueness of man. Other forms of life have evolved, undergone adaptive radiation, been modified by character displacement from jacks to specialists in the process known as niche diversification; and all have passed to extinction with the inevitable onset of environmental change to which they have been too specialized to adapt. Man has evolved essentially by *cultural* speciation. Trophic displacement and niche diversification therefore affect only cultural practices. As one culture moves to extinction, the morphological and behavioral characteristics of the jack remain, largely unmodified, to give rise to another culture.

Our anatomical, morphological, physiological, and behavioral characteristics are not, however, entirely immutable. The influence of selection pressures has undoubtedly produced modifications of gene frequencies and resulted in adaptation in these types of features, as have certain independently operating genetic phenomena. But such change is slow. From *Homo erectus*, through *Homo sapiens*, and on into the future, we really have one population, slowly but continuously evolving under selection pressure; eventually behavioral rituals will supply the knowledge to control these pressures. Only then shall we be able, if we wish, to stabilize gene frequencies and control further physical and behavioral evolution.

PHYSICAL CHARACTERISTICS OF *H. ERECTUS*

It seems likely that most earlier forms of *H. erectus* were about half the size of the average modern American, weighing approximately 60 lb. The carriage, as judged by the form of the pelvis, was just as upright, and the rest of the skeleton varied little (Figure 4-1). Estimates of cranial capacity range from 800 to 1100 cm^2, which overlaps that calculated for normal functioning in modern man (800–2000 cm^3). The large teeth also fall within the modern human range. Such proportionately large teeth would make the face somewhat prognathous (protruding), with a back-sloping chin and a receding forehead. For several reasons, *H. erectus* must have been effectively naked.

The Naked Ape

This naked condition of man, unique among the 193 surviving species of monkeys and apes (*Anthropoidea*) which are covered in hairy fur, has inspired a variety of theories (Morris, 1967). One of the most plausible accounts for the "naked ape" condition on a basis of our virtually exclusive diurnal vision, which probably did not differ significantly in *H. erectus.* Most predation by top carnivores is completed at dusk or dawn, and these larger carnivores all have some degree of night vision. Forced to operate, because of lack of night vision, in tropical or subtropical temperatures in full daylight—at a pace more likely to wear down rather than overtake a prey—*H. erectus* would soon have built up too much metabolic heat to be dissipated without a pause in activity. There would have been strong selection pressure for any mutants producing a reduced body fur covering. Supposedly there was a parallel and compensatory selection of mutants for shivering, which is estimated to provide up to three times the resting heat production (Harrison, *et al.*, 1964); otherwise the nights may have proved a little chilly before the cultural acquisition of fire and clothing.

Modern game animals normally rest in the shade during the heat of the day, and soon become exhausted if forced to run at this time. Any predator which has adapted to effective metabolic heat dispersal by loss of a furry covering and the development of sweat glands will obviously have a high rate of successful kills, even of animals many times larger, provided they can be stampeded into running. Nakedness would, however, have one other drawback in addition to the possibility of excessive chilling when at rest. Because it would permit still further exposure of the skin to ultraviolet rays, the possibility of *hypervitaminosis D* would be increased. For this reason it

Figure 4-1. *Confrontation between* Homo erectus *and* Paranthropus at Olduvai in Tanzania. The two *erectus* males have no body hair, and have a basic social division of labor which permits them to be away from their family base on a hunting expedition. *Paranthropus* retains body hair and lacks this division of labor; females and young all move with the band, each member of which gathers food only for itself. *H. erectus* would probably increasingly in geological time attack, kill, and eat young or disabled *Paranthropus* when opportunity arose, but not the contrary. While hunting, *H. erectus* would have the huge advantage of a greater facility in dispersing metabolic heat through his sweating and naked skin during a prolonged midday chase. Time period circa 600,000 BP. (After painting by Jay H. Matternes, © National Geographic Society, 1965. Reproduced with permission of the publisher.)

has been assumed that all the hominids considered here were heavily pigmented, even more so than the fur-covered protohominids like *Proconsul.*

The fact that none of the other 192 species of monkeys and apes are hairless is explained according to this predation theory by the circumstance that none of them is so exclusively carnivorous. Although many may have a significant secondary consumer element in their omnivorous diet, this comes from eating insects, small rodents, scorpions, worms, and other small animals rather than larger ones which have to be run down on foot.

The diverse opinions regarding many salient features of human evolution are well illustrated by contrary views on the origin of hairless skin. Bresler (1968) reproduces excerpts from eight letters to the editor of the journal *Science* prompted by a provocative statement of H. Bentley Glass (1968) referring to ". . . loss of certain unnecessary structures, such as bodily hair once clothing was invented. . . ." Alternative suggestions accounting for the loss of hair ranged from that described here, through a nutritional explanation, to one involving ticks and body lice.

CULTURAL CHARACTERISTICS OF *H. ERECTUS*

Clark (1963) provides a graphic description of the life of a small group of *H. habilis* on the bare open mud flats bordering the Lower Pleistocene Olduvai lake. The culture he describes persisted for more than 600,000 years from its first potassium-argon confirmed date of occurrence in 1,700,-000 BP (Strauss and Hunt, 1962) before being superseded by that of *H. erectus.* The essential features of the life of *H. habilis* Clark considers first to have been a hunting and gathering economy, that is, meat eating supplementing a vegetable diet, and second the collection in a central place of the results of foraging. Stone and more rarely bone equipment was developed to deal with this food supply. According to Clark, the temporary camp at Olduvai was made by several individuals only. The accompanying animal remains were either juvenile or small mammals, frogs, lizards, and other creatures of similar size. Virtually every bone that could have contained marrow was broken (Clark notes that a modern African hunting and gathering group is known to use bone marrow as the first solid food for infants). Artifacts used as implements in the camp were of five types: natural cobbles, "bashing stones," pebbles flaked to make choppers, and small nodules which could represent the end product when fashioning the choppers and obtaining the last category, flakes, used in cutting and scraping (Figure 4-2).

Figure 4-2. *Some of the major groupings of artifact types* characterizing particular cultural stages of human social evolution. The use of tools for dating purposes tends to produce circular arguments, so that absolute dating procedures, such as radiometric techniques, are preferable. The geographical variation in the times at which various cultures appeared, as revealed when absolute dates are available, illustrates the wide range in the chronological sequences of earlier cultures.

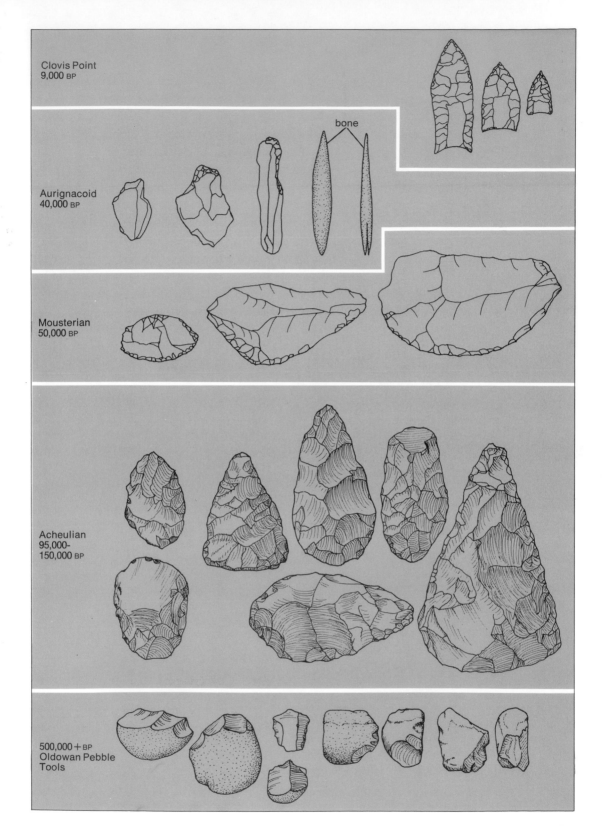

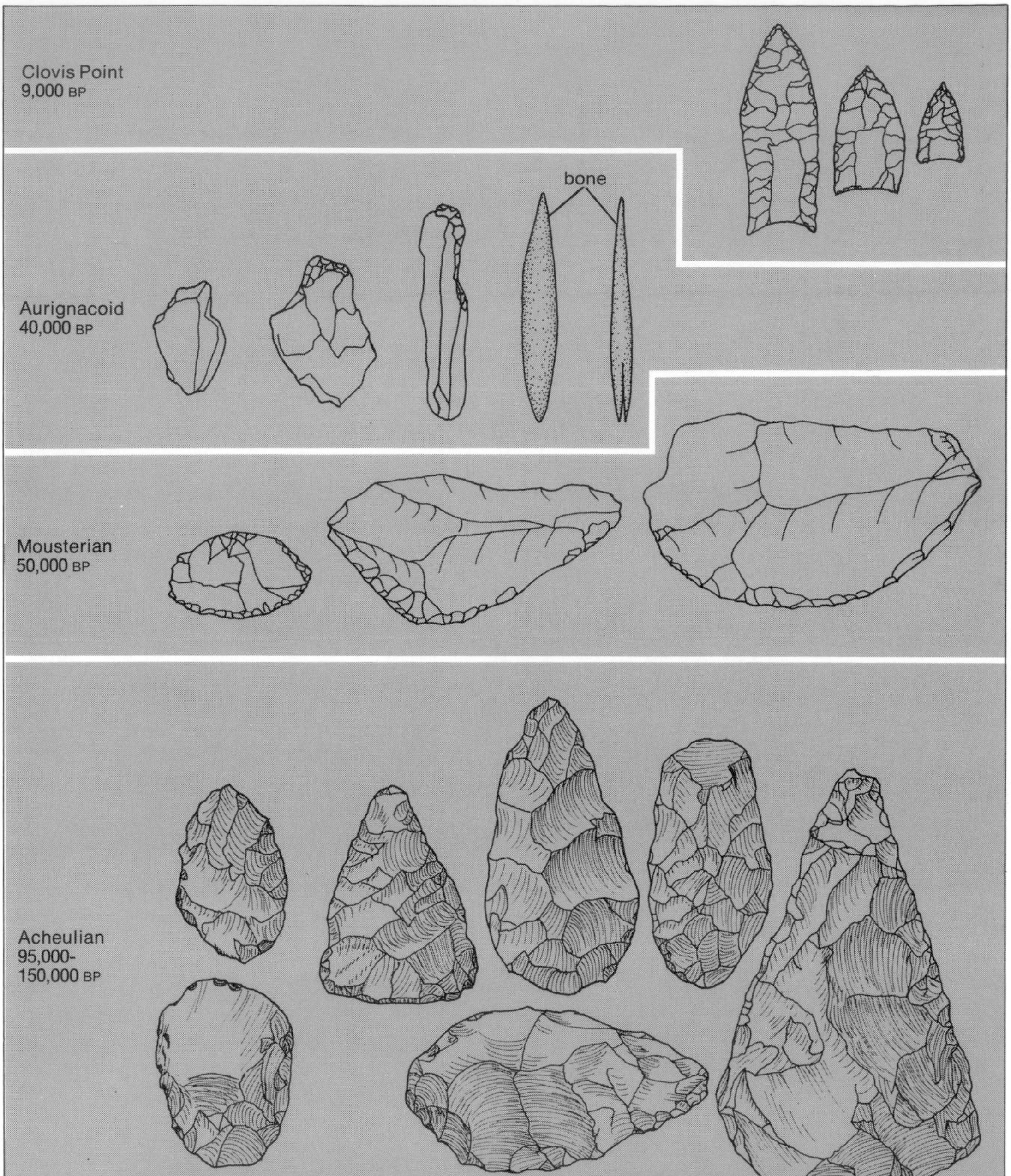
Clovis Point
9,000 BP
bone
Aurignacoid
40,000 BP
Mousterian
50,000 BP
Acheulian
95,000-
150,000 BP
500,000+BP
Oldowan Pebble
Tools

Chelles-Acheul Cultures

Clark proceeds from this human culture of *H. habilis* to examine its successor, that of the more advanced and complex *H. erectus*, the "handaxe culture" known as the Chelles-Acheul (Figure 4-2). He believes this African hunting-gathering paleolithic culture of the Middle and Upper Pleistocene had appeared by 500,000 BP and in some places persisted until 50,000 years ago. By at least 60,000 BP, as determined by radiocarbon dating, *H. erectus* lived in medium-sized groups in open country marginal to water supplies, camping around open hearths. Wooden spears, clubs, and stones were used for hunting quite large animals (Figure 4-3), although dead ones were still scavenged, fruit and honey (Figure 4-4) gathered, and wooden digging sticks used to unearth plant storage material. Large animals were probably driven into boggy ground, dispatched by stoning and spearing, dismembered, and eaten on the site (Figure 4-26). There had to be some form of language to permit coordination of these varied activities.

Figure 4-3. *An* erectus-sapiens *group in Africa* at a Chelles-Acheulean phase about 70,000 BP conjectured as gathering wild honey. Note the bark platter hacked out on the spot using a hand axe. Honey is still an important element of the diet of pygmy peoples in Africa, and an early type of beehive is commonly hung in natural vegetation by many other contemporary African groups. A bird group known as honey guides will direct any animal which will take notice (including man) to a wild bees' nest by repeated calls and flutterings. (Adapted with the permission of the author from J. D. Clark, *The Prehistory of Southern Africa,* London: Penguin, 1959, p. 134.)

Figure 4-4. *Hunting techniques of* erectus-sapiens *populations in Africa.* A hunting group of Broken Hill men dismembering a rhinoceros caught in a pit-trap. Lower Gamblian pluvial phase, about 70,000 BP. (Adapted with the permission of the author from J. D. Clark, *The Prehistory of Southern Africa,* London: Penguin, 1959, p. 138.)

Behavioral Features of *H. erectus*

Archeologists such as Clark base their assessments of behavioral patterns on factual evidence. Behavioralists like Morris (1967) must be more speculative. From the latter's viewpoint, it can be supposed *H. erectus* exhibited some major behavioral features, the most important of which would be *pair-bonding.*

In *H. erectus* the sexual behavioral pattern probably changed as a result of selection pressures favoring greater parental care for the young. Pair-bonding between the male and female parent would provide this; an extension of female receptivity both into pregnancy and into times of the menstrual cycle other than the few days of potential fertility would be a factor strengthening the pair bond. It would need no new triggering device, for the original physiological and behavioral stimuli which initiated copulation procedures—what we call "falling in love"—would also establish the arrangement.

In surviving social anthropoids there is no special individual pairing during periods of sexual activity. In a baboon troop (Washburn and de Vore, 1961) a female coming into estrus presents to any available and interested male. She works her way up to the dominant dog baboons, with one of which she may form a temporary attachment in the final stages of estrus. Beyond protecting individuals of the troop threatened by predators, no male baboon shows any further interest in what may or may not be his own offspring, or in the females he has impregnated.

Pair-bonding would appear to have selective advantages for a terrestrial social group. It would permit the lengthening of the females' period of receptivity without precipitating fighting among the males. This in turn would facilitate elaboration of a division of labor necessitated by the demands of increasingly long periods of juvenile dependence. The females would be able to specialize in child rearing around a home base while the males foraged for animal protein, some of which would be brought back to the now dependent pair-bond family.

Exogamous Mating

The practice of exogamous mating within bands or hordes may have been an early social development after the establishment of pair-bonding. Sahlins (1960) suggests that such behavior would assist in reducing sexual competition; it would also have implications for the rate of further social and physical evolution. A theoretical example of how such exogamous behavior would operate is illustrated in Figure 4-5, largely modified from Sahlins.

Incest taboo rituals frequently reinforce this exogamous mating behavior in surviving stone age societies. At the same time, they establish kinship ties which must considerably modify territoriality behavior, and which tend to establish a concept of tribal territory shared by intermarrying bands or hordes. Moreover, exogamy will increase the introduction of new loan words evolved by individual bands, and therefore increase the rate of language change and evolution.

Division of Labor

Pair-bonding may thus be considered as aiding extension of the division of labor. The male can scavenge and hunt unimpeded by the lesser mobility of his pregnant or child-encumbered mate. The patient female can concentrate on the more time-consuming labor of digging up edible portions of plants and breaking open bones for marrow extraction, while nurturing and caring for the infant and juvenile offspring of the pair bond.

The comparatively equal loss of body hair and equal performance in walking, running, jumping, and climbing ability between the sexes of modern man strongly suggests that these adaptations were made in a social stage before any such division of labor occurred. A marked lack of throwing ability among modern human females implies that from the time of *H.*

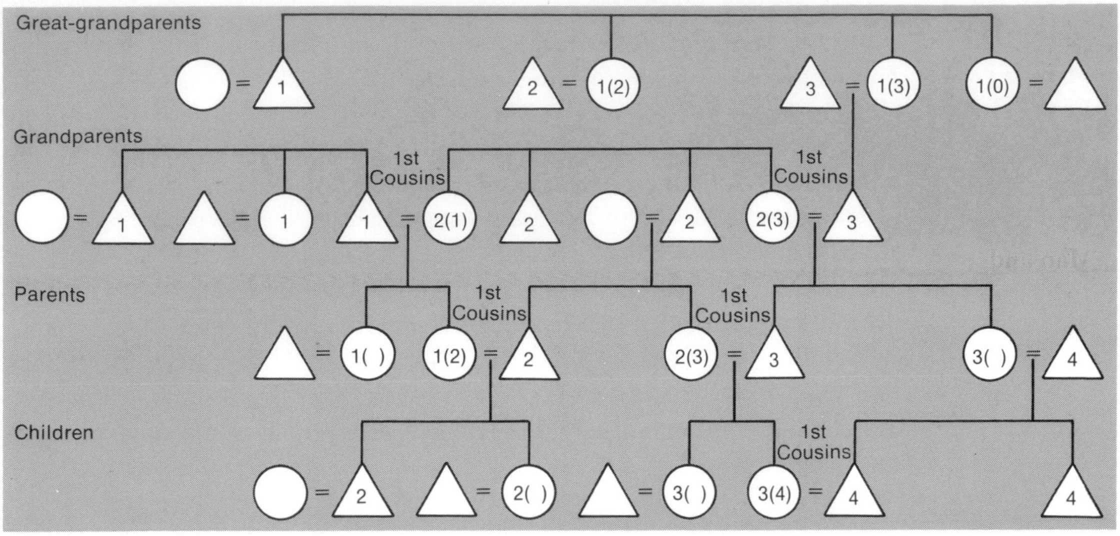

Figure 4-5. *Diagramatic example of exogamous mating* operated by hypothetical contemporary hunting-gathering bands. Group selection for such behavior probably occurred early in the history of *erectus-sapiens* populations. Selection pressure favoring such behavior would develop because of the need to avoid intraband rivalry over mates, and to prevent possible genetic consequences of close inbreeding which would produce potentially disadvantageous homozygosity for many recessive genes. This system can result in frequent first-cousin matings, which could have this same result. △ = male ○ = female; four different bands indicated by numbers 1, 2, 3, and 4. Mated females transfer to the band of male mate, indicated by the number in parentheses. Blanks instead of numbers indicate bands other and additional to those labeled 1, 2, 3, 4.

erectus, when temporary camps had evolved, women no longer participated in hunting expeditions, so were not further selected over the next 250,000 years for greater throwing accuracy and ability. At the same time their dexterity with a needle and thread demonstrates they continued to use, and perhaps manufactured, particular ranges of preparatory tools. Once fire was associated with the temporary camp, women would have fire tending and cooking added to the tasks of child care and plant digging.

It is interesting to speculate that with such divisions of labor in *H. erectus* there would be selection pressures operating on mental characteristics such as better-than-average aptitude for short-term strategic planning, aggression, and a command language in males, and longer-term policy planning, patience, and a descriptive language in females. The generally thicker head hair covering of modern females as compared with males suggests that even in *H. erectus* there was not always complete accord in a pair bond. Blows may occasionally have been traded, which afforded a selective value to the thicker hair protecting the portion of the body most susceptible to fatal damage. By the same token, the lesser head covering of the male suggests that blows were rarely exchanged between males temporarily associated in hunting parties. This implies the probable existence in such bands of some kind of accepted social hierarchy system, perhaps based on known hunting skills.

Speculation as to selection for specific behavioral traits in *H. erectus* could be continued almost indefinitely, but supporting evidence is so nebulous as to make such speculation unprofitable. What appears certain is that changes in gene frequencies of particular alleles were more rapidly made; selection pressures favoring particular alleles resulted in more speedy adaptation during the earlier periods of the almost 4 million years' existence of *H. erectus* and *erectus-sapiens* populations than has been possible at any subsequent time in *Homo sapiens*' history. For one thing, the time span for the *H. sapiens* grade has been very much smaller; for another, selection can operate only through a differential survival rate or differential production of offspring, and *sapiens* grade man has increasingly buffered this effect. The old adage that "human nature does not change" is substantially correct, although the vast numbers of modern man may require some amendment of this generalization.

FIRE AND COOKING

The only positive evidence of the earliest association between *H. erectus* and fire in Africa is from deposits as recent as 50,000 years BP (Clark, 1959). This can be interpreted two ways: either African populations of *H. erectus* were very late in acquiring the use of fire, or, alternatively, no evidence of earlier use has so far come to light.

In the case of Peking man the association of *H. erectus,* burned bones, and charcoal in caves is very much older, dating back to 400,000 BP (Figure 4-6). This does not imply any more than the *capturing* of fire from lightning strikes, volcanoes, or other such natural occurrences. It was probably a very, very long time before the making of fire was discovered.

The importance of *preserving* fire still retains its significance in present-day rituals, where an "eternal flame" is an important symbol in many cultures. The vestal virgins of Rome were responsible for keeping a fire going, and in some modern tropical forest communities, women may be seen walking from one site to another bearing burning brands on their heads (protected by several layers of leaves).

It is sometimes argued that cooking meat in a fire made it more digestible for *H. erectus.* Whether this is true or not, the meat would certainly be easier to consume, especially by the young, and by the middle-aged whose teeth had begun to wear down or decay. The significance of cooking might therefore lie more in its effects in reducing mortality in the young and the old, rather than in providing a greater digestibility.

There is circumstantial evidence that *H. erectus* in Europe was also using fire early, by about 300,000 BP (Figure 4-7). This evidence comes from a site at Farralba in Spain, where bones of many specimens of megafauna, including deer, horses, aurochs, and elephants, have been found in association with charcoal and showed signs of being broken. However, no trace of hominid skulls or skeletons has been located.

Figure 4-6. *Tableau depicting life of asiatic Homo erectus* (Peking Man) approximately 300,000 BP. Division of labor in the family unit is presumed to require females to remain around the cave shelter as fire-tenders (fire may have been captured rather than created at this time), vegetable food gatherers, and attendants for the young. Males hunted, butchered, made tools, and maintained the territory, while keeping in contact with other similar bands of the tribe to facilitate exogamous mating arrangements as daughters became nubile or sons matured. (Published by permission of the Trustees of the British Museum [Natural History]).

Perhaps this early use of fire in Europe and Asia, together with the use of clothing, was an essential prerequisite for an extension of *H. erectus* into colder latitudes, while populations remaining in equatorial Africa required no such protection against cold, so only adopted fire much later, and clothing often not at all.

GEOGRAPHICAL FORMS OF *H. ERECTUS*

Extrapolating from the studies of Loomis on pigmentation discussed in the previous chapter, it must be assumed that what ecologists are accustomed to call geographic races, which will here be termed *geographic forms* to avoid confusion, had developed in *Homo erectus* contemporaneously as migration carried these hominids into the temperate zones. While "Peking

Figure 4-7. *Tableau depicting life of European* erectus sapiens (Swanscombe Man) approximately 200,000 BP during the Riss-Würm interglacial. A group of males from the same tribe, but representing several bands, has driven a reindeer (caribou) into a bog, where it can more readily be killed with sharpened stakes and shafted tools. This would be one of the known localities within the tribal territory where such a hunting technique could be executed; animals previously dispatched on this spot included the aurochs. Butchering must have been effected with tools either left around, or manufactured as the occasion demanded. (Published by permission of the Trustees of the British Museum [Natural History]).

man" was marginal at 40° N, some lightening of the skin had probably occurred. "Heidelberg man," at nearly 50° N latitude, must have been *white,* although he developed a marked sun tan in summer. Such depigmented north temperate groups of *H. erectus* would be paralleled by southern groups in temperate Africa. It is not surprising to find there in modern times white groups as represented by the virtually extinct Hottentots, and brown groups such as the Bushmen of the Kalahari.

Genetic Continuity

Although such geographical groups would be established concurrently with migration north or south of the tropical zone, the uniformity of cultural artifacts throughout the area of dispersal of *H. erectus* demonstrates that cultural contact remained between the scattered populations. Where there was cultural contact it can confidently be assumed that breeding contact remained. Either mutual admiration or the vicissitudes of local fighting would be sufficient to overcome to at least some extent any cultural barriers against intergroup mating. In the case of highly selected characteristics such as skin color, the progeny of such crosses would sometimes tend to be less fit than the parents and would not significantly modify the gene pool of either group by introgression. In other traits less obviously of selective value, such as wavy versus straight hair, intergroup crossing must have ensured that mutant alleles eventually spread into all groups.

That some measure of breeding isolation did exist between major groups is evidenced by the present distribution of certain traits which appear to have no selective value. The most extensively studied series of such traits are *blood groups,* details of whose global distribution are known more fully than any other genetically determined system.

Blood Groups

The blood serum of some individuals can clump the red cells of certain others. From this reaction, three basic types of blood groups were initially recognized, A, B, and O. A fourth, AB, was later added to this early classification. The differences are believed to be caused by slight variations in the mucopolysaccharide materials at the blood corpuscle's surface, and there is some indication now that diet as well as heredity may influence their occurrence.

It is interesting to look at the same three areas when discussing skin color groups, where it may be supposed that East Africa had black-skinned forms of *H. erectus,* Heidelberg had white, and Peking brown or yellow. The maps in Figures 4-8 and 4-9 ignore for this purpose the blood groups of other parts of the world.

With regard to the gene *G* for blood group O, equatorial Africa has the highest frequency (70–80 per cent), Europe is lower (60–70 per cent), with tongues reaching south in Africa, and Asia is the lowest (40–50 per cent), with higher frequencies in coastal regions.

With gene G^B for blood group B, Asia has the highest (20–30 per cent), again lower on the coast; equatorial Africa lower (10–15 per cent); and Europe the lowest (5–10 per cent) frequencies.

In the case of gene G^A for blood group A, Europe has the highest frequency (25–30 per cent); Asia a lower figure (15–20 per cent), lower in coastal areas; and equatorial Africa the lowest (10–15 per cent), with some central intrusion of 15–20 per cent frequencies.

Putting these figures together in another way, with the area's most common blood group first, the next most frequent second, this gives

Europe	A	(O)
Equatorial Africa	O	(B)
Asia	B	(A)

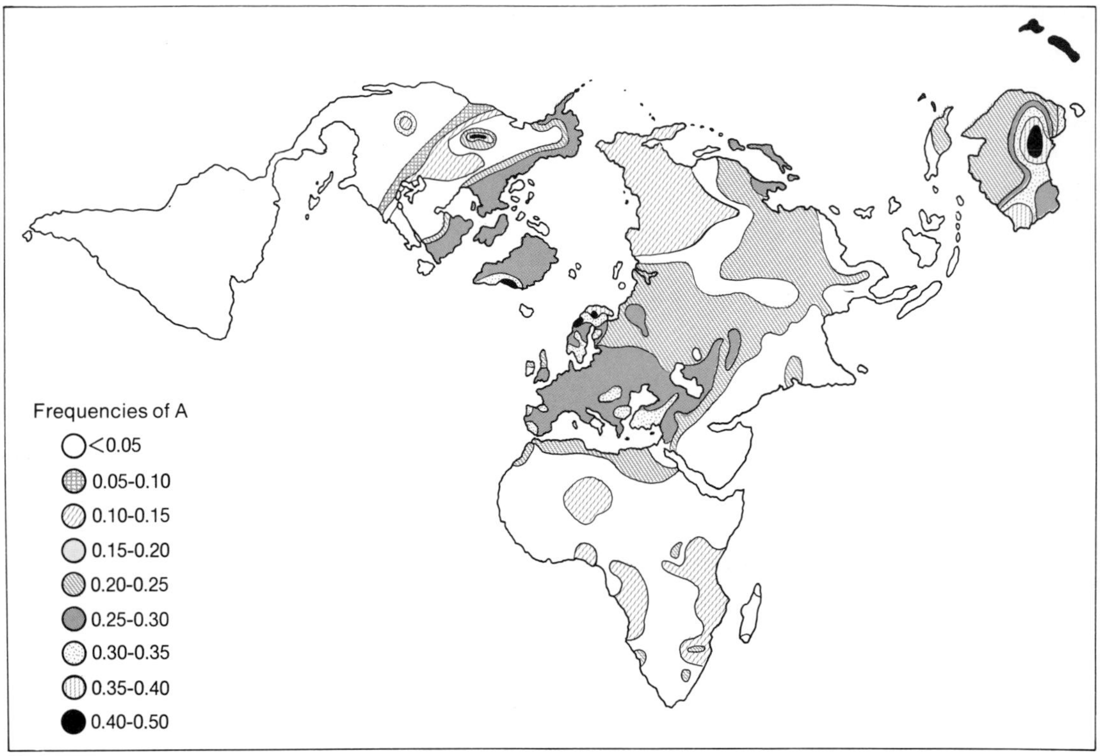

Figure 4-8. *The distribution among contemporary aborigine human populations of the gene* I^A which produces the A blood type. The frequency of this gene is highest in populations of the Caucasoid group, lowest in early Mongoloids of the Americas.

Boyd (1953), who examined the question of a more detailed range of blood groups in relation to major groupings of human populations, arrived at a scheme similar to the above. It differs only in identifying as separate entities two splinter groups, Amerindians and Australian aborigines. The scheme he arrived at, omitting these last two, may be summarized as:

Caucasoid.	High frequency of Rh cde and CDe, moderate of other blood group genes. M usually above, N below 50 per cent
Negroid.	Very high frequency of Rh cDe, moderate frequencies of other blood group genes
Mongoloid.	High frequency of B, little if any cde

It is tempting to argue that such groupings of an apparently nonselective character in modern human populations result from genetic differences which arose between *H. erectus* groups as mutations for skin color permitted some of them to migrate from the parent stock in equatorial Africa and form distinct geographic groups in higher latitudes. The possible migration routes which might have been followed have been considered during studies of an interrelated problem, the origin of the human populations of the New World.

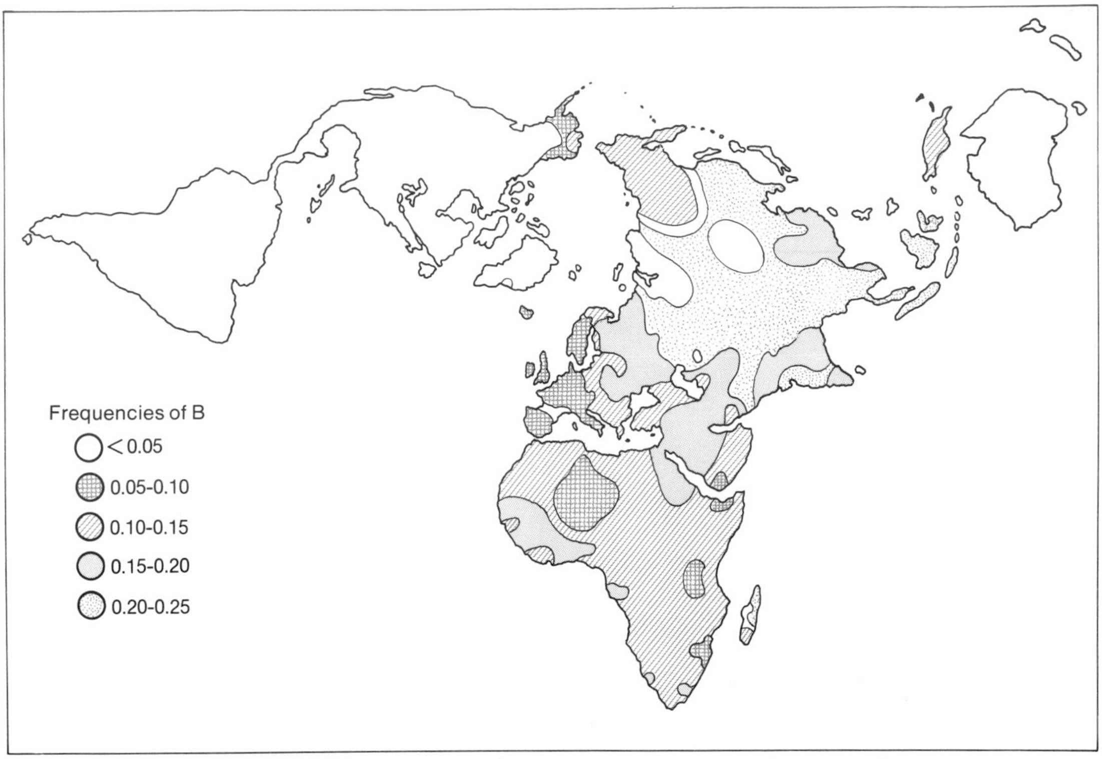

Figure 4-9. *The distribution among contemporary aborigine human populations of the gene* I^B which produces the B blood type. The frequency of this gene is highest among recent Mongoloids, but it is quite absent from the early Mongoloid populations of the Americas, probably because of the operation of the "Founder principle."

EARLY MIGRATIONS

The restrictions imposed by the spread of ice sheets in the Old World on territory suitable for hominid occupation have been considered by Weckler (1957). He illustrates the probability that during an ice age most of Europe would have been quite uninhabitable, although because of lowered sea levels, there may have been land routes across the Mediterranean Sea. Populations in Asia would have been isolated there by a southern extension of Caucasian ice sheets to the Persian Gulf (Figure 4-10). The same almost complete isolation would be true of Asian populations during an interglacial period because of the substitution in this Caucasus-Persian region of a dry zone for an ice sheet barrier (Figure 4-11).

As the climate moderated after a glacial interval, migration into western Europe would be possible, but factors of time and distance probably prevented European hominid groups from extending sufficiently eastward to encounter similarly migrating Asiatic populations spreading westward.

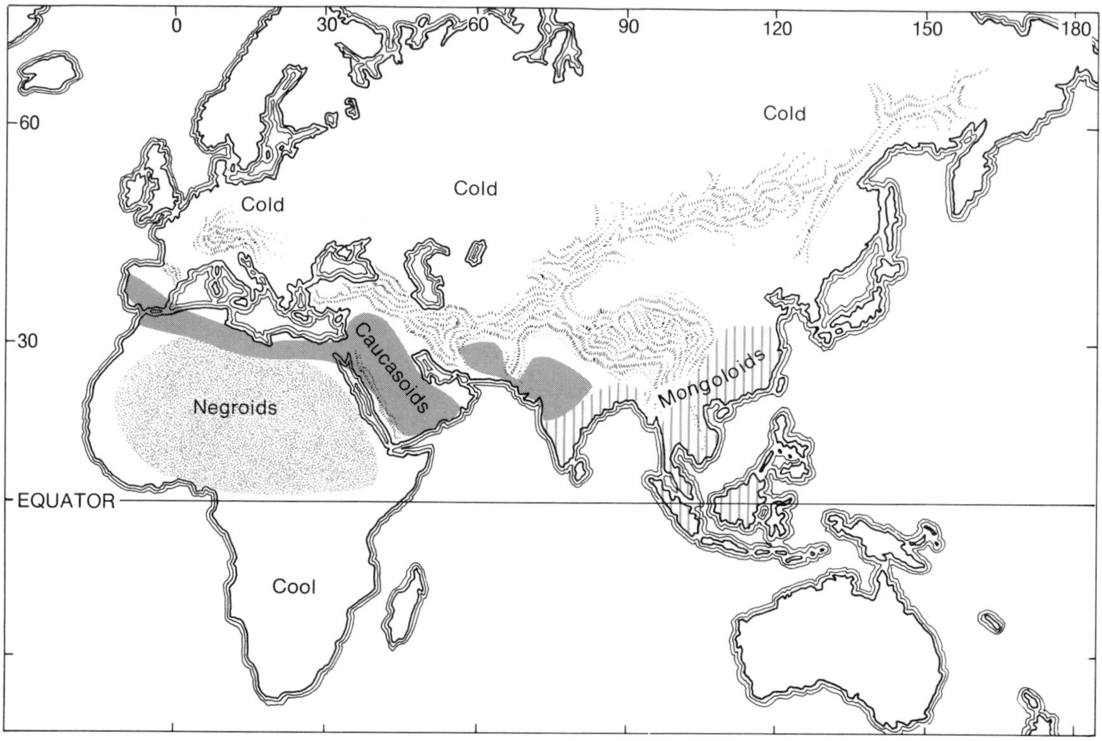

Figure 4-10. *Eurasia during a glacial episode of the Pleistocene.* Mountain glaciers effectively isolate any *erectus-sapiens* populations that have penetrated east of the Caucasus Mountains. In Europe the alpine glaciers may similarly have isolated any European populations, although lowering of sea levels may have permitted dry crossings of the Mediterranean Sea area.

Pleistocene barriers to migration therefore appear to confirm the suggestion from an examination of such traits as blood group differences that essentially white European groups, black African groups, and yellow or brown Asiatic groups of *erectus-sapiens* populations were evolved as distinct geographic entities in comparative breeding isolation (Figures 4-12 to 4-15).

NEANDERTHAL MAN

The concepts of human evolution developed so far indicate the existence of three geographical forms of *erectus-sapiens* populations which developed independently in response to their differing environments. However, all possessed a common Chelles-Acheul culture and undoubtedly were still undergoing some gene exchange throughout the dispersal area of this hominid stage.

So far we have ignored the complications which arise from the undisputable existence of another hominid form whose discovery antedates that of *H. erectus* historically, and whose remains and associated artifacts quantitatively far exceed those of any other hominid yet considered. The first

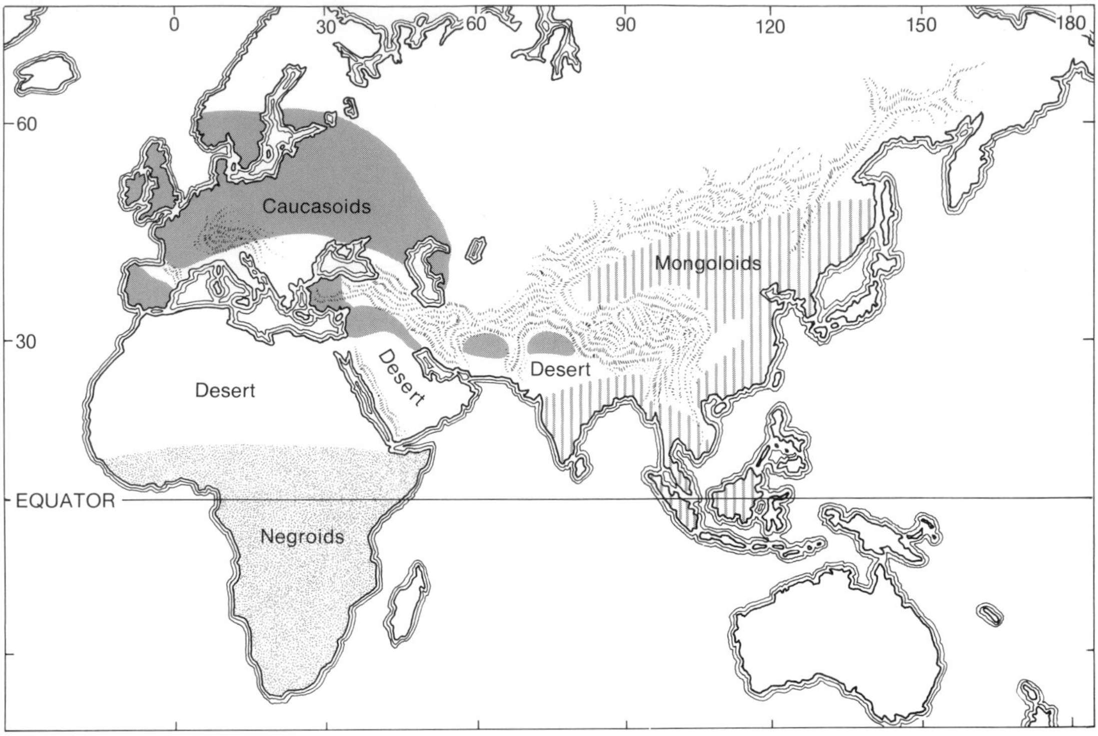

Figure 4-11. *Eurasia during an interglacial episode of the Pleistocene.* The warmer and drier conditions would impose a desert barrier tending to isolate any *erectus-sapiens* populations which had succeeded in penetrating east of the Caucasus Mountains. The Mediterranean Sea and desert conditions in North Africa would similarly tend to isolate any European populations.

report of artifacts of this form appeared ten years previous to the publication of Darwin's *Origin of Species,* in 1849, when M. Boucher de Perthes described some fashioned flints found in Somme river gravels in France. In an imperious manner not entirely unfamiliar to us today, the current French establishment pronounced its judgment on this report: "*L'homme fossile n'existe pas.*"

That this was not to be the last word on the subject was first conclusively demonstrated with the unearthing of thigh and arm bones, ribs, clavicle, pelvis, and skull cap sections from a cave in Germany. It was situated in a valley a little to the east of Dusseldorf, which had been named "Neanderthal" after the nom de plume *Neander* formed by translating into Greek the name of a seventeenth century poet which by sheer coincidence was Neumann (new man). Confusion and controversy surrounded these finds for many years, as they did more scanty but earlier remains of "Gibralter man." Although appropriately named by an astute Irish professor of anatomy, William King, as a new species of man, *Homo neanderthalensis,* support for this view was not generally received until after a dozen or so similar finds were unearthed in Europe between 1870 and 1880.

Controversy and doubt persist, and it is still not clear beyond reasonable

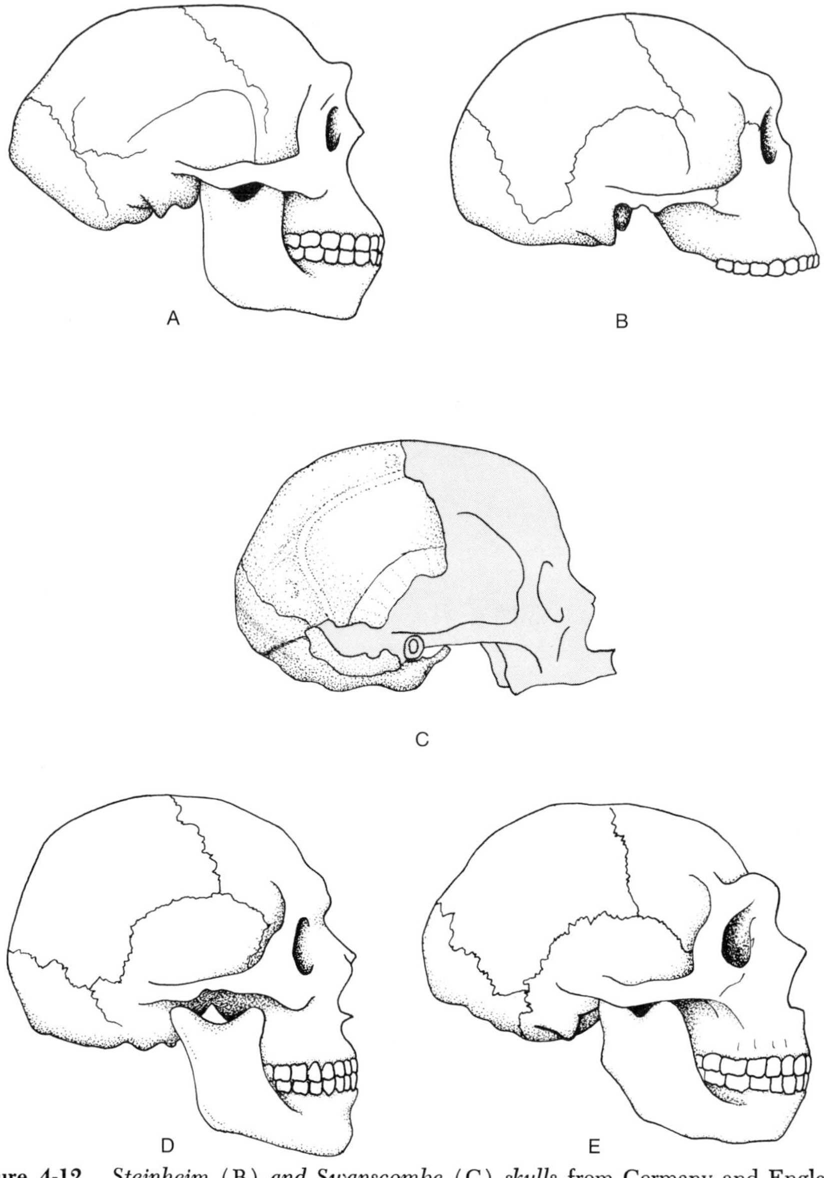

Figure 4-12. *Steinheim* (B) *and Swanscombe* (C) *skulls* from Germany and England, respectively. These skulls, which date between 200,000 and 300,000 BP, are intermediate in many characters between *H. erectus* (*A*) and *H. sapiens* (*D*). Their cranial capacity is considerably larger than that of *Homo erectus,* and the brow ridges are less pronounced than in Neanderthals (*E*). They provide fragmentary evidence at best; one interpretation could be that *erectus-sapiens* populations in Europe gradually evolved from an *erectus* grade by approximately 70,000 BP. A schematic representation of stages in this progression is given in Figure 4-14. Acheulian tools were associated with the Swanscombe fragment and evidence of fire.

Figure 4-13. *Scheme illustrating the possible evolution of the negroid* Homo sapiens *grade* from *Homo erectus* (*A*), illustrated here as of about 1,250,000 BP, occurring during the comparative isolation illustrated in Figure 4-10: through Rhodesian man (*B*), circa 750,000 BP, to modern Bushmen (*C*), Negros (*D*), and Pygmies (*E*). During interglacials (Figure 4-11) Negroids would be at various times in contact with caucasoid

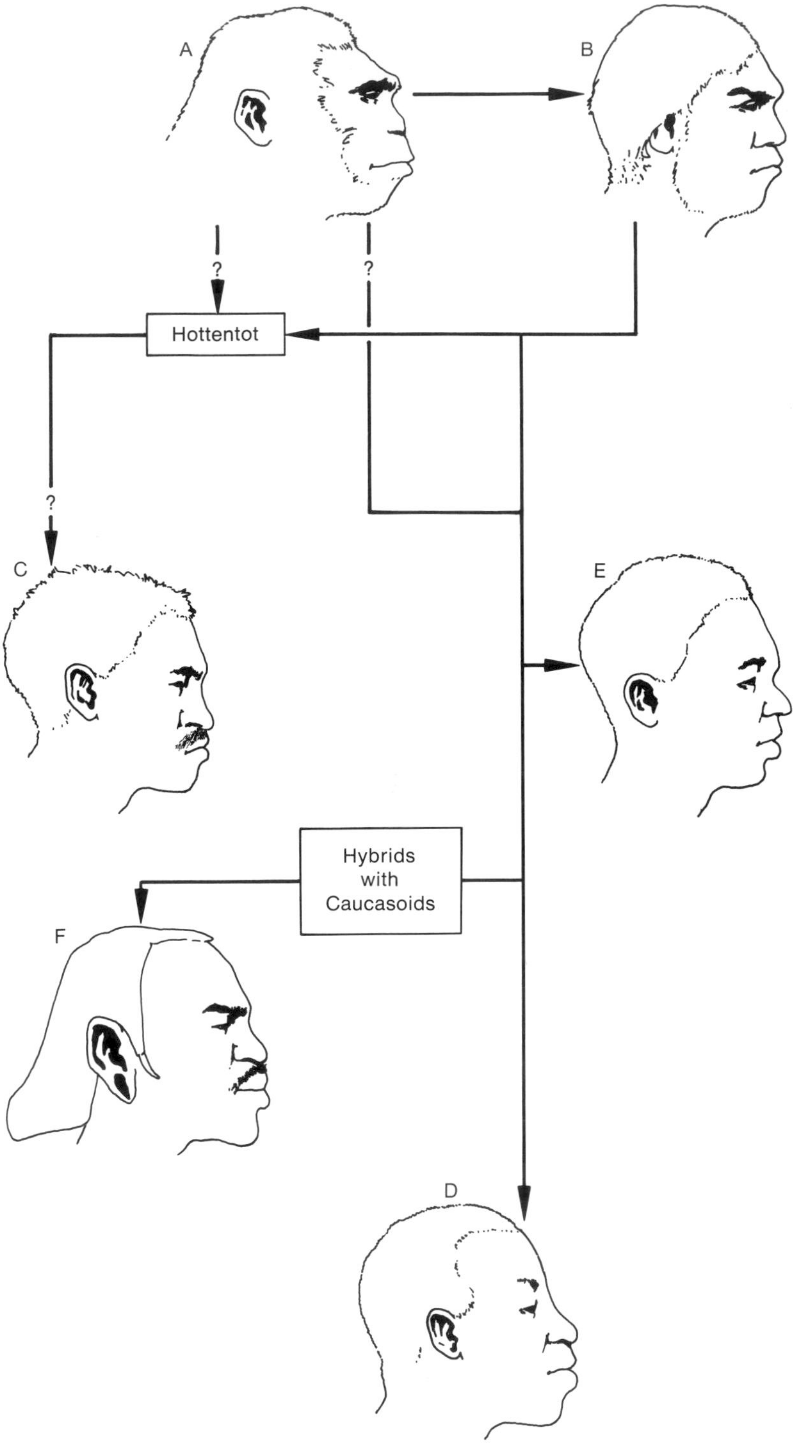

stocks, apparently producing such modern hybrid groups as those known collectively as the Bantu (*F*).

The arrows interrupted by queries offer possible alternative derivations, and the whole scheme is hypothetical: sufficient evidence of various kinds may eventually accumulate to permit more substantive schemes to be prepared.

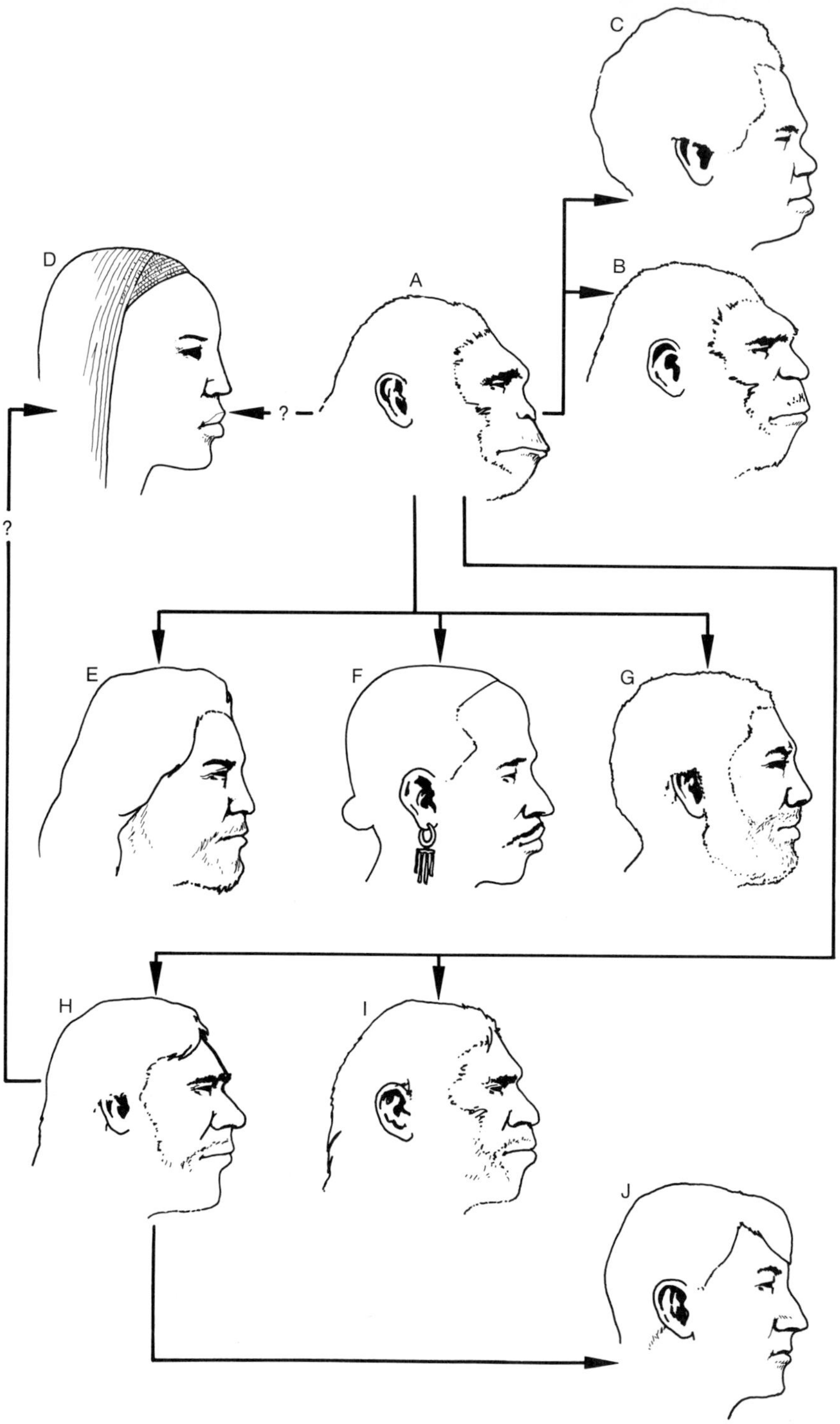

Figure 4-14. *Scheme illustrating the possible evolution of the caucasoid* Homo sapiens *grade* from *Homo erectus* (*A*), as in figure 4-13. Migration during interglacials (Figure 4-11) and comparative isolation during glacials (Figure 4-10) led to the evolution of such forms as Solo man (*B*), Indonesia circa 1,000,000 BP, and the now extinct Tasmanian man (*C*), as well as to modern Caucasoids such as the Ainu (*E*) of Japan,

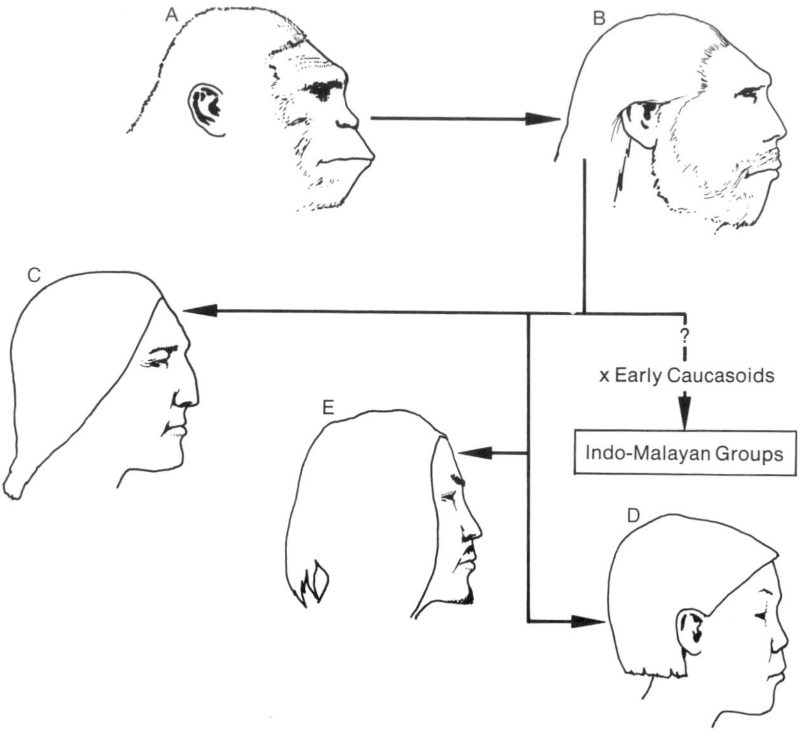

Figure 4-15. *Reconstructions illustrating possible evolution of mongoloid group of* Homo sapiens *grade from* H. erectus *grade. A. H. erectus* (Africa) circa 1,250,000 BP. *B.* Peking Man (China) circa 1,000,000 BP. *C.* Paleo-Indian. *D.* Recent Mongoloid female (China). *E.* Bering Sea Mongoloid (Alaska). All males unless otherwise stated.

question whether modern man evolved through a Neanderthal stage, or whether this was a specialized evolutionary form selected from the white geographical group of *H. erectus* which eventually died out without contributing any new alleles to the gene pool of modern man.

Neanderthal Characteristics

It is now generally agreed that Neanderthal man is associated with a particular stone-axe culture known as *Mousterian* (Weckler, 1957) (Figure 4-16). Apart from two controversial sites, Mount Carmel in Israel and Broken Hill in Zambia, all Neanderthal remains have been found in western continental Europe. There are no significant anatomical differences between Neanderthals and modern man except in the face and dentition. The teeth were very large, which partially accounts for the characteristic prognathy.

Dravidians (*F*) of India, and Australian aborigines (*G*). Modern Libyans (*D*) may be related to Swanscombe man (circa 250,000 BP), who could have been ancestral to Cro-Magnon man (*H*) (circa 50,000 BP) and to Neanderthals (*I*) (circa 50,000 BP), also probably such forms as the modern mid-East Caucasoids (*J*). All males apart from *D*. The same remarks about the speculative nature of this scheme as in Figure 4-13 apply also here.

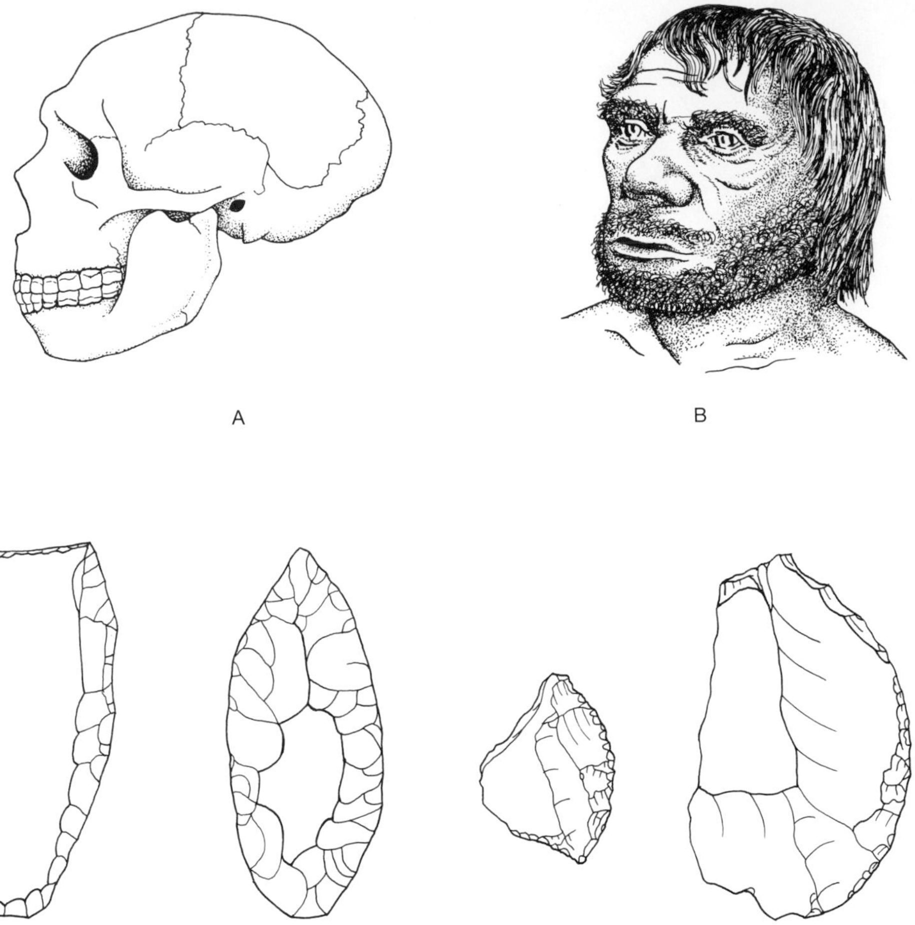

A B

C

Figure 4-16. *A "classical" Neanderthal skull and Mousterian tools,* both typical of forms dating to about 60,000 BP. Indisputable Neanderthal remains are not found outside Europe, but cultural artifacts identified as Mousterian are widespread over Eurasia, suggesting that this typically Neanderthal culture was adopted by other peoples. Such cultural spread indicates some degree of cultural contact between populations located in widely scattered regions of the Old World. (Based on a painting by Z. Burian. Reproduced with permission of the artist and *Artia,* Foreign Trade Corporation for Import and Export of Cultural Commodities, Prague, Czechoslovakia.)

The cranial capacity was the largest known in hominids, ranging from 1300 to 1600 cm^3. Earlier or "progressive" types of Neanderthals date from the last interglacial, the Riss-Würm, which began about 100,000 years ago. These "progressive" types graded into the "classical" types of the Würm glaciation, the latest remains known having been dated to an interstadial about 40,000 years ago. Perhaps "progressive" Neanderthals arose even earlier, toward the close of the Riss glaciation about 150,000 years ago. Fossil remains indicate Neanderthal populations were most abundant from the onset of the last (Würm) glaciation, dated at 75,000 $\pm$ 5000 BP radiometrically, to the temperate interstadial, which began about 42,000 years ago and lasted about 10,000 years. This represents a mere 30,000 $\pm$ 5000 years' allowing, perhaps only 1000 ± 250 generations, but more time than it took for differentiation of the American Indian populations.

Summarizing the characteristics of *H. neanderthalensis,* he lived and died (sometimes apparently being buried) either in caves which were heated by fires, but *not* yet decorated, or in the open. His stone tools were principally worked flint, including knives, scrapers, cleavers, borers, and saws, the last indicating that perhaps some flakes may have been hafted. He hunted and brought back portions of the kill to his hearths. Remains indicate his prey included such animals as woolly rhinoceros, mammoth, reindeer, musk-ox, ibex, glutton, chamois, fox, wild horses and oxen of various species, and marmots. He may have had to kill large predators such as cave lions, bears, and hyenas.

This megafauna typified a European periglacial ecosystem, highly productive in summer as the Arctic tundra is today. To survive the winter cold, *H. neanderthalensis* must have migrated into somewhat warmer climates and more wooded country. (Figure 4-17). He must also have dressed and worn furs, judging from the abundance of scrapers.

Trophic Position of Neanderthals

It is tempting to dismiss *H. neanderthalensis* as a variant of the white geographic group of *H. erectus* which had specialized in an exclusively hunting economy. As a top carnivore the population density could never become very high, development of new hunting techniques might always result in overkill of particular prey species and permanently disturb the tundra ecosystem. The facial characteristics, which became progressively more pronounced, are consistent with the need for such a top carnivore (as in the case of the modern Eskimo), to chew not only meat, but also hides in order to prepare skins for use as clothing.

Trophic isolation of this exclusive white hunter group would separate it from the still unspecialized hunting-gathering populations of the Mediterranean region, Asia, and Africa. The climatic amelioration of the Würm interstadial may have destroyed the game species on which *H. neanderthalensis* depended exclusively for his survival, an event to which overkill may have contributed.

Such a simplified view of Neanderthals quite ignores two major items of controversy already noted. The first is the discovery of possible intermediates on Mount Carmel in Israel (Binford, 1970), the second the so-called "Rhodesian" or "Broken Hill" man, exhibiting "boskopoid" tendencies, the African version of Neanderthals according to some workers (Figure 4-14). One plausible explanation of these apparent anomalies is that early Neanderthals, "Rhodesian man," and "Solo man" represent parallel stages in the progression of caucasoid, negroid, and mongoloid populations, respectively, to modern man. Classical Neanderthals would then be an extinct subspecies.

Figure 4-17. *A Neanderthal band setting out on its northward spring migration.* After overwintering in a wooded area of central Europe, this small band is heading north with all its possessions, tools, skins, and small game provisions to exploit the rich summer hunting resources of the more northerly tundras. Time period toward the close of the Riss-Würm interglacial about 80,000 BP, and relatively warm. (Based on a painting by Z. Burian.)

CRO-MAGNON MAN

The possible overemphasis on Neanderthals arising from the circumstances of their location in Western Europe may equally apply to the last major fossil series to be discussed. This has come to be called *Cro-Magnon* man, based on a rather imperfect skull found in a cave shelter near a great rock (*cro-magnon*) in the village of Les Eyzies in southwestern France in 1868 (Baker, 1968). Although the teeth are missing, all the skull measurements fall within the range of those of living Europeans. Indeed, photographs of contemporary individuals closely resembling this type have been published.

This first Cro-Magnon skull was that of a man about fifty. Subsequently in the same locality remains of two other adult men, a woman, and an unborn child were found. All date from the Göttweiger interstadial, approximately 30,000 years ago, and related artifacts represent upper paleolithic tools. It is thought that by this time the European group of *erectus-sapiens* had assumed the anatomical form of now-living descendants (Figures 4-12 and 4-14). The same may well have been true of the African group (Figure 4-13), but it was not quite applicable to the Asiatic forms, as subsequent migration into the Americas from Beringia revealed (Figure 4-15). Despite the comparative absence of any further physical evolution from this time, the immense range of late paleolithic, mesolithic, and neolithic cultures still had not evolved, and many major migrations had yet to occur. Some of these were undoubtedly prompted by further climatic change. In considering the diversity of modern man, a number of these points will be amplified later. Cultural changes other than those exhibited in worked stone tools will now be briefly examined.

Migration of *H. erectus-sapiens* Populations

As has been noted several times, dispersal of the various hominid stages about the world was remarkably wide (Figure 4-18). While it is true that as a top carnivore, which most species of the genus *Homo* proved to be, hominids could be expected to have the widespread distribution which fossil remains indicate, even the largely vegetarian species of the genus *Paranthropus* seem to have been widely dispersed. Several factors may have been responsible for this. The greater intelligence resulting from the proportionately larger brain and the possession of early forms of cultural behavioral patterns would permit more ready adaptation to somewhat differing habitats and ecosystems. This adaptability in turn would facilitate the accommodation of any population surplus in new territories. Feedback mechanisms, which in other animals might provide for regulation of population numbers by restricting births or increasing mortalities, or both, may therefore have not restricted population growth because emigration prevented overexploitation of any particular habitat or ecosystem. Emigration has been a constant feature of the development of all human societies, although in modern times restrictive laws have sometimes reduced this flow to a level where its selective nature causes it to be known as the "brain drain."

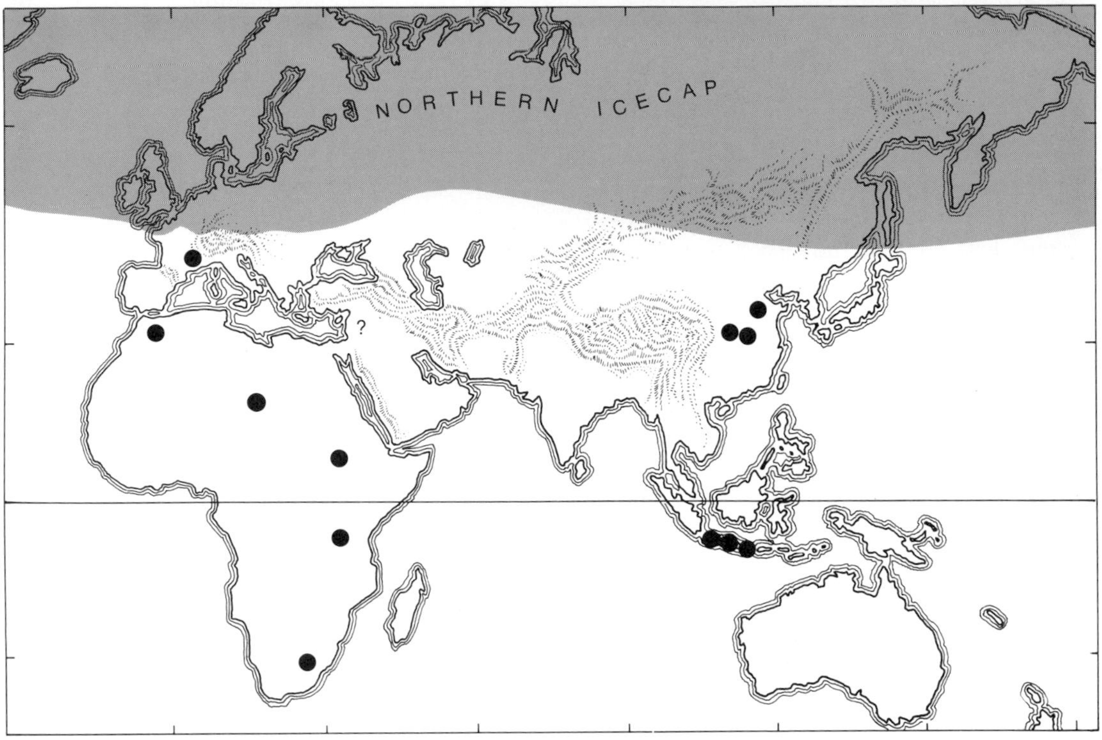

Figure 4-18. *Distribution of finds of skeletal remains attributable* to Homo erectus. Shaded area indicates position of polar ice sheet and European alpine glaciation about 500,000 BP, which is the approximate date for many of these finds. By contrast with *Paranthropus, Homo africanus,* and *H. habilis,* remains of which have not been found outside tropical areas, *H. erectus* could exist in a wide range of climates, from tropical to arctic.

As far as *erectus-sapiens* populations are concerned, we are discovering more about one major migration, the occupation of the New World during the closing stages of the Pleistocene.

OCCUPATION OF THE NEW WORLD

No remains of any hominid, or of any anthropoid other than *Homo sapiens,* have ever been found in the New World. It has therefore been concluded that until the appearance of *Homo sapiens* pongid and hominid evolution were restricted entirely to the Old World. This unexplained circumstance is somewhat curious in view of the fact that other forms of mammalian evolution were proceeding in the same period and about as extensively in both the eastern and western hemispheres. Moreover, camels, horses, bison, and elephants appear to have actually originated in the New World and migrated to the Old. Such migrations would not have been possible except across what is generally known as the *Bering land bridge.* More precisely, these mammals migrated by way of *Beringia,* for during the period when readjustments of sea level relative to land exposed a continu-

Plate 4. *Evidence of Paleo-Indian cultures in the American continents* is slowly being assembled by carefully and scientifically planned digs, such as this one in Wyoming. Archeological evidence from such digs is more readily accessible when modern earth-moving machinery can be used to remove the overburden. Stratigraphical and other spatial relationships are now more precisely recorded, and a wide range of techniques from other disciplines can be employed to convert what might otherwise be pure conjecture into quantified probabilities.

ous land mass between North America and Asia, this was at least 400 miles wide, which would in no way constrict animals into a narrow migration passage (Figure 4-19). Any movements through Beringia would therefore have been a normal pattern of territorial dispersal similar to that which would occur on any continental mass.

The Bering Land Bridge

If human migration into the Americas was by land—and there is presently no evidence to suggest that it was by sea or occurred more than once—it could have taken place only at three possible dates in the Upper Pleistocene (Figures 4-19 and 4-20). The first was from about 70,000 to 50,000 BP, the second from about 32,000 to 28,000 BP, the third from about 22,000 to 15,000 BP. These are the dates determined by the stratigraphical, palynological, and radiometric evidence of when sufficient areas of Beringia would have been exposed to permit migration from Asia to North America. Considerable archeological evidence suggests that the last date was probably the most likely for this spread of *Homo sapiens* populations into the western

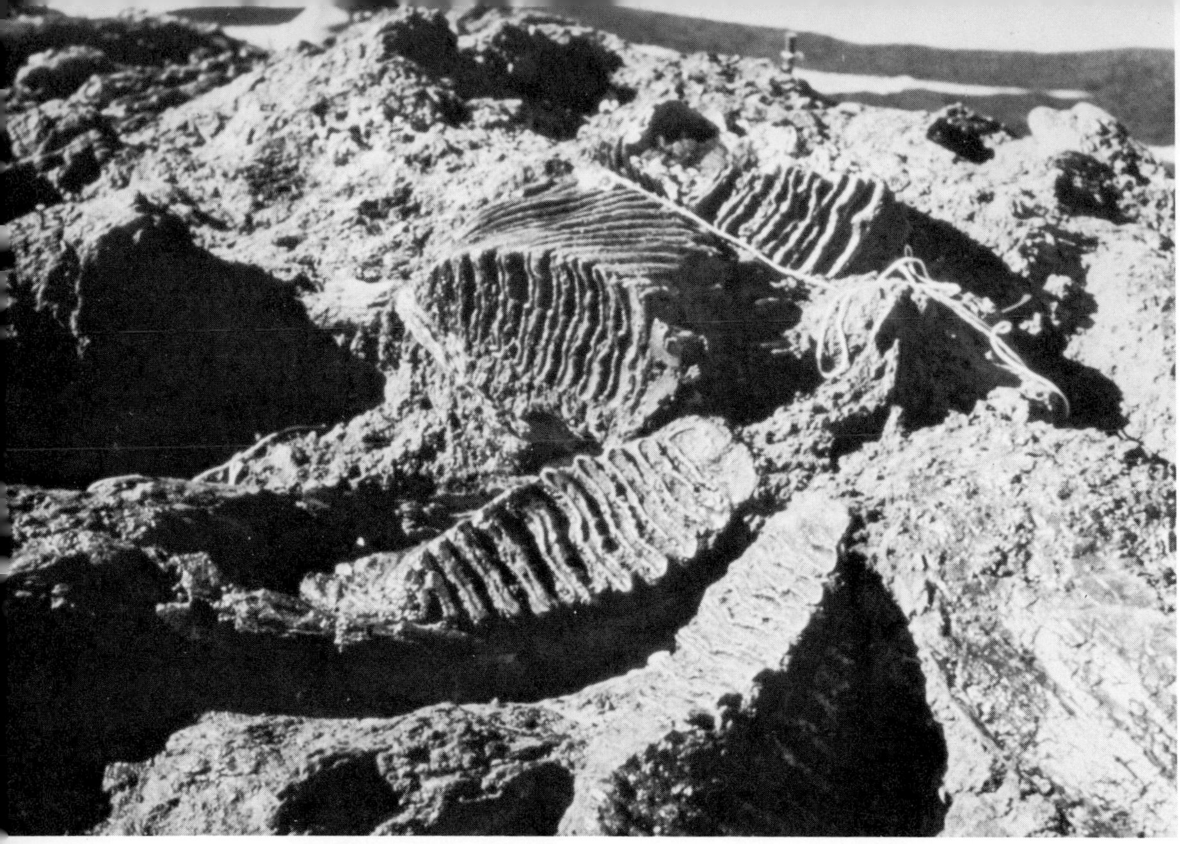

Plate 5. *Evidence of Paleo-Indian cultures in North America* frequently demonstrates that large animals were butchered, if not killed. The four teeth of this fully grown mammoth, the last of its three sets, and the rest of its skeleton were littered with several hundred Clovis tools broken, dropped, or discarded when it was butchered. This skeleton, provisionally dated to about 12,000 BP, was found recently in an arroyo some miles east of Tucson, Arizona.

hemisphere. It agrees with the oldest radiometric dating of any presently known Paleo-Indian remains of *Homo sapiens* in North America, that on "Laguna woman" dated to 17,000 BP (Berger, 1969). Although claims of earlier finds predating this period have not been substantiated, it should be remarked that while a considerable body of archeological opinion supports this dating, it does not preclude the movement of other cultures at an earlier date. This problem has recently been discussed in a survey by C. Vance Haynes (1969), and the two illustrations in Figure 4-20 which schematically summarize the present position are taken from this work.

Early Mongoloids

From about 18,000 BP, hunting-gathering groups of a nomadic pre-Mongolian type known as *Early Mongoloids* were spreading northward through the Pacific hinterland of northeastern Asia. They are termed Early Mongoloids, because the flattening of the face and the loss of brow ridges and certain other characteristics of the recent mongoloid had not yet reached their fullest development. Fossil remains of these people are always associ-

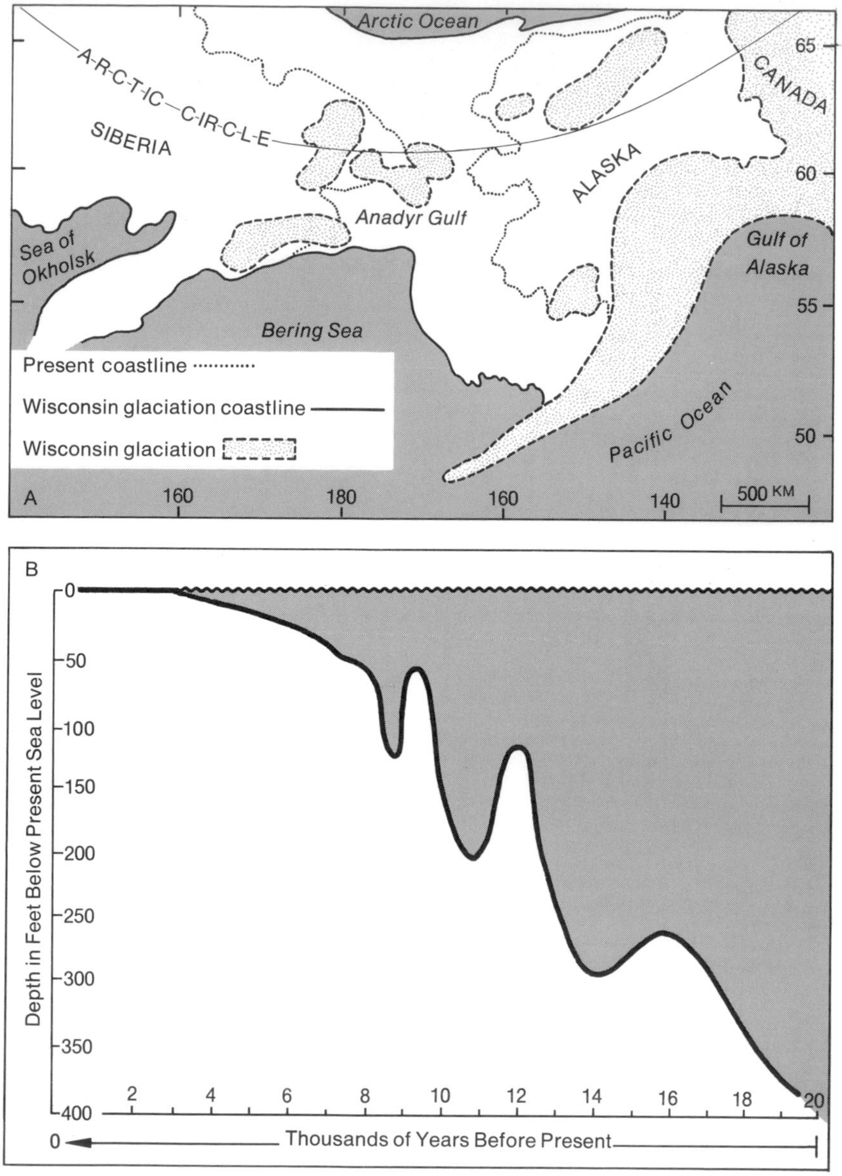

Figure 4-19. *The Bering land bridge* showing (*A*) the land area exposed during the maximum marine regression and (*B*) the fluctuating Pleistocene sea levels. See text for further explanation.

ated with a cultural tool known as the "projectile tip," in which the spear heads, supposedly hafted, have been secondarily flaked to provide a sharp apex (Figure 4-21). It is thought that such bands were hunting the large game animals which characterized these Upper Pleistocene times, and the projectile tip was necessary to provide penetration of the thick hides.

Remains of projectile tip peoples have been found as early as 18,000 BP in the northeastern section of Asia adjoining the now-inundated land of Beringia. The earliest such remains in Alaska are dated at 12,000 BP. No

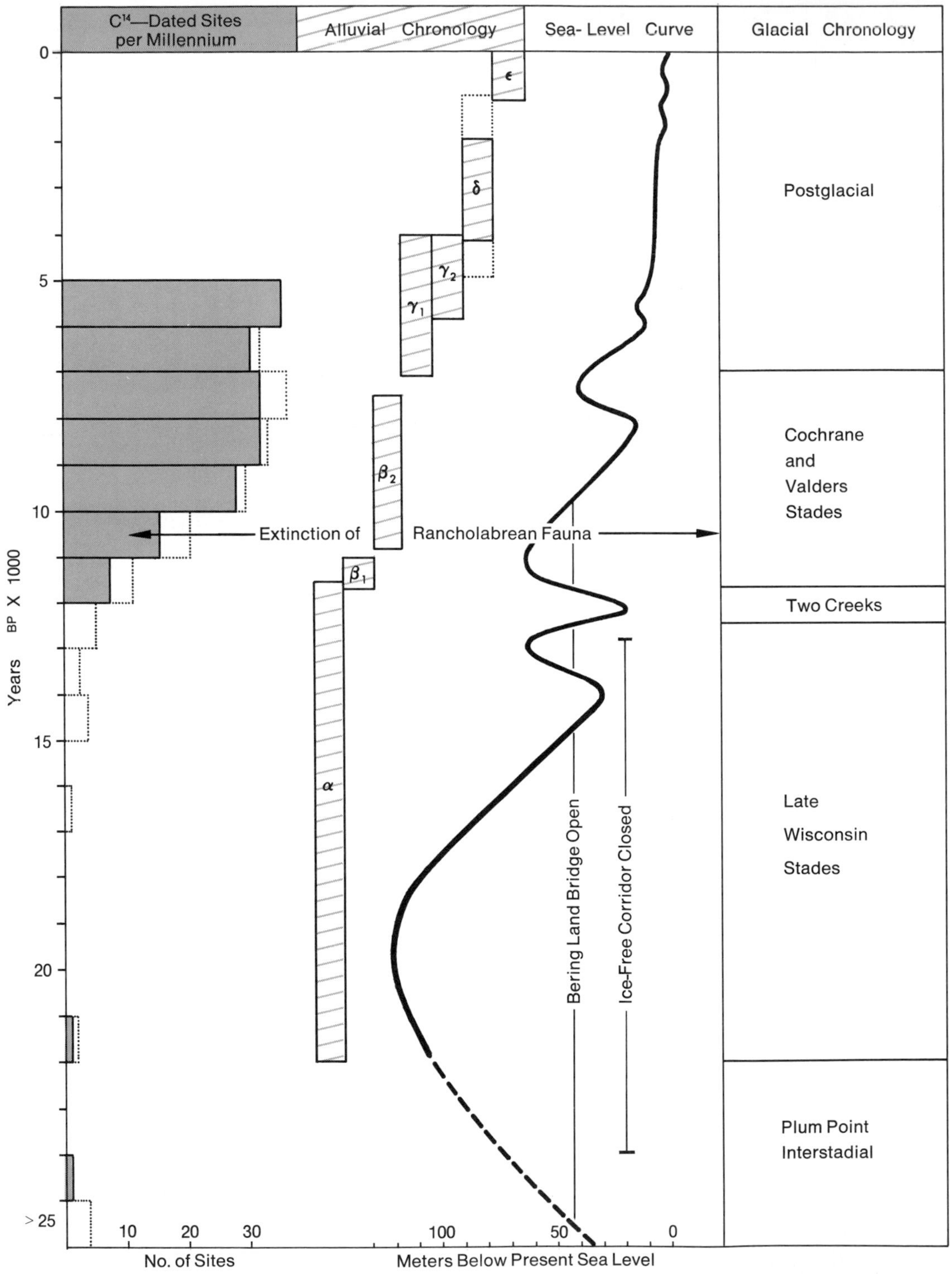

Figure 4-20. *Correlations between Pleistocene fluctuations in sea level, glacial chronology, alluvial deposition, and Paleo-Indian sites in North America.* (Reproduced with the permission of the author and publisher from C. V. Haynes, Jr., *Science,* **166:** 710, 711, 1969. Copyright 1969 by the American Association for the Advancement of Science.)

A B

Figure 4-21. *Tools of the general type known as projectile tip.* These occur extensively in northeast Asia, from about 18,000 BP, and forms shown in *A* are found later over a wide area of North America. The tools were believed to have been hafted, the point being used to penetrate the hide of large mammals. Folsom (*B*) is the name given to a common North American type of the general projectile tip class occurring from about 12,000 to 7000 BP.

remains have yet been located from the submerged areas of the Bering Straits.

However, similar projectile tips of about the same date have been found much further south in the North American continent. For them to have reached such a distance, it is presumed that the occupation of Beringia must have been completed by 15,000 BP. The term *occupation* is perhaps a misnomer. One, or at most several, bands of a projectile-tip hunting-gathering population were probably all that ever occupied this territory, and it is doubtful whether they even realized they were crossing from one continent to another. If it was indeed only one band, it could have numbered as few as 100 individuals. The so-called *founder principle,* which appears to apply to certain genetic traits of American Indians, provides circumstantial support both for the supposition of the unique event of migration to the Americas, and to the very small size of the migrating group.

Migrations in the Americas

The area of the land in North America available for colonization in this final major marine regression of the Upper Pleistocene would be comparatively restricted. The great ice sheets of the Wisconsin still stretched over the whole of Canada, apart from the so-called *nunatak,* or exposed ice-free tundra, covering much of Alaska. The Cascade and Sierra Nevada mountain chains were only just beginning to be elevated. Between them and the Pacific Ocean would lie most of the exposed land surface north of the most southerly extension of the Wisconsin ice sheets, which in the central part of the country would probably be at least as far south as Colorado and Kansas (Figure 4-22).

While the nomadic projectile-tip hunter-gatherers would be living in

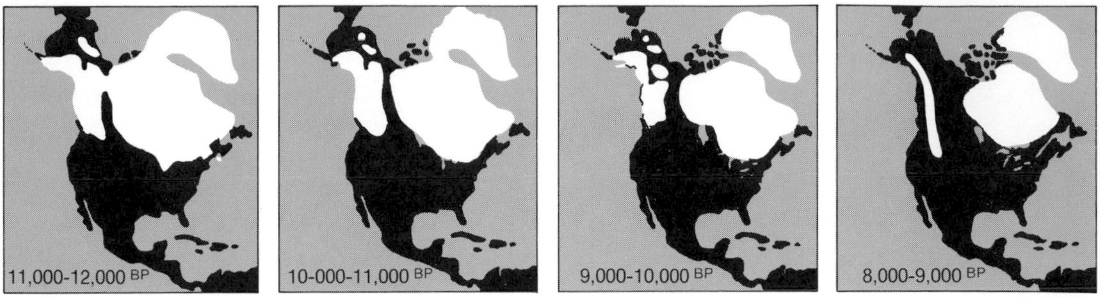

Figure 4-22. *Glaciation in North America at various times* as correlated with absolute dates obtained from radiocarbon measurements. Even during the several glacial episodes illustrated here, a western corridor and portions of Alaska remained clear of glaciers.

tundra in Beringia, as they penetrated further and further south through the Pacific Northwest they would encounter increasingly luxuriant ecosystems. These would mainly be of a coniferous forest type, interspersed with grasslands on which an extensive megafauna had evolved. Many remains of this megafauna have been found in the tar pits around Los Angeles, and the fauna has been named the *Rancho La Brea fauna* after the largest of these tar pits to be examined to date, on the old Spanish land holding of Rancho La Brea (Figure 4-23). Radiocarbon dates show that the remains form a sequence from about 40,000 to 10,000 years BP (Ho *et al.*, 1969).

The Rancho La Brea Fauna

The Rancho La Brea fauna has been extensively described and illustrated. It was composed of horses, camels, bison, elephants, mammoths, several species of sloth, saber-tooth cats, lions, wild dogs, dire-wolves, a number of large bird species, and many smaller genera and species of modern rodents. The projectile-tip nomadic bands would already have a long cultural history of hunting such animals, many of which (or their ecological equivalents) are known from Asia at this time. The American populations of these animals would, however, never previously have been exposed to any hominid-type predator, and they had no prior selection for predator-prey relationships in connection with hominids. The larger animals would be easily killed by the invading Mongoloids (Figure 4-24).

Pleistocene Overkill

It could be surmised that with such an abundance of easily obtainable food, there was a population explosion among these hunter-gathering bands, which would rapidly increase in number and in territory occupied. There is still much controversy as to the large animal-man interrelationships. One school of thought considers that what has come to be called the "Pleistocene overkill" occurred between about 15,000 and 12,000 BP, when many of the

Figure 4-23. *The Rancho La Brea fauna:* a few of the commoner large mammals typical of this South Pacific community. *A. Megalonyx* (giant sloth). *B. Arctodus* (giant bear). *C. Smilodon* (saber-toothed cat). *D. Camelops* (camel). *E. Titanotylopus* (*protogiraffe*). *F. Preptoceras* (giant ox). (Reproduced by permission of the publisher from P. S. Martin and H. E. Wright [eds.], *Pleistocene Extinctions,* New Haven: Yale University Press, 1967.)

Figure 4-24. *A Paleo-Indian hunt.* Folsom man attacking a camel near Tule Springs, Nevada. (From a painting by Jay H. Matternes, reproduced by permission of the National Geographical Society.)

genera of the Rancho La Brea megafauna passed to extinction (Figure 4-25). Simultaneously, remains of hunting-gathering early mongolian projectile-tip or "Clovis tip" peoples began to appear in scattered areas of western and southern North America. At this time camels, horses, sabertooth cats, elephants, mammoths, all species of sloth, lions, hunting dogs, dire-wolves, several forms of deer and antelope became extinct. The only forms of larger animals surviving to the present time from this rich fauna are bison and pronghorn antelopes.

P. S. Martin (1966, 1967) was the first to draw attention to the phenomenon which he called "Pleistocene overkill." He examined the disappearance rate of genera of game animals which it might be supposed *erectus-sapiens* populations were hunting and killing. He found that although during various epochs of the Tertiary period such extinction had proceeded at a relatively smooth and steady rate, the Late Pleistocene was characterized by sudden surges of extinction proceeding at far higher rates and appearing to coincide in some instances with new migrations or major cultural advances in *erectus-sapiens* populations.

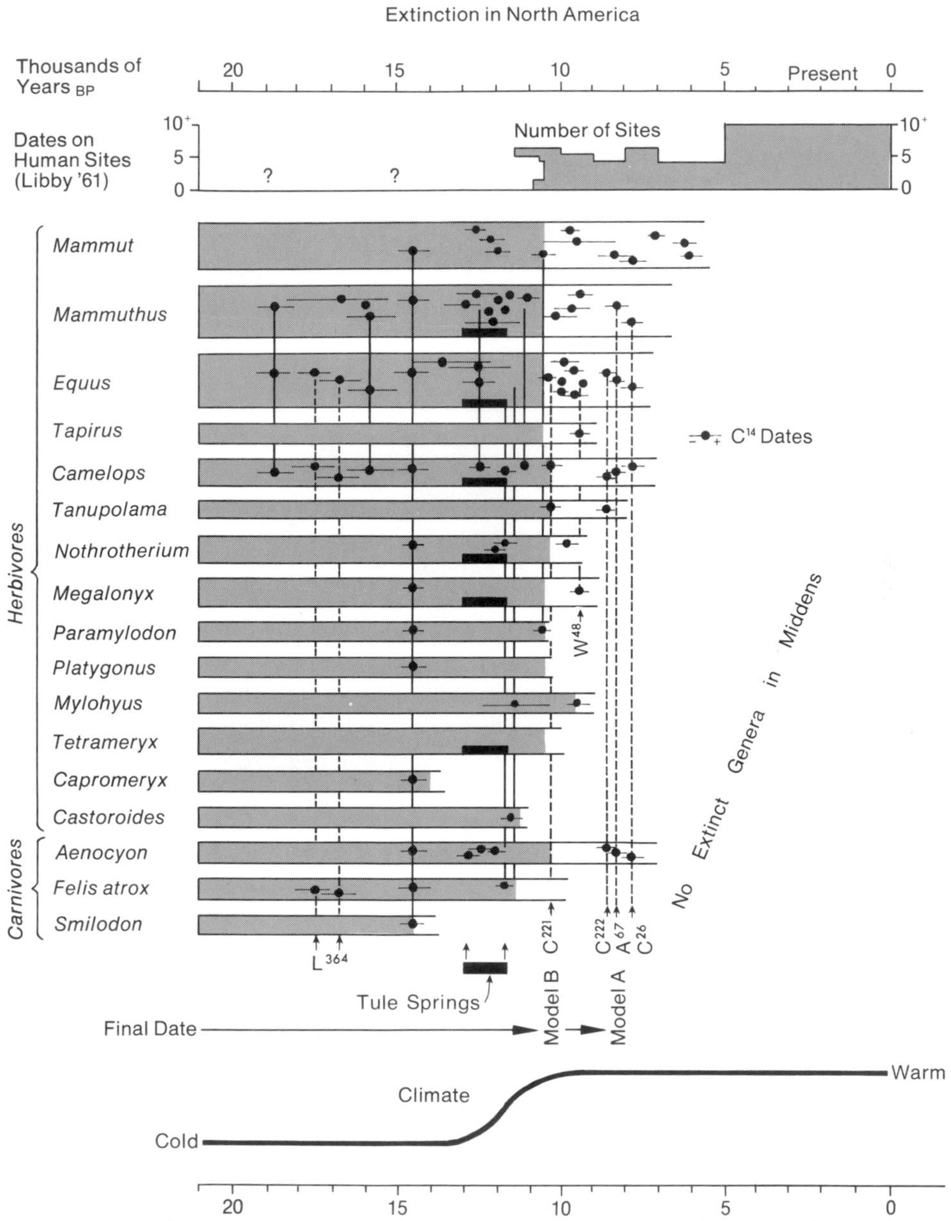

Figure 4-25. *Pleistocene overkill in North America.* See text for further explanation. (Reproduced by permission of the publisher from P. S. Martin and H. E. Wright [eds.], *Pleistocene Extinctions,* New Haven: Yale University Press, 1967, p. 95.)

African Overkill

In Africa the megafauna had been in contact with hominids for at least 4 million years, perhaps a little longer if hominid evolution can be extended backward into the Pliocene for any significant length of time. During this long period a predator-prey relationship would have developed in which any evolutionary advance permitting hominid predators to kill prey more readily would be paralleled by selection of the prey for a greater ability to escape this enhanced predation.

Such evolutionary balances are essential for the maintenance of stability in any predator-prey relationship. What would seriously disturb this balance would be cultural rather than morphological or physiological evolution occurring in the hominid predators. The speed at which cultural selection and adaptation could take place in the predator would be entirely beyond the prey's capacity to match by selection and adaptation of morphological and physiological features alone.

Martin notes that with the appearance of the utilization of fire and hafted weapons in Africa, apparently about 50,000 years ago, 40 per cent of the megafauna genera passed to extinction (Table 4-1).

Table 4-1* ***Pleistocene Overkill in Tropical Africa*** This table shows the date of extinction of various genera of large African mammals. The peak of these extinctions occurs about 50,000 BP, when it is believed fire-using was first introduced to this continent. This could have led to a fundamental change in hunting techniques, in which fire was used to drive animals into swampy areas. Such a radically new technique could have seriously unbalanced the precious predator-prey relationships and led to the extinction of some species.

	Villafrancian and Early Middle Pleistocene (1·0–2·0 Million Years)	*Late Middle Pleistocene Extinction (Last 100,000 Years)*	*Living Genera*
Primates	Gorgopithecus Dinopithecus Cercopithecoides Australopithecus Paranthropus Telanthropus Parapapio	Simopithecus	Pan Gorilla Mandrillus
Carnivora	Lycyaena Meganteron Homotherium	Machairodus	Actinonyx Panthera Hyaena Crocuta
Tubulidentata			Orycteropus
Proboscidea	Anancus Stegodon Deinotherium	Archidiskodon Gomphotherium	Loxodonta
Perissodactyla	Metaschizogherium Serengeticeros	Stylohipparion Eurygnathohippus	Equus Diceros Ceratotherium
Artiodactyla Suidae	Potamochoerops Omochoerus	Potamochoeroides Mesochoerus Notochoerus Tapinochoerus	Potamochoerus Sus Phacochoerus Hylochoerus

		Stylochoerus Metridiochoerus "Kolpochoerus" Orthostonyx	
Hippopotamidae			Hippopotamus Choeropis
Camelidae		Camelus†	
Cervidae		Megaceroides	Cervus
Giraffidae		Libytherium	Giraffa Okapia
Bovidae	Pultipkagonides Numidocapra	Homoioceras Bularchus Pelorovis Lunatoceras Megalotragus (Gen. nov. 1) (Gen. nov. 2) Makapania Phenacotragus	Tragelaphus Boocercus Taurotragus Syncerus Cephalophus Kobus Redunca Hippotragus Oryx Addax Damaliscus Alcelaphus Beatragus Connochaetus Aepyceros Litocranius Gazella Capra Ammotragus
Total	19	26	40

* Reprinted by permission of the publisher from P. S. Martin, *Nature,* **212:** 340, 1966.
† Living species surviving in Eurasia.

Hunting Innovations

There is a supposition that the general method of game hunting practiced by *erectus-sapiens* populations in Africa prior to this time was to drive animals into swampy areas, where their mobility would be greatly restricted (Figure 4-26). They were slaughtered before they could extricate themselves (Clark, 1959). A line of fire across a savanna would be far more effective in driving and speeding game downwind than a thin line of shouting, waving men.

Likewise, a hafted weapon would be more effective and far less dangerous in killing a bogged-down animal than a handheld one.

Pleistocene Overkill Elsewhere

If Martin is correct, Africa lost 40 per cent of its game genera as a result of these two cultural "mutations," but North America lost nearly all its larger game genera contemporaneously with migration of early Mongoloid bands into the area.

Figure 4-26. *Hunting techniques of* Homo erectus *in Africa.* Chelles-Acheul men driving a now-extinct giant antelope into a swamp, about 500,000 BP. Fire was not apparently used at this time in Africa to drive animals or indeed for any other purpose. (Reproduced with the permission of the author from J. D. Clark, *The Prehistory of South Africa,* London: Penguin, 1959, p. 108.)

By 1200 BP virtually all the large animal species had disappeared, as judged from the skeletal remains of this age encountered in the tar pits. While there were climatic changes during this interval, which have been carefully and critically considered by Axelrod (1967), they appear insufficient to account for such a large-scale and dramatic extinction (Table 4-2).

SUMMARY OF MAMMALIAN MEGAFAUNAL EXTINCTION AND SURVIVAL

	Africa	*U.S.A. + Canada*
1. Living genera (50 kg)	40	14
2. Later Pleistocene extinction	26+	35
3. Earlier Pleistocene extinction	19	13
4. Normal Pleistocene megafauna	66+	49
5. Later Pleistocene extinction intensity	39 per cent	71 per cent

As has already been mentioned, Early Mongoloid hordes using projectile-tip weapons had been migrating northward in northeast Asia from about 30,000 BP. From their weapons and the animal bones associated with them, it is apparent they were nomadic hunter-gatherers experienced in hunting a megafauna very similar in general composition to that of the Rancho La Brea. Geomorphologists have estimated that one or more of these hordes could have penetrated to Beringia from 22,000 to 15,000 BP, when it was an exposed tundra-covered land mass. The end of the Wisconsin glacial period and a further melting of glacial ice again inundated this

Table 4-2* ***Extinction of Larger Mammals in North America in the Late Pleistocene*** This seems to have reached a peak about 12,000 BP, and to have virtually ceased by 10,000 BP.

Order	*Irvingtonian + Blancan Extinction*	*Rancholabrean Extinction (Last 15,000 Years)*	*Living (1·5–2 Million) Years)*
Edentata	*Glyptotherium*	*Megalonyx*	
	Glyptodon	*Nothrotherium*	
		Paramylodon	
		Eremotherium	
		Boreostracon	
		Brachyostracon	
		Chlamytherium	
Carnivora	*Borophagus*	*Aretodus*	*Euarctos*
	Ischyrosmilus	*Smilodon*	*Ursus*
	Chasmaporthetes	*Dinobastis*	*Felis*
		Aenocyon	*Panthera*
		Tremarctos†	*Canis*
Proboscidea	*Rhyncotherium*	*Mammut*	
	Stegomastodon	*Cuvieronius*	
		Mammuthus	
Artiodactyla	*Pliauchenia*	*Platygonus*	*Cervus*
	Titanotylopus	*Mylohyus*	*Odocoileus*
	Hayoceros	*Camelops*	*Oreamnos*
	Platycerabos	*Tanupolama*	*Ovibos*
		Sangamona	*Ovis*
		Cervalces	*Rangifer*
		Capromeryx	*Antilocapra*
		Stockoceros	*Bison*
		Tetrameryx	*Alces*
		Bootherium	
		Symbos	
		Euceratherium	
		Preptoceras	
		Saiga†	
		Bos	
Perissodactyla	*Nannippus*	*Equus*†	
	Plesippus	*Tapirus*†	
Rodentia		*Castoroides*	
		Neochoerus	
		Hydrochoerus†	
Reptilia (Testudinata)		*Geochelone*†	
Total	13	36	14

* Reprinted by permission of the publisher from P. S. Martin, *Nature,* **212:** 339, 1966.
† Living species surviving south of the United States or in Eurasia.

area to open the Bering Straits, and the horde or hordes would be edged out into Alaska proper. From there, migrations would have occurred in the normal manner for establishing territory; the first confirmed date of 17,000 BP for penetration to the Los Angeles area fits well with this theory (a recent unreported discovery may take this date back approximately another 1,000 years).

Nevertheless, many workers still object to the hypothesis that within some 5,000 years Pleistocene overkill could have exterminated such an abundant megafauna (Table 4-3). Yet it was not in this instance merely a

Table 4-3 ***List of the Larger Animals Recorded from the Rancho La Brea Fauna***

Tetrameryx	Pronghorns	*Chlamytherium*	Armadillos
Stockocerus	Pronghorns	*Dinobastis*	Saber-toothed cats
Capromeryx	Pronghorns	*Smilodon*	Saber-toothed cats
Mammut	Mastodons	*Neochaerus*	Capybaras
Curieronius	Mastodons	*Hydrochoerus*	Capybaras
Mammuthus	Mammoth	*Euceratherium*	Shrub-oxen
Megalonyx	Ground sloths	*Preptoceras*	Shrub-oxen
Paramylodon	Ground sloths	*Tapirus*	Tapir
Northrotherium	Ground sloths	*Bootherium*	Bovid
Eremotherium	Ground sloths	*Cervalces*	Moose
Platygonus	Peccaries	*Brachyostracon*	Glyptodon
Mylohyus	Peccaries	*Saiga*	Antelope
Camelops	Camel	*Symbos*	Musk-ox
Equus	Horse	*Bison antiquus*	Long-horned bison
Castoroides	Giant beavers		
Arctodus	Bear		

case of a cultural change unbalancing a predator-prey relationship. This North American megafauna had never before had to cope with predation from bands of cunning anthropoid apes armed with effective weapons and perhaps 500,000 years of cultural experience with this type of hunting.

Australia had only two carnivorous animals, the Tasmanian wolf and the Tasmanian devil—neither of them social animals—so that again the megafauna, in this instance essentially a marsupial one, would be unable to respond by morphological, physiological, or behavioral adaptation. Many marsupial genera also disappeared about this time.

The most recent extinctions to occur in the world at large were not so much of whole megafauna, but rather of one particular element, large, flightless birds. The Maoris maintain that moas had disappeared from New Zealand before their arrival (Figure 4-27). European sailors have no such alibi for Mauritius, where the last dodo was killed in about 1680. The arrival of a Polynesian group to populate Madagascar for the first time in 1,000 BP coincides with the date of disappearance of the giant *Aepyrornis maximus*.

With the reduction in members of megafauna in these extensive game ecosystems, whether from climatic change or Pleistocene overkill, the hunting-gathering bands must have undergone cultural evolution directed more to the gathering aspects of the economy than had been true when game was abundant. This change of emphasis may have promoted the so-called "agricultural revolution" which originated in various parts of

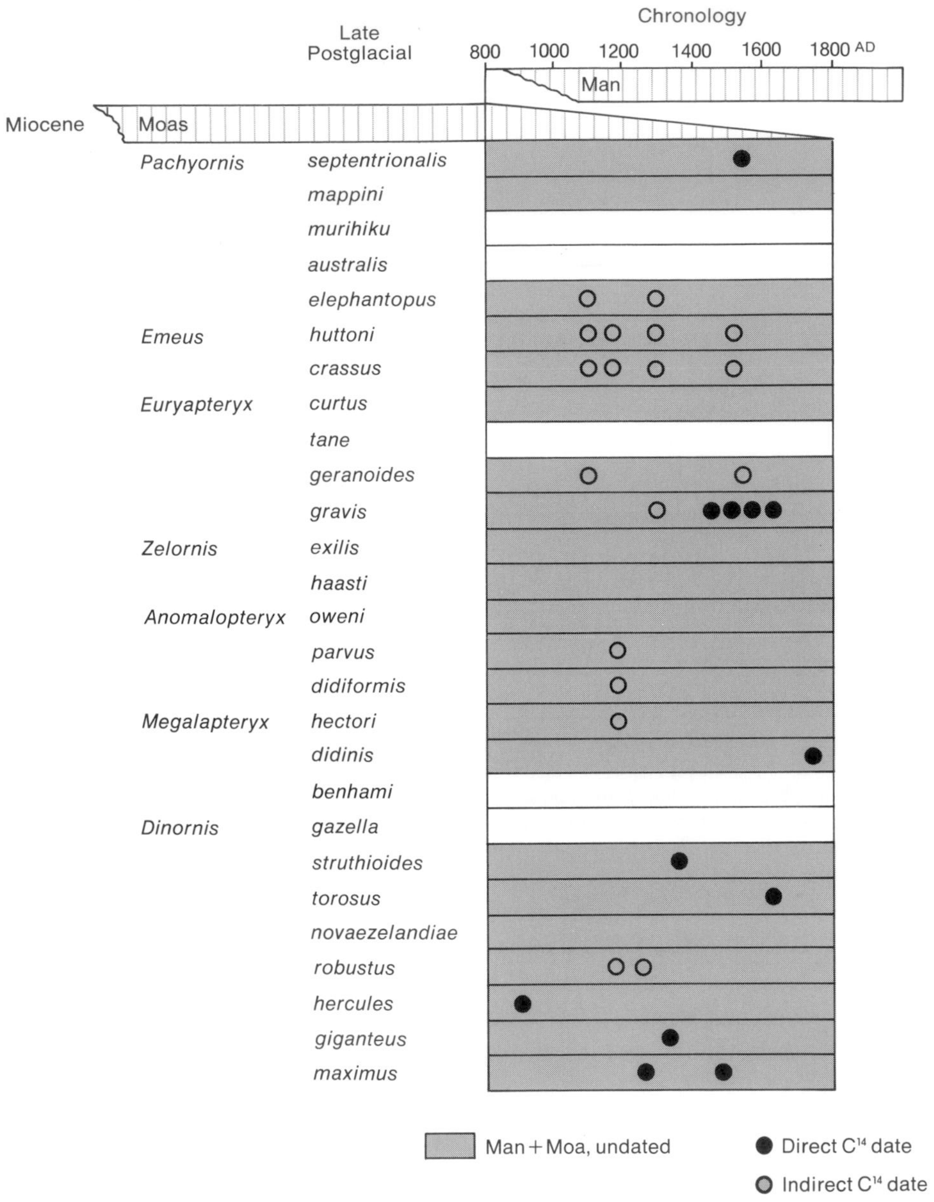

Figure 4-27. *Extinction of the moas in New Zealand* correlated with absolute dates obtained from radiocarbon dating. See text for further explanation. (Reproduced by permission of the author and publisher from C. A. Fleming, *Notornis,* **10:** 114, 115, 1962.)

the Old World and at least once and perhaps several times in the New World, where agricultural groups were clearly established by 5,000 BP.

Migration of Aleuts and Eskimos

The movement of a projectile-tip people through Asia and into the Americas was followed by the eastern and northern progression of later

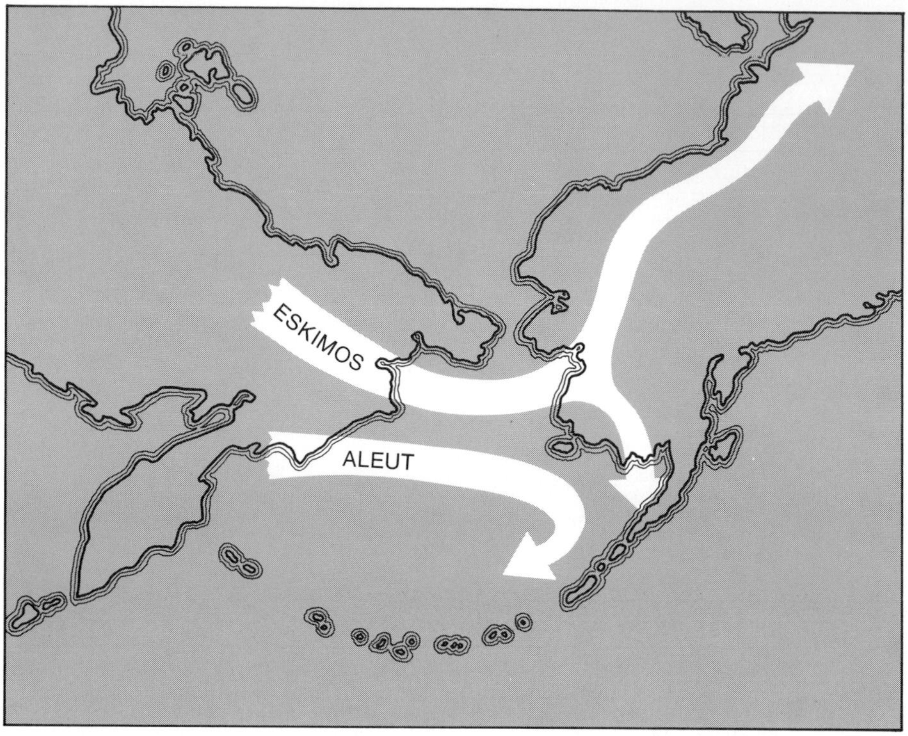

Figure 4-28. *Migration routes of recent Mongoloids in North America.* The areas occupied by Aleuts and Eskimos can be identified from artifacts of the general Auragnicoid type (Fig. 4-2). These include a number of bone tools and weapons and, besides being widely distributed in Eurasia at sites younger than those with projectile tip artifacts, occur also in Alaska and the Aleutian Islands and provide the evidence for the postulated migration routes.

groups, with physical characteristics more closely approaching those of present-day mongoloids. Invariably associated with these later mongoloids is a type of culture known as Aurignacoid, in which extensive use was made of bone and bone tools (Figure 4-28). The comparatively rapid migration of these peoples along the Pacific Coast of Asia may have been facilitated by two related factors. First, they were both hunters and fishermen, and the consumption of fish livers may well have provided the vitamin D necessary for a fairly deeply pigmented group to penetrate into northern latitudes without undergoing mutation toward lighter skin color. Second, they may have already possessed a form of kayak or umiak which permitted them both to venture into coastal waters and to move northward along the coast as population pressures developed in their original territories.

Arriving in Beringia, these later mongoloids apparently divided into groups, according to the nature of the boats utilized. The kayak was an individual hunter's boat of great maneuverability, which permitted the hunting-fishing band to penetrate further north into the inclement habitats. The umiak was an open boat, less seaworthy, less maneuverable, and handled by a small crew. Those using it would need to supplement their hunting and fishing by land operations. This would include the catching of anadromous fishes which periodically returned to the rivers of Beringia.

It appears that later mongoloids of both kinds arrived in Beringia by about 5,000 BP, almost coincidental with the final submergence of that land mass and the establishment of the Bering Straits. The more southerly group continued their mixed hunting and fishing operations, and persisted on the Aleutian Islands following the complete submergence of Beringia. They are represented by the present-day Aleuts. The other group followed the retreating ice across Canada and along the coast of Greenland with their highly specialized and exclusively hunting-fishing operations and became the present-day Eskimos (Giddings, 1967).

OTHER PREHISTORIC MIGRATIONS

The Americas were not the only continental masses excluded from early hominid and all pongid evolution. Australasia, although a part of the Old World and located not too far from Indonesia with its quite extensive and well-established hominid and pongid occupations, has so far produced no records of hominid remains earlier than 18,000 BP.

Australasia

Like North America, the island of Australia appears to have been invaded in prehistoric times by land, when the accumulation of polar and continental ice sheets lowered sea levels so as to expose traversable portions of the continental shelf. There is some evidence that it was occupied by at least two separate groups, the Tasmanians, who traveled down the east coast, and the Murrayians, who moved into the more arid regions (Birdsell, 1957). There is one record from Indonesia of an Australianlike skull dating to 50,000 BP which suggested that an ancestral group originated in this region. Unfortunately, the knowledge of the relative levels of sea and land between New Guinea and the island of Australia is not so extensive as for Beringia, and it is not possible to say when dry land connection between these two island masses was exposed, or even whether one has ever existed. There is also little circumstantial evidence on the possible timing of migration. The date for the domestication of dogs by *Homo sapiens* in Eurasia appears to fall between 50,000 and 100,000 BP. The dingo is the only eutherian predator known from the Upper Pleistocene of Australia, and it seems a reasonable conclusion that the dingo was a domesticated dog which moved into Australia with the earliest hunting-gathering aborigine bands, who had learned this practice through cultural contact with Eurasia.

Aborigine Australians with the earliest forms of culture still used nonhafted tools and weapons. The effect of mounting weapons on wooden shafts on extractive efficiency is very apparent, and it seems that the island of Tasmania was separated from the Australian mainland at a date which separated the people with nonhafted tools from those which later developed them. Tasmanians, the last of whom was exterminated in the nineteenth century, never developed hafted tools. Graphic eyewitness descriptions from early European travelers describe how Tasmanians used hand axes, for example, in climbing trees.

Island Migrations

Besides these major movements into the continental masses of the Americas and Australasia, many migrations have occurred by sea into smaller and sometimes larger islands. For example, the island of Madagascar appears to have been colonized by Polynesian groups about A.D. 1000. Other contemporary movements of Polynesians by sea into the islands of Oceania have been suggested and are further discussed in Chapter 6.

Migrations in Historical Times

Migrations of human groups have not yet entirely ceased, although modern national frontier regulations tend to prohibit mass movement. When considering human diversity it should be remembered that, with few exceptions, all human societies have resulted from the eventual incorporation into one territorial group of population elements from a series of migrations, conquests, slave captures, colonization, and other kinds of movement which have been continuously proceeding not only in *Homo sapiens* grade communities, but also among other species of this genus and even among earlier hominid forms.

In this account of migration, no consideration has been given to the question of what form of *Homo sapiens* grade was involved, or whether the migrating groups were indeed referable to this species grade. It must not be assumed that Cro-Magnon man evolved once and only then in Europe, and thence radiated out over the whole globe. There is considerable evidence for the supposition that each of the three main geographical groups already discussed independently evolved from an *H. erectus* grade to an *H. sapiens* grade. Support for such speculation is further discussed in Chapter 6.

Bibliography

REFERENCES

Axelrod, D. I. "Quaternary extinction of large mammals," *Univ. Calif. Publ. Geol. Sci.*, **75:** 1–42, 1967.

Baker, J. R. "Cro-Magnon Man 1868–1968," *Endeavour,* **27**: 87–90, 1968.

Berger, R. Personal communication.

Binford, S. R. "Late middle Paleolithic adaptations and their possible consequences," *Bioscience,* **20**: 280–83, 1970.

Birdsell, J. B. "Some population problems involving Pleistocene man," *Cold Spring Harbor Symposia on Quantitative Biology,* **22**: 47–69, 1957.

Boyd, W. "The contributions of genetics to anthropology," in A. Kroeber's *Anthropology Today,* Chicago: University of Chicago Press, 1953, pp. 488–506.

Bresler, J. B. (ed.) *Environments of Man,* Reading, Mass.: Addison-Wesley ("An Exchange of Views," pp. 169–76), 1968.

Clark, J. D. *The Prehistory of S. Africa,* Harmondsworth, England: Penguin, 1959.

Clark, J. D. "The evolution of culture in Africa," *American Naturalist,* **907**: 15–28, 1963.

Coles, J. M., and Higgs, E. S. *The Archeology of Early Man,* New York: Faber and Faber, 1969.

Coon, C. S. *The Origin of Races,* New York: Knopf, 1963.

Giddings, J. L. *Ancient Men of the Arctic,* New York: Knopf, 1967.

Glass, H. B. "The ethical basis of science," *Science,* **150**: 1245–61, 1965.

Greene, D. L. "Environmental influences on Pleistocene hominid dental evolution," *Bioscience,* **20**: 276–9, 1970

Harrison, G. A., Weiner, J. S., Tanner, J. M., and Barnicot, N. A. *Human Biology,* New York and Oxford: Oxford University Press, 1964.

Haynes, C. Vance. "The earliest Americans," *Science,* **166**: 709–15, 1969.

Hester, J. J. "Ecology of the North American Paleo-Indian," *Bioscience,* **20**: 213–17, 1970.

Ho, T. Y., Marcus, L. F., and Berger, R. "Radiation dating of petroleum-impregnated bone from tar pits at Rancho La Brea, California," *Science,* **164**: 1051–52, 1969.

Howell, F. C. "Upper Pleistocene men of the Southwest Asian Mousterian," in G. H. R. Van Koenigswald (ed.), *Neanderthal Centenary,* Utrecht: Kemink en Zoon N. V., pp. 185–98, 1958.

Howells, W. W. "The distribution of man," *Scientific American,* **203**(3): 112–27, 1960.

Howells, W. W. "*Homo erectus,*" *Scientific American,* **215**(5): 46–53, 1966.

Martin, P. S. "Africa and Pleistocene overkill," in P. S. Martin and H. E. Wright (eds.), *Pleistocene Extinctions,* New Haven: Yale University Press, 1967, pp. 75–120.

Morris, D. *The Naked Ape,* New York: McGraw-Hill, 1967.

Mourant, A. E. *The Distribution of Human Blood Groups,* Springfield, Ill.: Thomas, 1954.

Mulvaney, D. J. "The prehistory of the Australian Aborigines," *Scientific American,* **214**(3): 84–93, 1966.

Oakley, K. "The earliest fire makers," *Antiquity,* **30**: 102–107, 1956.

Reed, C. A. "Extinction of mammalian megafauna in the Old World late Quaternary," *Bioscience,* **20:** 284–88, 1970.

Sahlins, M. D. "The origin of society," *Scientific American,* **203**(3): 76–87, 1960.

Strauss, W. L., and Hunt, C. B. "Age of zinjanthropus," *Science,* **136:** 293–95, 1962.

Washburn, S. L., and DeVore, I. "The social life of baboons," *Scientific American,* **204**(6): 62–71, 1961.

Weckler, J. E. "Neanderthal man," *Scientific American,* **197**(6) 89-96, 1957.

FURTHER READINGS

Baker, P. T., and Weiner, J. S. *The Biology of Human Adaptability,* Oxford, England: Clarendon Press, 1966.

Crow, J. F. "The quality of people: human evolutionary changes," *Bioscience,* **16:** 863–67, 1966.

Darwin, C. *The Descent of Man,* London: Murray, 1909.

Dobzhansky, T. *Evolution, Genetics, and Man,* New York: Wiley, 1955.

Haynes C. V. "Elephant-hunting in North America," *Scientific American,* **214**(6): 104–12, 1966.

Hooton, E. A. *Up from the Ape,* rev. edit., New York: Macmillan, 1946.

Howell, F. C. *Early Man,* New York: Time-Life, 1965.

Howells, W. W. *Mankind in the Making: The Story of Human Evolution,* rev. edit., New York: Doubleday, 1967.

Hundert Jahre Neanderthaler/Neanderthal Centenary, Gedenkbuch der Int. Neanderthal Feier Düsseldorf, 26–30 August 1956, Utrecht (Netherlands) (Kemink en Zoon), 1958.

Klein, R. G. "Mousterian cultures in European Russia," *Science,* **165:** 257–65, 1969.

Leakey, L. B. S. *Olduvai Gorge 1951–1961, Fauna and Background,* Cambridge, England: Cambridge University Press, 1965.

Lee, R. B., and DeVore, I (eds.) *Man the Hunter,* Chicago: Aldine, 1968.

Martin, P. S. "Pleistocene niches for alien animals." Bioscience, **20:** 218–21, 1970.

Moore, R. *Man, Time and Fossils,* 2nd ed., New York: Knopf, 1963.

Race, R. R., and Sanger, R. *Blood Groups in Man,* 4th ed., Oxford: Blackwell Scientific Pub., 1962.

Sheppard, P. M. "Blood groups and natural selection," *Brit. Med. Bull.,* **15:** 134–39, 1959.

Simons, E. L. "Some fallacies in study of hominoid phylogeny," *Science,* **141:** 879–89, 1963.

Spuhler, J. N. (ed.) *The Evolution of Man's Capacity for Culture,* Detroit: Wayne State University Press, 1961.

Steward, J. H. *Theory of Culture Change: The Methodology of Multilinear Evolution,* Urbana: University of Illinois Press, 1969.
Warner, W. L. *A Black Civilization,* New York: Harper & Row, 1964.
Washburn, S. L. "Tools and human evolution," *Scientific American,* **203** (3): 62–75, 1960.
Washburn, S. L. (ed.) *Social Life of Early Man,* Chicago: Aldine, 1961.
Weidenreich, F. *Anthropological Papers,* Memorial Volume, compiled by S. L. Washburn and D. Wolffson, New York: The Viking Fund, 1949.
Westermarck, E. *The History of Human Marriage,* London: Macmillan, 1921.
Wunderly, J. "The keilor fossil skull: anatomical description," *Mem. Nat. Mus. Melbourne,* No 13, 1943.

The Origin of Urban Civilization

5

The previous four chapters have considered the ecological evolution of human populations from the first living organisms on this earth through primate and ground-ape stages to *erectus-sapiens* grades of the genus *Homo.* At this last level, human populations had evolved a sophisticated communication system and social order, were equipped with considerable manual dexterity which enabled them to fashion a range of artifacts adequate for their ecosystem roles, and had covered most of the earth with a mosaic of nucleated territories more or less stable and basically adequate for the support of the total global population, estimated as falling between 5 and six million persons (Deevey, 1960).

The further cultural evolution of these *erectus-sapiens* populations is closely correlated with selection for a "concentration" characteristic. That is, a tendency was introduced into the cultural activity which caused the formation of interacting groups of ever-increasing size and density. The most obvious selective advantage of this tendency is that it aids information accumulation and exchange. Hunting-gathering bands could make individual discoveries, but much time would elapse before these could be incorporated into the ritual behavior patterns of all extant societies. Greater concentrations of individuals and still further improved verbal systems would lead to accelerated dissemination of ideas, until with modern methods of communication this process of cultural exchange mushroomed into what is often called the "information explosion." This "concentration" trait would have to be selected for concurrently with the tendency to form permanent settlements.

THE EARLIEST SETTLEMENTS

Hunting-gathering cultures of *erectus-sapiens* populations were essentially nomadic, although they might seasonally or cyclically occupy a

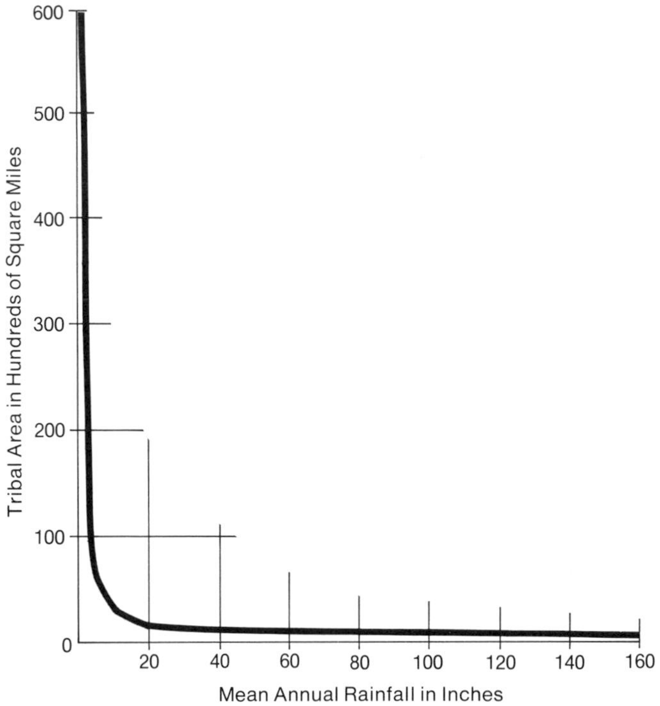

Figure 5-1. *Correlation between the mean annual rainfall and the territory size* for Australian aborigine tribes. The area needed by the tribe is larger with a low rainfall, smaller with a higher rainfall, as would be anticipated. (Reproduced with the permission of the author and publisher from J. B. Birdsell, *American Naturalist,* **87**: 179, 1953.)

specific section of territory. As Birdsell has demonstrated, the size of the territory occupied was determined by limiting environmental factors (Figure 5-1). This obligatory nomadism, dictated by seasonal resources depletion, is still exhibited by a few survivors of this type of culture such as the Bushmen of South Africa, or the Australian aborigine hordes. In some instances, however, a chance combination of microecosystems could have provided on the same site a sufficient overlapping succession of resource productivity peaks to permit continuous occupation of the site (Figure 5-2).

Drinking Water

The first requirement for such a permanent site is an assured supply of drinking water. This is found, for example, on the coast, where shallow wells can tap the fresh water which floats on the salt-water table below the sand dunes. At the close of a Middle Pleistocene glacial, or the beginning of an interstadial, there would also be many suitable fresh-water lake and river sites.

Food Supplies

All such permanent sites, whether coastal or interior, would also have readily accessible supplies of invertebrate food at any time of year (Sauer,

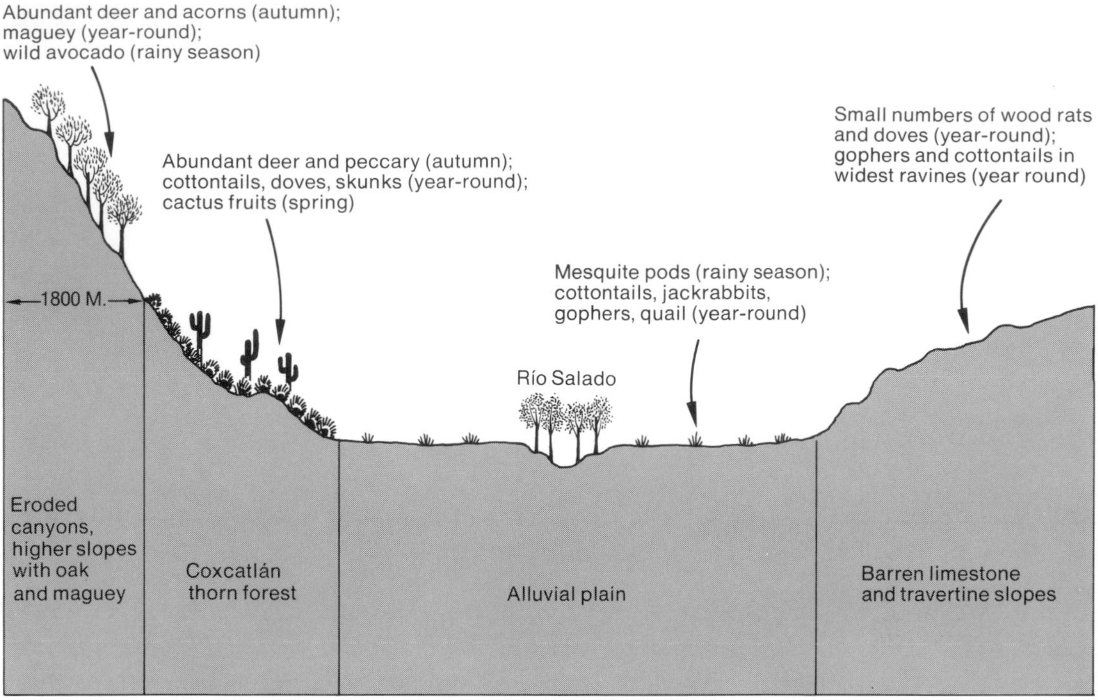

Figure 5-2. *Schematic representation of a microenvironmental series* sufficient to permit *permanent* human occupation of the area. The transect illustrates conditions across a 20-km section of the Tehuacan Valley, Puebla, Mexico. (Reproduced with the permission of the authors and publisher from M. D. Coe and K. V. Flannery, *Science,* **143:** 652, 1964. Copyright 1964 by the American Association for the Advancement of Science.)

1962). Supplemental gathering activities might be seasonal, such as the harvesting of acorns along the Pacific Coast of North America, or picking fruits of the *Grewia* species along southern African rivers. Hunting similarly might have been restricted to a breeding season, when the more readily taken juvenile animals were available.

Such village settlement patterns must have arisen many times in these types of favored locations long before the so-called "agricultural revolution." Indeed a number are known from the mid-East dating between 8,000 and 11,000 BP (Cambel and Braidwood, 1970). The permanent nature of the settlement would facilitate accumulation of cultural equipment, both material and behavioral (Figure 5-3). The provision of shelter around each pair-bond hearth, to cite a simple example, must have been among the earliest innovations. Once its effectiveness had been demonstrated, it would rapidly be copied and improved.

EARLY SETTLEMENT LIFE

It is tempting to conjecture as to the life of such early *erectus-sapiens* settlements. From contemporary survivals persisting in out-of-the way places some educated guesses can be made. Along many tropical shore-

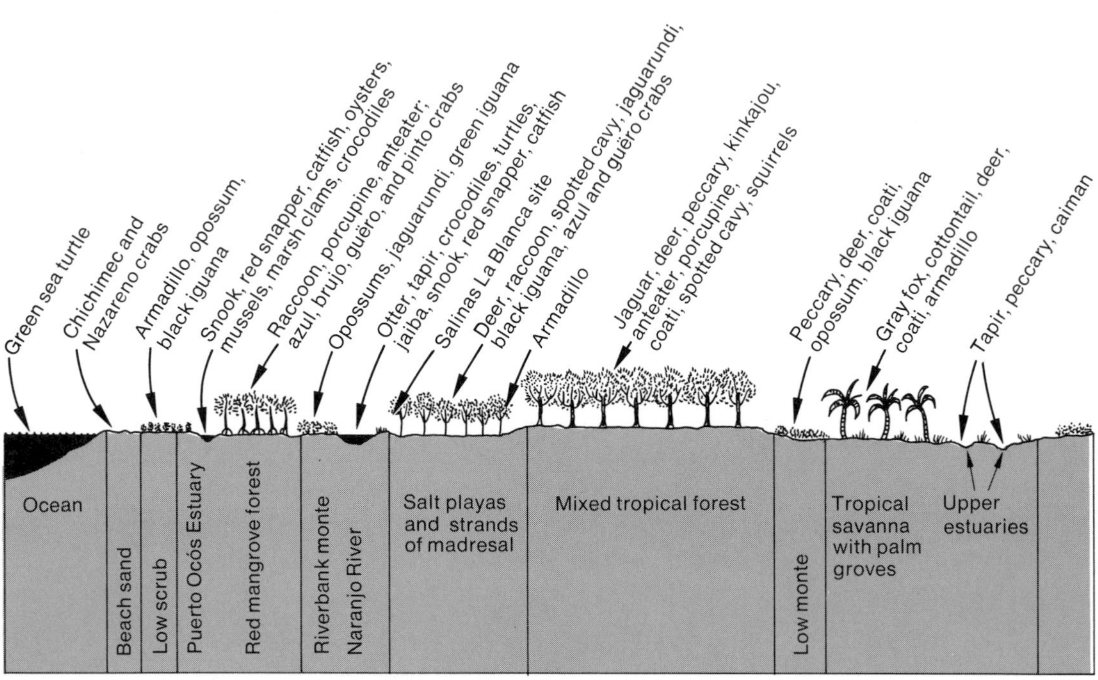

Figure 5-3. *A coastal site with sufficient microecosystems to support a permanent settlement.* A transect of the Ocoo area of coastal Guatemala about 15 km long. This is taken at the site of a pre-Columbian settlement now known as Salinas la Blanca. (Reproduced with the permission of the authors and publisher from M. D. Coe and K. V. Flannery, *Science*, **143**: 652, 1964. Copyright 1964 by the American Association for the Advancement of Science.)

lines small coastal villages can be encountered which have no road access, and very little connection by boat with neighboring settlements. Judging from the size of the kitchen middens, the village sites have often been occupied for a considerable length of time. Proceeding backward in time the life of such an early village as it was at first may have been somewhat as follows.

The settlement included fewer than 100 persons, and little more than a dozen hut clusters. The huts were built from coconut palm fronds and trunks, with coconut fiber constituting the main tying, binding, and knotting material, as it did in many other such operations. Fishing was a continuous year-round occupation for the men and youths, but was carried out on an individual basis, using spears or a ring or cast net. The women collected shellfish of various kinds from beach areas, and discarded shells piled up in middens near the village huts. Domestic water came from shallow wells from 6 to 10 feet deep dug through the sand immediately behind the shoreline. Toward the end of the dry season this water became more brackish and rather unpleasant to drink.

Besides collecting shellfish, drawing water, gathering dead coconut fronds and flotsam cast up on the beach for domestic fuel, the women rather casually tended small overgrown beds of nut grass (*Cyperus escu-*

lentus), which has a small underground rhizome, edible when boiled. Even today this is one of the few crops which will grow in close proximity to the beach, because of the driving salt spray which blows over coastal villages. Nut grass probably represents a very early selection from some naturally occurring ubiquitous tropical sedge species such as *Cyperus rotundus*. Women also foraged out on food-gathering expeditions behind the shoreline (Figure 5-4).

Diet

The diet of fish, shell food, nut grass, berries, nuts, and coconut was periodically varied with game meat, such as when, at differing times of the year, the several local species of turtle came ashore to breed. The telltale tracks the female turtles left in the sand led to their detection and slaughter, and to the unearthing of the eggs which they had concealed in the sand above the tide line. Other dietary bonanzas occurred when a whale or other large marine animal became stranded on the shore.

Domestic Animals

Dogs roamed around the village, but as scavengers; they were not fed or watered. At some time the settlement acquired a herd of swine. Like the dogs, the pigs were not fed, but lived especially on sand crabs from the beach and by scavenging on the middens. A few chickens, likewise unfed, were also obtained at some later stage. They were killed and eaten only on ceremonial occasions.

Division of Labor

In such an early village there was very limited communal sharing or division of labor, although the population had the social structure of an extended family. The women of the pair bonds would associate in groups during their various gathering activities, but each returned with the fruits of her labors to her own hearth. Her daughters might assist her when they reached puberty and before they were married. The female activities were essentially gathering ones. Males fished individually, and likewise returned their catch to their own huts. The only times food might be shared were the few occasions when turtles or marine mammals were killed or washed ashore. Some fish would be smoked or dried and used to barter for tools and other artifacts, clothing materials, and probably brides; marriage would be exogamous, and wives would be obtained by trading with neighboring settlements.

Cultural Activities

Life in such a village would not be so continuously exhausting that there would be no time for leisure, and some crafts would develop as

would communal dancing and storytelling. Perhaps the earliest specialization, with some women more proficient than others, would be weaving coconut fronds into baskets, fans, and other articles. Among the men, specialization may have taken the form of net-making, or carving further bone tools, which eventually progressed to boat building. Therefore, both sexes probably had some early division of labor, but there would be no communal schooling, and special skills would pass on by social learning and some degree of inherited adaptation from mother to daughter, father to son. Population regulation would result from mortalities following spasmodic fights over wells and coconut areas, by accidental drownings, and perhaps by outbreaks of food poisoning from eating infected shellfish.

ORIGIN OF CULTIVATED PLANTS

Inland settlements of similar complexity, size, and activity such as that just described must have been scattered along river and lake banks throughout much of the area first occupied by *Homo erectus* grade peoples, then later by evolving *erectus-sapiens* populations. Such favorable occupation sites would continue to be inhabited as *erectus-sapiens* populations graded by imperceptible stages into a *Homo sapiens* grade, whenever this might have occurred in such inland settlements. Perhaps occasional waves of a more highly evolved intermediate form would sweep over the settlements of a given region, just as one tribe was frequently observed to be in the process of overrunning another in eighteenth and nineteenth century Africa.

The First Cultigens

Food-gathering would continue to be a major occupation of the women, and a wide variety of gathered seeds would be brought back to the village. Reaped wild grasses might have been brought back for threshing and winnowing. It is not difficult to imagine that some of these grass seeds would fall on the piles of debris which comprised the kitchen middens, the first urban garbage disposal enterprise. Essential characteristics of these middens would be a high mineral content, from the decomposing bones and shells (of snails in inland settlements) which were thrown there, and also from fecal matter deposited on them. The disturbed nature of the soil would be coupled with good drainage of these loosely packed

Figure 5-4. *A hypothetical tropical African coastal settlement* in a mesolithic and preagricultural phase. This kind of settlement, although formed by Negroids, is very similar in structure and activity to that of Salinas la Blanca established by early Mongoloid Paleo-Indians in Guatemala and illustrated in Figure 5-3. Hunting-gathering bands probably quite independently established such permanent settlements along all tropical coasts, wherever the diversity and productivity of microecosystems were sufficient to support them, several millennia previous to the agricultural revolution.

dumps, which would in any case be on raised ground, with the huts, above the general flooding level. It is not surprising that the cereal crops like wheat and barley, which appear to have been those first cultivated, would require soils with good drainage, high nutrient content supplied from artificial or natural manures, and an open soil structure attained by plowing and harrowing, or digging and hoeing the soil in seed-bed preparation. Because of their heavy requirements for soluble nitrogenous salts, such cultivars are technically described as *nitrophilous* plants, although their phosphate requirements frequently are almost as great.

THE FERTILE CRESCENT

According to present evidence, the first plant taken into cultivation appears to have been wheat (Braidwood, 1960). The area where this occurred probably was in the so-called fertile crescent of Iraq and Iran, roughly the upland area separating the valleys of the Tigris and the Euphrates from Turkey to the north and Iran to the east (Figure 5-5). In the upland areas (averaging about 1000 m altitude) of this fertile crescent there was an adequate winter and spring rainfall, and herbaceous plants were abundant between and within the woodland communities. As early as perhaps 50,000 years ago, grinding stones were apparently employed in preparing food, presumably the harvested seeds of such herbaceous plants. Flint sickle blades have been found together with these milling and grinding stones, suggesting that wild cereals were actually reaped and brought to the settlement for threshing.

Early Farming Villages

The two earliest village-farming communities so far extensively explored date from 7000 and 6500 BP, although recently a site dating to at least 9500 BP has been described (Cambel and Braidwood, 1970). Jarmo, the more ancient, and Tepe Sarab are approximately 120 miles apart in modern Kurdistan in northeastern Iraq. Jarmo was a permanent settlement with about two dozen mud-walled houses. It has been estimated that about 150 people lived there with dogs and other animals. Some tools were made from obsidian, the nearest source of which was 200 miles away.

Two different kinds of cultivated wheat and one of barley have been found at Jarmo, together with lentils, peas, and a kind of vetch, although it is not certain that the last three were actually cultivated. Goats, dogs, and perhaps sheep were domesticated animals in the village, while wild species of goats, sheep, cattle, pigs, horses, asses, and dogs were all present in the surrounding areas.

Archeologists have considered that this settlement of Jarmo and others

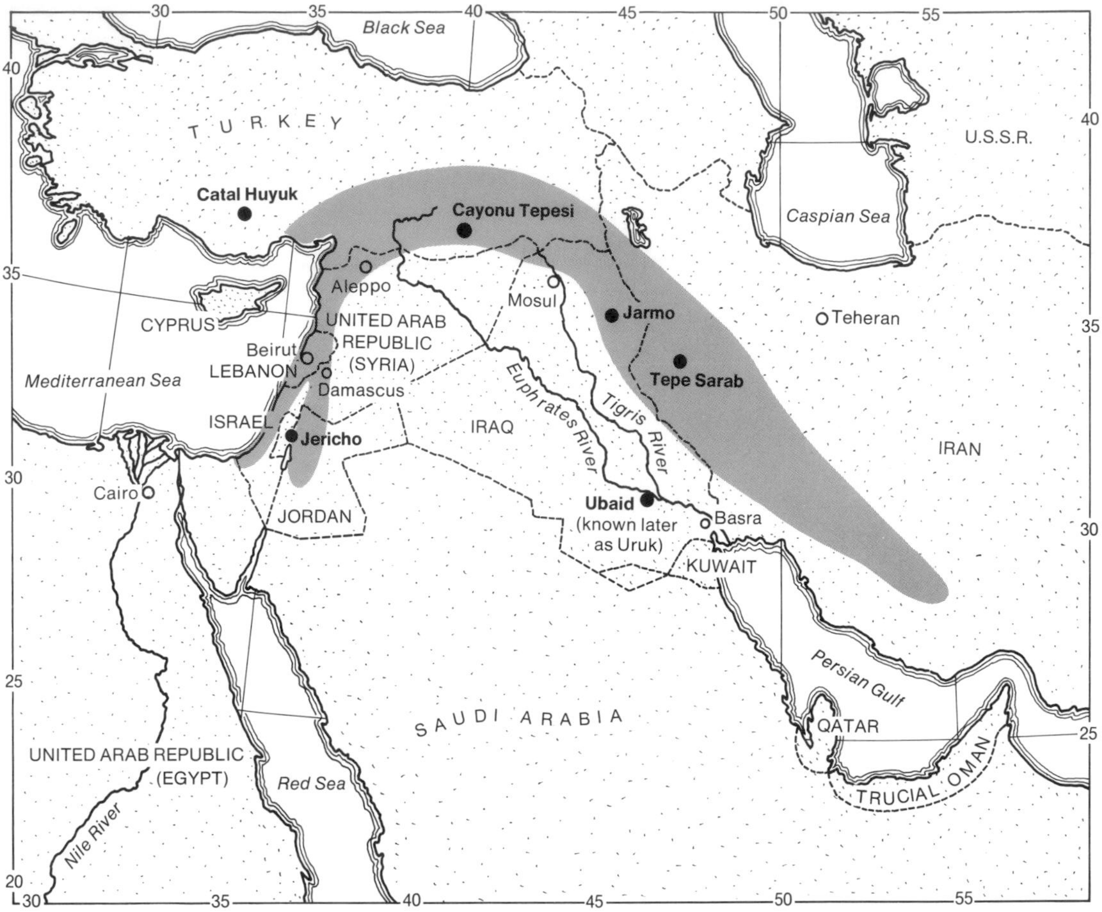

Figure 5-5. *The geographical area covered by the fertile crescent* which lies in the region known at the beginning of this century as Mesopotamia, now allocated between Iraq, Iran, Turkey, Jordan, and some other national territories. Although the cultivation of plants and domestication of animals developed independently in other areas, the fertile crescent is most significant in that cereal crops appear earlier here than anywhere else, and more animal species were domesticated here than in any other region.

like it represent a relatively sophisticated stage of the first agricultural societies, and that the actual origins of agriculture should be sought still earlier, a view now substantiated by the work of Cambel and Braidwood at Cayonu Tepesi. Some further support for this view has come with the excavation of a city known as Catal Huyuk, on the Anatolian Peninsula of Turkey, by British archeologist James A. Mellaart (1963).

TRADING SETTLEMENTS

Catal Huyuk is an early neolithic settlement, whose first occupation levels can be dated to 9000 BP. It was at first a prepottery settlement, as evidenced from its oldest occupation level. It appears to have been estab-

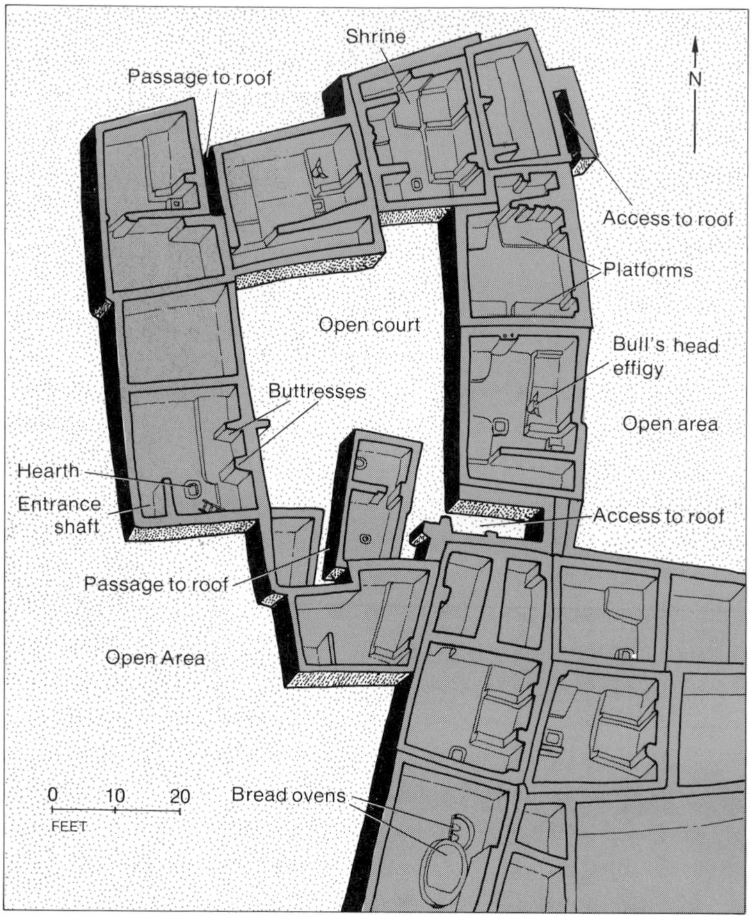

Figure 5-6. *A plan of the condominium accommodations in the neolithic city of Catal Huyuk* reconstructed to show how the house walls probably stood, but without including any roof structures. This Turkish city, at this time about 8000 BP, had remarkably advanced agricultural and commercial activities. (From James Mellaart, "A Neolithic City in Turkey," *Scientific American,* **210**[4]: 95, 1964. Copyright © 1964 by Scientific American, Inc. All rights reserved.)

lished along a river bank, and to have covered about 32 acres, although not all of this was necessarily occupied at one time. Evidence that it was more than a village of farmers comes from the variety of cultural materials encountered—especially the abundance and range of tools made from obsidian—together with the quality and consistent planning of the mud-walled houses (Figure 5-6).

Agricultural Activities

Among the cereal grains identified from the oldest levels are six-row barley and a hexaploid type free-threshing wheat. Grain bins were found in every house, together with mortars for husking grain and querns for grinding it. Domestic animal remains include sheep, cows, dogs, and goats, but no pigs; wild animal bones indicated wild cattle, reindeer, wild asses, wild sheep, boars, and leopards. The dead were buried underneath the houses, and the disproportionate number of females found interred suggests that many men died away from the settlement, on foraging, hunting, or trading expeditions. Clothing worn by both sexes was made of leopard skin, fastened with bone pins.

An Early City

Mellaart considers that because of the obvious prosperity of this settlement of Catal Huyuk, which must be called a city because of the many activities which took place in it as compared with those of an agricultural village, it is clear that obsidian was extensively traded there. The nearest source of obsidian to the city is only 50 miles to the east, and other active volcanoes which would have produced this natural glass were not much further distant. Obsidian is not commonly encountered in this region of Asia Minor or Europe; it was the most superior material from which to fashion the cutting tools of the Neolithic period, a use first encountered in the Mesolithic period.

City Origins

Jacobs (1969) has speculated on the influence which this obsidian trade played in the development of such a city. She hypothesizes that about 12,000 BP a hunting-gathering group had located deposits of obsidian at a site at first unintentionally incorporated within its territory. As this material was discovered and worked into cutting tools by the group, it was found that the material, the tools, or both could be traded with adjoining hunting-gathering groups in return for products of the hunt such as live or dead animals, and for gathered food like berries, nuts, and wild cereal grains.

Barter

Such would be the demand for this obsidian trade that a permanent area would be established within the group territory where barter could be carried on. This would not be at the site of the obsidian deposits themselves, which would be kept secret and protected, but rather some distance from them, probably on the perimeter of the group's territory. This obsidian trading settlement would rapidly grow in size and prosperity as more representatives came in to offer hunting-gathering materials in trade.

Jacobs supposes this was the situation several millennia previous to the first known occupation of Catal Huyuk, perhaps as early as 12,000 BP at a time before there were cultivated plants and domestic animals to be traded. She postulates that some of the wild animals brought in for barter were alive, and that grain bins were filled to overflowing with all kinds of gathered wild plants.

Appearance of Cultivars

Seed of all these wild plants would inevitably be scattered around the settlement accidentally. Some would germinate to become established on kitchen middens, at first being ignored. The plants more successful in propagating themselves on such sites would occasionally hybridize with other forms, a process facilitated by the admixture of species resulting from the obsidian trade. Eventually the more prolific of these natural hybrids, which may also have meanwhile mutated to give a more vigorous form or one with a higher yield, would come to the attention of one or more of the citizens, who might hit upon the idea of gathering its seed and scattering it over the midden to extend the plant's area.

Origin of Domestic Animals

In the case of the live wild animals received in trade, the quieter ones would be left alive in preference to the more obstreperous beasts, which would be killed first because they were such a nuisance to keep or to feed. The former, which might forage for themselves around the settlement and were no great trouble, might have been allowed to remain alive even long enough to produce offspring. It would be an easy transition from this to domestication, although there seems little doubt that cattle were first domesticated for religious purposes rather than for actual consumption.

According to Jacobs' suppositions, the agricultural revolution resulted from the development of at most a few trading settlements, *not* from the activities of the small permanent occupation sites which would have become generally established over a wide area during the *erectus-sapiens* phase of human evolution. There is increasing evidence that in Mesopotamia from about 9500 to 8500 BP agricultural villages and hunters villages coexisted (Perkins and Daly, 1968).

THE AGRICULTURAL REVOLUTION

Whatever the origins of agriculture, there can be no doubt that once cultivated plants and domestic animals had been developed, their use would spread rapidly. The pattern of permanent settlement was already laid down, social contacts had been established through exogamous mating, and knowledge of the techniques of this new culture could disseminate quickly. In the 2 millennia from 9000 to 7000 BP, neolithic agricultural cultures had become widespread throughout the Middle East, and especially in the valleys of the Tigris and the Euphrates and across the Sinai

Peninsula in the Nile Delta. Baker (1965) estimates that by the year 3800 BP Assyrian and Babylonian irrigation systems using brick-lined canals were irrigating an area of 110,000 acres from the waters of the Tigris and the Euphrates.

PARALLEL DEVELOPMENT OF AGRICULTURE

The origins of agriculture in other parts of the world are with one exception less well explored, although they likewise have been the subject of much speculation.

The New World

The exception is the New World, where many efforts have been made to trace the origin of corn (Mangelsdorf *et al.*, 1964) in connection with the Maya civilization, and of various legumes and cucurbits. Despite much research, the real origin of corn (maize), which archeologists estimate dates back some 7000 years (Bartlett *et al.*, 1969), has not yet been clearly established—as to date, parentage or place—although this probably was somewhere in Central America or in the northern part of the Andes. Both areas seem to have been possible centers of origin for another major crop, the "Irish" potato, while manioc (cassava), peanut, sweet potato, and a number of lesser crops such as tomato, cocoa, rubber, cocaine, and tainus (*Xanthosoma*) yam also originated in the New World (Figure 5-7).

Asia

In Asia, paddy rice, which is now the staple food of half the world's population, must have been among the first crops cultivated. There are a number of surviving wild species of this genus (*Oryza*), some of which are still gathered for food.

Other Tropical Areas

In other tropical areas there was probably an independent discovery of various forms of cultivated plants. For example, in West Africa, the oil palm (*Elaeis guineensis*) and various forms of *Dioscorea* yam were probably among the earliest cultivated crops. Both groups occur on the margins between forest and savanna, which was probably the most favored occupation site for the temporary camps of hunting-gathering people. It would be merely a question of extending the area of clearing around naturally occurring wild plants of these two species in order to create something of a garden.

Sauer (1952) has argued for a wild root origin of cultivated plants be-

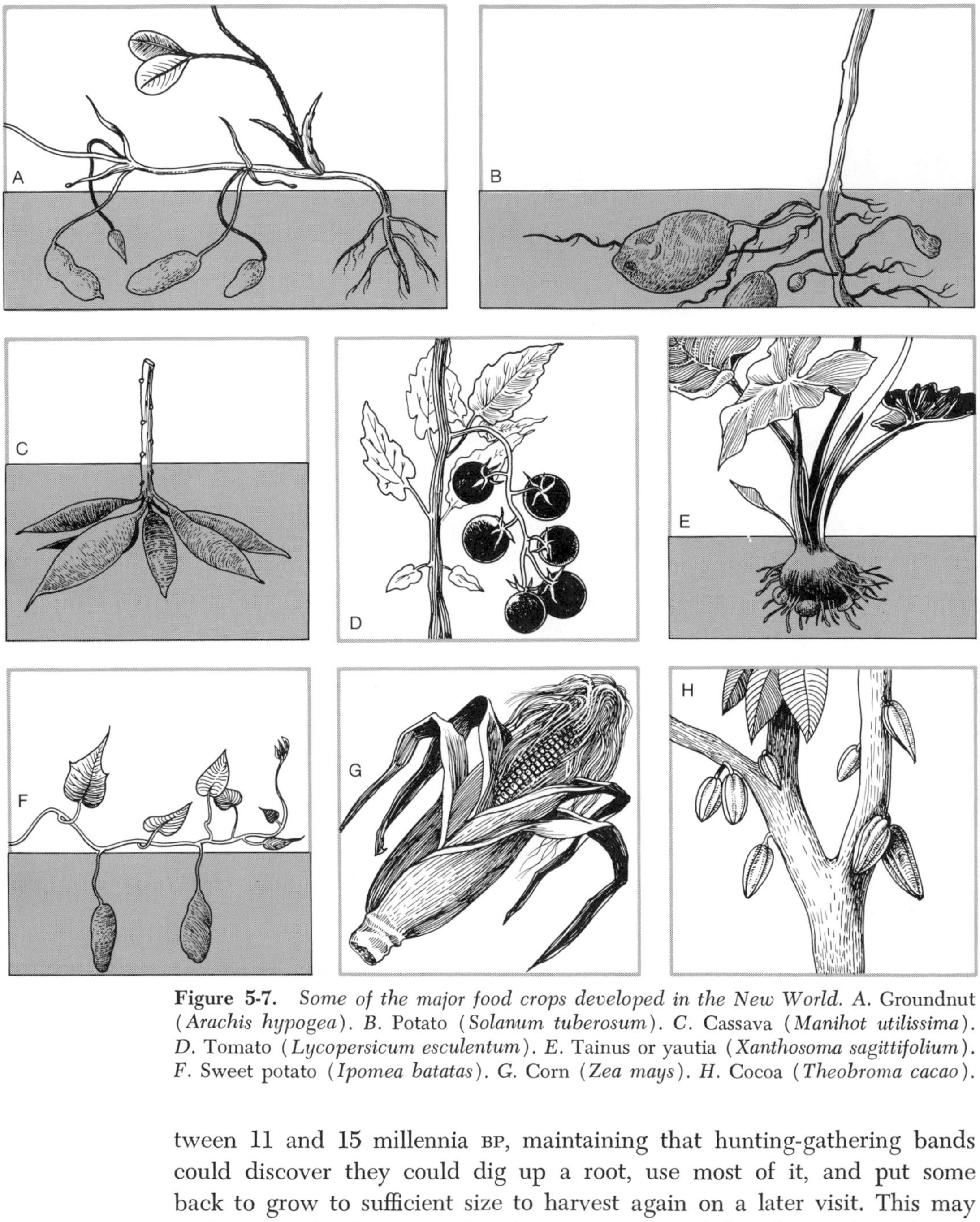

Figure 5-7. *Some of the major food crops developed in the New World. A.* Groundnut (*Arachis hypogea*). *B.* Potato (*Solanum tuberosum*). *C.* Cassava (*Manihot utilissima*). *D.* Tomato (*Lycopersicum esculentum*). *E.* Tainus or yautia (*Xanthosoma sagittifolium*). *F.* Sweet potato (*Ipomea batatas*). *G.* Corn (*Zea mays*). *H.* Cocoa (*Theobroma cacao*).

tween 11 and 15 millennia BP, maintaining that hunting-gathering bands could discover they could dig up a root, use most of it, and put some back to grow to sufficient size to harvest again on a later visit. This may explain the development of such crop plants as *Colocasia esculenta* (taro) in Asia and *Xanthosoma* (tainus yam) in South America, but cereals like barley and wheat in the Middle East appear both to antedate the appearance of any other major crop and to exert the strongest cultural influence (Figure 5-8). Curiously, some major clusters of hunting-gatherers, like Australian aborigines, never developed any cultivated plants, cereals, or

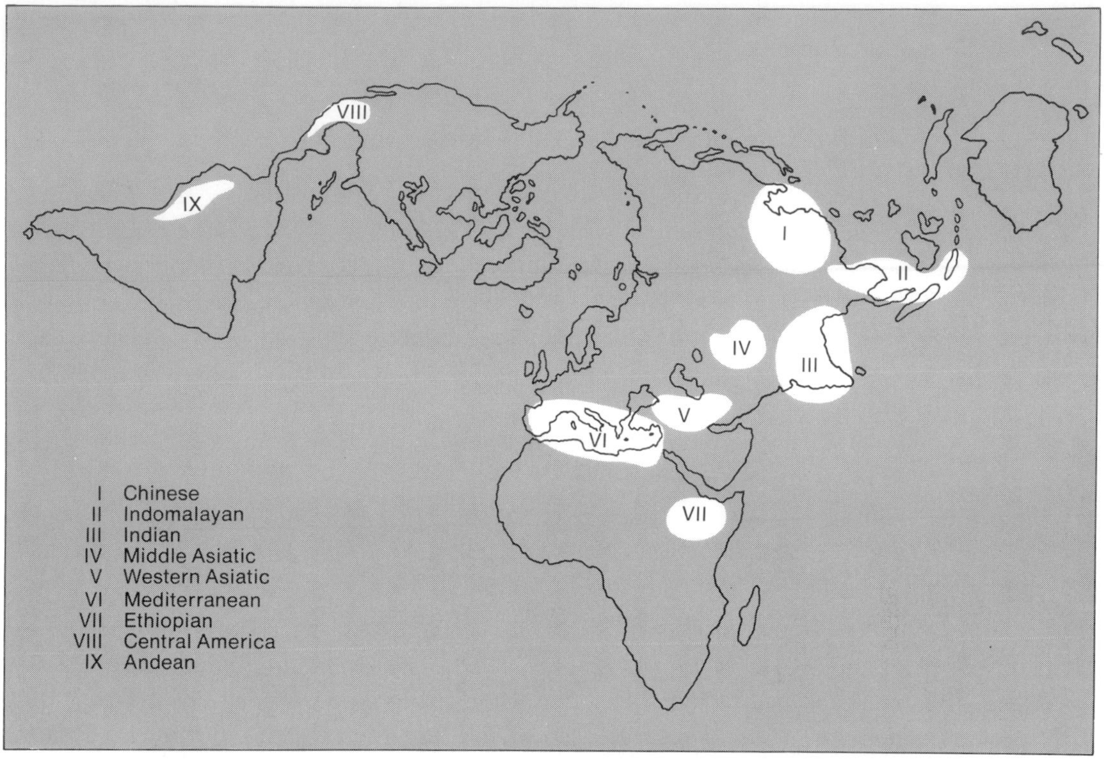

Figure 5-8. *The centers of origin of cultivated plants* as demonstrated by the Russian geneticist Vavilov. Some of these coincide with the known early centers of urban civilizations, for example V, the western Asiatic, and VI, the Mediterranean centers. On the other hand, the Ethiopian center is not associated with any known early urbanized society. The Eurasian belt from China to Spain, which includes centers I, III, IV, V, and VI, is the primary area for grain crop origins. Only two major cereals, sorghum (Africa) and maize (tropical America), originated outside this area, and it is possible that early cities only developed in such grain-raising areas. Root crops, which more particularly evolved in center II, were too bulky and sometimes too perishable to be transported any distance for purposes of barter; city evolution was not associated with them.

roots, perhaps because this continent provided an insufficient number of sites suitable for permanent settlement.

DOMESTICATION OF ANIMALS

Archeologists have developed a technique which enables them to decide when an animal species has been domesticated. By analysis of the fossils of a megafauna found at various levels of an occupation site over a given time interval, it is possible to detect a shift to a larger consumption of a prodomestic wild species. A second shift is detectable by changes in the age at which these prodomestic animals are killed. If these two shifts are associated with a continuing increase in the proportional representation of the prodomestic species in the total animal remains found in the area, the shifts and the increase together demonstrate that cultural control over the species has been obtained, that the animal has become domesticated.

Animal Domestication in the Middle East

Using this method of analysis it is apparent that in the Near East, domestication of animals had taken place generally by the beginning of the seventh millennium BP, although, as already noted, domestic animals occurred at Catal Huyuk 5000 years previously. It did not develop in Europe until at least a thousand years later, and—in central, eastern, and southwest Asia—2 millennia later, 5000 BP. In the New World it had hardly begun with the llama and its relatives, and Australian aborigines have only the dingo, which they may have taken from some other group before reaching Australia.

DOMESTICATION OF CATTLE

Of all the problems which have interested the cultural historian, the ethologist, and the geographer in relation to animal domestication, the most fascinating has been the origin of domestic cattle. The concept that nomadic hunters first domesticated cattle for religious purposes has long been rejected in favor of the hypothesis which asserts that it was sedentary farmers who did so (Isaac, 1962). Some archeologists, with well-documented support, contend that *human* sacrifice preceded animal sacrifice.

Bos primigenius

It is generally believed that all domestic cattle are derived from one wild species, *Bos primigenius,* the wild urus or auroch (Figure 5-9). This species at one time ranged widely from the Pacific coast of Asia across Eurasia into Europe and North America. Although the last member of this wild population is believed to have died in 1627, a synthetic population has since been recreated by the selective breeding of cattle in domestic herds with urus or auroch characteristics. With this wide distribution of urus there was linked a considerable range in form, size, and probably also in coat color, from the time when the animal first appeared in the fossil record during the Riss glacial period.

Religious Motivation of Cattle Domestication

That the domestication of the urus may have been undertaken in the first instance for religious reasons is suggested by the resemblance between the huge curved horns of the species and the young moon. In fact, his-

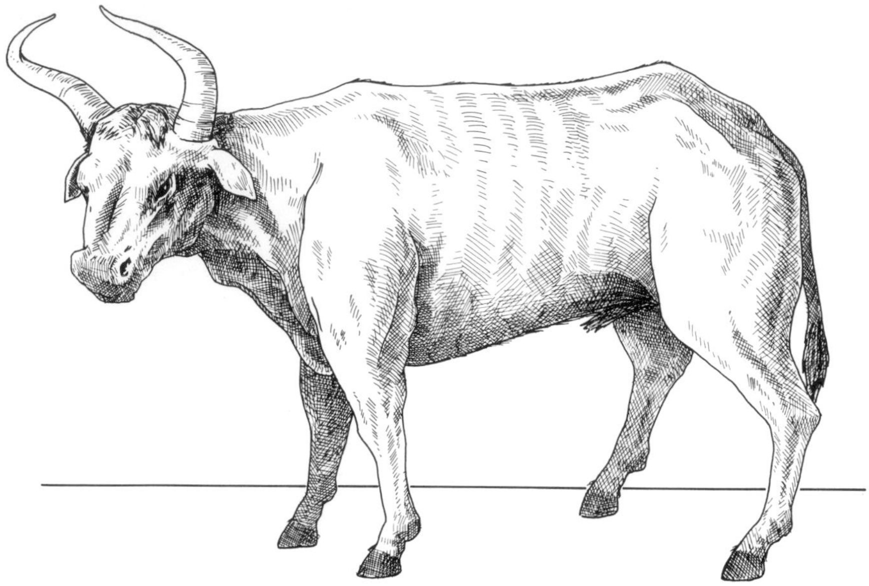

Figure 5-9. *The aurochs* or urus (*Bos primigenius*), the wild cattle species which was widely distributed over temperate and subtropical Eurasia in the early Holocene, and survived in a wild form until the seventeenth century. All breeds of domestic cattle are believed to have been developed from this ancestral stock.

torical studies suggest that the urus was regarded as a symbol of the moon goddess and was ritually killed in a charade symbolizing death and resurrection. It is supposed that captured wild animals were kept in corrals for sacrificial use at such ceremonies, and that here some young would be born and receive more protection than they would in the wild state. Infant mortality would be lower, and there would be a tendency for somewhat unusual forms to survive in greater numbers. Similarly, castration in bulls probably developed as a ritual before the effect which this operation has in taming animals and in improving the amount and quality of meat was discovered.

It is significant that the religious cult of the city of Catal Huyuk was apparently based on cattle; representations and remains indicate a cattle altar in every dwelling (Figure 5-10).

Early Forms of Domestic Cattle

Quite early there seems to have been a selection for large horns in the domesticated form which has been known as "primigenius" (*Bos taurus primigenius*) and shorter horns or polled types (*Bos taurus longifrons*). While it is somewhat difficult to distinguish between the wild urus and early domesticated "primigenius" cattle probably maintained as a breed for ritual purposes, there is no problem with the short-horned or polled "longifrons" type, which appears to have been developed more for draft, beef, and milk production.

Figure 5-10. *A reconstructed shrine from the neolithic city of Catal Huyuk* showing the prominence given to animals and especially cattle heads. (From James Mellaart, "A Neolithic City in Turkey," *Scientific American*, **210**[4]: 100, 1964. Copyright © 1964 by Scientific American, Inc. All rights reserved.)

The religious aspects of the herding of cattle persisted into dynastic Egypt in the tombs of the bulls, which are ceremoniously buried under the Sakkara pyramid near Cairo, and even into modern times with the traditional Hindu sacred Brahman. Perhaps it is reasonable to suggest that this ritual has penetrated into and persisted in the New World with the rodeo and "ride the Brahman bull" event, and the Latin American bullfights.

Although domestication of cattle was at first for religious purposes, it may be concluded that carcasses of the animals were normally eaten, if they were not given any form of ritual burial. Just when the religious significance of the killing was abandoned, and the cropping of domestic cattle became solely an agricultural operation to provide food, is difficult to determine. It is possible that in some areas, simultaneously with the decline in the sacrificial motive, the milking possibilities rather than the beef potentialities received the greater attention.

There is some confirmation of this chronological account of animal domestication in the recorded use of cattle as the first kind of draft animals. Wheeled vehicles have been found among the items buried during royal funerals in the Middle East dating back to 5000 BP. In addition there are either the representations or the remains of sledges, plows, and oxen yokes commonly encountered in the area at one time called Mesopotamia, which includes parts of Turkey, Iran, Iraq, Syria, Jordan, Israel, and Saudi Arabia. In Mesopotamia cattle must have been used as draft animals at least for 7000 years, and perhaps the use of the oxdrawn sledge antedated even this.

During the 9000 years from the twelfth to the third millennia BP, it is probable that all the major plants and animals which have at one time or another been used in agriculture were domesticated or cultivated (Table 5-1). It is indeed erroneous to talk of *the* agricultural revolution, because although this process of domestication and cultivation probably first developed in the Middle East, it was repeated a number of times in peoples apparently, at least temporarily in complete cultural isolation, for example, the American Indians. Agriculture probably had similar independent origins in yet other relatively isolated human groups.

Table 5–1 ***Possible Origin and Date of Domestication of the Major Domestic Animals*** Domestication of animals was associated with the earlier stages of the urban revolution, and was likewise concentrated in the Eurasian belt in which cereal growing developed. A number of domestic pets subsequently appeared in many parts of the world, such as peacocks (India), budgerigars (Australia), canaries (Canary Islands), white mice and hamsters (Mideast), as well as a few more recently domesticated animals kept for food such as the eland (Africa). All dates given here are estimates, based often on slight circumstantial evidence; much additional work must be done before more precise statements can be made.

Area Where First Domesticated	*Date of Domestication*
EUROPE AND WESTERN ASIA	
Dog (*Canis familiaris*)	20–50,000 BP
Cattle (*Bos taurus, B. indicus*)	11,000 BP
Sheep (*Ovis aries*)	11,000 BP
Goat (*Capra hircus*)	11,000 BP
Pig (*Sus scrofa*)	? 11,000 BP
Horse (*Equus caballus*)	6,000 BP
Ass (*Equus asinus*)	6,000 BP
Cat (*Felis maniculata*)	4,000 BP
Dromedary (*Camelus dromedarius*)	3–4,000 BP
Rabbit (*Oryctolagus cuniculus*)	3,000 BP
Goose (*Anser anser*)	3,000 BP
Pigeon (*Columba livia*)	? 3,000 BP
EASTERN ASIA	
Chicken (*Gallus domesticus*)	4–5,000 BP
Elephant (*Elephas maximus*)	5,000 BP
Water buffalo (*Bos bubalus*)	3–4,000 BP
Yak (*Poephagus grunniens*)	3–4,000 BP
Bactrian camel (*Camelus bactrianus*)	3–4,000 BP
Duck (*Anas platyrhynchos*)	3–4,000 BP
NEW WORLD	
Llama (*Lama huancus*)	4–5,000 BP
Turkey (*Meleagris gallopavo*)	2–3,000 BP
AFRICA	
Guinea fowl (*Numida numida*)	2–3,000 BP

Cultivated Plants

The selection of cultigens during these several millennia certainly involved a wide range of plants. Something like 3000 plant species have

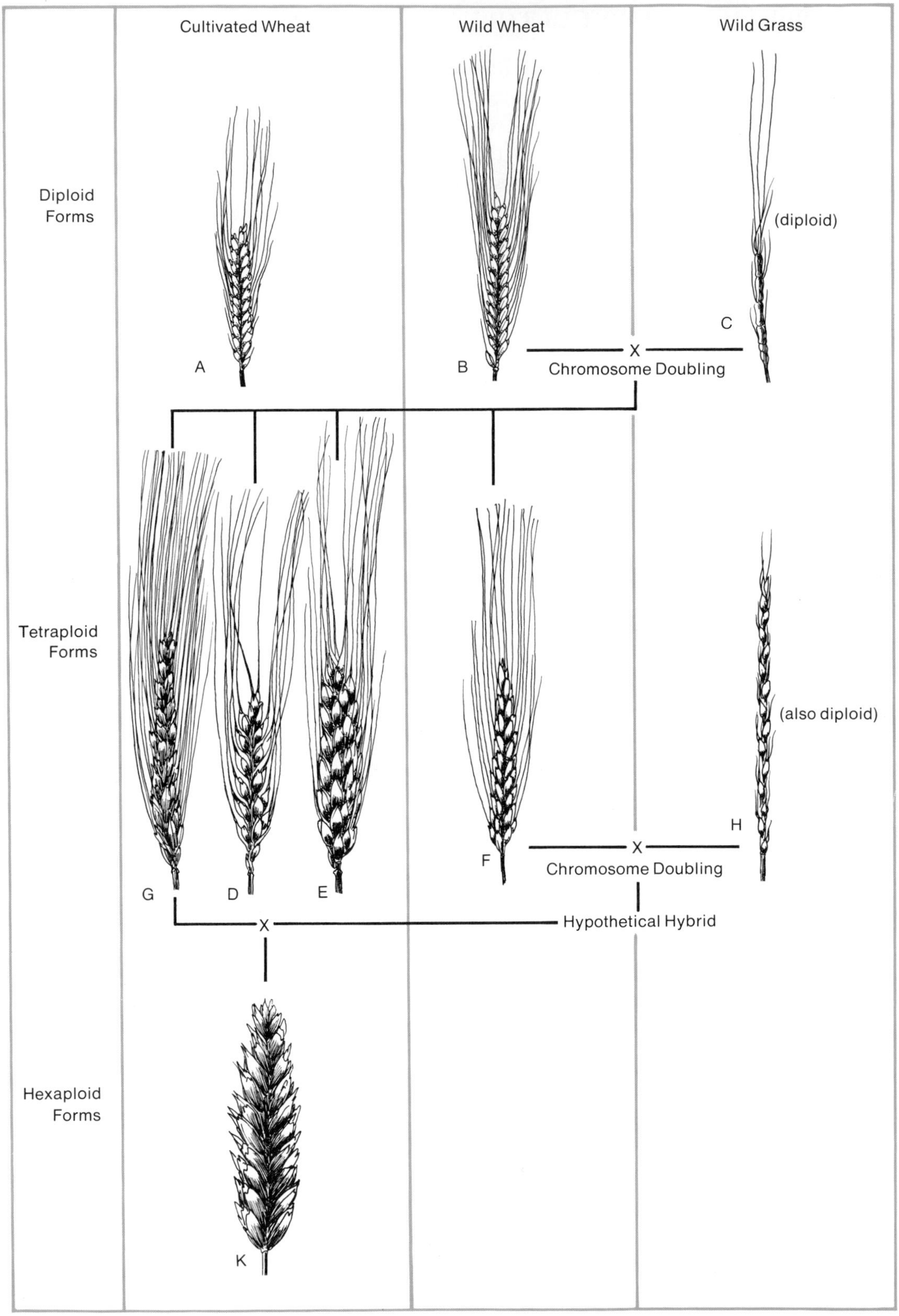
Cultivated Wheat
Wild Wheat
Wild Grass
Diploid Forms
Tetraploid Forms
Hexaploid Forms
A
B
C
(diploid)
X
Chromosome Doubling
G
D
E
F
H
(also diploid)
X
Chromosome Doubling
X
Hypothetical Hybrid
K

been utilized as cultivated plants throughout history. Partly because of increasing monoculture and mechanization practices, perhaps only about 300 of these now survive in sufficient acreage to be regarded as anything but botanical curiosities or "backyard vegetables." No more than a dozen of these provide the staple foods for 90 per cent of the world's population.

Much attention has been given in this century to the improvement of existing crop plants by concentrating upon their center of origin and searching out related plants growing there for use in crop-improvement breeding programs. Such activities have greatly increased our understanding of the various stages of development of many cultivars. One of the most imaginative workers in this area was the brilliant Russian geneticist N. I. Vavilov (1926). Among his many fundamental contributions is the concept of primary and secondary crop plants, and of centers of origin of cultivated plants (Figure 5-8).

Primary crop plants are those such as wheat and barley which are deliberately cultivated and distributed for their own merits. *Secondary crop plants* developed incidentally as *weeds* adulterating the primary crop. The spread of wheat from Asia Minor into Northwestern Europe, for example, also carried along some seeds of rye, and possibly of oats, as weed contaminants. In the colder and wetter areas to which they were introduced, both these species tended to grow and yield better than the wheat. In many such areas these secondary crop plants therefore replaced the wheat which had been the intended introduction.

WHEAT

Wheat is not only one of the most important food crops of the world and a primary crop, but it illustrates very well the kind of evolutionary history characteristic of many cultigens. In the wheat genus *Triticum* there are some 14 different species, some wild, others known only in cultivation, but all originating in the Old World. These species can be arranged in three groups according to the number of chromosomes their cells contain: *diploids* (14), *tetraploids* (28), and *hexaploids* (42). Their interrelationships are shown in Figure 5-11.

Figure 5-11. *Cultivated wheats and their interrelationships. A.* Cultivated einkorn, *Triticum monococcum. B.* Wild einkorn, *T. aegilopoides,* which is believed to have hybridized with (*C*) a diploid wild grass *Aegilops speltoides.* Following doubling of the chromosome number of this hybrid, it produced a tetraploid series including (*E*) macaroni wheat, *T. durum,* (*F*) wild emmer, *T. dicoccoides,* (*D*) emmer, *T. diococcum,* and another tetraploid type, Persian wheat (*G*). The wild emmer is believed to have hybridized with a second wild grass species *Aegilops squarrosa* (*H*), to produce a hybrid which, following chromosome doubling, further hybridized with Persian wheat to produce the bread wheat series in *K*.

Diploid Wheats

The diploid wheats, with two sets of chromosomes, are assumed to be both the most ancient of the series and the foundation from which this crop was developed. Two diploid species are recognized, *Triticum boeoticum* and *T. monococcum.* The first, known as wild einkorn, is a wild grass native to southern Europe and the Middle East, and is one of the supposed parents of cultivated wheats. The second, einkorn (the name referring to the occurrence of one seed per spikelet), is thought to be a cultivated form of the first, with slightly larger seeds and less fragile heads.

In both species, however, the flower stalks are very brittle and the heads break so easily that there is inevitable loss during harvesting. Moreover, the glumes remain firmly attached around the seed, making the grain difficult to hull. Einkorn is still grown for animal consumption in certain areas of Europe and the Middle East.

Tetraploid Wheats

The seven wheat species usually recognized in this group are considered to have arisen by hybridization of wild einkorn with another wheatlike Mideastern wild grass, *Aegilops speltoides,* and followed, as frequently happens in the case of such crosses, by a doubling of the hybrid chromosome number to give a tetraploid form. Among these tetraploids is a wild emmer, *T. dicoccoides,* and an emmer, *T. dicoccum.* Both of these species have been identified in the charred wheat grains found at Jarmo. The fact that tetraploid rather than diploid wheats are represented there suggests either that Jarmo is indeed, as surmised, a fairly advanced agricultural settlement, or that cultivation and gathering of tetraploid wheats preceded that of diploids.

Emmer was extensively grown in the early civilizations of the Mediterranean region to as far north as Britain. It retains the disadvantageous features of einkorn, brittle heads and attached glumes, so that where it is still grown it similarly is used as an animal feed.

Another cultivated tetraploid species, *T. durum* (durum), is also still grown; its exceptionally high gluten content makes it suitable for the preparation of spaghetti and macaroni.

Hexaploid Wheats

Hexaploid wheats are known only in cultivation, and the five principal forms are sometimes lumped under one species, *T. aestivum,* sometimes given separate specific names. All are believed to have developed by hybridization between a diploid wild grass species, *Aegilops squarrosa*—common as a weed in wheat fields in the Middle East—and tetraploid wheat, followed by a doubling of the chromosome number. Common bread wheat, which if distinguished as a species is labeled *T. sativum* or *T. vulgare,* is supposed to be the result of such a cross with a variety of emmer known as Persian wheat occurring in the region which is now northern Turkey or the adjoining area of Russia.

Varieties of bread wheat have firm stems which do not tend to shatter when reaped, and glumes which open readily to release the grain when threshed. It may be found necessary to predate the time of development of such free-threshing hexaploid wheats, because, as already noted, grains of one have now been identified in an early occupational layer of Catal Huyuk.

Preparation of Wheat

Because of the difficulty of hulling diploid and tetraploid wheats, whose clasping glumes retain the grain, it seems probable that after light roasting these wheats were soaked in water and made into gruel. If this preparation were left around for several days it would become contaminated with wild yeasts. The working of these yeasts may have prompted the subsequent development of leavened bread on the one hand and the brewing of cereal grains on the other, but the concept of alcoholic beverages appears to have had many independent origins.

The preparation of wheat flour by grinding grain, and the baking of bread from this, seems to have developed only with the selection of free-threshing hexaploid wheat varieties.

Domestic Animals

Considering the abundance of wild species available, the number of animals domesticated is comparatively few (Table 5-1). The early domestic forms developed from naturally occurring species in the Middle East included dogs, cattle, horses, donkeys, goats, sheep, cats, two species of camel, poultry, ducks, and geese. The New World contributed only the llama, its relative the alpaca, and the turkey. Europe provided the reindeer, and Asia the yak, the water buffalo, and the elephant. Two continents, Australasia and Africa, yielded no domestic animals at all, except the ostrich and guinea fowl, and excluding the African elephant. The one center in which it had been domesticated has not continued its operations following the independence of the Congo. The absence of domestic animals originating in Africa is exceedingly curious. The giant eland, for example, is readily domesticated; after corralling an animal for a day or so, it is difficult to drive it from the homestead. In South Africa herds of springbok and blessbok are commonly seen grazing with domestic animals on farms in the central regions. They are kept in this semiwild condition for game cropping purposes.

It is little more satisfactory to speak of the urban revolution than it is to speak of the agricultural revolution. It is certainly not correct that the agricultural revolution preceded and precipitated the urban revolution. As has already been discussed, the findings of recent archeological work, and the writings of such individuals as Jacobs (1969), indicate that the so-called urban revolution may have developed directly from trading settlements. In this case, at any rate, it actually preceded the agricultural revolution which developed from it.

Farming Villages

In a number of global regions, however, the agricultural revolution did not lead to or was not associated with any urban development. This seems to be true of the Maya civilization in the New World. Despite the existence of the many fine Mayan temples and other stone works, a city—defined as a center of multifarious manufacturing industries—did not exist. Nor did the city first arise in Egypt, despite the similar existence of temples. In dynastic Egypt, civilization probably developed under the Pharoahs for 2 millennia before true cities began to appear.

In the fertile crescent of southwestern Asia, village farming communities had become fully organized by 7500 BP, and for the next 1500 years at least they continued to exist and to spread from the upland areas into the alluvial plain between the Tigris and the Euphrates rivers. It is in this valley that archeologists have excavated the early Mesopotamian cities which seem to be the world's first real urban civilizations.

City Development

One reason for this city development may have been the increased productivity made possible by the use of irrigation water in agriculture; another may have been the need to develop some kind of control organization to limit and direct the utilization of irrigation water. The city would also provide the organization necessary for storage and barter of the additional productivity of such civilizations.

Middle East Cities

A number of settlements known to have been at this city level by 6000 BP have been excavated. Archeologists recognize four periods in the development of these cities, the earliest of which is named after Ubaid, the first site to be found. This first stage lasted for a couple of centuries, to give way to the even briefer Walda. The third period, the Protoliterate, produced the first written records, and occupied the rest of the fourth millennium.

The last and final phase is known as Early Dynastic. During this period, between 5000 and 4500 BP, independent city-states reached the height of their prosperity in the Tigris and Euphrates valleys and in Lower Egypt. The Early Dynastic period is characterized by the replacement of a ritual priest class by an hereditary ruler group. Before this, temples and their priestly hierarchies had supervised a multitude of economic and ritual activities (Adams, 1960). Afterward, short-term war leaders had their political authority continued into succeeding peace periods. Temple organizations nevertheless continued to prosper and acquired or held great estates of their own. The palace was concerned with raising and supplying its army, and constructing and maintaining the defensive wall of the city.

Uruk

This early dynastic series may be illustrated by the city of Uruk in southern Mesopotamia, which extended over 100 acres and probably had a population of about 50,000 people (Adams, 1960). Records from the time indicate that one of the temples within Uruk had a total congregation of 1200 people, including 90 herdsmen, 80 soldiers-laborers, 100 fishermen, 125 sailors, pilots, and oarsmen, 25 scribes, 20 or 25 craftsmen (carpenters, smiths, potters, etc.), and 250 to 300 slaves. Presumably the rest of the inhabitants, the cultivators and women and children, were not listed. While such a city and others like it in southern Mesopotamia and in the Nile Delta and lower and upper Nile regions were based on military organizations and engaged in military activities, parallel developments in the Indus Valley in Pakistan illustrate that this was not an essential feature of city evolution. Nevertheless the division of labor among craftsmen had apparently already become extensive.

THE FURTHER EVOLUTION OF HUMAN SOCIETIES

If we assume for the sake of the present review that the agricultural and urban revolutions were elaborations of the ritual behavior of human societies, there has been comparatively little time for their spread and evolution through all the widely scattered and sometimes partially isolated segments of the human population. Despite the ever-accelerating pace of exchange of cultural information, it is inevitable that some areas are still occupied by populations which are unable for one reason or another either to appreciate the significance of this information or to utilize it. A contemporary review of human societies on a global basis therefore reveals a mosaic of varying degrees of social evolution, with numerous stages of adoption of the many ritual and cultural behavioral patterns which have evolved. The many elements of this mosaic can be arranged to indicate the existence of a continuum, or rather a series of continua. Alternately, if a very broad classification is adopted, certain distinct grades or stages may conveniently be distinguished, and the mosaic can then be segmented into six somewhat arbitrary but convenient categories (Boughey, 1971) as follows:

1. Hunting-gathering groups
2. Early agricultural groups
3. Advanced agricultural societies
4. Industrializing societies
5. Colonial societies
6. Advanced industrial societies

This arrangement of categories is developmental and on an evolutionary ecological basis. The groups become larger as the series advances, which is why the term *societies* replaces *groups* in the later categories. Examples can be cited from the contemporary world of all these categories. It is also possible to maintain that any category except the first has had an evolutionary history which involved proceeding through the earlier categories. Special circumstances permitted some advanced industrial societies to internalize the fifth stage. The United States and Australia, for example, had undeveloped frontier areas within their own territories which absorbed the surplus population. Some small countries were able to achieve demographic changes which also enabled them to avoid passing through a colonial phase.

HUNTING-GATHERING GROUPS

Hunting-gathering groups still have a few representatives, the best known of which are the Bushmen of southwest Africa and Australian aborigine groups, although these are no longer in a mesolithic or any other form of stone age culture.

EARLY AGRICULTURAL GROUPS

Early agricultural groups are still found, and some from New Guinea have been recently described (Rappaport, 1967) in terms which explain the ecological significance of the feedback mechanisms which regulate their population size.

ADVANCED AGRICULTURAL SOCIETIES

Neither of the first two categories is associated with any permanent settlement of any size, or of any greater significance than a village of farmers. In the advanced agricultural societies the villages become in many cases market towns, with a primary significance as barter trading settlements. Quite frequently the market's importance may be judged from the frequency with which it is held, whether it is a three-day, a four-day, or a five-day market and so forth. When it becomes of sufficient importance to be a daily affair, it may become associated with streets of various kinds of artisans, leatherworkers, metal workers, potters, weavers, dyers, and so forth. The city of Kano in central Nigeria represents such a market, where these various activities appear to have been established for at least a thousand years.

INDUSTRIALIZING SOCIETIES

The advanced agricultural societies constitute many of the now-independent nations of the tropical world in Africa, Southeast Asia, and south Central America. They have only recently ceased to be politically dominated by the Western powers, which experienced the last of the major revolutions, the so-called industrial revolution, in the eighteenth century, as they evolved into the fourth category of industrializing societies. They then underwent a population explosion, becoming in the nineteenth century *colonial societies.*

ADVANCED INDUSTRIAL SOCIETIES

This advance carried most of the Western nations into the last category, advanced industrial societies, by the beginning of the twentieth century. Japan only reached the stage of an industrializing society appreciably later and thus did not enter the colonial category until the beginning of this century. Some nations, for example Egypt, may only just be evolving from the fourth category of an industrializing society and trying to move into a colonial society although it no longer has any expansion area in which to accommodate the surplus of individuals resulting from her population explosion.

THE ECOLOGICAL DEVELOPMENT OF HUMAN SOCIETIES

This series or sequence of society development can be interpreted as an *ecological succession.* The characteristics of an ecological succession are displayed on a *society* instead of a *community* basis in the progression through the six categories arbitrarily recognized—increasing diversity, competition, and structural complexity, and decreasing dominance and net productivity. Such an application of the succession concept represents an extension of its original use. Previously it has been applied to a series of communities, each with differing groups of dominants, rather than different social organizations dominated by the same species at different cultural levels. Further examination does, however, seem to confirm the parallel.

Diversity

There is, for example, an increasing diversity of the various elements of these societies. This is illustrated by the division of labor which is essentially lacking except as between sexes in the pair bonds of a hunting-gathering group, but which begins to develop in the agricultural categories and is extensive in the guild systems of industrializing societies. Advanced industrial societies have an even more diversified division of labor, or degree of specialization, as is documented in the U.S. "DOT," the *Dictionary of Occupational Titles.* Expressed in ecological language, this extreme subdivision of tasks into many specialties is known as *niche diversification.* The division of labor does not necessarily follow the same route in every instance, but may result from branching at differing points. This leads to the evolution of *ecological equivalents.*

Competition

Increasing specialization results from adaptation to a steady heightening of competition between the various elements which develop in each successive society category. The jack-of-all-trades of one category rarely survives the evolution of society to the next grade. In the severe competition between specialists in the advanced industrial societies, redundancy is a very real threat to many trades and professions. It is now quite common to see magazine advertisements which begin, "Is your husband obsolete. . . ." For management and labor this problem of the constant movement toward redundancy of many specialists because of ever-intensifying competition presents both practical and moral problems.

Dominance

Whereas the two first features of evolving societies tend to increase in degree, there is a parallel trend toward a reduction of dominance by one or more elements over the rest. As has been noted, the early civilizations were dominated by priests joined by, or sometimes superseded by, hereditary rulers. Generally in more modern societies priests and hereditary rulers no longer dominate; power has passed to smaller and more numerous circles of dominance which build around various types of individuals such as sportsmen, entertainers, politicians, scientists, and sometimes professional figures.

Succession

What causes succession, or what directs the movement from one stage in this series to the next is an *energy differential* known in ecological terms as the net primary production. It is the difference between the total gross productivity of an ecosystem and the amount of energy which that ecosystem disperses in maintaining itself, mostly in the form of heat and respiration, some as stored energy. In a hunting group such as Eskimos, or a hunting-gathering group like the Bushmen or Australian aborigines, there appears to be too little difference between the amount of energy absorbed and the amount dispersed to move the group into a higher social category. Early agricultural groups in the tropics appear to have sufficient net primary production to cause this further evolution; however, a number of feedback mechanisms limit the gross productivity, as described by Rappaport (1967). When these feedback mechanisms are interrupted, gross and net productivity rise, and the group moves forward into the category of an advanced agricultural society.

In the past such societies were frequently exploited by colonial powers, who creamed off the surplus portion of the gross production in the form of raw agricultural and mineral products, which they then transferred for processing in their metropolitan factories. After attaining independence, such groups progressed by utilization of their considerable net primary productivity into the category of an industrializing society.

THE METAL AGES AND THE INDUSTRIAL REVOLUTION

This essentially ecological approach to the evolution of human societies largely ignores the sequences obtained when this process is considered in relation to other criteria. The progress of civilization can be examined, for example, in terms of the metals used for tool manufacture, the type of fuel energy utilized, and the degree of automation.

An extensive literature has developed concerning the successive use of stone, bone, copper, bronze, and iron into the "alloy age." Recent works have suggested that the transition from stone-working to metal-working occurred in the obsidian trading cities of western Asia which have been described here (Braidwood *et al.*, 1969; Cambel and Braidwood, 1970). The progress from wood to coal, to oil, to atomic energy, with a side turn to water and wind power, provides a different but equally instructional view of civilization. The industrial socioeconomic theory may well recede somewhat in importance in what Hardin calls the synthetic *computer-slave-automated-atomic* society. Many books can be and have been written about such aspects of societal evolution, but further consideration of them is incidental to the main purpose of the present work. It is necessary, however, to examine further certain aspects of city ecology.

THE ECOLOGY OF THE CITY

Considering the central importance of cities in our modern civilization, it is almost incredible that so little attention has been paid to an analysis of the ecological processes which control their establishment, growth, and survival. During this century various attempts have been made to establish model cities, including a few modern capitals such as New Delhi and Brasilia, but the basic treatment of these appears to be architectural rather than ecological, a point which only a very few schools, such as that developed by Ian McHarg at the University of Pennsylvania, have appreciated.

Generally speaking, cities, even capital cities, have just happened. Moreover, the reason why migration to them from rural environments occurs is largely unexplored.

Migration from Rural to Urban Environments

In the United States, where agricultural production in terms of per capita output is more efficient than in any other country, there has been a continuous migration from rural to urban environments (Figure 5-12). This has created city centers in various regions, of which 26 now have populations totaling over 500,000 inhabitants. Such city centers are by no means assured of perpetual growth by this migration process; some have already, by their own projections, been shown to have entered a phase of population decline (Table 5-2).

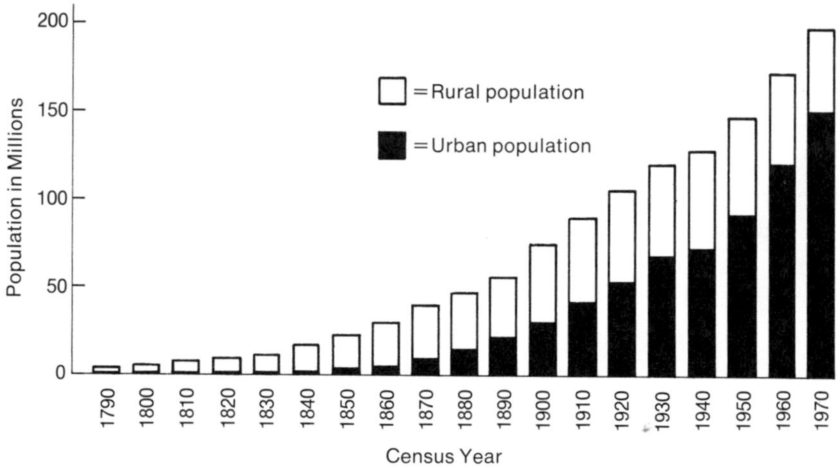

Figure 5-12. *Growth of the urban population of the United States as represented in census figures* 1790 to 1960. The rural population needed to maintain agricultural production has increased very little in size during this present century, despite a virtual doubling of the total population, because of increases in per capita agricultural productivity. At the same time there has been a continuous migration of population from rural to urban areas.

There has been much speculation as to the causal factors of this city decline. Some of the most stimulating ideas have been presented by Jacobs (1969), who relates it to loss of industrial diversity. She contrasts the economic growth of two English cities, Manchester and Birmingham, over the past century. Manchester at the beginning of this period was a great textile center, but its industry was specialized in this one activity. Birmingham was a diversified jumble of much smaller enterprises, but now its industries are expanding on this diversified basis. Manchester has stagnated with the relative decline of its textile industry as international competition heightened.

Jacobs goes on to identify the same kind of factors in operation in the

Table 5-2 ***Actual and Projected Population in Selected Cities.*** Statistics are rounded to the nearest 10,000 and given in 1000s. The largest cities, New York, Chicago, and Los Angeles, will continue the steady rise in population through this generation, as will a number of smaller cities like Oakland, Calif. Some smaller cities such as Nashville, Tenn., Tampa, Fla., and San Antonio, Tex., will undergo a more spectacular increase in size, while the population of a few large cities, such as St. Louis, Mo., will actually decline.

	1950	*1960*	*1965* (*Thousands*)	*1970*	*1980*
New York	7,890	7,780	8,100	8,240	8,550
Los Angeles	1,980	2,480	2,740	3,000	3,670
Chicago	3,600	3,550	3,680	3,600	3,770
Nashville	170	170	450	470	520
Oakland	380	370	390	400	420
Tampa	120	270	300	350	440
San Antonio	410	690	680	780	950
St. Louis	860	750	700	670	660

United States. Los Angeles, she notes, made its remarkable recovery from the loss of its aircraft industry, which had mushroomed during World War II, by diversifying into the electronics and other sophisticated industrial fields, thereby conforming to the Birmingham type of expanding city. Detroit, with its automotive industry, or Pittsburgh with its steel mills, conforms to the Manchester type.

This is actually only a portion of the argument which Jacobs develops for city expansion and decline. There is a considerable similarity between her full thesis and the process of ecological succession, just as was noted in the case of society development. There are, however, other aspects of city ecology which must be considered besides economic diversification and population size, of which transport represents one of the most intriguing. Doxiadis (1968) has evolved a theory relating the expansion of a city to its varying modes of transport.

City Transport

According to Doxiadis, the city limits are determined by a given time interval from its center, usually from 10 to 15 minutes. City evolution occurs in such a way that the suburbs are never more than 15 minutes away from the city center. When the only form of transport was on foot, 15 minutes represented roughly 1 mile. Medieval walled cities such as Sienna in Italy, Kano in Nigeria, or the City of London therefore attained a maximum size of 1-mile radius. As various forms of city transport developed, this radius could be expanded. On the outer perimeter subsidiary city centers would be developed again related to transport, but to less rapid forms. Finally, with a municipal tram or bus service, a city could sprawl over an area with a radius of up to 10 miles, and contain up to a dozen or so suburban centers on its periphery, which people would proceed to on foot from areas 10 to 15 minutes' walk away.

In the megapolis, a flight of 10 to 15 minutes by air sets a radius of about 50 to 100 miles. High-speed nonstop rapid transit may achieve the same magnitude of city size.

The Flight to the Suburbs

Toffler (1970) has recently developed the idea that we are moving toward *superindustrial* societies. This would be the new climax of the society succession discussed in this chapter. In these superindustrial societies, city concentrations lose their significance in the promotion of information exchange. In Toffler's view, the modern media for information transmission, in particular the electronic ones such as radio and television, have removed the necessity for face-to-face confrontation. The suburbanite can be as well-informed and up-to-date as the dweller in the inner city. By implication he forecasts a decline in city life and an increasing localization of industry and domiciles in suburbia.

Cities will stagnate or decay for many reasons, and this extraordinarily complex subject is now being extensively investigated for the first time. Economy and transport are just two of the many factors which may be responsible for bringing about a decline. Another way of investigating this problem is to build special experimental cities, a further procedure which is being explored (Spilhaus, 1968).

The Experimental City

Proposals to build experimental cities have developed from a number of directions, and a further approach is discussed in Chapter 13. One particular proposal, the Experimental City project in Minnesota, has been presented by a group representing federal, state, university, industrial, and private interests (Spilhaus, 1968). This group started from the premise that if the present population of the United States were accommodated in 800 cities of approximately 250,000 inhabitants each, evenly dispersed over the country, environmental crises such as traffic congestion, riots, and pollution would be nonexistent. They further consider that the future emphasis in cities will be on the trading of *mentifacts* rather than *artifacts,* the exchange of ideas rather than goods. Basically, as this chapter has tried to explain, this opportunity for cultural exchange is the city's primary attraction for people, and the essential causal ecological factor promoting migration from rural to urban environments.

The Experimental City group projects into a theoretical future and notes that the approximately 2 to 3 billion acres of land surface on the earth by A.D. 2068 will have to accommodate an estimated 15 billion people. These could be dispersed in 60,000 cities of a quarter of a million inhabitants, each surrounded by 40,000 acres (64 square miles) of open land.

Having thus established the theoretical global feasibility of such an approach to urban life, the group proceeded to outline details of the controlled city. Essentially it would be a self-contained, self-perpetuating ecosystem, in which all energy and material transfers are internalized, so that cycling processes prevent the accumulation at any point of unused wastes. It is beyond the scope of this text to pursue details of the experimental city further (they are provided in the paper by Spilhaus), but the opinion may be hazarded that if the Minnesota group succeeds in founding such a city, they will experience no difficulty in locating a quarter of a million individuals willing to move in.

ENVIRONMENTAL CONFRONTATIONS

The surface of this earth is now almost completely occupied by human groups and societies at the different stages of evolution which have been specified here. One of the elemental problems which this circumstance presents arises from the fact that no feedback mechanisms such as were imposed by the environment in category one, or by behavioral ritual in category two, are now operating to restrict population growth in any of the society categories except the last. This is the basic cause of the present environmental crises which have been too slowly noticed, at least in the advanced industrial societies. For some of the other societies, the consequences of this fundamental but inescapable situation do not have to be understood; they are only too apparent. Famine and undernourishment are found only in very local areas in the so-called advanced industrial nations, but they are a way of life for the great majority in most of the advanced agricultural societies. In attempts to remedy this situation, wholesale use is made of pesticides without reference to possible longer term and more widespread consequences. There has also been 25 years of such use in the more advanced industrial societies, and this has many manifestations. These advanced industrial societies deliberately release huge quantities of wastes as well as pesticides into the air and water of their environment, indeed into the whole biosphere.

There is a tendency to attribute all present difficulties to the "population explosion." While this is essentially true as regards the occurrence of famine, disease, poverty, lack of education, lack of opportunity, and low standards of living, it is not the sole cause of our misery. A second major contributing factor is the inexorable and seemingly inevitable expansion of city life and activity. In successive chapters the pathological and autotoxic by-products of the urban revolution will be considered individually. Essentially technological problems of human ecology, they have technological solutions. They are the particular aspects of human ecology which presently cause most concern because disregard of the effects of any single one now threatens to bring almost immediate disaster. The threat from any of them is just as real as would follow the outbreak of atomic warfare, and the chances for survival of even a small segment of our global human population would be at about the same level. If such an environmental disaster were to befall the human race, and if there were accidentally to be a small segment of survivors, there is some question as to whether even the present levels of Western civilization could ever again be attained. The total resources of the earth have already been so far exhausted that the succession of society categories as described here, which was made possible by the attainment of a particular level of net primary productivity, could not be repeated. Because of this despoiling of resources, it might never again be possible to achieve a sufficient net primary productivity in a critical mass adequate enough to permit the succession from a surviving pioneering segment to the full flowering of advanced industrial societies which has been obtained in the middle of this century.

To control population growth is the first and most urgent step which must be taken, but many other measures must simultaneously be instigated. What must be done, and the eoclogical basis for such actions, will be described after an examination in the next chapter of the diversity of contemporary human populations which parallels this review of the origin and development of contemporary societies.

Bibliography

REFERENCES

Adams, R. M. "The origin of cities," *Scientific American,* **203**(3): 153–68, 1960.

Baker, H. G. *Plants and Civilization,* Belmont, Calif.: Wadsworth, 1965.

Bartlett, A. S., Baghorn, E. S., and Berger, R. "Fossil maize from Panama," *Science,* **165:** 389–90, 1969.

Birdsell, J. B. "Some environmental and cultural factors influencing the structuring of Australian aboriginal populations," *American Naturalist,* **87:** 171–207, 1953.

Boughey, A. S. "Society succession," in preparation, 1971.

Braidwood, R. J. "The agricultural revolution," *Scientific American,* **203**(3): 130–48, 1960.

Braidwood, R. J., Cambel, H., and Watson, P. J. "Prehistoric investigations in Southeastern Turkey," *Science,* **164:** 1275, 1969.

Cambel, H., and Braidwood, R. J. "An early farming village in Turkey," *Scientific American,* **222**(3): 50–56, 1970.

Coe, M. D., and Flannery, K. V. "Microenvironment and mesoamerican prehistory," *Science,* **164:** 650–54, 1964.

Deevey, E. S. "The human population," *Scientific American,* **203**(3): 194–204, 1960.

Doxiadis, C. A. "Man's movement and his city," *Science,* **162:** 326–34, 1968.

Isaac, E. "On the domestication of cattle," *Science,* **137:** 195–204, 1962.

Jacobs, J. *The Economy of Cities,* New York: Random House, 1969.

Mangelsdorf, P. C., MacNeish, R. R., and Galinat, W. C. "Domestication of corn," *Science,* **143:** 538–45, 1964.

Martin, P. S., and Wright, H. F. (eds.) *Pleistocene Extinctions: Search for a Cause,* New Haven, Conn.: Yale University Press, 1967.

Mellaart, J. "Deities and shrines of neolithic Anatolia: excavations at Catal Hüyük, 1962," *Acheology,* **16:** 28–38, 1963.

Mellaart, J. "A neolithic city in Turkey," *Scientific American,* **210**(4): 94–104, 1964.

Perkins, D., Jr., and Daly, P. "A hunter's village in Neolithic Turkey," *Scientific American,* **219**(5): 98–106, 1968.

Rappaport, R. A. *Pigs for the Ancestors,* New Haven: Yale University Press, 1967.

Sauer, C. O. *Agricultural Origins and Dispersals,* New York: American Geographical Society, 1952.

Sauer, C. O. "Seashore—primitive home of man?" *Amer. Philosoph. Soc. Proc.,* **106:** 41–47, 1962.

Spilhaus, A. "The experimental city," *Science,* **159:** 710–15, 1968.

Toffler, A. *Future Shock,* New York: Random House, 1970.

Vavilov, N. I. "Studies on the origins of cultivated plants," *Bull. Appl. Bot., Genet., Plant Breed.,* **16:** 139–248 (English summary), 1926.

FURTHER READINGS

Anderson, E. *Plants, Man and Life,* Boston: Little, Brown, 1952.

Burkhill, I. H. "Habits of man and the origins of cultivated plants of the Old World," *Proc. Linn. Soc. London,* **164:** 12–42, 1953.

Byers, D. S. (ed.) *The Prehistory of the Tehuacan Valley,* 2 vols. Austin: Peabody Foundation and University of Texas Press, 1968.

Cain, S. A. "Man and his environment," *Bulletin,* **22:** 96–103, 1966.

Cockrill, W. R. "The water buffalo," *Scientific American,* **217**(6): 118–25, 1967.

Fava, S. F. (ed.) *Urbanism in World Perspective: A reader,* New York: Crowell, 1968.

Flannery, K. V. "The ecology of early food production in Mesopotamia," *Science,* **147:** 1247–56, 1965.

Grist, D. H. *Rice,* London: Longmans Green, 1953.

Harlan, J. R., and Zachary, D. "Distribution of wild wheats and barley," *Science,* **153:** 1074–80, 1966.

Harris, M. "The cultural ecology of India's sacred cattle," *Current Anthropology*, **7:** 51–56, 1966.

Helback, H. "Ecological effects of irrigation in ancient Mesopotamia," *Iraq*, **22:** 186–96, 1960.

Helbark, R. "Domestication of food plants in the Old World," *Science*, **130:** 365–72, 1959.

Heiser, C. R. "Some considerations of early plant domestication," *Bioscience*, **19:** 228–31, 1969.

Hutchinson, J. (ed.) *Crop Plant Evolution*, Cambridge: Cambridge University Press, 1965.

Leeds, A., and Vayda, A. P. (eds.) *Man, Culture, and Animals: The Role of Animals in Human Ecological Adjustments*, American Association for the Advancement of Science, Pub. 78, Washington, D.C., 1965.

Lorenz, K. Z. *Man Meets Dog*, London: Pan Books, 1959.

Lowry, W. P. "The climate of cities," *Scientific American*, **217**(2): 15–23, 1967.

Mason, I. L. *A World Dictionary of Breed Types and Varieties of Livestock*, Commonwealth Bureau of Animal Breeding Genet, Techn. Commun. No. 7, 1951.

Mumford, L., *The City in History: Its Origins, Its Transformations and Its Prospects*, New York: Harcourt, Brace and World, 1961.

Reed, C. A. "Animal domestication in the prehistoric Near East," *Science*, **130:** 1629–39, 1958.

Tindale, N. B. "Ecology of primitive man in Australia," in A. Keast *et al.* (eds.), *Biogeography and Ecology in Australia*, Monographiae Biologicae No. 8: 36–51, The Hague: Junk, 1959.

Ucko, P. J., and Dimbleby, G. W. (eds.) *The Domestication and Exploitation of Plants and Animals*, London: Duckworth, 1969.

Wright, H. E., Jr. "Environmental changes and the origin of agriculture in the Near East," *Bioscience*, **20:** 210–12, 1970.

Human Diversity

6

The nature of *Homo erectus* and the further evolution which occurred in *erectus-sapiens* populations during the estimated 3 to 4 million years of their existence was reviewed in Chapter 4; the last chapter examined the urban revolution which represents the latest quantum advance in contemporary man's cultural development. There is still an overemphasis on the importance of selecting the particular stage of this evolutionary ecological progression which is clearly identifiable with "man." Some homologous, or at least analogous human characteristics, as has been noted, can be identified in anthropoid species dating as far back as the Miocene. At the same time some ape traits, such as the prominence of the canine teeth, or dominance cliques, may still be traceable in contemporary human populations.

The emergence of "man" has been a continuous progress from one stage or grade to another. Some small isolated populations are still a little way back in the *erectus-sapiens* progression; others may already be moving into the stage which will succeed *H. sapiens*. The second 12,000 years of exposure to the selection pressures of city ecosystems are certain to produce further cultural adaptations to urban civilization which will make modern man appear in retrospect as ill-adjusted to these ecosystems as we presently consider a chimpanzee riding a bicycle. Our descendants of those futuristic days, geologically but a moment away, will undoubtedly regard with tolerant amusement our clumsy attempts to elevate to a unique pedestal an evolutionary stage of the *Homo sapiens* grade they will doubtlessly classify with Neolithic man.

The purpose of this chapter is primarily to examine the ecological features of the morphological and physiological diversity of contemporary man, and to relate them to any environmental factors with which there appear to be adaptative evolutionary relationships. In the course of such a review it will be apparent that biologists have had to base their theories solely on observational analytical experience. The amount of experimental work as compared with, for example that which has been carried out in order to obtain a similar understanding of the fruit fly *Drosophila,* the mold *Neurospora,* or the bacterium *Escherichia coli* is negligible. At the same time, although ethical considerations will always impose a limitation on studies of human adaptations, in no other organism is there such a huge population available for study, such an accumulation of precisely recorded data, or such strenuous efforts made to preserve all offspring of all matings. We have only begun to exploit the opportunity which these unique circumsances present.

The nature of the more obvious differences between the various modern populations which we classify as *Homo sapiens* has awakened as much interest and promoted as much controversy as the question of man's origin. Such differences have also been the source of considerable misunderstanding, great bitterness, and some conflict. On the one hand there have been the well-intended but overenthusiastic protagonists of the point of view that discernible differences are slight, and the situation so variable as to make it impossible to recognize any valid group patterns. At the other extreme are dogmatists who insist that appreciable differential adaptation has occurred, sufficient to produce significant differences in mental as well as physical attributes.

CONTINUOUS VERSUS DISCONTINUOUS VARIATION

In human populations as in all species it is sometimes convenient to group discernible differences of form, function, and behavior into either *continuous* or *discontinuous* variations. Continuous variations, sometimes described as *quantitative* differences, are measurable in some abstract way, and there are no discrete breaks between one expression and another of the diversity. There are tall men and short men in a given human population, but between these two extremes is a continuous series of men of intermediate height. Continuous variation is polygenic; it is controlled by a complex system of genes and is an expression of the total effect of all the genes involved, modified normally by interaction with the environment.

Discontinuous variation, providing *qualitative* differences, has no such gradations. Although it also can be modified somewhat by interaction with environmental factors, the differences never intergrade into one another. For example, circus dwarfs usually exhibit a variant known as *achondroplasiac dwarfism.* They may vary somewhat in height, but there is a discrete break in this variation as compared with that in the height of individuals not exhibiting this condition. Achondroplasiac dwarfism results from a single gene difference in the usual genotype, as do many examples of discontinuous variation.

Another obvious discontinuous variation in human populations is the distinction between male and female individuals, in this instance produced by differences in a whole chromosome rather than a single gene. In other animals, and more particularly in plants, study of the chromosome complements has frequently led to a greater understanding of the causes of diversity. In human populations such studies have been undertaken only within the last decade or so. Meanwhile both continuous and discontinuous variations have been investigated using methods developed from environmental ecology or from genetic-physiological studies.

HUMAN CYTOGENETICS

The normal diploid chromosome number in *Homo sapiens* is 46 (Tjio and Levan, 1956). This karyotype or chromosome complement has been classified by size on the "Denver system," which numbers and groups the 44 autosomes

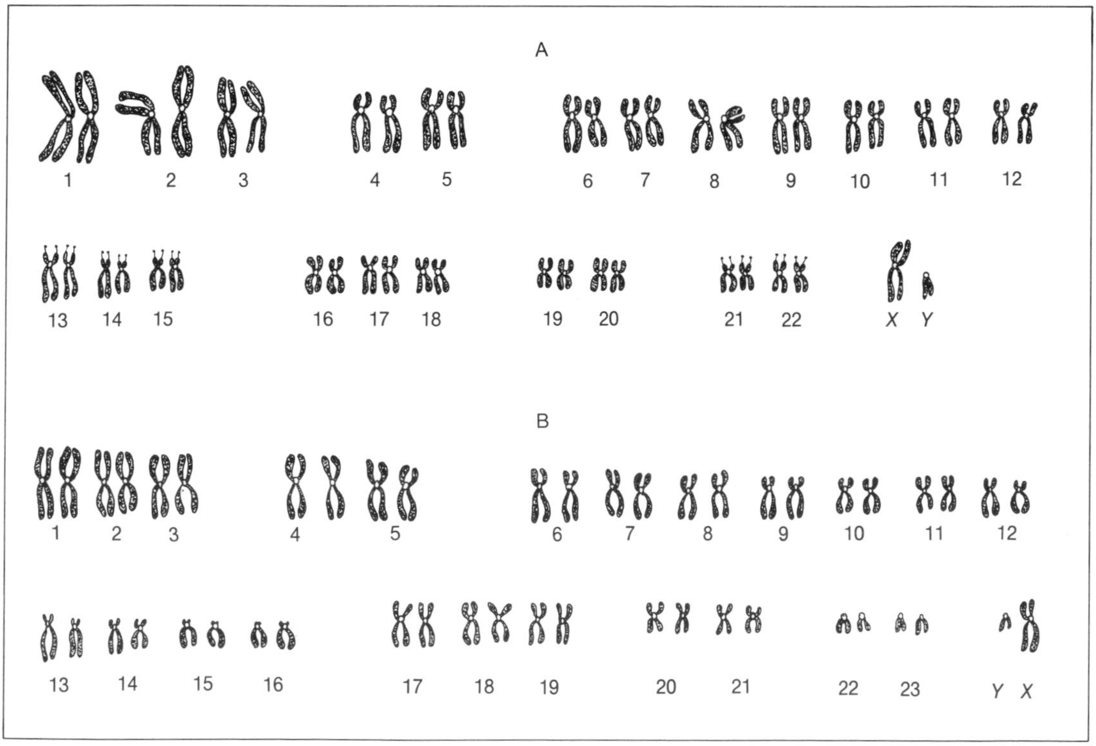

Figure 6-1. *Human karyotype contrasted with that of a pongid.* Apart from the additional homologous pair of chromosomes (pair 16) in the male chimpanzee (*Pan troglodytes*) karyotype shown in B, the chromosomes are morphologically very similar to those of the male human (*Homo sapiens*) karyotype shown in *A*. This close similarity is further emphasized by the occurrence of an aneuploid, trisomic 21, causing Down's syndrome (mongolism) in man, and a similar syndrome in chimpanzee, as recently reported by McClure *et al.* (1969). Because of the extra pair of chromosomes in the chimpanzee karyotype, this syndrome is designated as trisomic 22 in chimpanzee, but it is apparently in each case the same morphologically similar homologous pair of chromosomes which are involved.

into "large" pairs, 1—5; "medium-sized," 6—12; and "small," 13—22. Of the two sex chromosomes, X can be classified as medium-sized, but its length varies both between individuals and between cells of the same individual. Y is small but usually distinguishable by its shape. In numbering the autosomes, the longest is placed first, the shortest last, and the others sequentially in order of length (Fig. 6-1).

Other Primate Karyotypes

Diploid chromosome numbers vary considerably in other primates, as may be seen from Table 6-1. Prosimians range from 38 to 80, Old World monkeys from 42 to 72, and gibbons from 44 to 50; gorillas and chimpanzees are 48. Morphologically, the chimpanzee karyotype, apart from an extra pair of chromosomes and differences in pair 22, appears quite similar to that of humans (Fig. 6-1). For the present, any such similarities provide no evidence supporting particular theories of affinities among the primates in their relationship to the Hominoidea, any more than they can be used to identify group diversity in man.

Table 6-1 ***The Range of Primate Karyotypes***

Primate group	*Diploid number*
Prosimii	
Tupaia glis	62
Tarsius bansanus	80
Lemur nongaz (mongoose lemur)	60
Lemur nacaco (black lemur)	44
Galago crassicaudatus	62
Galago senegalensis	38
Nycticebus coucang (slow loris)	50
Perodictus potto (potto)	62
Ceboidea	
Callithrix chrysoliucos	46
Ateles paniscus	34
Cebus apella	54
Cercopithecoidea	
Cercopithecus mitis	72
Cercopithecus mona (mona monkey)	66
Cercopithecus neglectus	60
Ceropithecus patas (patas monkey)	54
Macao fuscata	42
Papio galada (gelada baboon)	42
Hominoidea	
Pongidae	
Hylobates moloch	44
Hylobates syndactylus	50
Pan gorilla (gorilla)	48
Pongo pygmaeus (orangutan)	48
Pan troglodytes (chimpanzee)	48
Hominidae	
Homo sapiens (man)	46

Observations on human karyotypes are now made by the culture in vivo of blood lymphocytes which are stmulated to divide. This technique has permitted the identification of many chromosome abnormalities with particular clinical conditions, but it has not yet been extensively applied to investigations of population cytogenetics. Court Brown (1967) suggests that when this is done, at least 1 per cent of newborn children will be found to show chromosome abnormalities. About half of these will be structural rearrangements, one-quarter autosomal aneuploids, the rest abnormalities in the sex chromosomes (Table 6-2).

Table 6-2 ***Frequency of Occurrence of Chromosome Aberrations in Newborn Human Infants***

Type of Abnormality	*Per Cent Occurrence in Population*
Trisomy 21 (Down's syndrome: mongolism)	0.15
Trisomy 13/15	0.07
Trisomy 17/18	0.50
Aneuploidy in sex chromosomes (XXY:XXX:XXXY:XX:XYY, etc.)	0.18
Total anomalies	0.90

Individual abnormalities in chromosome numbers in human karyotypes have been correlated with a number of congenital defects, but there is so far no suggestion of intergroup variation. There is, however, an apparent correlation between the occurrence of XYY forms and height. More than half the males with this aneuploidy who have been measured are over 6 feet tall (Court Brown, 1969). The same author also reports that an additional Y chromosome somewhat increases the chance of a male developing psychopathic features.

ANTHROPOMETRY

The first and to date the only class of scientists to embark upon extensive mensuration of group differences in contemporary human populations in an impartial manner were the physical anthropologists, who concentrated essentially on morphological characteristics such as height, weight, sitting height, head length, skin color, nature of hair, and width of nose (Ashley-Montagu, 1960). The result of their labors was the compilation of a huge mass of physical measurements, whose highest potential value will probably never be fully exploited, because such work generally neglected to record simultaneously the precise environmental parameters relating to each group studied. Unfortunately also for *anthropometry*, the subject which embraces such studies, the more dimensions are measured, the less likely they are to be independent. Moreover, ecologists now tend to minimize correlations with macroenvironmental factors, emphasizing instead considerations of the microenvironment.

Before examining some conclusions of the physical anthropologists based on an examination of anthropometric data, it is pertinent to review the geographical situation in respect to the Old World distribution of *Homo erectus* in the Middle Pleistocene, and to look again at any possible connections between this and the distribution of distinct groups in contemporary man.

MAJOR GROUPINGS OF *HOMO SAPIENS*

As was noted earlier, it seems reasonable to postulate that populations of a *Homo erectus* grade evolved gradually into *Homo sapiens* grade level, undergoing, as far as physical characteristics are concerned, changes in only a few features such as cranial capacity and teeth size. As a result of these changes, facial and skull characteristics became somewhat modified. Because we are still uncertain of when this evolution occurred, and because there could not really be any abrupt transition, it seems better to refer to an *H. erectus* grade and an *H. sapiens* grade. The term *erectus-sapiens population* can then be used to refer to transition groups between these two grades.

In regard to *behavioral characteristics,* by contrast with physical features there was an extensive further evolution in developing *erectus-sapiens* cultures. As the number of individual hordes or bands increased, territoriality would begin to impose a restriction on additional wide migration of these evolving populations. There would also be an additional stabilizing territorial effect with the appearance of permanent settlements in favored microenvironments. Therefore it seems most likely that the gradual evolution from the *H. erectus* grade to the *H. sapiens* grade proceeded, albeit at somewhat varying rates, in all geographical areas, developing from the existing groups already occupying those areas.

The skulls of all early and recent Mongoloids are characterized by certain features such as a more or less flattened face, a somewhat larger cranial capacity, and so forth, and are thereby distinguishable at all stages from the skulls of Caucasoids and Negroids occurring in the two other main geographical areas.

In the same way the characteristics of the Cro-Magnon skulls and associated skeletal remains are caucasoid in nature, clearly not early or late mongoloid, and recognizably different from negroid.

Some major movements of populations over long distances surely occurred as *erectus-sapiens* populations approached the last few millennia preceding historical times. The most spectacular of these movements resulted in the first occupation of the continents of North and South America and of Australasia. Despite such exceptions it nevertheless seems legitimate to suppose that by the time *erectus-sapiens* populations entered recorded and illustrated history, three major geographical groups of *sapiens* grade could be recognized, described, and diagnosed as different from one another on a number of criteria. These latter include the skull characters which permit physical anthropologists to work from both contemporary and extinct populations by a comparison of skeletal remains. It also appears reasonable to postulate that evolution from the *erectus* to the *sapiens* grade took place at approximately the same geological time in all three groupings.

The ancient geographic groups which emerge on this hypothesis have been labeled *Caucasoid, Negroid,* and *Mongoloid;* they characteristically occur in western Europe, tropical Africa, and eastern Asia, respectively. As already noted, there is every indication that genetic and cultural continuity among these geographical groups was never lost for any significant period of time. Their isolation was therefore only a matter of a greater or lesser degree of separation, varying with the conditions prevailing in the macroenvironment, and with the particular ritual behavioral patterns involved.

DISTRIBUTION

When examining the distribution of *erectus-sapiens* populations in previous chapters, it was noted that hunting-gathering assemblages with relatively stabilized territories had become established over most of the habitable regions of the Eurasian and African continents by, at the latest, about 200,000 BP. Major land migrations, notably into the "empty" continents of the Americas and Australasia, occurred subsequent to this date, followed by extensive and repeated migrations into Oceania by sea. In occupied territories, however, migratory movements of this kind must have been more difficult, as they would involve fighting and possibly a temporary depletion of resources. It can be assumed, therefore, that for at least 2–300,000 years ancestral groups of contemporary man adapted and evolved, each in its own territorial area and within the particular parameters of a great variety of differing ecosystems.

It would then be reasonable, by extrapolation from experience with other animal species under these circumstances, to expect the following:

1. Varying gene frequencies between various major geographic human groups
2. Some mutant alleles unique to a particular major geographic group
3. Phenotypic acclimation to particular environmental factors
4. Genotypic variation as a result of the selection of particular morphological, physiological, and behavioral characteristics, sometimes in the same direction as changes resulting from acclimation

5. Examples of genetic drift
6. Examples of the founder principle

In this chapter, as we review the diversity of contemporary human populations, numerous instances will be observed where one or other of these phenomena is in operation. In each case they have produced a new form which was "fitter" in relation to some circumstance at some time. The characteristic need no longer provide a "fitter" phenotype, indeed rather the opposite. "Fitter" is not in any case to be equated with "superior."

It would be intellectually dishonest to deny or minimize diversity in human populations arising from such ecological causes. It is most likely that the selection for "fitter" phenotypes at some time in the 4 million-year history of *erectus-sapiens* populations has produced diversity not only in morphological and physiological but also in behavioral or mental characteristics. In its time and place each of these selections would be uniquely superior to all other variations subject to the same selection pressures. They are therefore of ecological interest in this respect, and also in regard to their present representation in contemporary populations. A number of recent books on the potentially inflammatory subject of the "races" of mankind, which discuss human diversity at some length, are listed in the items for further reading at the end of this chapter. This subject becomes inflammatory only if it is taken out of its ecological context and given emotional overtones.

In Chapter 4 the salient features of the evolution and continental migrations of *Homo erectus* were reviewed. It was noted that major topographical environmental discontinuities—mountain barriers, seas, and ice sheets—had at different times isolated various sections of global populations of this *abiotically* imposed isolation within which these several geographical sections of *erectus-sapiens* groups evolved before reaching the *sapiens* grade. It is not surprising to find that virtually all workers who have examined the diversity of contemporary human populations are agreed that a Negroid group can be defined in the continent of Africa, a Caucasoid group in Europe, and a Mongoloid group in Asia. Other continents have presented a greater confusion of opinion. For this reason, Amerindians and Australian aborigines are usually separated as fourth and fifth groups, and care is taken to avoid discussion of the present inhabitants of the diverse islands commonly grouped together under the heading Oceania.

The speculations on evolution and migrations presented in Chapter 4 can be logically extended to include these other groups, and this subject is therefore taken up again here. In doing so, one basic assumption has to be made on an issue which in most previous texts has been ignored. "Modern man" is tacitly assumed in most descriptions to be a type of Cro-Magnon man or a development from this form. This cannot possibly be so if there has been the degree of continental isolation postulated in these pages. The last common ancestor of all men was *Homo erectus.* Because the subsequent adaptation of *erectus-sapiens* populations has been basically the result of selection leading to cultural evolution, mental characteristics have developed very much along parallel evolutionary lines. Because physical characteristics have not been changed extensively since early Pleistocene times, no breeding barriers have developed. Our various geographic forms have therefore remained interfertile in both theory and occasional actuality. This is an implication which cannot be side-stepped or glossed over; it must be subjected to scientific scrutiny.

Negroids

Africa south of the Sahara contained during the Late Pleistocene the most homogenous group of hominids of any continent. This area seems to have been both the center of origin of australopithecines and the region of sympatric interaction between *Homo* and *Paranthropus* which eventually led to the selection of *H. erectus* which had adapted to a human ecological niche. While several waves of hominid migration have left the continent of Africa, none apparently returned, at least until the Holocene, or postglacial times. African *erectus-sapiens* populations therefore were little influenced by mixture with other groups and had a longer period of undisturbed regional evolutionary history than any other such groups. This is reflected in the vast range of cultural behavior, as described by social anthropologists, which exceeds that of any other geographical area, and the considerable morphological variation, again more extensive than in any other region of comparable size.

The possible interrelationships of major negroid groups are illustrated in Figures 6-2 and 4-13. These schemes are based partly upon archeological finds which are illustrated in Figure 6-2, again arranged in a sequential evolutionary pattern. Further and intensified work could substantiate, disprove, or modify such very tentative hypotheses of negroid interrelationships. In any case, these became much obscured by waves of southerly migrations of various Caucasoid stocks from the Mediterranean area, which developed more especially during and after the last glacial period. This led to the establishment in tropical Africa of pure Caucasoid groups such as the Red Sea Hamitics including tribes like the Beja, Beni Amer, and Hadendoa (Figure 6-3), together with synthetic Caucasoid-Negroid populations like the Bantu, who have come to occupy much of the tropical African savanna regions. Negroid groups remained generally pure in forested areas because these Holocene caucasoid invaders were inseparable from their domestic grazing animals for whom there were no suitable fodder plants in the tropical rain forest.

That negroid stocks were evolved from forms very close to the earliest form of *H. erectus* is also evidenced from the occurrence elsewhere in the

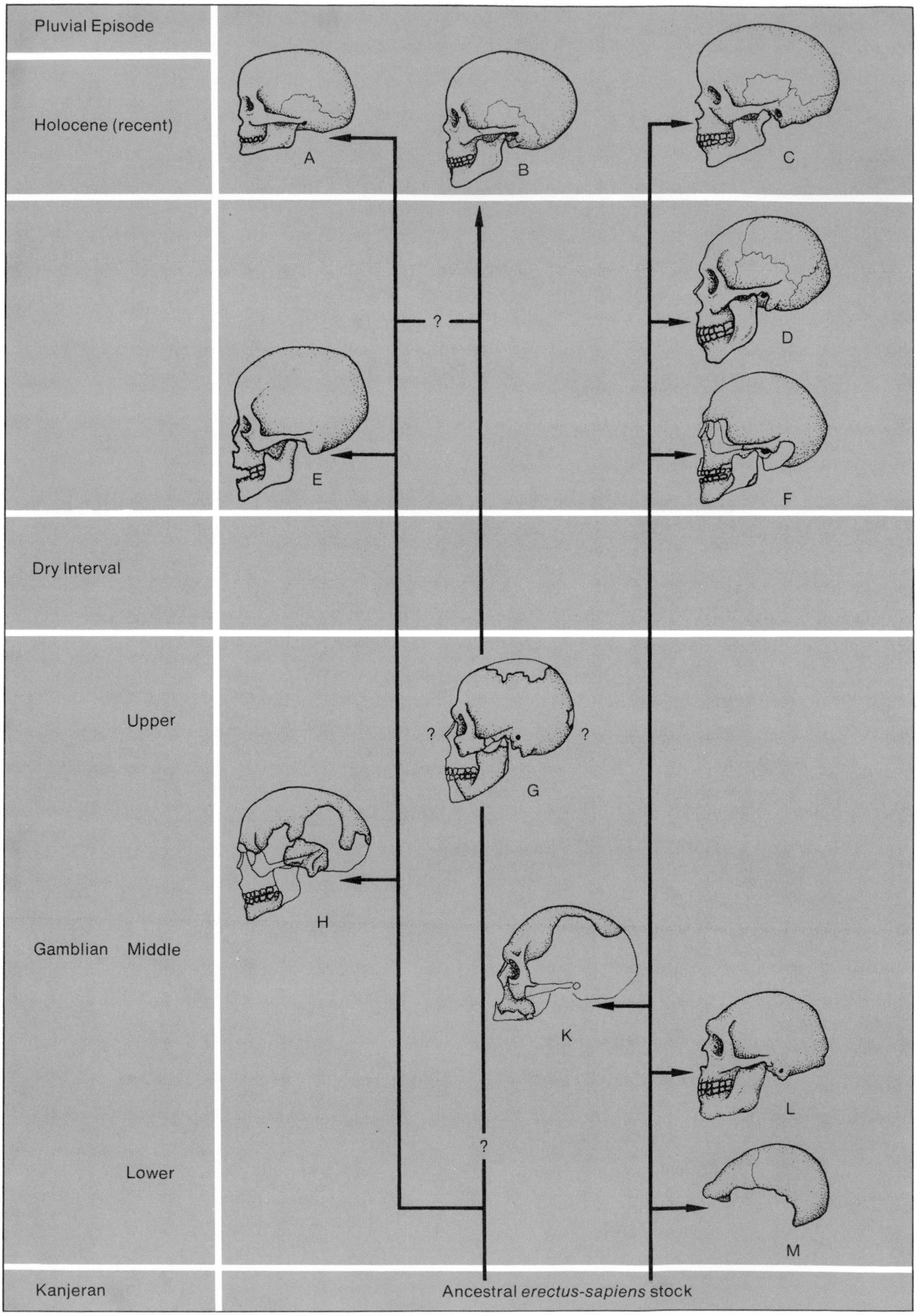
Pluvial Episode
Holocene (recent)
A
B
C
?
D
E
F
Dry Interval
Upper
?
?
G
H
Gamblian
Middle
K
L
?
Lower
M
Kanjeran
Ancestral *erectus-sapiens* stock

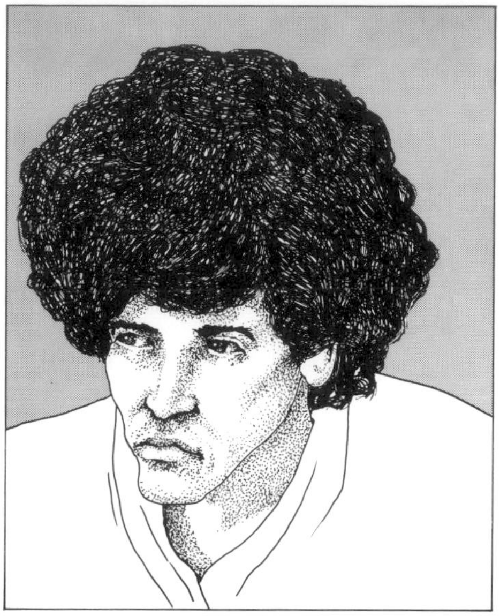

Figure 6-3. *Hadendoa male* showing the caucasoid features characterizing several allied tribes collectively classed as Red Sea Hamites, occupying the Red Sea hills of the Sudan and the former territory of Eritrea, on the western shores of the Red Sea. These pastoral Caucasoids are believed to have emigrated from the central portion of the southern Mediterranean coast at a time in the Late Pleistocene or early Holocene when the Sahara ecosystem was more productive, partly at least because of a higher rainfall.

tropics of such fossil forms as *H. soloensis* or Solo man. All these *erectus* forms must have had very slow hair growth, and "kinky" hair or "wool." Negroes, Bushmen, Hottentots, and Congo pygmies display this feature, as do Pacific groups regarded as "primitive"—the Kanaks of New Caledonia, the Papuans, and the Negrito pygmies of New Guinea, the now-extinct Tasmanians possessed it also. It could be an environmentally determined feature like the black skin which characterized all tropical inhabitants whatever their origin, but the balance of evidence is against this, especially as it seems to be linked with small external ears, and perhaps other as-yet uninvestigated traits.

Figure 6-2. *Interrelationships of negroid erectus-sapiens populations* as conjectured from some recent and fossil material representing such forms as (*A*) Bushman (contemporary), (*B*) Hottentot (South Africa, extinct twentieth century), (*C*) Negro (contemporary) (*D*) Elmenteita A (Kenya), (*E*) Matjes (South Africa), (*F*) Cape Flats (South Africa), (*G*) Tuinplaats (South Africa), (*H*) Boskop (South Africa), (*K*) Florisbad (South Africa), (*L*) Rhodesian man (Zambia), (*M*) Hopefield (South Africa). An ever-increasing accumulation of such skeletal material may eventually make possible a statistical evaluation of the significance of any observed and measured variation in it. Improvements in dating techniques are gradually providing an absolute chronology, and increasing paleoclimatic knowledge is supplying an ever more reliable paleoecological background. Combined with biochemical, genetic, and morphometric studies of contemporary populations, these should eventually permit the construction of a conjectural scheme depicting the evolution of the *sapiens* grade in Africa and elsewhere. For the sake of simplicity here, prehistoric (Hamitic) and historic (Semitic) intrusions into Africa from the north are ignored.

Caucasoids

As *H. erectus* produced mutant lighter pigmented forms, so populations were able to penetrate from the tropics into northern latitudes. Simultaneously there seem to have been other morphological changes. For example, in the method and rate of growth of the hair which became longer and more or less wavy or curly. Perhaps this was an adaptation to provide better head protection during the colder winter season which would be experienced at the higher latitudes.

Although Caucasoids, like Negroids, appear to have migrated until historic times only by land, subtropical forms must have penetrated the northerly margins of the *H. erectus* Asiatic areas of dispersal. Such groups as the Dravidians of India, Vedda of Ceylon, Ainu of Japan, and especially the "Murrayian" types of Australian aborigines, with caucasoid features such as long wavy hair and medium large ears, can be accounted relicts of such a former distribution, except that the Australians must have headed south across the tropics.

In Figure 4-14 a diagram represents some of these caucasoid interrelationships. Australians, Ainu, and so on not only have the caucasoid features mentioned, but show an *absence* of features of other main groups. The Ainu are not Mongoloid, although now isolated in a sea of Mongoloids; the Murrayian Australians are not Negroid, although some live within the tropics and have black skins.

Caucasiods occupied Europe for a long time, long enough for two events to occur which did not happen in any other primary group. The first was that a major Late Pleistocene section of *sapiens* grade, the Neanderthals, differentiated, became very abundant, and passed to extinction. In other primary geographic groups major Late Pleistocene subsections of *sapiens* grade did not apparently pass to extinction, at least not until the twentieth century. The second unique event was that Caucasoids occupied the higher latitude regions with weaker sunlight long enough for depigmented mutations to spread through the population; this affected hair, eye, and skin color. Depigmentation of the skin has occurred in all groups, but only in Caucasoids did this extend to other epidermal structures.

Mongoloids

It is difficult to avoid the conclusion that Mongoloids evolved parallel with Caucasoids and from the northerly area of distribution of the earliest *H. erectus* form. No prehistoric mongoloid forms are found in Europe or Africa. Later mongoloid forms are reminiscent of late Neanderthals in that they appear to be specialized forms further adapted to a particular mode of existence. In the case of recent Mongoloids, these forms appear to have evolved adaptations to a particularly rigorous winter period such as is encountered on the Asiatic steppes. This adaptation enabled the Eskimo groups to spread, for example, along the northern shore of Canada and occupy parts of the Greenland coast. Some of these mongoloid migrations were by sea, and either this habit was copied or *erectus-sapiens* populations had now simultaneously in many areas evolved a *sea-exploration grade*. In either case in the Late Pleistocene and persisting into historical times, many previously unoccupied islands became settled, often by people of synthetic populations apparently resulting from recent Mongoloid admixture with early Mongoloid or even with direct descendants of early *H. erectus* stocks. These explorations by sea involved especially the smaller islands of Oceania, the last virgin territories uninvaded by man. All the islands on continental shelves had by now been occupied during one interval or another of marine regression during a glacial period.

Oceanic Groups

The problem of classifying the contemporary populations of Oceania on the basis of three primary geographical groups involves even more speculation; authorities such as Garn (1961) take the line of least resistance by designating them as distinct populations. A plausible hypothesis which involves some confirmable deductions would run something as follows: *Homo erectus* was widely distributed throughout the Old World. An early wave of tropical forms of this species spread rapidly through the Old World tropics and is represented by Solo man in Java and Rhodesian man in Africa. Pygmy types developed by parallel evolution from these forms, represented by the contemporary Congo pygmies in Africa and Negritos in New Guinea (Figure 6-4). Papuans, according to this hypothesis, are the *Homo sapiens* grade evolved from Solo man (Figure 6-5). They have some negroid features, notably slow-growing kinky hair and small ears—which, as already noted, are not specifically negroid but rather traits of the earliest *erectus-grade* forms. Papuans and similar groups form what are often called the Melanesians, who have no mongoloid features.

Another wave of the early *H. erectus* stock moved eastward into Asia after evolving into proto-Caucasoid stocks. These eastern migrants continued east to form the Ainu of Japan, left a remnant behind as the Vedda of Ceylon and the Dravidians of India, and penetrated by land routes into Australia to form the Murrayian groups of Australian aborigines. They also had no mongoloid features. In all these migrations into Australia, Ceylon, and Japan, these early groups moved across the continental shelves when they were exposed during a stadial period (Figure 6-6).

Some of these migrating proto-Caucasoid stocks mingled with early Mongoloid stocks in Southeast Asia. About the third or fourth millennium BP they became sufficiently skilled in boat-making to succeed in making long ocean crossings (Goodenough, 1955). Sailing originally from the Malayan peninsula, they penetrated the whole of Oceania in successive *Polynesian* migrations, of which New Zealand, for example, probably re-

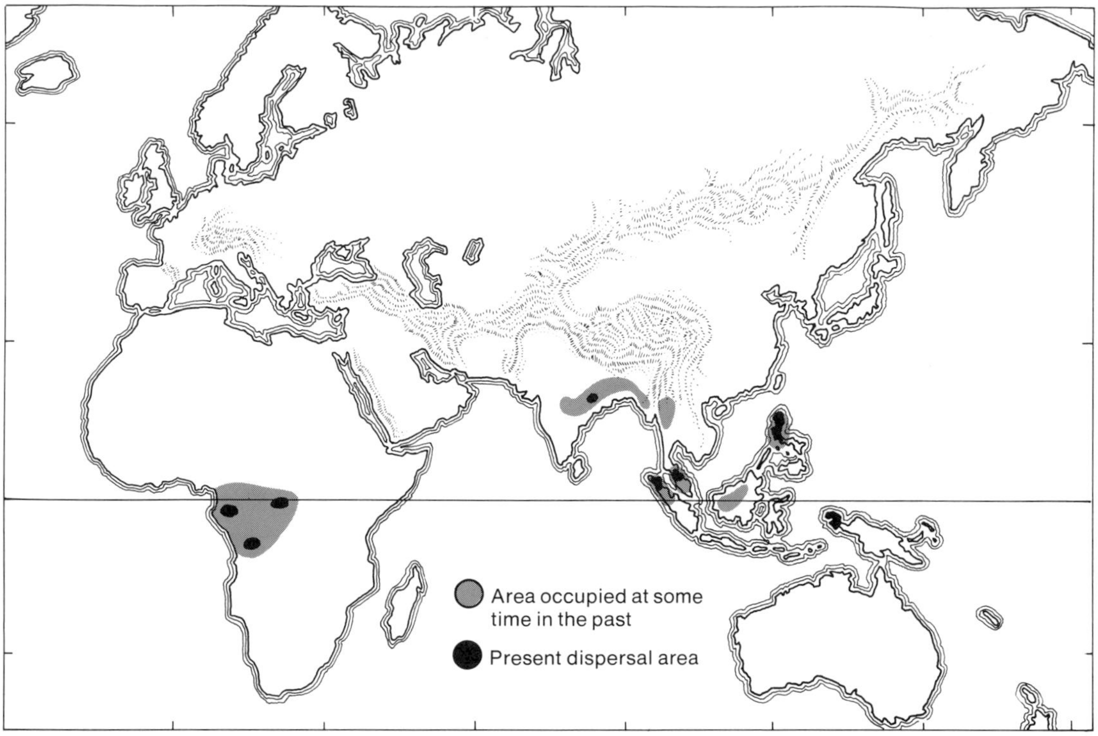

Figure 6-4. *Past and present distribution of pygmies.* The shaded area represents the conjectural distribution at the close of the Late Pleistocene, the solid area the modern distribution of pygmy groups in Africa and Negrito peoples in Southeast Asia. There are at least two hypotheses as to the origin of such groups; one supposed that they arose independently as an adaptation to high-temperature regimes, the other that their stature has varied little from the *africanus-erectus* stock from which it is surmised they evolved. The second hypothesis receives additional support from the circumstance that negritolike forms were the first human invaders of Australia, and the *only* prehistoric occupants of Tasmania.

ceived two before the main Maori invasion of the fifteenth century A.D. (Figure 6-5). Madagascar was reached by the Polynesians about the tenth century A.D. Some of the Polynesian groups fused with Melanesians to invade the small islands which comprise Micronesia.

The distribution of the main language groups in Oceania (shown in Figure 6-7) does not conflict with this broad hypothesis. Language relationships are, however, noted for their unreliability as evidence of ancestral relationships. Until much more archeological and anthropological work has been undertaken in Oceania, it is not really profitable to speculate even this far as to group origins and relationships.

Because of this partial segmentation of the global populations of *erectus-sapiens* into distinct interbreeding units, an ecologist would attempt to recognize and establish two kinds of diagnostic characters typifying particular units. The first class of characters would be genetically determined, the second the result of environmental response. Moreover, some environ-

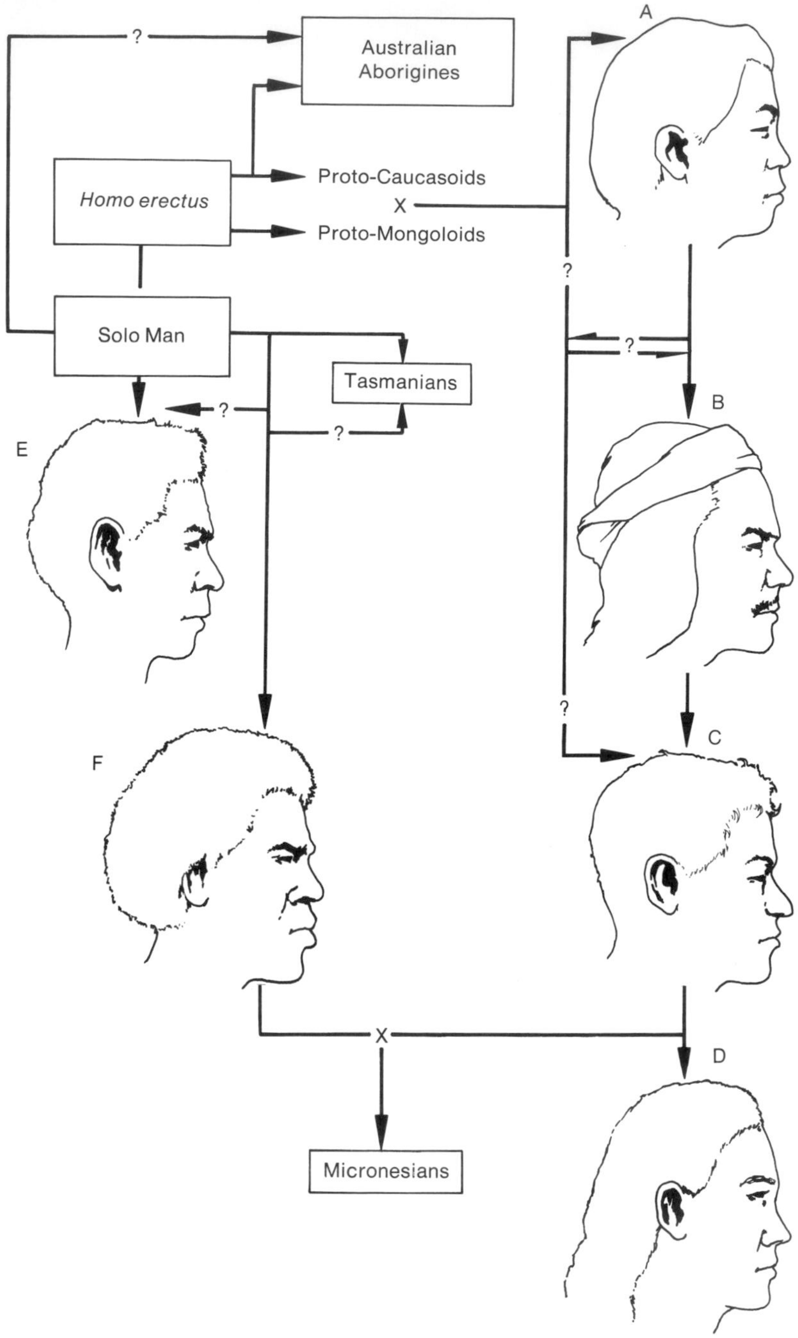

Figure 6-5. *Oceanic groups. A.* Indo-Malayan (Thai). *B.* Philippino. *C.* Polynesian (Hawaii). *D.* Maori female (New Zealand). *E.* Negrito (Philippines). *F.* Melanesian (Papua). The Polynesian group here represented by *B–D,* and Micronesians are sometimes considered to be derived from sea-going migrants related to the inhabitants of the Indo-Malay peninsula (*A*), derived from admixture between early Mongoloid stocks and a partially differentiating Caucasoid group. Melanesians (*F*) and Negritos (*E*) may have differentiated directly from a Pacific group of *erectus-sapiens* stock established in Oceania before any of the later migrant groups arrived, as may the southern group (Tasmanians) and more northerly groups of Australian aborigines.

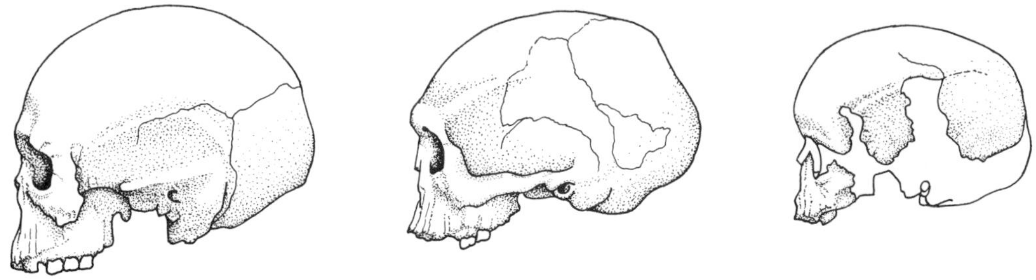

Figure 6-6. *Evidence of Australian aborigine origin,* which is very fragmentary at present, is provided by these three skulls. *A.* This skull, found near Melbourne and dated to 18,000 BP, represents the oldest human remains found in Australia. *B.* Closely resembling the skull in *A*, this comes from Wadyak in Java, and its age has not yet been positively determined. *C.* An adolescent skull from Sarawak believed to be approximately 40,000 years old and to belong to the same population group as the two other skulls.

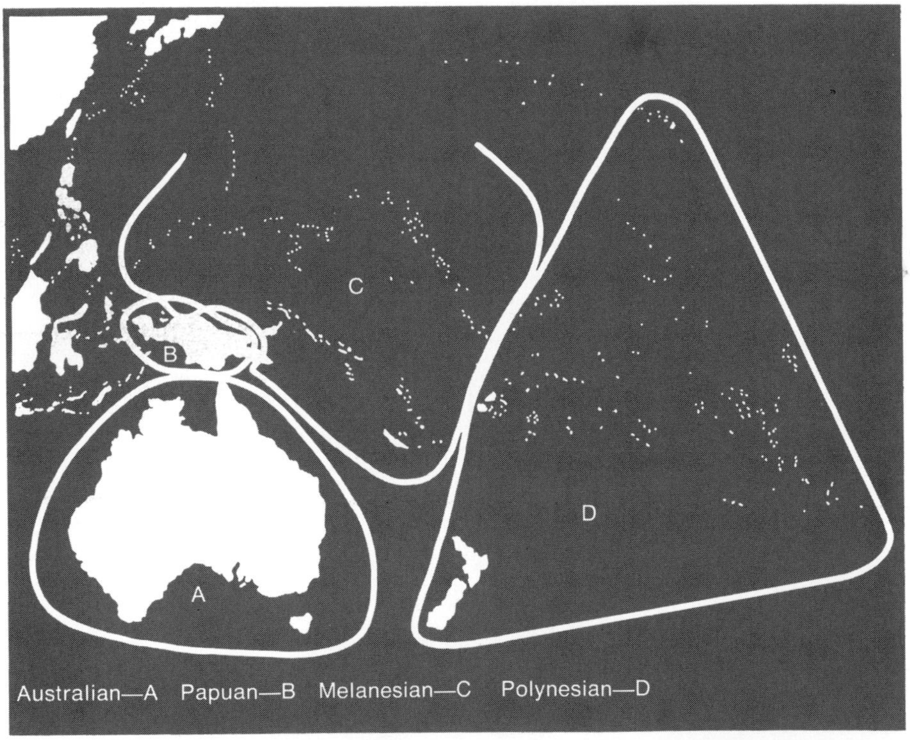

Figure 6-7. *The distribution of Oceanic languages* agrees with the major migrations through Oceania suggested in the text. A Polynesian group (*D*) essentially coincides with the area occupied during the principal Polynesian movements by sea and contrasts with *A*, the language group of the aborigine Australians who moved in earlier by land. The Papuan forms (*B*) are distinct from *A* and *D*, as would be expected if such peoples are ancient relict groups. Melanesian languages (*C*), used in this sense to exclude Papuan, would be expected to differ both from the languages of such ancient stocks and also from the language of Polynesian peoples, as unlike the latter, they contain no mongoloid admixture.

mental modification of the expression of particular genetically determined characters would be expected. Stated in ecological terms, there should be detectable differences of a *genotypic* nature, which had arisen because of differences in genetic inheritance, and variations of *phenotypic* origin resulting from the responses of the same genotypes to different environments, or through the operation of the same environment on different genotypes. In making their careful and extensive measurements on the morphological characteristics of various groups, physical anthropologists generally neglected to distinguish between diversity arising from these two different sources. Numerous attempts nonetheless have been made to establish relationships between these measurements and features of the macroenvironment.

ECOLOGICAL RULES

Two rules were early established regarding temperature responses. These classical ecological laws which have been known generally as Bergman's rule and Allen's rule, hold that variation in *size* in the first, and *body form* in the second, over a given geographical range of a homoiotherm group, are related to thermal gradients in that range (Table 6-3). Traditionally animal ecologists have considered the size relationships, and anthropologists have attempted to apply the body-form correlations (Figure 6-8).

Temperature is one of the limiting ecological factors operating on a global scale. It broadly determines the nature of the biotypes and ecosystems of particular latitudes and altitudes, and may be shown to be correlated with such ecological phenomena as species diversity and productivity. The relationship between temperature and body-heat regulation in homoiotherms has been extensively explored in recent years, and the validity of these two rules has been seriously questioned. Physiologists in particular have challenged both of these so-called rules on the grounds that there are too many exceptions. Some also maintain that adaptations to particular ranges of environmental temperature characteristics are physiological rather than anatomical. There are those human ecologists who would admit the general applicability of the rules to animals, but who also maintain that man's culture enables him to modify the effects of temperature without any biological adaptation. This last view largely ignores the circumstance that if the *sapiens* grade is regarded as a species population, *Homo sapiens* has probably been in existence for an estimated minimum of 200,000 years. Cultural adaptations which significantly render him independent of external temperatures, and especially the exploitation of fire, have been operating universally under extensive control for approximately one quarter of this time, and in more sophisticated cultural patterns for perhaps only 2 or 3 thousand years. Even in modern times, many economically structured societies still expose their less privileged members to considerable extremes

Table 6-3 ***Environmental Adaptations of Body Form*** Each of the three main contemporary groups listed here is graded downward in terms of increasing mean ambient temperature. There are associated clines of decreasing height and weight in each group, as would be anticipated according to Bergman's rule. There are also clines in the ratio of height to weight, as would be expected from Allen's rule. See text for further explanation.

Population	*Stature*	*Weight*	*Ratio*
CAUCASOID			
Finland	171.0	70.0	2.44
United States (Army)	173.9	70.2	2.48
Iceland	173.6	68.1	2.55
France	172.5	67.0	2.57
England	166.3	64.5	2.58
Sicily	169.1	65.0	2.60
Morocco	168.9	63.8	2.65
Scotland	170.4	61.8	2.76
Tunisia	173.4	62.3	2.78
Berbers	169.8	59.5	2.85
Mahratta (India)	168.8	55.7	2.94
Bengal (India)	165.8	52.7	3.15
NEGROID			
Yambasa	169.0	62.0	2.78
Kirdi	166.5	57.3	2.90
Baya	163.0	53.9	3.02
Batutsi	176.0	57.0	3.09
Kikuyu	164.5	51.9	3.17
Pygmies	142.2	39.9	3.56
Efe	143.8	39.8	3.61
Bushmen	155.8	40.4	3.86
MONGOLOID			
Kazakh (Turkestan)	163.1	69.7	2.34
Eskimo	161.2	62.9	2.56
North China	168.0	61.0	2.75
Korea	161.1	55.5	2.90
Central China	163.0	54.7	2.98
Japan	160.9	53.0	3.04
Sudanese	159.8	51.9	3.08
Annamites	158.7	51.3	3.09
Hong Kong	166.2	52.2	3.18

of heat and cold, and selection pressures promoting anatomical and physiological adaptations in relation to temperature cannot be ignored.

Biometric Studies of Body Form

Schreider (1964) analyzed body build in order to quantify it for mensuration purposes and permit a more scientific determination of possible correlations with environmental parameters such as temperature. He studied ten metric characters in eleven human populations and discovered that the volume to surface ratio is very similar in groups as distinct as Parisian workmen and Somali nomads. More specifically, he found that this volume to surface ratio figure fluctuates around 0.5 liter per square decimeter, and

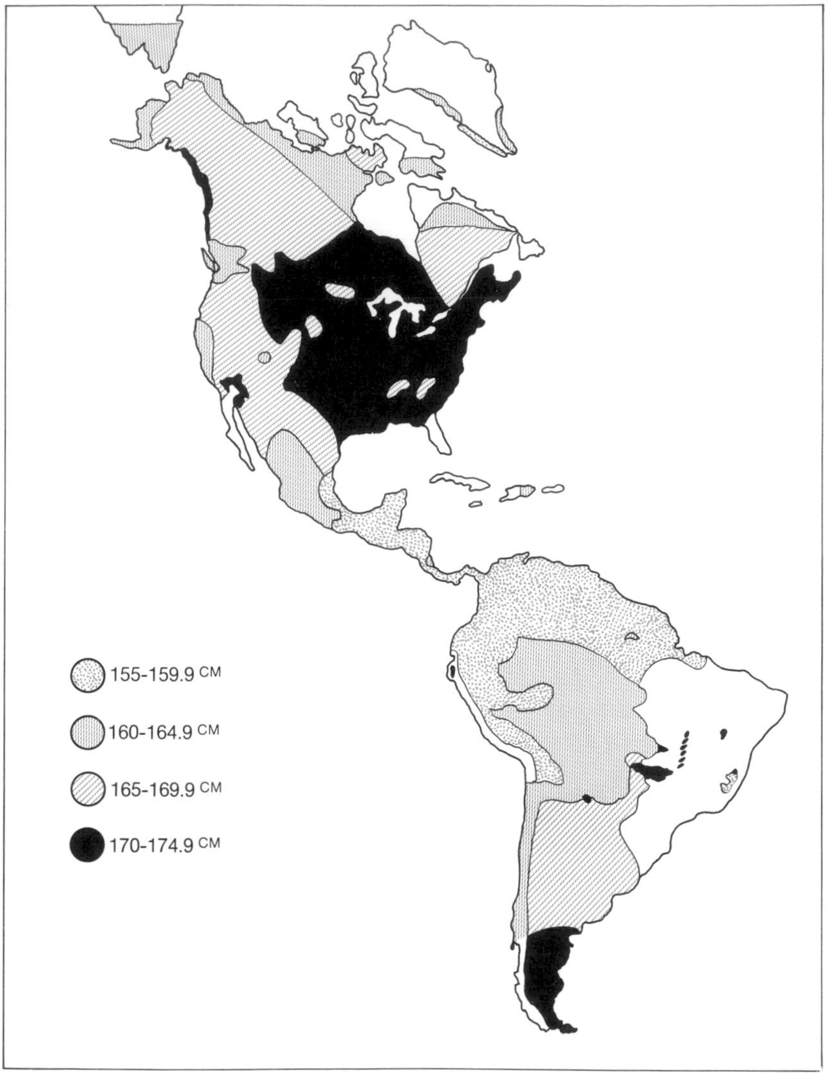

Figure 6-8. *Bergman's rule* postulates that body size in a widely distributed homoiotherm *increases* with *decrease* in temperature. This holds true for Amerindian populations which show clines of increasing stature with increasing latitude north and south of the equator. Environmental selection for this characteristic cannot on present evidence have been operating for more than 20,000 years. Similar correlations hold for sitting height, head size, and other anthropometric statistics. In the far north these correlations are not significant, because in this case the measurements are taken from Eskimos, who have probably had less time in which to adapt to prevailing temperatures. (After N. T. Newman, *American Anthropologist,* **55:** 314, 1953; reproduced with the permission of the publisher.)

concluded that despite the obvious imperfection of his methods, the ratio appears higher in European than in tropical populations. The body weight to estimated trunk surface ratio likewise revealed two distinct groups, one in the temperate, the other in the tropical zone (Table 6-4).

Schreider supposed from these analyses that a geographical gradient exists for the body weight to body surface ratio in human populations. He found

Table 6-4* ***Limb Length/Body Weight Ratios (cm/kg) for Adult Males*** *Allen's rule* postulates that in a widely distributed homoiotherm the length of the extremities tends to increase with increasing temperature. These figures relate arm and leg length to body weight, so that the greater the limb length relative to the body weight, the higher the ratio. The limb length in the anthropometric statistics used in this table increases from cooler regions (Europe) through subtropical (Mexico, Mideast) to hot regions (equatorial Africa, India).

	Limbs to Weight Ratio Average	*Body Height Average*
73 Parisian workers	4.88	168.8
47 Finns	4.89	169.5
80 French soldiers	4.91	166.2
50 French students	4.94	174.6
300 British soldiers	5.00	170.9
113 French soldiers	5.02	168.9
504 Ukrainians	5.08	167.3
120 Sicilian soldiers	5.09	169.1
100 Tonkinese	5.37	159.9
82 Otomis (Mexico)	5.51	157.6
31 Arabs (Yemen)	5.63	162.2
18 Asheraf (Somalia)	5.64	170.9
119 Nhungues (Mozambique)	5.66	167.9
123 Darod (Somalia)	5.74	172.2
119 Rahanoween (Somalia)	5.83	169.4
51 Gobaween (Somalia)	5.90	168.4
47 Dir (Somalia)	6.01	172.9
26 Antumba (Mozambique)	6.06	164.9
87 Hawyah (Somalia)	6.21	170.0
18 Korana (S. Africa)	6.21	159.8
35 Indians (Madras)	6.61	168.4
95 Aka Pygmies (Congo)	6.98	144.1
115 Basua Pygm. (Congo)	7.03	144.3

* Reprinted by permission of the publisher from E. Schreider, *Evolution,* **18:** 4, 1964.

it impossible to develop these particular analyses further because of a dearth of measurements using these criteria. He therefore had to utilize the more extensively recorded parameters of body height and weight. These generally conformed to the geographical gradient of the weight to body surface ratio, but he discovered a more complex situation than was originally supposed. From this complexity it was concluded that either there were exceptions to these ecological rules, or that a number of distinct gradients exist for each of the groups examined.

These and other considerations led Schreider to restate Bergman's rule: "In races of closely related homoiotherm species, the relative value of the body surface, expressed as a volume of the mass, increases in climates which at least during part of the year subject the thermolitic mechanisms to stress. The inverse tendency appears in climates which over-facilitate the elimination of heat."

Examining the assumptions of Bergman's ratio, Schreider considers that the universally quoted examples of Eskimo body form and the Nilotic

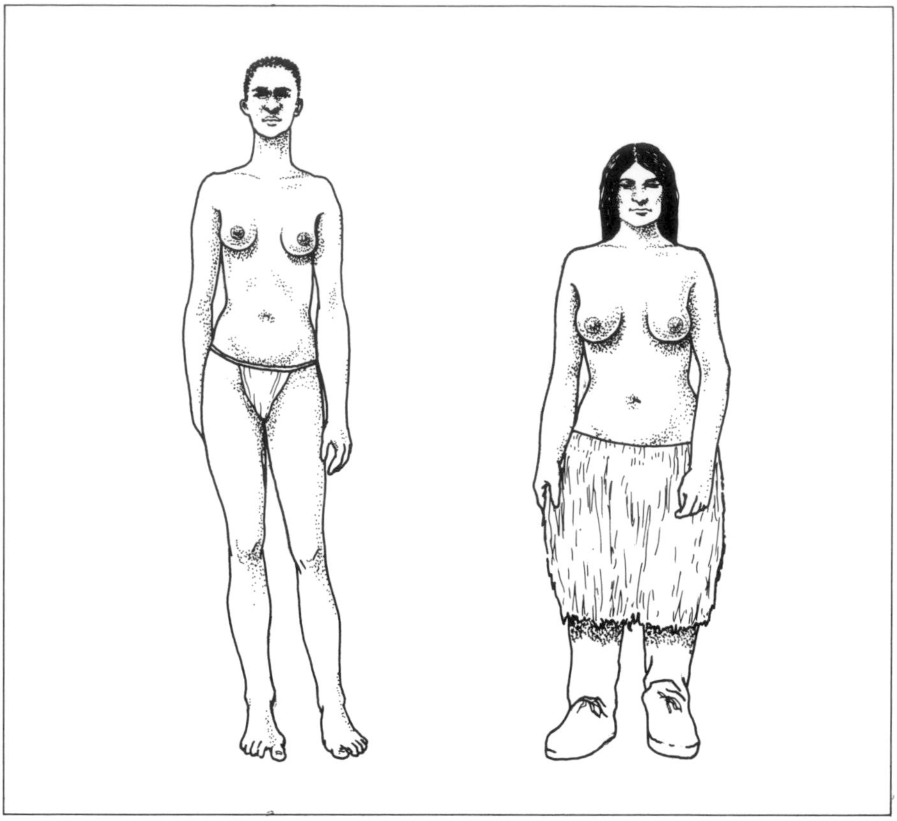

Figure 6-9. *Correlations between body size and form and prevailing temperature.* The attenuated limbs of the Dinka woman from the Southern Sudan on the left have been related by Allen's rule to a direct correlation between limb length and temperature. This same rule requires that the Eskimo (right) have relatively foreshortened limbs, as seems to be the case.

anatomy are in some way fallacious and may lead to error (Figure 6-9). He supposes that there is a convergence for these biologically significant ratios in human groups, but considers that corrected formulae may, when applied, still reveal some sort of relationship supporting the original hypothesis. He concludes that the limbs to weight ratio does play a part in thermoregulation, that with an environmental temperature of 35–36.9° C the negative correlation between the body temperature and the ratio is significant. However, Schreider admits this correlation is not very marked, and that there is no reason to expect that it should have been so, because the anatomical conditions of thermoregulation are not the only causal factors influencing this ratio. The plurality of cross factors partly explains why physiological correlations are generally low.

Extreme Variations in Body Form

The greatest extremes of body form in contemporary human populations are encountered on the African continent (Figure 6-10). They are the

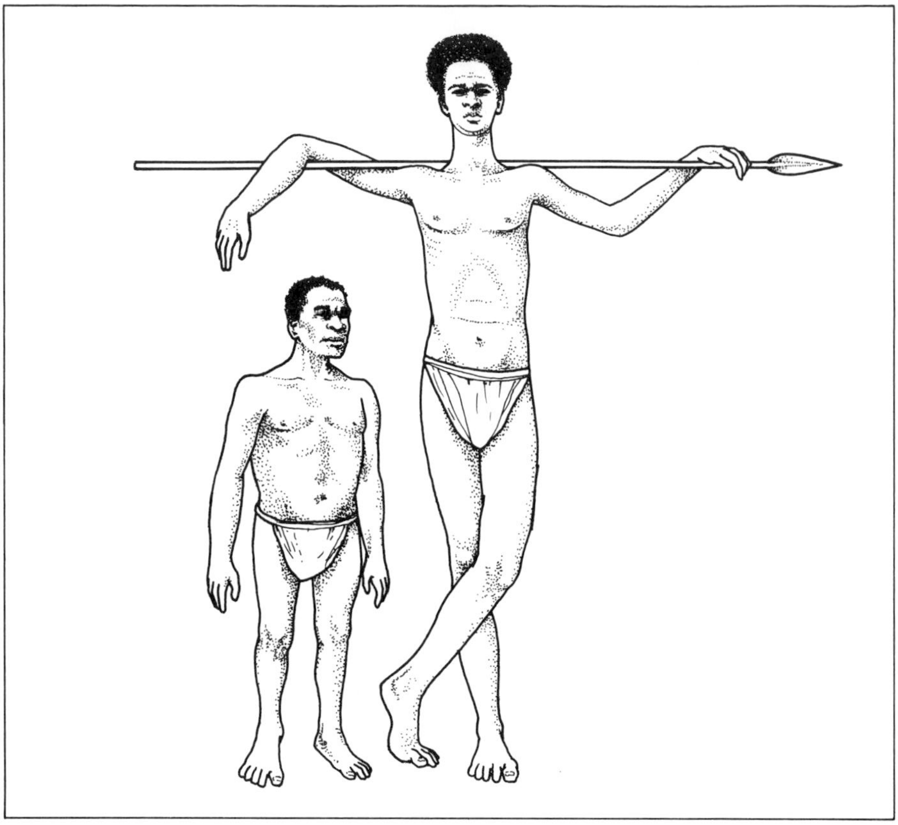

Figure 6-10. *Extremes of body form* as shown by the Watusi (right) and the pygmy (left) illustrated here. These two African groups live in approximately the same temperature regimes, and within 500 miles of one another, although the first prefers savanna, the second, forest habitats. The usual explanation for this contrast is that both forms are adaptations to increase the rate of heat loss. See text for further explanation.

several groups of pygmies, where the Ituri group, for example, average about 1.44 m (4 feet 8 inches) in height; and such other groups as the Nilotics (Dinka, Nuer, Shilluk) of the Sudan, Masai of East Africa, and Watusi of central Africa, the first group of which averages approximately 1.78 m (5 feet 10 inches).

Current explanations for the evolution of such contrasting morphological forms in relatively close geographical proximity suppose that both are selections for increasing the rate of heat dispersal into the environment. Pygmies achieve this because of their increased surface area to bulk ratio. The very tall groups are tall by virtue of attenuation of the limbs and trunk associated with little if any increase in bulk. In other words, pygmies are conforming to Bergman's rule, Nilotics to Allen's. Pygmies are moist forest hunter-gatherers whose supply of protein is limited. Nilotics, Masai, and Watusi are pastoralists, with a relatively high protein diet. The additional skeletal material can be added without the risk of attendant dietary problems.

If these explanations are correct, there should be other pygmy groups in the moist forests of other continents, and this is indeed so. Pygmies are found in the Andaman Islands and in New Guinea, and it seems more plausible to argue their appearance there as an example of parallel evolution rather than as long-distance dispersal from a common African ancestral pygmy stock. However, pygmy morphology and genetics could be read in a somewhat different way, if their close approximation to the height and weight of early forms of *Homo erectus* is stressed. Pygmies would not then be regarded as genetic variants of *erectus-sapiens* stocks, but as retaining for nearly four million years the ancient body form characteristics of *H. erectus.*

PIGMENTATION

Of all the differences among contemporary human groups, skin color has been the most obvious, the most controversial, and the most misunderstood. The term race has frequently been intended implicitly or explicitly to refer to a group with a particular range of skin color, and has provoked more territorial behavior reactions than any other human characteristic. The latest hypothesis accounting for the presence of pigments in the superficial layers of the human epidermis, presented in Chapter 2, affords a plausible explanation for most of the phenomena which have been observed in relation to this characteristic.

Distribution of Pigmentation Levels

Skin color is an inherited trait determined by a polygenic system whose individual phenotypic expression is modified within certain limits by environmental interaction. In other words, individuals inheriting a particular gene combination will be somewhat lighter or darker pigmented than the average individual with this particular gene combination if they have more or less than average exposure to the sun's untraviolet rays.

Throughout history there has been, until modern reinforced diets appeared, strong selection pressure in respect to this characteristic of skin color. The selection pressure was of this high intensity because, according to Loomis's theory, in regard to a particular latitude individuals with too deep pigmentation would have too little vitamin D synthesis; individuals who were too pale would have too much. Neither group would be likely to survive to breeding age.

The original human population of the Americas is known to have been on this continent for at least some 17,000 years, and it may have developed from a population very limited in number, and almost devoid of skin color. The occupation by this "white" founder band or bands of a region of as high latitudes as Beringia could only have been achieved by depigmented populations, or by still pigmented people receiving an adequate supply of vitamin D through the consumption of fresh fish livers. It is generally agreed that the founder Paleo-Indian populations were not fishermen; they therefore must have been depigmented.

At the opening of the European era the range of pigmentation exhibited in American Indians showed a close inverse correlation with latitude (Figure 6-11). Those groups occupying the tropical zone of Central America are almost as heavily pigmented as any black group encountered in the Old World. As this extent of pigmentation had to be produced by adapta-

Figure 6-11. *Distribution of skin pigmentation in aboriginal Amerindian populations.* The darkest peoples occur in the tropical and subtropical areas of Central America. The lightest are the Fuegians (extreme south) and the Iroquois (extreme north). The Eskimos are anomalous; see text for further explanations. (Reproduced with modification by permission of the publisher from C. L. Brace and M. F. Ashley Montagu, *Man's Evolution,* New York: Macmillan, 1965, p. 272.)

tions to the selection pressures developing as the originally white early Mongoloid stock of the Americas penetrated further into low latitudes, it would be expected that the genetic system controlling pigmentation in Amerindians would differ from that encountered in the Old World. This possibility does not seem to have been investigated.

Other Clines of Skin Color

Each of the geographical groups Negroid, Caucasoid, and Mongoloid contains populations which show similar correlations between latitude and skin color. In the first group the greatest amount of pigmentation is found in West African Negroes of the forest areas. The Bantu peoples of the upland plateau outside the equatorial forest areas are somewhat lighter in skin color, becoming reduced to "brown" in the region of the Tropic of Capricorn with people like the Zulus. Bushmen of the Kalahari Desert, generally classified as Negroid, are similarly brown-skinned. The Hottentots, also Negroid, who at one time occupied the southern areas of South Africa, were almost completely depigmented.

Mongoloids show the same inverse correlation with latitude, varying from the depigmented peoples of Mongolia to very dark-skinned Indonesians. Theoretically this dark skin would be controlled by the same polygenic system as in representatives of the Negroid stock, but again this does not appear to have been studied.

Caucasoids, like Mongoloids, appear to have been selected for depigmentation during a northward migration through the northern hemisphere, supplying the brown-skinned populations of the Mediterrean region and the white-skinned groups of Northern Europe.

It is possible that one of the pale-skinned Caucasoid populations which had adapted to higher latitudes later migrated south and east through Eurasia, leaving relicit populations behind, and founded an Australian aborigine group. If this is true, these early Caucasoid colonizers of Australia—like the early Mongoloid settlers of the New World—would have had to adapt to lower latitudes again. Their pigmentation, which is very heavy in the northern Australian tribes occupying the tropical zone, would be expected to be controlled by a separate genetic system from that encountered in Negroes of Negroid stock. In this particular instance there is literature describing work which appears to confirm this theoretical expectation.

Hair Color

Because it is derived from epidermal cells, hair color would not be expected to differ significantly from that of the skin itself. This holds true with one qualification, which is necessary because a relatively small amount of pigmentation in the epidermis will produce in the hair a much darker color than it does in the skin. Depigmentation as an adaptation to high latitudes will therefore have more obvious effects in lightening the skin than in lightening the hair color. Although Negroid and Mongoloid populations with depigmented skin are known, only Caucasoids are ever encountered with blond hair. This suggests the possibility that the adaptation of Caucasoid groups to the highest latitudes occurred very much earlier than in these other two main groups. With Mongoloids and Negroids there has not been sufficient time for mutant forms to be selected which exhibit a complete depigmentation in the epidermal apparatus.

Likewise, there is a curious red coloration of the hair, associated with the clumping of minor pigmentation into freckles on the skin, correlated with the predominance of the pigment carotene, which appears to have developed exclusively in Caucasoids.

Albinos

There have been albino forms reported from all three main geographic groups. Because the production and distribution of melanin is controlled by polygenic systems, the occurrence of such mutants suggests that changes may take place in the enzyme pathways leading to the production of melanin which can be blocked by a single mutational change.

Eye Color

The amount of pigment in the epidermis is reflected not only in skin and hair color, but also, by its presence in the iris, in the eye color. There is a general, but not complete, correlation between hair and eye color. Dark eyes are more common, and the function of the pigment appears to be prevention of damage to the sensitive eye tissues by ultraviolet light.

In northern Caucasoid groups, brown eyes are dominant over blue in a simple mendelian arrangement, but eye color in general is under polygenic control. This character is thus of limited use in reference to group differences or the study of environmental interactions.

HAIR TEXTURE AND FORM

Considering hair texture and form, there appears less reason why this should show as marked environmental adaptations as skin color. Hair can be classified into three categories, long and straight, long and wavy or curly, short and crinkly or kinky. The distribution of these three hair types in the Old World conforms very closely with what would be expected if they characterized modern peoples derived from Mongoloids, Caucasoid, and Negroid groups, respectively. The most extreme form of crinkly hair is found in the tight spirals of the Bushman's head; this would indicate directional evolution which has proceeded to an extreme in this ancient form of Negroid stock.

In Mongoloids the hair is not only straight but has a greater surface area in section than in Negroids and Caucasoids. That is, individual hairs are thicker than those of the other two groups, although the total head covering is not.

Baldness

Even though the *form* of the hair may thus be less a matter of environmental adaptation than its color, its *persistence* during life appears to show adaptation as a result of environmental pressures or, in this case, the removal of environmental pressures. The various patches of hair which are still distributed over the surface of the human body are sometimes referred to as *ornamental* hair. If this were literally true, this relict hair covering would be solely decorative, and subject only to selection pressures associated with sexual selection. However, the skull has the thinnest layer of subcutaneous fat of any part of the body, and the brain tissues are the most susceptible to damage of all body organs. An intelligent guess might be made that head hair therefore has at least an ancilliary protective function. This being so, cultural developments which introduced the use of artificial covering such as helmets would be expected to reduce the selection pressures for maintenance of this protective covering, and be associated with the random spread of mutations away from this character.

This is largely what has been found. In those areas of the Mideast where the "metal ages" appeared about 7000 BP, several millennia before they developed in other parts of the world, the incidence of premature baldness is far higher than elsewhere. The genetic system producing premature baldness in man is located in the sex chromosomes, so that males heterozygous for this character will bald early, whereas a heterozygous female will be just as persistently covered as one who is a homozygous dominant. Only the homozygous recessive female will be prematurely bald, so this is a quite rare condition.

EFFECTS OF SELECTION PRESSURE REMOVAL

This tendency of hair characteristics to mutate away from the genes producing them when selection pressures no longer operate against such mutants may be expected eventually to affect all such characteristics of human morphology, physiology, and behavior. Because additives in the form of vitamin D are now extensively used in temperate countries, and clothing has been adopted in tropical ones, the interaction between latitude and skin pigmentation is no longer so important. Movement of populations to different latitudes is relatively (but not completely) free from selective disadvantage of skin color inappropriate to a changed climate. Thus, after a lapse of time which will certainly run to many millennia, it is likely that skin pigmentation will disappear, and with it at least one cause of intergroup friction which arises as a result of human diversity. Long before this, however, it is equally certain that chemical control of genes will make possible the creation of any desired level of pigmentation or form of hair.

Face Form

Face form is clearly a very complicated characteristic, controlled by different but interconnected genetic systems. Nevertheless, terms have been applied which generalize observable differences. Two such terms are *flat-faced* and *prognathous.* Some of these forms are the result in particular of variation in another characteristic, the size of teeth.

Teeth Size

The presence of very large teeth, as in Neanderthals, necessitated a corresponding protrusion of the lower portions of the face in order to accommodate them, and resulted in the appearance of what is sometimes called a receding chin. Reconstructions of Neanderthals (Figure 4-17) always show this marked prognathy and the receding chin feature.

Among living forms the largest teeth known are those of the Australian aborigines. These are associated similarly with a receding chin and a degree of prognathy which are not, however, as pronounced as that of Neanderthals (Figure 6-12).

The size of the teeth is considered an adaptation resulting from positive

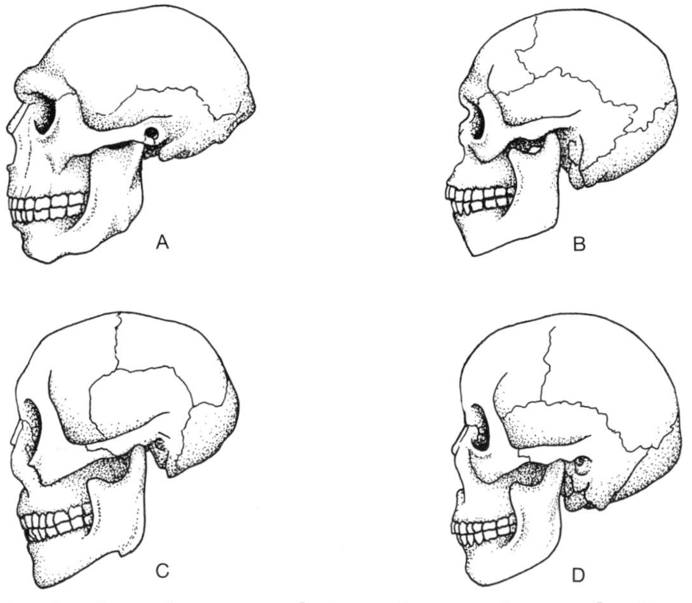

Figure 6-12. *Correlation between tooth size and extent of prognathy.* Large teeth as in Neanderthals (*A*) require more facial volume for their accommodation than the small ones of a mid-East Caucasoid (*D*). Aborigine Australians (*B*) have the largest teeth of any contemporary group; those of Eskimos (*C*) are almost as large.

selection pressures of the environment. In prehistoric times the food of Australian aborigines was apparently cooked in the ashes of a fire, then eaten, ashes and all. The abrasion resulting from the incorporation of gritty ash in the food contributed to the rapid wearing down of even these large teeth. By middle age the incisors were worn down to the gums, a circumstance which led to early death because of the inability to consume enough food.

Another factor contributory to this abrasion was the use of teeth for gripping items while they were being worked with the hands. This wears the incisors in particular, unlike the chewing effects which especially affect the molars. Among Australian aborigines the incisors were the teeth to suffer the most excessive wear by middle age. The top and bottom sets came together instead of overlapping in what is now known as the overbite. Worn incisors would be prevented from meeting by the projection of the molar crowns and would no longer be able to grip anything small.

Selection for Large Teeth

In such a population as the pre-European aborigine peoples of Australia, any random mutation resulting in smaller teeth, particularly in smaller incisor size, would shorten the life span of the individual bearing it. There would thus be a reduction in the number of offspring with this trait in the next generation. By contrast, positive selection pressures would gradually increase the size of the teeth to the point where some other factor began to interact which balanced the advantages of larger teeth against the disadvantages of further increases in their size.

Among extant populations, the next largest teeth to those of the Australian aborigines are found in Eskimo populations, and selection for this trait can again be explained on a cultural basis. Eskimos too use the incisors for gripping objects which are being worked with the hands; even more significantly, they chew skins to tan and soften them in preparing furs as garments. Eskimos also have no overbite, or at least did not have one until the present generation, which is no longer rigidly observing traditional cultural practices.

Evolution of Small Teeth

When the relative size of teeth in the Old World is mapped (Figure 6-13), it appears that populations with the smallest teeth are centered in an area where agricultural communities first developed extensively. This suggests that with the change from the consumption of wild plants and roots to that of gruels and other preparations made from the flour of ground cereals, lesser demands were placed on the teeth. Mutations resulting in the development of smaller teeth were no longer eliminated by the operation of strong selection pressures.

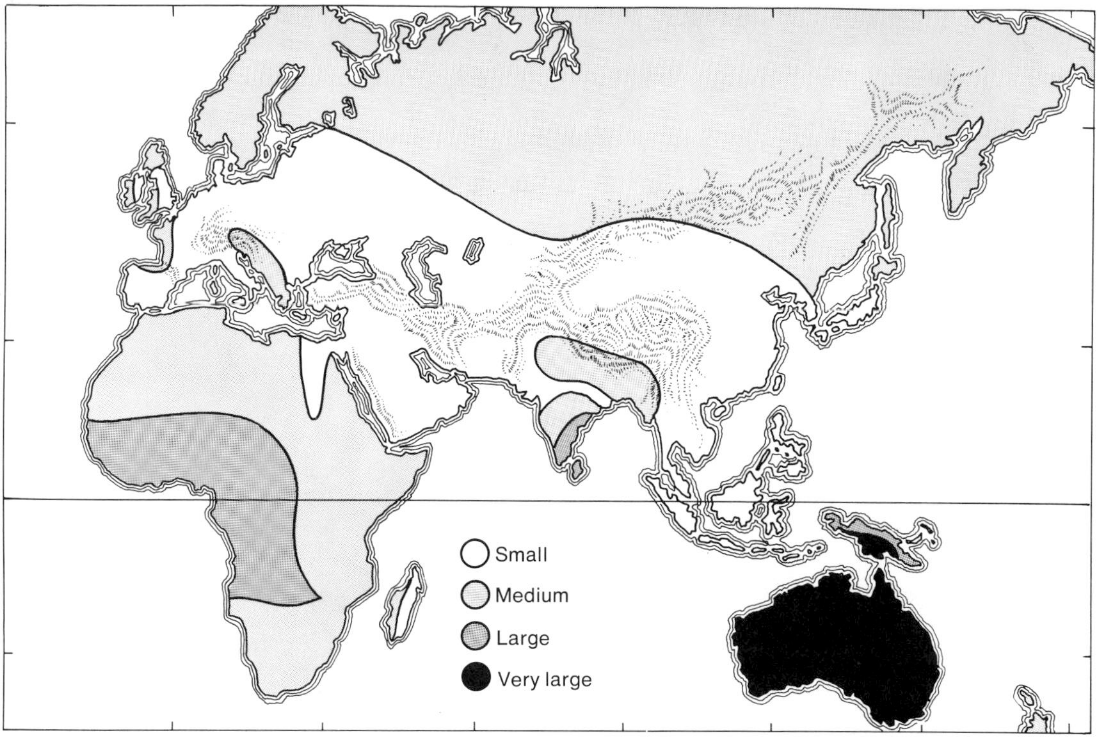

Figure 6-13. *Distribution of relative tooth size* in aborigine human populations of the Old World before the major migrations of the nineteenth and twentieth centuries. The smallest teeth occur in the Eurasian region where cereals, especially wheat and barley, were first cultivated beginning some 11,000 years ago. The crude figures of teeth size used for this table were adjusted to *relative* figures by allowing for an obvious correlation with body size. (Reproduced by permission of the publisher from C. L. Brace and M. F. Ashley Montagu, *Man's Evolution,* New York: Macmillan, 1965, p. 300.)

Distribution of Teeth Size

A belt of small-toothed people stretches from the Pacific Coast of China to northwest Europe, including both Mongoloid and Caucasoid populations. Combined with the fact that the occurrence of large teeth is found equally in peoples derived from Negroid, Caucasoid, and Mongoloid stocks, this strongly suggests that teeth size is determined by interaction with the cultural practices of individual peoples, both as to the preparation and nature of the food consumed, and the extent teeth are used as a clamp.

There is a further complication in the diversity encountered in tooth form, the presence in some groups of shovel-shaped incisors. This also has been explained environmentally as another mutation away from large teeth in people with advanced food cultures.

NASAL CHARACTERISTICS

The form and shape of the nose are, like the degree of prognathy of the face, partly correlated with the size of the teeth, rather than a specific indication of a particular ancestry. Large teeth increase the frontal width of the lower face. This increase widens the breadth of the base of the nose, and results in extended nostrils. Peoples as widely apart geographically as Australian aborigines (Caucasoids), West African Negroes (Negroids), and Eskimos (Mongoloids) are found to have such wide noses and flared nostrils, supposedly for this reason. Contemporary populations of the Middle East, with agricultural food cultures believed to precede any others by several millennia, not only have small teeth but also correspondingly thinner lower faces, narrow noses, and small nostrils.

Nose Form

Physical anthropologists record nose form, as opposed to the width and the size of the nostrils, by using the *nasal index.* This is arrived at by expressing the breadth of the nose as a percentage value of its length (Hóóton, 1960). A low nasal index (47) therefore is associated with a long, narrow type of nose, a high index (51) with a relatively short, low one. Although correlations can be obtained between this index and certain environmental parameters, the nasal index is not generally considered a good character to use. Despite this lack of confidence in it, low, short noses appear to be more characteristic of the tropics, and long, high noses typical of more temperate areas (Figure 6-14 and Table 6-5).

Long noses and high bridges are also characteristic of peoples living in desert areas. It is sometimes suggested that such long noses are adaptations

Table 6-5* ***The Correlation Between Nasal Index and Climate*** A low index, a short wide nose, is correlated with warm, moist climates; a high index, characterizing long, narrow noses, is correlated with a cool or cold dry climate.

Nasal Index of 146 Populations Correlated with	*Correlation Coefficient*	*Standard Error*
Dry-bulb temperature	0.63	0.050
Relative humidity	0.42	0.068
Dry-bulb temperature and relative humidity	0.72	0.040
Wet-bulb temperature	0.77	0.034
Vapor pressure of the air	0.82	0.027

* Reprinted with permission of the publisher after G. A. Harrison, J. S. Weiner, J. M. Tanner, and N. A. Barnicot, *Human Biology,* New York and Oxford: The Clarendon Press, 1964, p. 459.

to selection pressures arising from dry or cold air or a combination of these, all being a type of environment in which the air requires dampening, warming, or both, in long nasal passages before it enters the lungs.

In the tropics, where the air is both moist and warm, there is no selection pressure for the development of longer nasal passages, nor is there any pressure to select against mutations resulting in somewhat shorter nasal passages. The short, low, squat nose with small but flared nostrils is supposedly the type which all peoples would eventually develop if we all lived in air-

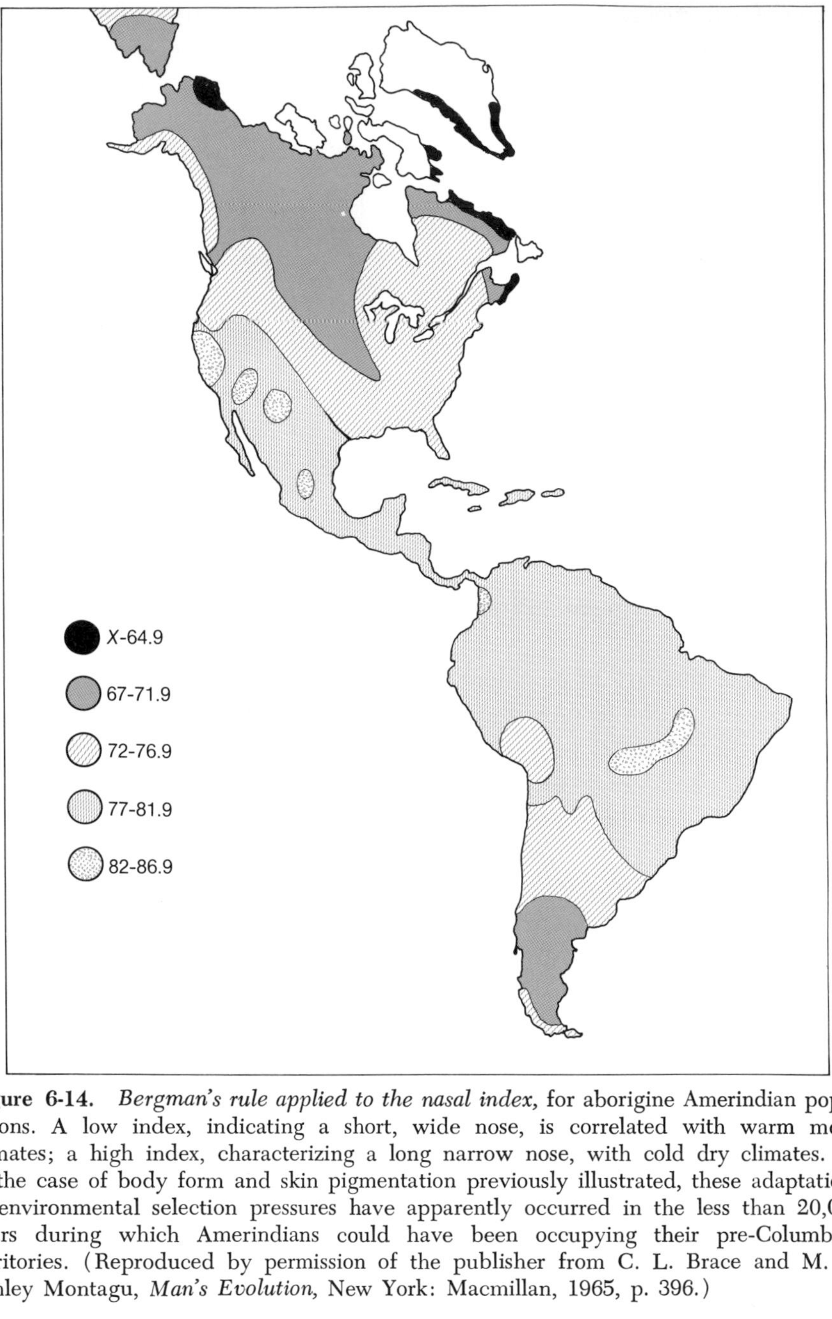

Figure 6-14. *Bergman's rule applied to the nasal index,* for aborigine Amerindian populations. A low index, indicating a short, wide nose, is correlated with warm moist climates; a high index, characterizing a long narrow nose, with cold dry climates. As in the case of body form and skin pigmentation previously illustrated, these adaptations to environmental selection pressures have apparently occurred in the less than 20,000 years during which Amerindians could have been occupying their pre-Columbian territories. (Reproduced by permission of the publisher from C. L. Brace and M. F. Ashley Montagu, *Man's Evolution,* New York: Macmillan, 1965, p. 396.)

conditioned homes with the thermostat turned up rather on the warm side, and effective humidifiers. Similar results would occur if everyone lived in moist tropical regions.

Mongoloid Adaptations

There are some objections to a purely environmental explanation of nose form, for the flattened faces of Mongoloids are associated with a relatively low and comparatively small nose, despite the usual explanation for this face form as an adaptation to extremely cold conditions. The broad fat-padded cheeks, eyelids, and forehead of recent Mongoloids, if indeed they are genetic adaptations to the cold, are the latest major morphological adaptation in *erectus-sapiens* populations. Such adaptations must have occurred within the last 500 or 600 generations. They were not present in 25,000 BP when early Mongoloids were entering Beringia, and climatic conditions had ameliorated throughout the world by 10,000 BP.

Mongoloid Eye Fold

The slitlike form of the eyes in Mongoloids is accentuated by the deposition of fatty tissues in an exterior fold of the upper eyelid (Figure 6-15). This is a characteristic which is exhibited in its most extreme form among modern Asiatic populations of northeast Asia. It is also present to a lesser extent in Amerindians, and is therefore judged to have been a feature of the early Mongoloids.

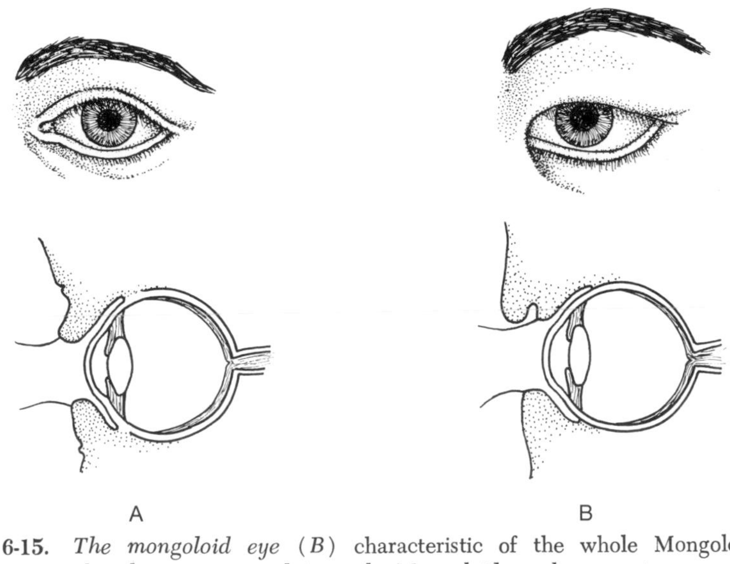

Figure 6-15. *The mongoloid eye* (*B*) characteristic of the whole Mongoloid geographic group, but less pronounced in early Mongoloids such as contemporary Amerindians, contrasted with a caucasoid eye (*A*). The mongoloid eye is narrowed dorsiventrally, and the additional fatty fold shown in the sectional view gives it a slanted appearance. The narrowing of the eye aperture is considered an adaptation to provide relief from sun glare off snow. The fold is thought to have a protective function against cold wind, to which the rather flat mongoloid face exposes the eyes.

The usual explanation for this deposition of fat in the eyelids is that under conditions of extreme cold it protects against frost damage to this comparatively thin membrane. Likewise the general form of the eye, the tendency to assume a slitlike apperture, is considered to be the result of selection pressures favoring reduction of the amount of light entering the eye, an adaptation to conditions of high light reflectance which is obtained in a snow-covered landscape. Wooden masks are sometimes worn by hunters in such areas, which similarly reduce the glare by having only narrow slitlike appertures for the eyes (Figure 6-15). Interestingly, the Bushman groups, who stare at distant game against perpetually bright skies, have also developed a partially slitlike eye form. This has sometimes been regarded as suggesting Mongoloid ancestry.

The lesser development of both eyefold and the slitlike shape in early Mongoloid forms, or in modern groups descended from early Mongoloid forms, suggests that although these two characteristics may first have been adaptations to selection pressures exerted by cold winds and snow-covered landscapes, directional evolution through random drift has continued even when the selection pressures which initiated such adaptations diminished.

Negroid stocks essentially restricted to the African continent never experienced extremes of low temperatures and would not be expected to have developed these particular cold-protective adaptations. Caucasoid groups, however, in Late Pleistocene times could be expected to have been exposed to somewhat similar conditions. Considering their greater extent of depigmentation, the length of this exposure would be for a longer period. These particular eye characteristics do not appear in Caucasoid stocks, possibly because the ameliorating effect of the Gulf Stream somewhat reduced the severity of the winter conditions in northwestern Europe.

Thus the mongoloid type of eye seems to provide an example of a characteristic which was environmentally determined, but was an adaptation which occurred in only one of the three major geographic groups of *erectus-sapiens* populations.

OTHER MORPHOLOGICAL VARIATIONS

Two minor variations in the morphology of the head—small ears and thick lips—appear to characterize at least some Negroid stocks. For neither of these features would there appear to be any obvious selective value, either presently or in the past. Some Caucasoids have very large ears, but there is no record of the auditory mechanisms performing any differently with such large appendages as compared with small ones. A possible thermoregulatory function does not fit the circumstances either. It is possible that the ear flaps are in the process of reduction to a vestigial condition, and that the mutations leading to this reduction are more numerous in Negroids than in other groups.

The thick lips of Negroids may be the result of sexual selection. Tobias (1962) has argued that the *steatopygia* (Hottentot bulge) of Bushmen and Hottentot women, giving the hugely fattened buttocks, is another example of such a process of sexual selection (Figure 6-16). This might provide a better explanation of both phenomena than any theory of environmental selection, random drift, or mutation.

Considerable attention was once given to the varying occurrence of sweat

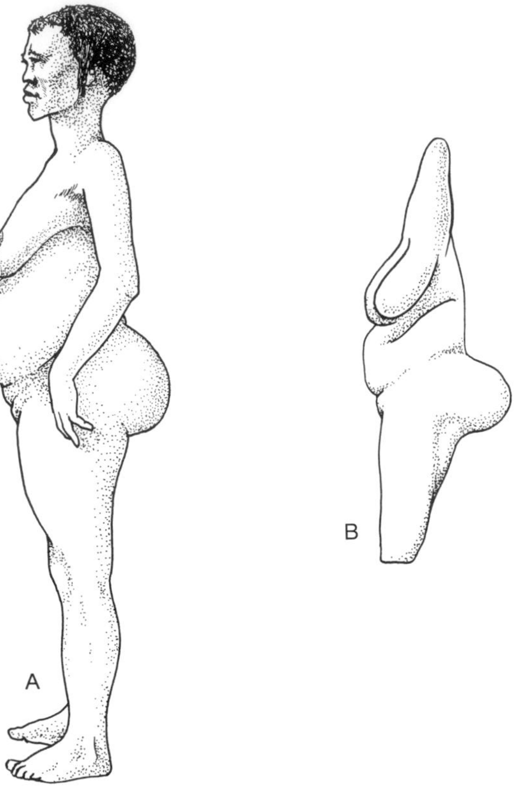

Figure 6-16. *Steatopygia: A.* Side view of female Bushman from the Kalahari Desert showing the outgrowth of fatty tissues in the buttocks to which the term *steatopygia* has been applied. This condition characterizes Bushmen and Hottentot groups, being considerably less exaggerated in the males and not found to occur in any other modern peoples. The relatively common occurrence in Europe from about the close of the Pleistocene of figurines such as that illustrated in *B* suggests that possibly steatopygia was a feature of early *Homo erectus* populations generally, but only survived in these two African groups. If this were substantiated, it would favor the food storage–heat exchange explanation of steatopygia rather than the sexual selection one.

glands in different human groups. There are from two to five million such glands on the body, and their density ranges from 150 to 350 per square centimeter. Figures were produced to support the view that acclimation to higher temperatures would increase the figure in an individual, and that there were also genetically fixed differences between various groups. Recent work suggests, however, that the number of sweat glands has already been determined at birth. Possibly the differences previously recorded may have arisen because observations were made on the number of glands actually functioning at a given time.

BIOCHEMICAL VARIATIONS

Some reference has already been made to the existence of different blood groups in contemporary human populations. The biochemical study of such diversity was the natural successor to the physical anthropologists' activities. In this instance, although the observations are mostly qualitative rather than quantitative, they have a scientific basis and are both repeatable and suitable for the application of statistical tests of validity. Furthermore, a major portion of the observable diversity in biochemical characteristics is genetic and inherited, not a phenotypic expression of environmental interactions.

Such characters are grouped here as biochemical variations because the application of biochemical tests is usually required for their detection. It is a purely arbitrary grouping which has no other significance than convenience. Included within this definition are the blood groups and hemoglobin mutants already considered; many other blood groups like the rhesus, P Lutheran, Kell, Duffy, Diego, and Gm systems; G-6PD deficiency haptoglobins; transferrins; BAIB excretion; and other examples of genetic polymorphism. The impetus which human immunological work received from what is fast becoming regarded as classical studies on genetic coding, and more recently in response to demands for a deeper understanding of organ and tissue transplant phenomena, is rapidly extending this list. At the risk of appearing biased, it is possible to select for mention some of these polymorphic situations which affect blood group systems, secretory, and taste functions.

The Rhesus System

Polymorphic situations arise when several mutant forms of an allele coexist in a population at such levels of gene frequency that their persistence must be related to factors other than the mutation rate alone. The *rhesus system* at one time was believed to result from the existence of two alleles, Rh and rh, giving rhesus positive genotypes RhRh and Rhrh, with the single recessive rhesus negative genotype rhrh. The presence of these alleles is determined by agglutination tests using rhesus monkey red cells in rabbits.

The effect of rhesus incompatibilities between mother and offspring is lethal to newborn babies. The rhesus factor genetic system is, however, more complicated than was first thought. A more recent hypothesis postulates rhesus alleles in closely linked combinations among three loci, C, D, and E. Using this last interpretation, considerable variation has been found in the rhesus system throughout the world, and some theories as to possible ancestry and migration routes of particular population groups have been based upon this (Table 6-6).

The Diego System

Some blood group systems, such as the Diego antigen, precisely coincide with one of the three main *erectus-sapiens* groups. The Diego antigen is of widespread occurrence in early Mongoloid populations of American Indians

Table 6-6* ***Distribution of Rhesus Genes in Populations from Different Geographical Groups*** These figures appear to support the proposition that gene frequencies for the rhesus factor lie at different levels in Caucasoid, Mongoloid, and Negroid populations; Eskimos and Amerindians are classifiable most nearly as Mongoloids, Australian aborigines as Caucasoids. However, a more critical examination of such statistics needs to be undertaken before indisputable conclusions can be drawn.

Geographical Group	*Genes*							
CAUCASOID	*CDE*	*CDe*	*CdE*	*Cde*	*cDE*	*cdE*	*cDe*	*cde*
Danes	0.1	42.2	0	1.3	15.1	0.7	1.8	38.8
Italians	0.4	47.6	0.3	0.7	10.8	0.7	1.6	38.0
Spaniards	0.1	43.2	0	1.9	12.0	0	3.7	38.0
Australians Aborigines (early Caucasoid)	2.1	56.4	0	12.9	20.1	0	8.5	0
MONGOLOID								
South Chinese	0.5	75.9	0	0	19.5	0	4.1	0
Japanese (both the above are recent Mongoloid)	0.4	60.2	0	0	30.8	3.3	0	5.3
Eskimos (Greenland)	3.4	72.5	0	0	22.0	0	2.1	0
Navaho	1.3	43.1	0	0	27.7	0	28.0	0
Blood	4.1	47.8	0	0	34.8	3.4	0	9.9
Chippewa (all these are early Mongoloid)	2.0	33.7	0	0	53.0	3.2	0	8.0
NEGROID								
Bushmen (early Negroid)	0	9.0	0	0	2.0	0	89.0	0
Shona (Rhodesia) (Mixed Negroid-Caucasoid)	0	6.9	0	0	6.4	0	62.7	23.9

* Reprinted by permission of the publisher from A. R. Mourant, *The Distribution of the Human Blood Groups,* Oxford: Blackwell Scientific Publications, 1954, pp. 383, 393, 394.

in both Americas, and also in Asiatic Mongoloids such as Japanese and Koreans (Table 6-7).

Abnormal Hemoglobins

Generalizations such as this supposed confirmation, from blood group biochemistry, of the hypothetical three independently evolving geographical groups of *erectus-sapiens* populations, inevitably involve much oversimplification. If this oversimplification is substantially ignored, and subspecies or races are erected on this basis (Coon, 1963), then, as Mayr (1963) has emphasized, these entities may nevertheless be entirely artificial and have no real evolutionary significance. It is therefore interesting to examine the situation in regard to the occurrence of *abnormal* as opposed to normal hemoglobins in modern human populations. The distribution of the genes producing these abnormalities is among the best known of the genetic systems operating in any naturally occurring population.

Table 6-7* *Frequency of Diego-Positive Phenotypes in the Major Geographical Groups of Contemporary Man* The figures provided are estimated percentage frequencies of occurrence of Diego-positive (Di [a+]) individuals in the population specified.

Geographical Group	*Population*	*Percentage Di (a+)*
MONGOLOID		
Early Mongoloid	Caingangs, Brazil	46
	Carajas, Brazil	36
	Guajiros, Venezuela	5
	Caribs, Venezuela	36
	Guahibos, Venezuela	15
	Maya Indians, Mexico	18
	Chippewa Indians, U.S.A.	11
	Appache Indians, U.S.A.	4
Recent Mongoloid	Japanese	12
	Koreans	6
	Alaskan Eskimos	1
CAUCASOID		
Early Caucasoid	Australian Aborigines	0
Caucasoid	U.S.A. whites	0
	Asiatic Indians	0
NEGROID	Liberia and Ivory Coast	0
	Bushmen	0

* Reprinted with permission of the publisher from G. A. Harrison, J. S. Weiner, J. M. Tanner, and N. A. Barnicot, *Human Biology,* New York and Oxford: The Clarendon Press, 1964, p. 275.

Hemoglobin molecules are formed by two different polypeptide chains known as the X and B chains, two of each occurring in each molecule. Formation of the X chains is controlled by a different gene from the one which controls the B chains. Detectable mutations occur very rarely in these genes; they result in the replacement of a single amino acid by another at a particular position on one of the X or B polypeptide chains.

Other mutations resulting in the production of abnormal hemoglobin occur which involve more extensive changes than a single amino acid replacement; sometimes even a change in chromosome structure is involved. In the heterozygous condition with most mutants the condition is not lethal, but tends to reduce the individual's life span.

With international agreement in 1952 the various abnormal hemoglobins were named A, F, M, S, etc. (Livingstone, 1964); and it is relatively simple to recognize these using electrophoretic techniques. Some had already been characterized by their clinical expressions. *Sickle-cell hemoglobin,* or *sickle-cell anemia* as it has alternatively been named, had long been recognized from the sickle shape which some red cells in a fresh blood film from an affected person assume when they are deoxygenated, particularly when this is done by adding sodium metabisulfite as a reducing agent. This condition was believed to be present in peoples of Negroid ancestry, and it is now known to indicate the presence of the hemoglobin labeled S, which is the

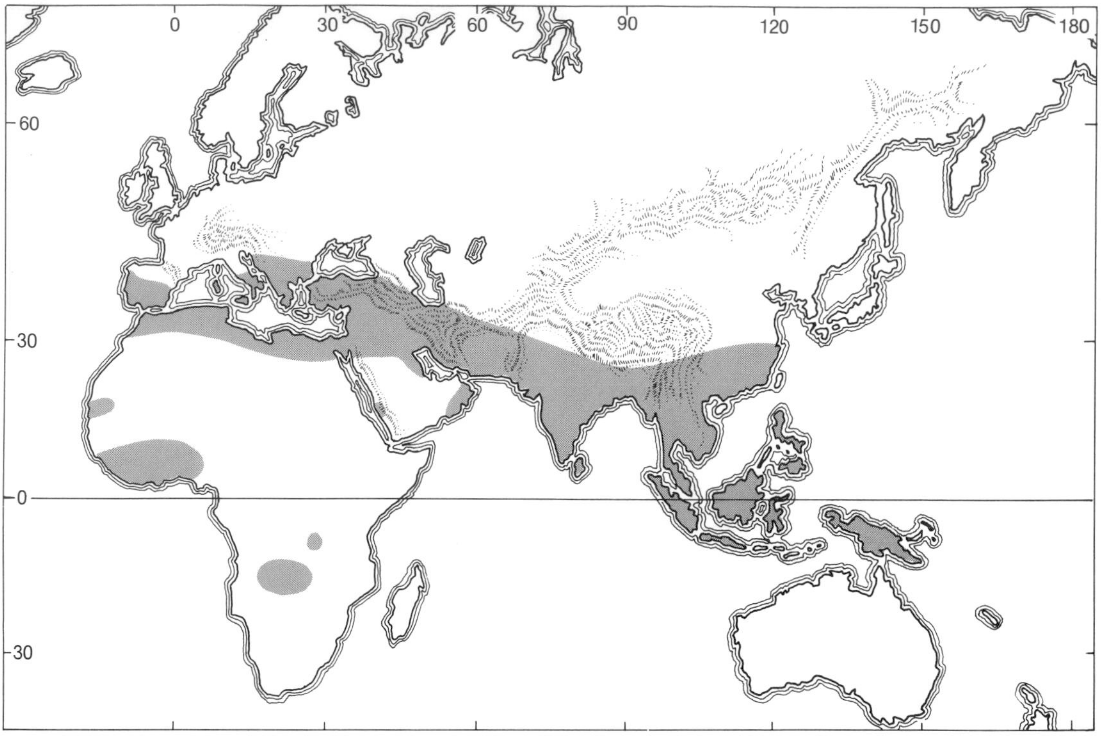

Figure 6-17. *Distribution of thalassemia in the Old World,* which is independent of the distribution of the three main human geographical groups. It therefore differs from sickle-cell anemia in this respect, but may similarly be correlated with the distribution of a form of malaria (see Figure 6-18). (Reproduced by permission of the publisher from J. Buettner-Janusch, *Origins of Man,* New York: Wiley, 1966, p. 542.)

result of a single amino acid replacement. The frequency of heterozygotes in a population may sometimes exceed 15 per cent.

Another inherited clinical condition, *thalassemia,* received its name because it was most often recorded among Mediterranean stocks (Figure 6-17). When it resulted in severe anemia, usually fatal during childhood, it was known as *thalassemia major* or *Cooley's anemia.* Milder forms of this anemia were called *thalassemia minor.* These mutants were associated with a wide range of red cell distortions.

Thalassemia results from a number of changes in gene composition and is a relatively common mutant, sometimes attaining a gene frequency in excess of 15 per cent.

Livingstone (1964) has considered the global distribution of these hemoglobin polymorphisms both in relation to that of various forms of malaria and of possible "breeding units." Thalassemia, which seems to convey some resistance to a widespread form of malaria due to *Plasmodium malariae* and *P. vivax,* almost coincides in its distribution with that of endemic forms of this malaria (Figure 6-18). It appears to be encountered extensively in peoples of Negroid, Caucasoid, and Mongoloid stocks, all of which are represented within this endemic malarial area. Hemoglobin S, by contrast,

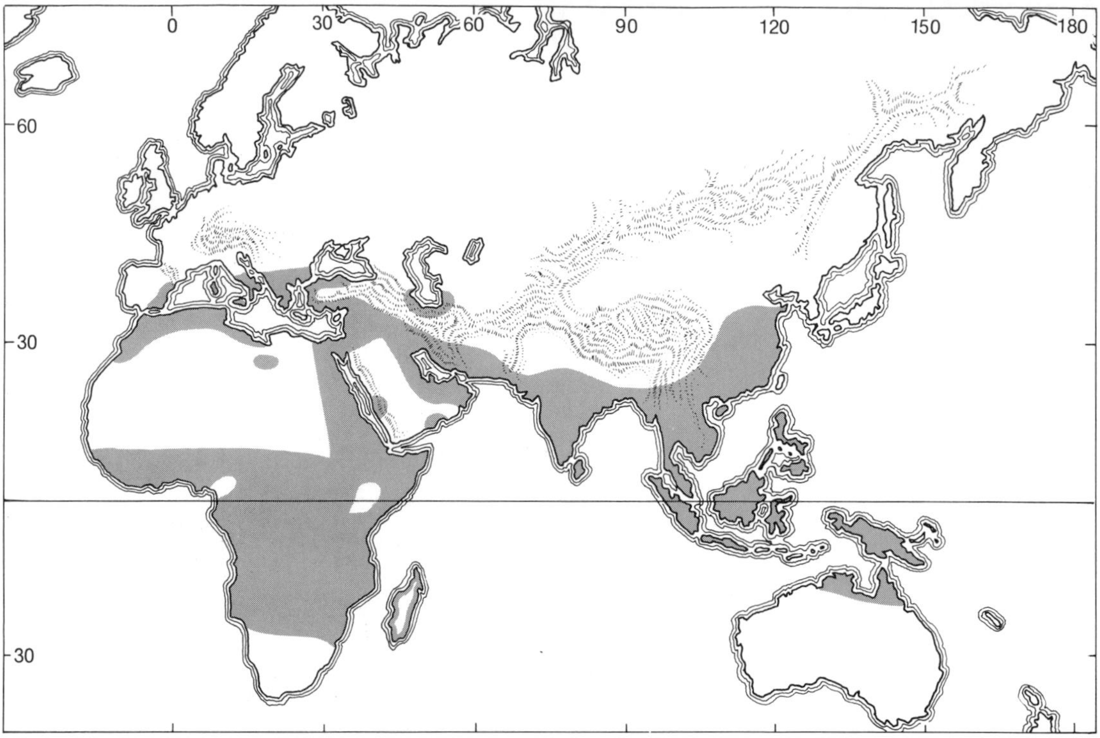

Figure 6-18. *Distribution of falciparum malaria in the Old World* which is correlated with the dispersal area of thalassemia shown in Figure 6-17. Falciparum malaria results from infection by either *Plasmodium malariae* or *P. vivax;* see text for further explanation. (Reproduced by permission of the publisher from J. Buettner-Janusch, *Origins of Man,* New York: Wiley, 1966, p. 546.)

appears to relate primarily to malaria resulting from infection by *Plasmodium falciparum.* This form of malaria is found especially in Africa, Greece, and India (Figure 6-18), and it is not therefore surprising that this sickle-cell trait is noted primarily in peoples of Negroid stock, less in Caucasoids, little in Mongoloids.

Thus Livingstone has established that a high incidence of malaria is associated with a cultural change from hunting-gathering to sedentary agriculture, which has taken place during approximately the past 10,000 years, and that the distribution of hemoglobin polymorphisms cannot be used as evidence supporting the establisment of any human stock breeding units at this time. Nevertheless, although he does not note this, it does provide evidence of genetic contact among the various human populations of the Old World in recent times.

TWINNING RATES

Before proceeding to examine some more complex correlations between human diversity and biotic or abiotic selection pressures, it would be possible to run through a whole gamut of apparently unrelated features

Table 6-8* ***Twinning Rates Contrasted Among the Three Major Geographical Groups of Contemporary Man*** Figures for dizygotic twins, those arising from the separate fertilization of two individual ova, are separated from those of monozygotic twins, which have resulted from the division of the one fertilized egg to form two individuals. While this second type shows no significant differences in occurrence among groups and is always low, dizygotic twinning rates are very much higher in Negroids than in the other groups. The one figure for Mongoloids indicates this group may have very low values. Perhaps the extent of dizygotic twinning was at one time subjected to negative selection correlated with the seasonal rigor of the environment.

Geographic Group	*Population Sampled*	*Rate of Dizygotic Twinning per 1000 Maternities*	*Rate of Monozygotic Twinning per 1000 Maternities*
NEGROIDS	Ibadan, Nigeria	39.9	5.0
	Kinshasha, Congo	18.7	3.1
	Negroes, Jamaica	13.4	3.8
	Salisbury, Rhodesia (Bantu)	26.6	2.3
CAUCASOIDS	Greece	10.9	2.9
	England and Wales	8.9	3.6
	Sweden	8.6	3.2
	Italy	8.6	3.7
	France	7.1	3.7
	Spain	5.9	3.2
MONGOLOIDS	Japan	2.7	3.8

* Reprinted by permission of the publisher from M. G. Bulmer, *Annals of Human Genetics*, **24:** 121–25, 1960. Copyright 1960, Cambridge University Press, New York.

which show such correlation in some measure. One of these is the rate of twinning in the three major geographical groups. The figures reproduced in Table 6-8 are comparatively old and very incomplete, but essentially similar figures have recently been published by Dyer (1969). It should be possible to obtain considerably more data on this subject from various parts of the world. Despite the complication that the twinning rate is related to age (Figure 6-19), these figures do suggest that monozygotic twinning rates lie at the same low value in all contemporary human groups, whereas dizygotic twinning rates show a marked inverse correlation with predictable rigors of the environment in the three areas of the world where these primary population groups evolved.

ATHLETIC PERFORMANCE

Once considerations are extended from morphological characters which can be precisely measured, to less tangible and less readily quantifiable traits, one enters the realm of controversy. Among the least controversial of such features are differences among the major human groups in athletic performance.

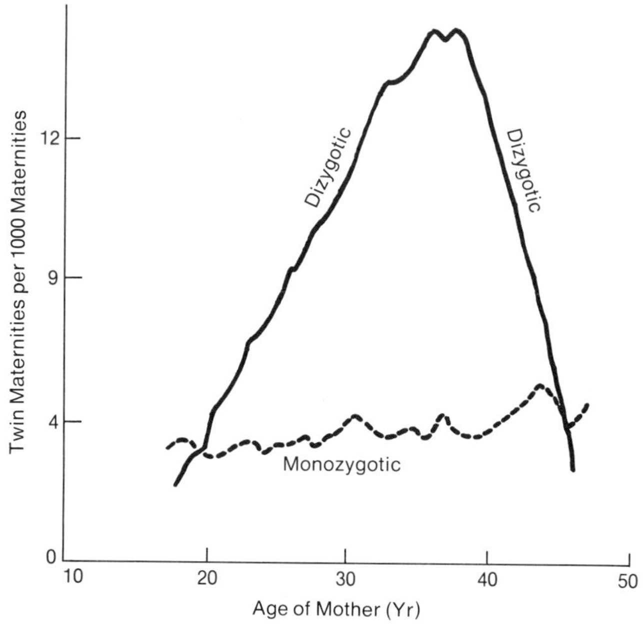

Figure 6-19. *Twinning rates* are affected by the age of the mother, insofar as dizygotic twins are concerned; the monozygotic twinning rate appears to be independent of the mother's age. This correlation will only affect the figures on geographical differences in twinning rates shown in Table 6-8 if it can be shown that the age periods of child-bearing are significantly different, which seems unlikely. (Reproduced with the permission of the author and publisher from M. G. Bulmer, *Annals of Human Genetics,* **23:** 455, 1958-59. Copyright 1958 Cambridge University Press, New York.)

Records of the Olympic games performances of athletes from many contemporary societies are now sufficient to indicate that individuals of Negroid ancestry are far more successful in the short distance races, the dashes or sprints (particularly those up to 400 m) than individuals apparently belonging to the other two major groups. There is no immediately obvious morphological or physiological explanation for this. Nor is the reverse true, that members of one or the other major group are more successful in the longer distance events. There is an added complication in respect to competitors in these long distance races, because when games are held at sites near sea level, the competitors who have been long adapted by residence to the more rarified atmosphere of higher altitudes are at an advantage. This is because they are conditioned to process oxygen at lower pressures. Through entirely unrelated circumstances there has apparently in recent Olympics been a greater proportion of such high altitude residents among competitors who are Negroid rather than Caucasoid or Mongoloid in ancestry, and a corresponding bias in the competitive performance of these individuals. The suggestion of a positive correlation between ancestry and performance requires a more critical examination than space permits here.

Athletic performance is still measurable in absolute terms. An extra-terrestrial form of higher life would be able to comprehend varying abilities in the time taken to cover a specific distance of the earth's surface in a given time interval. However, *cultural* features such as music have no such absolute values and cannot be detached in time and space from the populations for whom they are an expression of behavior ritual.

Musical Ability

It is tempting to generalize that Negroids are more responsive to musical tones and rhythms than Caucasoids or Mongoloids. Certainly among peoples of Negroid ancestry there are more musical scales known than between the other two groups combined. Caucasoids now utilize but a single eight-note musical scale and normally must be specially trained to adhere to that. "Tone deafness" commonly prevents many individuals of this group from detecting fluctuations in pitch up to half a tone away from these notes.

Linguistic Ability

This comparative lack of musical response may be associated with the absence of tonal elements in Caucasoid languages which are common in those of the other two groups. It may also account for the comparatively indifferent performance of Caucasoids as linguists. Many Negroids even today cope effectively with a staggering range of languages; A Negroid college student, for example, may be simultaneously fluent in five tongues. First is a home language, which may be quite different from that used in primary education. For historical reasons the secondary education will probably be in either French or English, but this is obtained in a residential institution, often in an area where the local *lingua franca* has to be learned to make a fourth language. Meanwhile the parental home may have been moved to a new area where a fifth language is the dominant *lingua franca*. Before embarking on a college career the student may therefore be speaking five different languages, varying in form from Romance, Teutonic, Semitic, and Bantu. Mongoloids not infrequently are presented with the same kind of necessity, Caucasoids sometimes also—as with the Scandinavians or the Dutch—but rarely contend with more than four languages, and these have either a Romance or Teutonic form.

MENTAL TRAITS

Next to diversity in skin color, possible variation in *mental ability* among the primary geographic groups has aroused more controversial interest than any other human attribute. Study of this aspect of diversity presents many other problems. First, it is impossible to provide a completely acceptable definition of intelligence. A simple statement such as "intelligence is essentially genetically determined, and heredity plays a dominant role in influencing its level in a given individual" becomes meaningless, because it is not clear just what is alleged to be inherited.

A distinction has been accepted between *intelligence* and *aptitude* (Guilford, 1968). In terms of this schism, intelligence had been defined as the ability to associate separate abstract ideas, and *aptitude* as the ability to perform particular specialized mental or physical activities. According to this definition, the musical and linguistic skills discussed above become aptitudes. At the same time it would appear that a certain level of intelligence is required before particular aptitudes may be expressed, as in mathematics. The most recent development of such a synergistic interaction is in the mathematical symbolism of computer programming. While there are good and bad programmers, many people lack either the aptitude or the intelligence or both and cannot even *begin* to do any programming. Considering the proportionately high wages programmers can command in advanced industrial societies, it may be surmized that until the demographic transition is quite completed, selection pressures will tend to increase gene frequencies for this ability, whatever its origins. It is also apparent that "brain drain" phenomena are tending to concentrate these abilities in regional centers (Lynn, 1969).

Measurement of Intelligence

Doubtless many sincerely impartial attempts such as the recent work of Jensen (1968) have been and will be made to define and measure intelligence, but for the present this would seem an unnecessarily disturbing approach. With the current stage of knowledge, "intelligence" could be regarded simply as an "aptitude," and measured as such, as Guilford (1968) suggests. That is, intelligence can be measured and rated as the ability to perform a particular type of mental exercise and *not* transfered from its specific context in relation to this type of exercise. It is unnecessary to attempt a measurement of the intelligence of computer programmers; it is sufficient to express a measure of their ability to program.

Aggression

Rather similar difficulties are encountered when considering diversity in another complex of traits sometimes labeled as *aggression.* There is an increasing tendency (Gilula and Daniels, 1969) to include under this heading not only violent expressions of human behavior, but also all the abilities to invent, innovate, "cope," and "drive." It would be a reasonable deduction that environments which are described as having a low predictability (Slobodkin and Sanders, 1969) would select for genotypes producing more aggression than those with a higher predictability. In the north temperate zone, predictability shows a broad inverse correlation with latitude. Of the 22 or 23 successive civilizations which historians commonly recognize in this portion of the globe, all but one have been overrun, or at least seriously threatened by barbarians from the north. The one exception is provided by the Moorish invasion of Europe following the rise of Islam. Northerners in Eurasian countries are frequently considered hardier or more aggressive than southerners. After a time, local migration of a brain-drain type may concentrate southern power in the hands of a northern caucus, simultaneously depleting the north of its most aggressive genotypes.

The level of aggression which an individual must possess to survive in a modern city ghetto relates to the situation of these possible north-south diversities. Movements such as the "hippie" groups may represent a social withdrawal from exposure to the more aggressive elements of modern society and the phenomena with which they may be associated.

During the long course of *erectus-sapiens* evolution, the persistence of such less aggressive groups in more predictable environments, with the greater leisure to innovate in other cultural directions which such an existence would provide, may well have made most important contributions both to the diversity of the human gene pool and to the store of cultural knowledge. Such considerations reinforce the obvious need to conserve as great a diversity as possible in human groups, and to resist cultural tendencies which impose a greater conformity.

ECOLOGICAL INFLUENCES ON HUMAN DIVERSITY

At the beginning of this chapter it was noted that if human diversity is entirely explicable on the basis of evolutionary theory as developed from a study of other organisms, it should be possible to detect the same kind of evolutionary phenomena as in these other populations. It is now possible to review the features previously outlined to see to what extent the diversity presented here may be attributed to such sources.

1. ***Varying Frequencies for the Same Genes as Between the Human Groups Considered to Have Been Differentiated.*** This kind of variation has been extensively illustrated here, and is consistent with the primary geographical grouping. Genetic systems producing such features as basic blood groups and rhesus factors are distributed with consistently maintained variations in gene frequencies between groups, even though no selection pressures can presently be identified. Where they can be, as in such traits as resistance to thalassemia, skin color, and teeth size, gene frequencies are clearly related to environmental selection pressures, not to ancestral groups.

2. ***Unique Alleles.*** A number of these have been mentioned, among them coarse hair and fatty upper eyelids in Mongoloids, steatopygia in southern Negroids, thick protruding lips in equatorial African Negroids, Negroid

pygmy groups, and Caucasoid freckles. Not all are morphological by any means. The occurrence of blonde hair solely in Caucasoids is of biochemical origin. Other less apparent unique biochemical traits are the Diego antigen in Mongoloids, the absence of cdE rhesus factor combinants in Negroids, and the presence of Cde combinants in Caucasoids.

3 and 4. ***Phenotypic Acclimation and Genotypic Fixation.*** Waddington (1957) discusses the circumstance that individual phenotypic responses to environmental stress are similar to the adaptations made as a result of selection pressures resulting from such stress. This has been illustrated by the density of *active* sweat glands in human skin. This will respond phenotypically when long periods of tropical residence are found to increase the number of glands. A higher density of sweat glands is also a genetic characteristic of equatorial Negroid populations. In a similar way, the amount of pigment in the skin will increase following considerable exposure to a higher ultraviolet content in sunlight. This also is a genetically determined trait.

5. ***Genetic Drift.*** This phenomenon has not been specifically identified here, because its major effects on human populations must have been far back in *erectus-sapiens* history. In these early times quite small migratory bands are thought to have existed. The early Mongoloid group ancestral to all Amerindians could have been, as has been noted, as few as 100 to 500 persons strong. From recent studies on groups as small as this, for example, on the Dunkers sect in the United States, it is certain that genetic drift would have occurred in such a band. Observations on this point have not yet been assembled in the literature.

6. ***Founder Principle.*** The same applies to studies of the founder principle insofar as it must also have affected these early migratory bands. The complete absence of the B blood group in Amerindians is believed to be the result of its exclusion from the sample represented by the original Beringian founder band. This blood group does occur in other Mongoloids, including Eskimos and Aleuts.

Causes of Diversity

In a text such as this, there is space to mention only the salient features of human diversity, but insofar as these have been considered, they appear to conform to the general pattern of evolutionary development which any widespread biological group would be expected to exhibit. While there is no difference in principle, there has been a considerable difference in emphasis. Evolution in *erectus-sapiens* populations, as is mentioned several times in this text, has related more especially to cultural evolution. It is the behavioral, that is, mental traits which have been especially and characteristically the material on which selection and adaptation have operated during the past 4 million years. We have no reason to suppose that such selection is not still a continuing process.

Cultural Evolution

The cultural adaptation which permits cultural evolution is very flexible indeed, and may occur one or several times per generation. In an attempt to define culture more closely, so that its evolution could be more critically examined, Huxley (1958) recognized three separate but overlapping aspects:

1. *Socifacts.* Direct behavioral acts such as rituals
2. *Artifacts.* Material results of socifacts, e.g., tools or music
3. *Mentifacts.* Potential behavior, assumptions, ideas, values, intentions, etc.; for example, "water flows downhill"

All higher animals possess socifacts, but artifacts are rarely produced by animal populations other than members of the genus *Homo*. Nevertheless, there is no great difference between them, one merely being the physical product of the other. Both types of culture can be learned by imitation; neither require either a society or a language (socifact) for their transmission.

Mentifacts, however, could not evolve before an effective communication language was developed. *Social learning* of mentifacts would also greatly accelerate the rate of familiarization of juveniles with accumulated mentifact stores. Once an effective language and mentifacts had become established in human culture, an extremely high selection value became attached to variants with a greater than average interest in them. Primates all show inquisitiveness, but intellectual curiosity in the form of *increasing educability* (Dobzhansky and Montagu, 1947) would be and still is a primary adaptation in *erectus-sapiens* populations. Morphological and physiological adaptation lagged far behind in the 4 million years of *erectus-sapiens* cultural evolution, but this was not significant because mentifacts and artifacts provided the adjustments which "biological" selection had failed to produce. It is possible now that continuing pressures, coupled with the size of the population, have resulted in the production of mentifacts at such a rate that they cannot all be properly integrated into global culture. Some resultant artifacts are accumulating as wastes, and no reducer or socifact process in our ecosystem has the information necessary to decompose and recirculate them.

Finally, a crucial point must be made about cultural as compared with physical evolution. The latter can take place only in populations and is achieved by selection which leads to adaptation within a population. Leaving aside those special cases in microbial groups where certain adaptations can be transmitted genetically from one to another, only the population subjected to the selection process will be able to adapt and thus evolve.

Cultural evolution is not restricted to the population in which it occurs;

any other population may *mimic* the socifact, *use* the artifact, *learn* the mentifact. The speed and ease with which this cultural exchange proceeds have attained such a value that in the advanced industrial societies possessing the modern artifacts which facilitate information dissemination on cultural advances, cultural diversity is more evident between generations than between groups.

This has brought to our modern world another threat of extinction of a portion of its human diversity. Those populations lacking artifacts to receive and utilize all this new cultural information will be unable to adapt by cultural evolution to the adjusted parameters of the abiotic elements of the new ecosystems. The very speed of our cultural evolution will therefore inevitably reduce some of our population diversity. The nineteenth and twentieth centuries will have witnessed the complete destruction of all hunting and hunting-gathering populations which were present when we entered this critical period. It is possible that the same inexorable fate may also extend to all agricultural societies, early and advanced. Conceivably only the advanced industrial societies, geared to the mass production of artifacts and the mass dissemination of mentifacts will survive into the next millennium.

Individual Adaptation

Any recent review of human evolution stresses population adaption, another vital change. Laughlin (1966), for example, states: "The crucial importance of the concept of population and of population thinking becomes obvious when it is appreciated that *evolution takes place only in populations. . . .*" [author's italics]. This is no longer true. *Cultural evolution now takes place in individuals.* The "fitter" individual has adapted to a changing environment, but not necessarily because of any trait which will be transmitted to a potentially larger number of offspring. The ability to adapt will depend on the individual's cultural history and cultural equipment. If he is surrounded by a suitable array of artifacts, has been provided with a sufficient store of mentifacts, and has been taught the socifact tricks of applying these, he will respond by individual adaptation to cultural change which would not even be perceived by someone deprived of appropriate artifacts. This fundamental change which cultural evolution has imposed has such far-reaching implications that this point will be discussed further in later chapters.

SYNTHETIC SOCIETIES

From this generalized and necessarily oversimplified account of human diversity, it may be deduced that during the approximately 4 million years of *erectus-sapiens* evolution there have been alternating periods of territorial stabilization and isolation succeeded by extensive migration, hybridization, and integration. The periods of comparative isolation in localized territories must have far exceeded in total time the almost cataclysmic episodes of migration and integration.

The most recent of these episodes resulted from the population explosions which were a consequence of the industrial revolution in northwestern Europe, which moved its previously largely agricultural societies into a colonizing phase. The subsequent migrations transferred Caucasoid groups into areas of the globe already inhabited by hunting-gathering and early agricultural groups of early Caucasoids (Australia), early Mongoloids (the Americas), and Negroids (equatorial and southern Africa). Return migrations were also promoted—Negroids into Caucasoid Europe, for example—as well as large-scale deportations, such as Negroids to early Mongoloid areas (North and South America).

Modern Migration Rates

A resurgence of nationalism among previously politically dominated groups, which was accelerated in the 1950s after the end of World War II, has vastly reduced the level and rate of migration. The position has once more become stabilized, each national group being within its own legally established territory. Some geographical regions have remained largely unaffected by the nineteenth century upheaval, and stabilization finds their populations little different in genetic composition from what they were in the last stable period. In the Scandinavian countries, especially Sweden, the genetic composition has varied little. The same applies in Switzerland, Albania, the Japanese islands, New Zealand, or Costa Rica.

Table 6-9 ***Ethnic Composition of the Synthetic Society of Honolulu County, Hawaii*** Estimated population averages for 1955–56 are arranged into primary groups and adjusted to the nearest 1000.

CAUCASOIDS		100,000
MONGOLOIDS		
Chinese	31,000	
Japanese	127,000	
Korean	6,000	164,000
OCEANIC GROUPS		
Filipino	36,000	
Hawaiian (or part)	63,000	99,000
OTHERS		12,000
	Total	375,000

Some islands, such as Hawaii, have received wave after wave of emigrants during this period. In Hawaii, an originally Polynesian people was infiltrated first by Caucasoids, then by Mongoloids from China and Japan, and finally by a complex of early and late Mongoloids, Caucasoids, and Negroids from the North American mainland (Table 6-9). Such a *synthetic society* affords tremendous genetic opportunities for gene recombination followed by selection of "fitter" genotypes, better adapted to such an environment.

The United States

The largest contemporary synthetic society, indeed the largest extensively diversified society ever known, is the 200-million strong population of American citizens (Table 6-10). There can be little doubt that despite modern medical care, welfare procedures, and tax differentials, selection is still operating on this massive gene pool to favor a greater reproduction or increased survival of offspring among the more "fit" (Reed, 1969).

The selection pressures in this instance have operated, at least until quite recently, through degree of economic success. For example, the high financial remuneration now provided major league basketball players permits a very big man, with massive food consumption and special expenses in terms of apparel, furniture, and other domestic appurtenances, to survive comfortably and afford, if he wishes, a large family. Previously such individuals existed miserably (e.g., as freak exhibits in a circus), and it can be supposed their fertility rate was low.

The number of magnificently coordinated and fast-moving giants in the United States is visibly increasing. The same selection factors are providing larger and faster football players; in the case of quarterbacks, at least, cor-

Table 6-10 ***Ethnic Composition of the Synthetic Society of the United States*** Ethnic origins are indicated by census statistics recorded in 1900. Figures expressed are thousands of individuals registered as foreign-born residents emigrating from the countries listed. It must be remembered that included in the other 66 million (87 per cent) of the population, were the surviving *Negroid* descendants of some 10 million Negro slaves brought to the United States in the eighteenth and nineteenth centuries, and, in the *Mongoloid* group, some one and a half million Amerindians who were the sole pre-Columbian inhabitants of the area.

Caucasoids		*Mongoloids*	
Austria	433	China	81
Great Britain	2,688	Mexico	103
Bohemia	157	Total	184
Canada			
(English language)	785		
(French language)	395		
France	104	Others	117
Germany	2,663	Grand total	10,046
Hungary	146		
Italy	484		
Netherlands	95		
Poland	383		
Russia	424		
Scandinavia	1,072		
Switzerland	116		
Total	9,745		

rect and fast response to strategic problem solving is being subjected to vigorous selection pressures.

This is the way four linebackers were recently described (Anon. 1969): ". . . . Larsen (6 feet 5 inches, 255 lb); his forte is an explosive initial charge . . . that opens the way for Page (6 feet 4 inches, 250 lb) and Eller (6 feet 6 inches, 255 lb). Both are extremely quick and boast exceptional agility. . . . The iron man who makes it all work is Marshall (6 feet 5 inches, 250 lb), [who] has a quality of balance as great as any man I've ever seen."

David might have had something more of a problem on his hands had he been faced with one of these modern-day Goliaths. Studies on the inheritance and number of offspring of individuals selected for these particular characteristics would be extremely interesting.

Selection for Aggression

In these synthetic societies—whether of the past, like Britain or Rome, or contemporary like the United States, Brazil, or Australia—one of the behavioral characteristics still subject to strong selection pressure is *aggression.* Gilula and Daniels (1969), as previously quoted, provide a wide definition of aggression, including the entire spectrum of assertive, intrusive, and attacking behavior . . . sarcasm, dominance, and "coping." They point out the complex origins of aggression, which may arise from selection, frustration, social learning. Creative aspects of aggression are usually described by the terms *drive, judgment,* and *intelligence.*

Boughey (1971) maintains that considerable selective immigration into the synthetic society of the United States is concentrating individuals who express strongly aggressive characteristics. These are attracted especially to the three areas of developing megalopoli, the southern Pacific Coast, the northeastern seaboard, and the southern Great Lakes. This local concentration of American citizens, he maintains, is supplemented with a brain drain of individuals with similar aggressive characteristics from other parts of the world (Fermi, 1968). According to Boughey, the higher gene frequencies for aggressive polymorphisms in such megalopoli will lead to assortative mating and the partial separation of distinct breeding units which may constitute the founders of a new species grade of *Homo, H. innovatus.* This will arise, or has already arisen, from cultural speciation. The new species will be characterized by a more stable and better accepted social hierarchy than in *Homo sapiens,* reproduction entirely separated from sexual intercourse, greater intelligence, and a harnessing of aggression into innovative and inventive directions. Individuals of this new species grade will possess the cultural equipment enabling them to adapt to cultural change.

Although he does not specifically say so, Toffler (1970) implies that *H. sapiens* has now reached the limits of his adaptability to an ever-accelerating rate of cultural change. The pathological syndrome which develops from overstimulation by the swelling flood of new ideas he labels *future shock.* Victims of future shock, according to Toffler, show symptoms ranging from anxiety, and hostility to authority, through senseless violence, to actual physical illness, depression, and apathy. They feel "bugged" or harassed and attempt various forms of withdrawal in order to reduce the number of decisions they must make. It may be conjectured that *H. innovatus* is being selected for variations providing a measure of resistance to future shock.

The gene frequencies of this new species will slowly introgress into the surviving populations of the *Homo sapiens* grade until this grade has passed to extinction. Meanwhile, all human populations of whatever grade are imminently threatened by environmental crises of immense, unprecedented proportions. These are a direct consequence of the removal of the feedback mechanisms which once regulated human population growth. The ever-increasing depletion of natural resources, the discharge of externalized wastes into air and natural waters, and the deliberate and accidental discharge of persistent poisons into natural ecosystems are technical problems resulting directly from either failure to comprehend, or a deliberate flouting of ecosystem requirements. Their explanation, effects, and possible remedies are aspects of human ecology which will be considered in the remainder of this text.

Bibliography

REFERENCES

Anonymous Extract from *Time,* October 17th, 1969, p. 62.

Ashley-Montagu, M. F. *A Handbook of Anthropometry,* Springfield, Ill.: Thomas, 1960.

Baker, P. T. "Racial differences in heat tolerance," *Amer. Phys. Anthropo.* **16:** 287–305, 1958.

Boughey, A. S. "The future of *Homo sapiens,*" in preparation, 1971.

Brace, C. L., and Ashley-Montagu, M. F. *Man's Evolution,* New York: Macmillan, 1965.

Buettner-Janusch, J. *Origins of Man,* New York: Wiley, 1966.

Bulmer, M. G. "The effect of parental age, parity and duration of marriage on the twinning rate," *Ann. Hum. Genet.* **23:** 454–58, 1959.

Coon, C. S. *The Origin of Races,* New York: Knopf, 1963.

Court Brown, W. M. *Human Population Cytogenetics,* New York: Wiley, 1967.

Court Brown, W. M. "Heredity and responsibility," *New Scientist,* **40:** 235–36, 1968.

Dobzhansky, T., and Ashley-Montagu, M. F. "Natural selection and the mental capacty of mankind," *Science,* **105:** 587–90, 1947.

Dyer, K. F. "Hidden variability in man," *New Scientist,* **44:** 72–74, 1969.

Fermi, L. *Illustrious Immigrants,* Chicago: University of Chicago Press, 1968.

Garn, S. M. *Human Races,* Springfield Ill.: Thomas, 1961.

Gilula, M. F., and Daniels, D. N. "Violence and man's struggle to adapt," *Science,* **164:** 396–409, 1969.

Goodenough, W. "A problem in Malayo-Polynesian social organization," *American Anthropologist,* **57:** 71–83, 1955.

Greene, D. L. "Environmental influences on Pleistocene hominid dental evolution," *Bioscience,* **20:** 276–79, 1970.

Guilford, J. P. "Intelligence has three facets," *Science,* **160:** 615–20, 1968.

Harrison, G. A., Weiner, J. S., Tanner, J. M., and Barnicot, N. A. *Human Biology,* New York and Oxford: Oxford University Press, 1964.

Hooton, E. A. *Up from the Ape,* Rev. ed, New York: Macmillan, 1960.

Huxley, J. S. "Cultural process and evolution" in A. Roe and G. G. Simpson (eds.), *Behavior and Evolution,* New Haven, Conn.: Yale University Press, 1958, pp. 437–54.

Jensen, A. R. "How much can we boost IQ and scholastic achievement?" *Harvard Educa. Rev.,* **39**(1): 1–123, 1969.

Laughlin, W. S. "Race: A population concept," *Eugenics Quart.,* **13:** 326–40, 1966.

Livingstone, F. B. "Aspects of the population dynamics of the abnormal hemoglobins and glucose-6-phosphate dehydrogenase deficiency genes," *Amer. J. Human Genet.,* **16:** 435, 1964.

Lynn, R. "Genetic implications of the brain drain," *New Scientist,* **41:** 622–25, 1969.

Mayr, E. *Animal Species and Evolution,* Cambridge: Belknap Press, 1963.

McClure, H. M., Belden, K. H., Pieper, W. A., and Jacobson, C. B. "Autosomal trisomy in a chimpanzee: resemblance to Down's syndrome," *Science,* **165:** 1010–12, 1969.

Newman, M. T. "The application of ecological rules to the racial anthropology of the aboriginal New World," *American Anthropologist,* **55:** 311–27, 1953.

Reed, T. E. "Caucasian genes in American Negroes," *Science,* **165:** 762–68, 1969.

Schreider, E. "Ecological rules, body-heat regulation, and human evolution," *Evolution,* **18:** 1–9, 1964.

Slobodkin, L. B., and Sanders, H. L. "On the contribution of environmental predictability to species diversity," in *Diversity and Stability in Ecological Systems,* Brookhaven Symposia in Biology No. 22, pp. 82–95, 1969.

Tjio, J. H., and Levan, A. "The chromosome number of man," *Hereditas,* **4:** 1, 1956.

Tobias, P. V. Personal communication, 1962.

Toffler, A. *Future Shock,* New York: Random House, 1970.

Waddington, C. H. *The Strategy of the Genes,* London: Allen and Unwin, 1957.

FURTHER READINGS

Ashley-Montagu, M. F. *An Introducation to Physical Anthropology,* 3rd. ed., Springfield, Ill. Thomas, 1960.

Bloom, H. F. "Does the melanin pigment of human skin have adaptive value?" *Quat. Rev. Biol.,* **36:** 50–63, 1961.

Boyd, W. C. *Genetics and the Races of Man,* Boston: Little, Brown 1950.

Brace, C. L. "A non-racial approach towards the understanding of human diversity," in M. F. Ashley-Montagu (ed.), *The Concept of Race,* New York: The Free Press, 1962

Brace, C. L., and Ashley-Montagu, M. F. *Man's Evolution,* New York: Macmillan, 1965.

Campbell, B. G. *Human Evolution,* Chicago: Aldine, 1966.

Dobzansky, T. *Mankind Evolving,* New Haven: Yale University Press, 1962.

Dobzhansky, T. "Genetics of race equality," *Eugenics Quart.,* **10:** 151–60, 1963.

Harrison, G. (ed.) *Genetical Variations in Human Populations,* Oxford: Pergamon, 1961.

Hulse, F. S. "Technological advance and major racial stocks," *Human Biology,* **27:** 184–92, 1955.

James, P. E. *A Geography of Man,* 2nd ed., London: Ginn, 1959.

Mather, K. *Human Diversity,* New York: Macmillan, 1964.

Mourant, A. E. *The Distribution of the Human Blood Groups,* Oxford: Blackwell, 1954.

Race, R. R., and Sanger, R. *Blood Groups in Man,* 4th ed., Oxford: Blackwell, 1962.

Roberts, D. F., and Bainbridge, D. R. "Nilotic physique," *Amer. J. Phys. Anthropol.* **21:** 341–70, 1963.

Sheldon, W. H., Dupertius, C. W., and McDermott, E. *Atlas of Men,* New York: Harper, 1954.

Washburn, S. L. *Classification and Human Evolution,* Chicago: Aldine, 1963.

Population Growth

7

The first six chapters of this book were concerned with the origin and evolution of the *erectus-sapiens* populations which have universally achieved a *sapiens* grade and now occupy the whole of the habitable globe. This chapter and the succeeding two are devoted to human population dynamics —the study of population size and structure, and fluctuations in numbers. Until the twentieth century the emphasis was on population fluctuations rather than population growth, if such matters were considered at all. Little account was paid to structure. The emphasis on population growth is of very recent occurrence, dating back no further in its present form than the early years after the Korean War. Even in literate societies many people still consider this emphasis misplaced; to illiterate societies the problem may be meaningless, although they may already feel the impact of our present failure to resolve it.

Until World War II any surplus population could always be accommodated on the appropriate frontier—the American West, the Canadian Northwest Territorities, the French Empire, the British Colonies, Java, the Belgian Congo, Manchuria, "up-country"—almost anywhere. Now the frontier is no more, the empires and colonies no longer the happy hunting ground for minor sons seeking fame and fortune. Such up-country as remains is barren and uninviting.

To understand why human population growth has so suddenly come to demand such alarmed attention, we must examine the size of *erectus-sapiens* populations as they evolved through the various ecological stages described in Chapter 5.

POPULATION SIZE IN THE PAST

The occupational floor which Clark describes for Olduvai *Homo habilis* (1963) may well have represented the base of activities of a single pair bond and their offspring. Among the King Bushmen of the Kalahari Desert Basin of southwest Africa, which possess one of the most primitive contemporary societies known, the band is still basically formed from such a family unit (Sahlins, 1960). The 1000 persons which comprise the Kung group are divided up into 28 *bands,* each of which is what anthropologists term an *extended family.*

A band might be composed of perhaps 17 adults and 14 children, comprising an older leader with an older and a younger wife, their four sons and four daughters, three sons-in-law, three daughters-in-law, two unmarried children, and 12 grandchildren. Such a nomadic band would occupy a territory of approximately 30 square miles (20,000 acres), if territorial arrangements did not overlap.

Population Density

The derived Bushmen densities (one person per square mile) are approximately the same as those of another surviving group of hunter-gatherers, the Australian aborigines, who—at the time of the continent's historical discovery—were estimated to number approximately 300,000 persons. The aborigine equivalent of the Bushman band is an extended family unit known as a *horde,* which usually comprised about 40 persons. A number of hordes together made up a *tribe,* the equivalent of the Bushman group, and an average tribe numbered about 500 persons. The size of the aborigine tribal territory varied with rainfall, the ecological factor most commonly limiting ecosystem productivity (Figure 5-1). Availability of marine foods also increased the population density of coastal and insular tribes, but it was the additional food resources of riparian habitats which provided the greatest increases in density.

The rainfall regimes of southwest Africa and Australia are not comparable, especially as the latter show variation of a continental scale. Birdsell (1953) quotes the widely varying densities as they relate to rainfall regimes in these two instances, and also as between Shoshoni in the Great Basin of the United States and Indians in central Baja California. Density of the last is more than 50 times that of the Australian aborigine, despite generally comparable climatic conditions. Aside from deserts and the polar regions, no part of this earth still has such a low population density. The carrying capacity for human populations has been forced upward by elimination of some competitors, or overexploitation of some resource, with a consequent overriding of the previous regulatory mechanisms restricting human population growth.

Trophic Relationships

Birdsell (1953) quotes a century-old work describing the food of Australian aborigine tribes along the southwestern coastal region. This illustrates well the fact that aborigine populations extracted all the food which could be economically obtained and prepared by the tools available at this stone-age cultural level from the several ecosystems they occupied. Arranged in categories according to the trophic level at which the human population had to function in utilizing each particular food source, the list of items eaten is shown in Table 7-1.

Table 7-1 ***List of Food Items in an Australian Aborigine Diet Indicating the Trophic Level at Which the Aborigine Populations Would Be Operating in Each Instance***

As a Primary Consumer (Herbivore)	*As a Secondary Consumer (General Carnivore)*	*As a Tertiary Consumer (Top Carnivore)*
29 kinds of roots	6 sorts of kangaroos	2 species of opossum
4 kinds of fruit	5 medium-sized marsupials	dingos
2 species of cycad nuts	9 species of marsupial rats and mice	1 type of whale
Seeds of several legumes	3 types of turtles	2 species of seals
2 kinds of mesembryanthemum	11 kinds of frogs	7 types of iguanas and lizards
7 types of fungus	29 kinds of fish	8 types of snakes
4 sorts of gum	All salt-water shellfish except oysters	
2 kinds of manna	4 kinds of fresh-water shellfish	
Flowers of several *Banksia* species	4 kinds of grubs	

Because in an ecosystem only about one tenth of the energy input is transmitted from one trophic level to another (the rest is dissipated in metabolic and locomotor activity and as heat), only one hundredth of the biomass is available when a human population acts as a tertiary consumer or top carnivore, compared with when it functions as a primary consumer or herbivore. This tends to make such items listed in Table 7-1 as whales, snakes, and dingos delicacies, relieving a fairly steady basic diet of roots interspersed with marsupials, fish, and other seafood.

Hunting-Gathering Carrying Capacities

During the Middle Pleistocene we can estimate, using such figures for population densities as those just discussed, that despite local overriding of regulatory mechanisms, the world's *erectus-sapiens* population did not exceed 3 million and could have been as low as 1 million (Table 7-2). The manner in which these communities existed is becoming more clearly defined by extrapolation from surviving hunting-gathering peoples (Lee and DeVore, 1968).

Special Characteristics of *erectus-sapiens* Populations

Throughout the 4 million years of their evolution, the species of the genus *Homo* have been characterized by three features which have ensured

Table 7-2* ***Increase in Human Population Density and Size Over the Last One Million Years.*** Improvement in efficiency resulting from cultural development of artifacts and socifacts is correlated with a slow increase in population density and size, but only the urban, agricultural, and industrial revolutions of the last 6000 years caused dramatic changes in both. Compare the estimated density for A.D. 2000 with those listed in Table 13-1.

Time BP	*Cultural Level*	*Average Density in Persons per Square Kilometer*	*Total World Population in Millions*
1,000,000	Lower Paleolithic	0.004	0.125
300,000	Middle Paleolithic	0.012	1.0
25,000	Upper Paleolithic	0.04	3.34
10,000	Mesolithic	0.04	5.32
2–6,000	Neolithic/farming	0.04–1	86–133
210–310	Farming/industrial	3.7–4.9	545–728
10–60	Farming/industrial	11–16	1,610–2,400
0–(A.D. 2,000)	Farming/industrial	<46	<6,270

* Partially from H. F. Dorn, *Science*, **135**, 283–90, 1962, by permission of the American Association for the Advancement of Science.

if not a high density, at least an always wide distribution. They have been what the zoo curator calls "opportunistic" in diet; that is, their food habits have never become highly specialized, and they have always possessed a considerable development of behavioral rituals which we call "culture." These first two features have interacted synergistically, providing a ready facility for rapid extension into new and previously unoccupied territory. The third behavioral feature is a *social nature,* which has ensured the speedy dissemination and adoption of cultural invention and innovation.

Consequently, by the time evolution in the genus had attained what is here labeled the *erectus-sapiens* stages, beginning perhaps 2 to 3 million years ago, the whole of the habitable world with the exception of the Americas and Australasia was becoming occupied and divided into nucleated hunting-gathering territories of varying size.

POTENTIAL FOR CONTINUING POPULATION GROWTH

Further increases in size of the global *erectus-sapiens* population could thus only be achieved by advances in what computer jargon labels "hardware" and "software." The "hardware" would be the physical equipment. Virtually no significant skeletal changes occurred in these last 2 to 3 million years of *erectus-sapiens* population development; it is only in somewhat larger cranial capacities that the physical equipment noticeably improved. Most further advances were achieved in the "software," the behavioral rituals which fashioned the cultural patterns, tools, and weapons of evolving societies, to which we have already applied the terms socifacts, mentifacts, and artifacts. The simultaneous enlarging of the brain supposedly supplied some reinforcement to this cultural evolution.

Carrying Capacities

Each cultural advance would permit an increase in the human secondary productivity of the individual group territory, thus increasing its *carrying capacity* for *erectus-sapiens* individuals. As the ecosystems contained in the territory did not receive any greater input of energy, this increased size of the *erectus-sapiens* population could only be achieved in one of two ways. It could be effected if there were a corresponding reduction in the size of competing species populations, for example, in the numbers of other top carnivores feeding on the same prey. Or it could be achieved by "mining" accumulated resources of the ecosystem, as when honey representing several years' production was collected from all the bees' nests in the territory, or all the animals of a particular species were killed and eaten. Increases in human population size were probably achieved in both ways.

Global Population Size

At the beginning of this *erectus-sapiens* period 2 to 3 million years ago, the human world population size is estimated at a figure of about 125,000 (Table 7-2). Two major cultural advances were achieved before the end of this stage, probably between 50,000 and 300,000 BP, depending on the region. One was the *hafting* of tools and weapons, which previously had been held directly in the hand. The other was the use of *fire* not only in domestic cooking but also in hunting. It is not yet certain which development was the earlier, but it is likely that their cultural spread was uneven, whatever their point of origin. The use of fire, for example, is not recorded in Africa until comparatively late, 50,000 BP; and the use of hafted tools in Australia appears to have been introduced about 15 to 20,000 BP. Tasmanian man, as previously noted, was isolated from the human populations of the Australian mainland before the development of hafted tools and did not independently devise them. Both these major developments of hafting and fire use in hunting could have arisen independently in a number of territories; it is not essential for them to have had a unique origin.

PLEISTOCENE OVERKILL

It is difficult to estimate the effect on population numbers of these two cultural advances, the use of fire and hafting, but no later than 50,000 BP there is notable evidence of their effects on at least some of the contemporary ecosystems. Indeed these might be regarded as the first evidence of the devastating and irreversibly destructive effects which human occupation has had subsequently and with increasing intensity on world ecosystems.

Overkill and Population Growth

During the time of this overkill in all continents, both food and water would have been in abundant supply, and the ample protein diet would have reduced infant mortality and extended the life span (Haynes, 1966). It can be supposed that in all the *erectus-sapiens* populations involved family size was large, and that the formation of new hordes and the occupation of any virgin territory was at a rate never again attained by hunter-gatherer populations. Birdsell (1958) believes such populations would double every generation. As shown in Table 7-2, the world population is estimated to have tripled during this period.

Such a population explosion must have been associated with the migration of hunter-gatherer *erectus-sapiens* stock into Australia as well as the Americas. The earliest reliable date on any *erectus-sapiens* fossil remains from Australia is 18,000 BP. Access may have been obtained to the continent before this, but not too early, for there is some evidence the dingo (a semi-domesticated dog) moved in at the same time. Early Mongoloids penetrating the Americas had no domestic dogs.

All these extinctions can be interpreted as the result of overexploitation of a food resource, which would establish larger and more vigorous *erectus-sapiens* populations than had previously existed. With the disappearance of much of the game, the same carrying capacity for the enlarged human population could be maintained only by assuming a primary consumer role and adopting a more vegetarian diet.

POPULATION GROWTH IN EARLY GROUPS

After these various Pleistocene overkill episodes, perhaps in some instances concurrently with them, the various agricultural populations established in the old hunting-gathering *erectus-sapiens* territories appear to have maintained balanced populations whose growth was regulated by a number of feedback mechanisms. These were perhaps the first *erectus-sapiens* populations which were *density-dependent,* and in which feedback mechanisms evolved which prevented utilization of ecosystem resources at a non-renewable rate.

To illustrate the kind of feedback mechanisms in such early agricultural groups, one tropical and predominantly vegetarian population is considered here, contrasted with a temperate and almost exclusively carnivorous group.

Population Growth in an Early Agricultural Group

Small isolated populations in moist forest areas of New Guinea have been known for some time to be head-hunters and have herds of domestic swine, while operating essentially on a "swidden agriculture" pattern of shifting cultivation. Rappaport (1967) has reported studies of one particular group

Plate 6. *Evergreen riparian forest* lining the bed of a seasonal river in Rhodesia. Rainfall in this area is low, averaging about 200 mm per annum. Crops such as sorghum millet, and in heavier rainfall years corn, can often be grown, but nothing in years of below average rainfall. Surface water is present in the shallow river bed for 3 or 4 months of the year; after that water is to be had only by digging in the riverbed. Nevertheless, this seemingly inhospitable microenvironment has supported permanent settlements of early agriculturalists for at least 1000 years.

of about 200 persons in which there is a cyclic progress through swine herd increase to warfare, to extended feasting and truce, and back to swine herd increase. This effectively maintains both the human and domestic animal populations at a level where no irreversible damage is effected in the microecosystems occupied.

The swine are not fed, but scavenge for themselves around kitchen middens, clearing up, among other items, human feces. They also feed in the moist forest. Whenever a sow farrows, as many males of the litter as can be caught are castrated. This reduces the number of boars to so low a figure that sows are most frequently impregnated by wild boars. The swine are not herded, killed, or controlled at this stage, and their number slowly builds until incidents of pig damage to gardens increase beyond a tolerable frequency. Formalized warfare of a highly ritualized form then breaks out between "offended" and "offending" parties, their relatives, and sympathizers. Some individuals are killed and others maimed in this warfare, which ceases when ritualized "honor" has been satisfied. Participants from both sides then join in an extended feast period during which virtually all the domestic pigs which can be caught are killed and eaten. When the swine herds have reached a very low density, the feast period is concluded, a truce is declared, and the group settles down to another slow build-up period for swine and human populations.

Plate 7. *Palm-wine preparation* from the palm *Hyphaene crinita* which occurs naturally in the riparian forest illustrated in Plate 6. The cut surface toward the tip of the stem of this palm exudes a sap which collects in the pot attached to receive it, as in this photograph. The sugar solution ferments because of contamination of the collecting pot by wild yeasts. The vitamins obtained from drinking this fermented preparation probably help to keep mortality rates in the permanent riparian settlements of this area relatively low. When most of the palm trees, even small suckers as here, have been tapped, the whole settlement moves a few hundred yards up or downstream, and the previously occupied area is allowed some years to recover.

The early agricultural "Sutu" peoples of these riparian communities have remained in this region for at least 10 centuries without overexploiting the riparian ecosystem or warring with other peoples.

The feedback mechanisms in the group which Rappaport studied were so effective in controlling both swine and human populations that a considerable area of virgin moist forest had remained uncut and not included in the "swidden" mosaic.

Population Growth in a Nomadic Pastoral Group

In contrast, the Bedouin populations of the Mideast are pastoral peoples with an almost complete dependence on an animal as compared with a vegetable diet. As recently recounted by Orians (1969), in the north Arabian deserts of Saudi Arabia the main food supply of the Bedouin is camel's milk, together with meat from male calves which are killed in order to conserve milk for human consumption. A single family unit requires from 15 to 20 milking camels for its maintenance. If cyclic drought reduces the forage in the territory of a particular tribe, this density of camels cannot be maintained. The tribe can therefore allow some of its camels to die and make good its needs by raiding or bartering with more fortunate neighbors, or it can resort to the same alternatives to obtain additional pasturage for its own camels. Either way a population control mechanism is likely to be invoked. Raiding will kill some male members of the groups involved. Bartering will lower productivity—or rather, slow the rate of build-up of net productivity—and probably, through an enforced postponement of marriage, reduce population growth.

ADVANCED AGRICULTURAL SOCIETIES

It is possible, as was described in Chapter 5, that advanced agricultural societies arose in two ways. Primarily they may have been derived directly under the influence of a barter-trade city such as Catal Huyuk. Secondarily, they may have developed through the superimposition of a trading function on a settlement in an early agricultural group. The founding of these advanced agricultural societies is estimated to have been associated with a rise in world population to somewhere in the neighborhood of 30 million. However these societies originated, it seems highly probable that, at least in their early history, advanced agricultural societies were independent of any feedback mechanisms regulating population growth.

Putting carrying capacity in terms of population density, Braidwood and Reed (1957) have estimated the increased carrying capacities which advanced agricultural societies were able to achieve in southwestern Asia as shown in Table 7-3.

Table 7-3 ***Estimated Carrying Capacities of Various Early Societies*** These figures, for density in a given land-use pattern, do not compare with the overall figures of Table 7-2, but related to Table 13-1 they suggest that Sumeria might have looked much like modern Egypt in terms of population density.

Type of Culture	*Population Density in Persons per Square Kilometer*
Mid-Pleistocene hunter-gatherers	0.01
Late Pleistocene hunter-gatherers	0.05
Early agricultural communities (circa 7000 BP)	10
Advanced agricultural community (Sumerian—circa 5500 BP)	20

Cultural monuments such as Mayan temples or Egyptian pyramids and numerous art works testify to the high level of net primary productivity which was available in this category of society for the expansion of cultural activities. It is nevertheless conceivable that this stage became a major hurdle for many evolving societies in all parts of the occupied world. Already some groups had remained at an earlier evolutionary stage, probably because environmental or behavioral limitations maintained a low net primary productivity. Thus Australian aborigines and Kalahari Bushmen were held at a mesolithic grade in the first successional category, New

Guinea settlements at the second. A study of West Africa illustrates the way in which many societies could be held at the third succession category of advanced agricultural societies.

West African Societies

The pattern of ecosystem development in West Africa from the ocean to the borders of the Sahara is closely associated with the rainfall patterns and regimes. Interaction between the conformation of the coastline, the Southwestern trade winds, and the cold Benguela current produces a set of isoclines of diminishing rainfall parallel with the coast. From an average total of over 1400 mm, the rainfall diminishes to as low as 200 mm per annum in the interior.

The first to observe the ecological correlations with this rainfall pattern was the French botanist and ecologist Auguste Chevalier (1933), who described a succession of forest and savanna zones (Figure 7-1). Subsequent workers have detailed how the human settlement pattern is intimately related to the ecosystem distribution with respect to these rainfall regimes (Harrison-Church, 1967).

The Moist Forest Zone

Until colonial times the moist forest zone was essentially a pattern of swidden agriculture or shifting cultivation societies. Many of these remained in comparative isolation in the category of early agricultural groups. They must have possessed population regulatory mechanisms; otherwise there would not have remained enough land to permit recovery of the forest areas which they cropped for three or four years before abandoning for between 15 and 40 years. They grew such foods as oil palm and *Dioscorea* yam which originated supposedly 5 or 6,000 years ago in this area.

Imposed on this swidden agricultural pattern in the forest were societies based on permanent settlements like Kumasi, Benin, and Enugu. They had become trading centers, the seats of tribal authority, and the focal points of political power for the advanced agricultural societies which dominated the forest region. These cities appeared to be in a phase of continuous population growth; surplus members migrated to form colonies in many other West African towns.

The Guinea Savanna Zone

The adjoining savanna belt to the north, the Guinea savanna, was scarcely populated, and there is still no entirely satisfactory explanation for this. It could have been because of the presence of human diseases, or animal diseases, or both, a seasonal lack of domestic water, or any number of other causes.

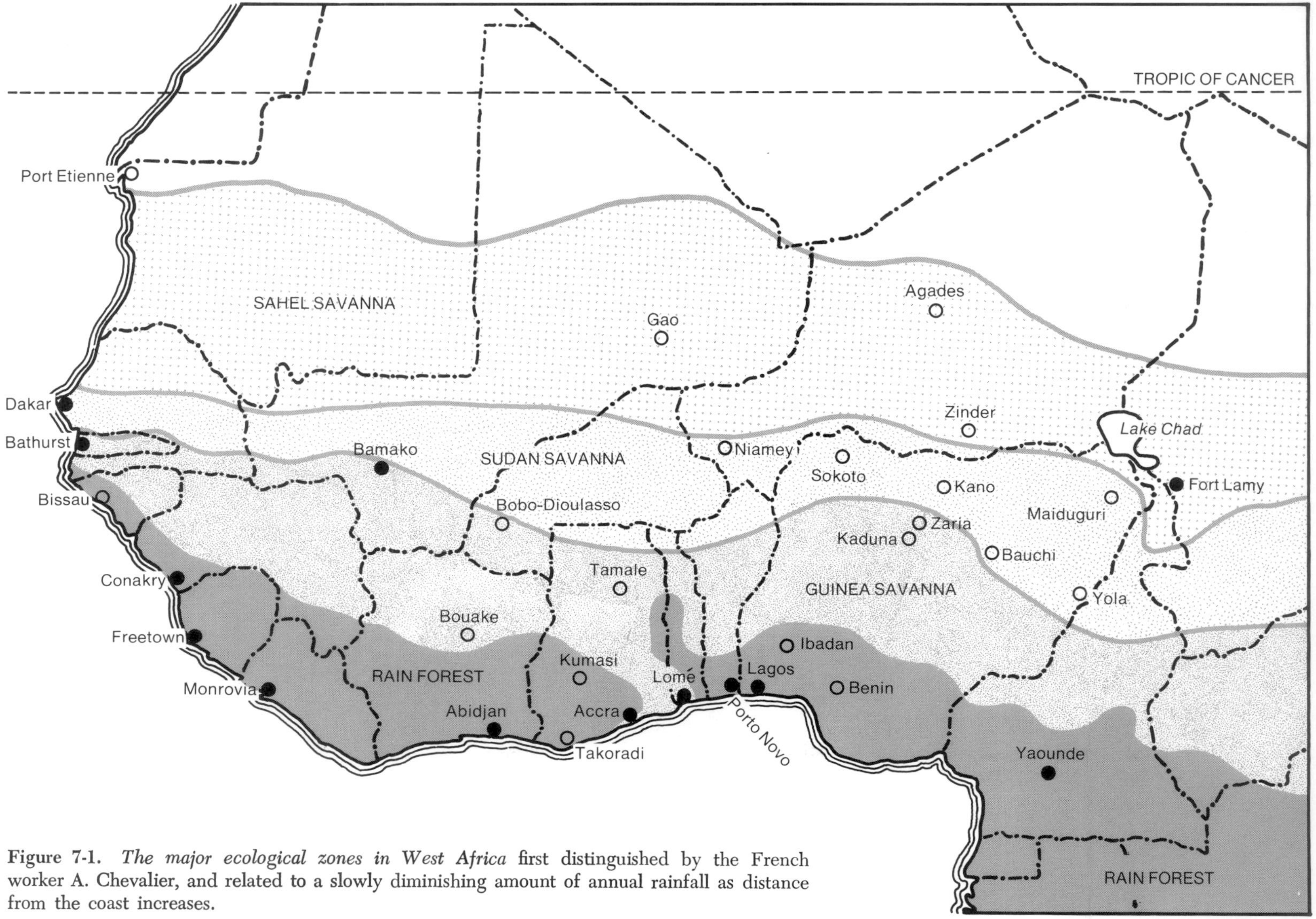

Figure 7-1. *The major ecological zones in West Africa* first distinguished by the French worker A. Chevalier, and related to a slowly diminishing amount of annual rainfall as distance from the coast increases.

The Sudan Savanna

The second savanna zone, the Sudan savanna, was heavily populated by sedentary agriculturalists practicing mixed husbandry. Market towns with a history of at least 1000 years were established there, among them Niamey, Kano, Zari, and Bamako. Lines of communication ran through the Sudan zone linking these towns and across the Sahara to the Mediterranean cities. They were walled towns, developed originally perhaps from such a pattern as originated in the Tigris-Euphrates valley, and with much the same kinds of activity.

There appeared to be no regulatory mechanisms on population growth in the Sudan zone. Although not yet describable as an industrialized society, this advanced agricultural society was already moving into a colonizing phase at the beginning of this century, and few villages or towns in the rest of West Africa lacked a "Hausa quarter." In such outside areas the Hausa handled the meat trade which distributed beef brought on the hoof from the Sudan and Sahel zones to the meatless forest zones.

The Sahel Savanna

The Sahel zone adjoining the desert to the north supported especially nomadic pastoralists, but included a few favored microenvironments along rivers and the shores of Lake Chad where permanent villages could be maintained. These pastoralists must originally, before the *pax colonia* of the late nineteenth century, have had population regulatory mechanisms similar to those described for the camel-owning Bedouin of northern Arabia. Raiding, local drought, and occasional outbreaks of rinderpest and other animal diseases would have prevented overexploitation of the Sahelian ecosystems. Now the Sahara desert is said to be expanding as a result of overutilization.

Modern Limitation of Population Growth

This admittedly oversimplified categorization of West African communities has been included to illustrate the problems which now confront developing societies, even when their net primary production is sufficient to permit a successional advance to a further category of society.

In Nigeria, the Hausa peoples of the Sudan zones are in a colonizing phase, but already their political influence over the whole country is resented and resisted. A federal prime minister from this society (Abu Bakr) was assassinated several years ago.

Advanced agricultural societies of moist forest areas are also lacking any population control. The Yoruba of Western Nigeria have inserted colonies into virtually every forest settlement in West Africa. The Ibo of eastern Nigeria, who had done the same in Nigeria, have been confronted with an intertribal power struggle which precipitated a genocidal war of distressing dimensions and consequences.

Unless immediate and drastic curbs on population growth in such forest and Sudan zone societies can be introduced, genocidal conflicts of these tragic dimensions are unavoidable. Meanwhile the habitats of these two areas are being changed irreversibly, as is that of the Sahel zone.

Growth and Stress

The inevitability of genocidal strife of one form or another would appear, in the continuing absence of population control measures, to threaten all advanced agricultural societies, which still accommodate a considerable majority of the world's 3 billion-plus inhabitants. Honduras and San Salvador make war essentially for the reason that the growth of the agricultural population has exceeded the supply of land. Trouble breaks out between Kikuyu and Luo in Kenya, which is discovering that the end of colonial rule has not solved problems of population pressures. Malay and Chinese-origin inhabitants of Malaya come into conflict; China and Russia stage a military confrontation over a relatively unproductive section of a micro-ecosystem. Emigrants from the West Indies and Pakistan, fleeing from population pressures, provoke color discrimination in Britain, a country with the longest traditions of liberalism of any extant society. A little nearer home, the central sections of all great American cities become ghettos for uncontainable multitudes of citizens of particular ethnic groups, tongues, or religions, mostly immigrating there from burgeoning advanced agricultural societies.

POPULATION STABILIZATION

This extensive preliminary approach to population growth has been inserted to explain how we, within a period of less than one generation, have been presented with a population problem which we did not immediately know how to handle. Indeed, we generally did not even recognize it as such until it was spelled out for us. For all these past millennia each human female had to produce on average five or six children; this has suddenly become far too many, and the rest of this chapter will explain why.

Advanced agricultural societies have to reimpose population controls if they are to preserve the net primary production necessary for progression to an industrialized society and avoid still further reduction of productivity potential by habitat degradation. Colonizing industrializing societies presently have no unoccupied territory available to accommodate their surplus populations; they must impose severe restrictions if their net productivity is not to be drastically reduced by overdispersion among too high a population. Advanced industrial societies are either multiethnic or multistructured, or both. Differential growth rates must all be equalized at zero population growth if city habitats as well as national resources are not to be irreversibly destroyed by a final overexploitation.

Global and national population growth figures do little more than give the dimensions of our world population crisis. There is a danger indeed that they can have a tranquilizing effect. It is easy to extrapolate from miracle rice and miracle wheat to how easy it will be to avoid the predicted famines for overcrowded populations of many underdeveloped areas. This tends to ignore the circumstance that such areas have sometimes been characterized by low productivity for so long that the people have been selected for, among other features, a small stature. For 2 or 3 million years *erectus-sapiens* populations have been penetrating into all areas of the earth, and with a few special exceptions like Madagascar and Oceania, by about 20,000 years ago they had entered all ecosystems capable of supporting human life, unless we are now to start living in ice caves, subterranean caverns, or skyscraper configurations.

A few advanced industrial societies have managed to achieve a population growth rate of zero; that is, they have simultaneously stabilized their population number and structure. To further illustrate population growth, we will examine the contemporary world situation.

WORLD POPULATION GROWTH

Various references have been made in the first part of this chapter to global estimates of population size in *erectus-sapiens* populations. The evidence on which these are based, which is always scanty, makes these subject to considerable margins of error. Even with modern census techniques, it is impossible to obtain demographic information which is completely without error.

Population Censuses

No regular population censuses were made prior to the beginning of the nineteenth century, although information on limited areas is available for periods dating as far back as pre-dynastic Egyptian times. Even about a century ago, a mere fifth of the world's population was included in censuses taken at intervals of not more than ten years.

Despite these reservations, it is possible to project approximate figures for global population size, and in a paper published several years before his death, H. F. Dorn (1960) supplied the statistics reproduced in Table 7-4. Some of this account of world population growth is based on the information he assembled in this paper.

Recent Increases in Population Growth

However such demographic statistics are obtained, they always exhibit the same features. It took some 2 or 3 million years for global *erectus-*

sapiens populations to reach a total of 250 million persons, a figure attained some two millennia back. By the beginning of the seventeenth century this figure had doubled, and in another two centuries it doubled again, reaching 1 billion.

Whereas the second half billion had taken two centuries to produce, the sixth took less than 11 years. At present rates of increase it will take only six or seven years to add the next half billion (Figure 7-2).

Forecasts of Population Size

When it became apparent that world population size was in this explosive phase of growth, demographers began to project expected increases. Dorn quotes several of these projections, including that prepared by the United Nations, which he considered the most authoritative; it is given in Table 7-4.

Table 7-4* ***World Population Increase in the Christian Era*** Until the beginning of the industrial revolution in Europe, the doubling rates for the total world population are estimated to have remained very modest; such increases would in any case be contained. The 1975 figure of 37 years is close to producing with each new generation an *additional* human population estimated to be greater in size than the total of all the people who have ever lived and died in the whole of our 4-million-year history.

Year (A.D.)	*World Population* (*Billions*)	*Doubling Time in Years*
1	0.25(?)	1650(?)
1650	0.50	200
1850	1.1	80
1930	2.0	45
1975	4.0	37
2013	8.0	?

* Reprinted by permission of the publisher from H. F. Dorn, *Science*, **135**, 283–90, 1962, and the Population Reference Bureau. Copyright from *Science* 1962 by American Association for the Advancement of Science.

From this table it may be observed that the world will double its population between now and A.D. 2,000. This staggering addition of between *3 and 4 billion* people is beyond normal human comprehension and must be broken down into more local increases to become credible. For example, the total increase in the population of Latin America during the last 50 years of this century will equal the total increase of population in the world prior to European settlement in the western hemisphere. The increase in Asia for the same 50 years will approximately equal the total population of the world as recently as 1958.

If the imagination boggles at such increases, it will be impossible to conceive the problem which a projected doubling of the world's population every 37 years presents. Assuming a life span of the biblical three score

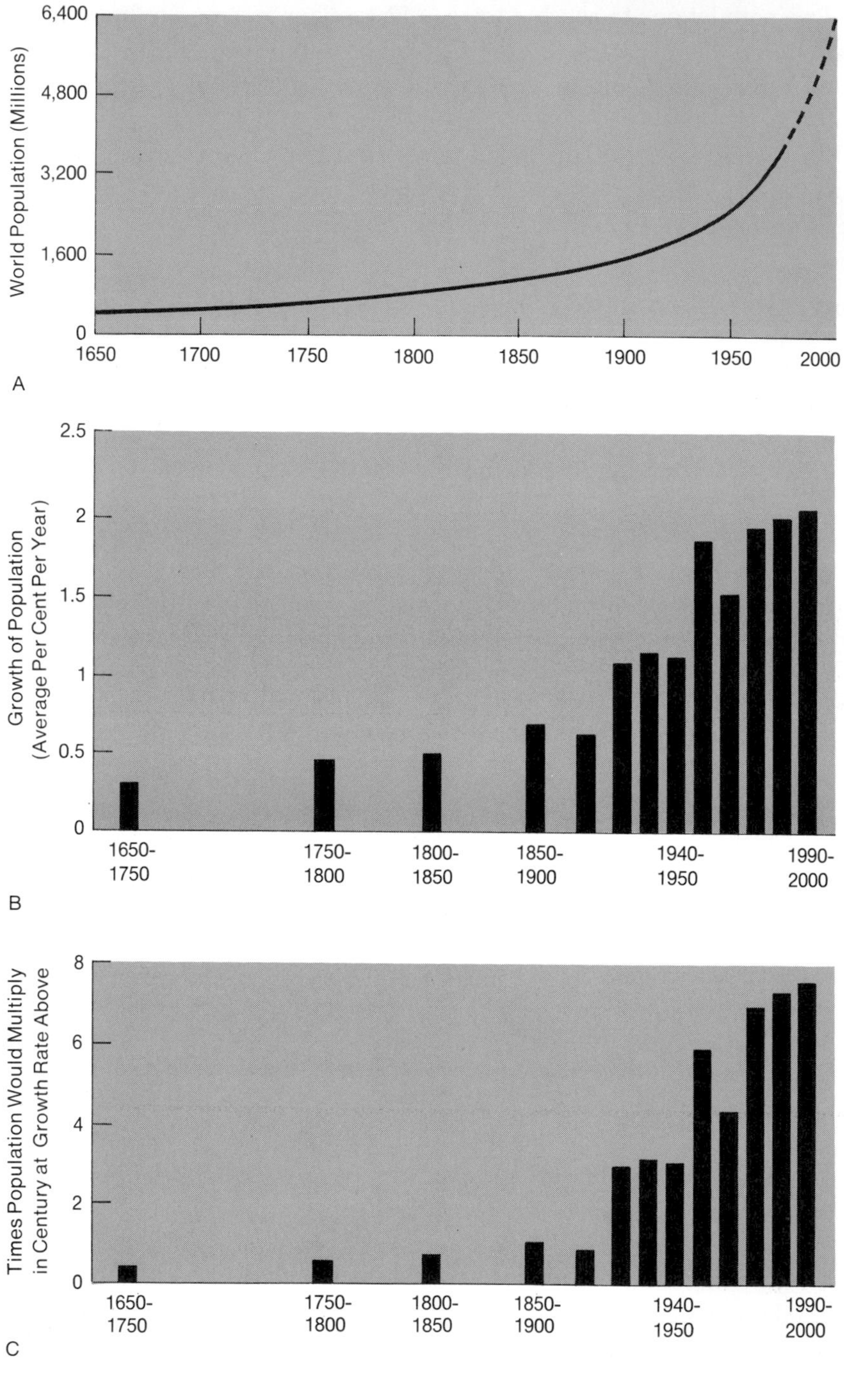

Figure 7-2. *World population growth between 1650 and 1950.* The first curve, *A*, represents the total persons alive at any given time. *B* shows the rate of population increase at various times, while *C* indicates the number of times the world population would double in a century, at the same time intervals. It is possible that the 1970 census figures when available and analyzed will show a slight reduction in the rate of increase and an extension of the doubling time, but unfortunately will inevitably have to record still further immense increases in the total world population.

years and ten, we each have to contemplate in our declining years as senior citizens not a carefree utopia, but a desperate scramble to survive on one quarter of the food and one quarter of the water in one quarter of the shelter in one quarter of the space existing when we were born.

To understand how this appalling world situation has come about, it is necessary to refer to some theoretical aspects of population growth.

FUNDAMENTAL CONSIDERATIONS OF POPULATION GROWTH

Population ecologists have long been concerned with the dynamics of population growth, and all standard ecological texts describe this concept and related terms. As applied to human population dynamics, the concept is very simply illustrated in the following way.

Theoretical Population Increase

Assuming that we are dealing with one of the occasional human situations in which consanguineous marriages are permitted (as in the Egyptian royal dynasty to which Cleopatra belonged) and that each such marriage produced two boys and two girls who lived to marry and produce two boys and two girls of their own, we could express the population growth in tabular form as in Table 7-5.

Table 7-5 ***Theoretical Population Growth in Initially Consanguineous Marriages Yielding Two Male and Two Female Offspring*** See text for further explanation.

Number of Generations	*Number of Marriages*	*Number of Children*	*Total Population*
1	1	4	6
2	2	8	14
3	4	16	28
4	8	32	56
5	16	64	112
6	32	128	224
7	64	256	448
8	128	512	896
9	256	1,024	1,792
10	512	2,048	3,548

If it can be assumed that there is an interval of 30 years between each generation, and that each parent survives to age 60 as a grandparent but does not become a great-grandparent, then in ten generations and in a time span of three centuries, the original pair have generated no fewer than 3584 descendants.

When plotted in graph form, this apparently modest ambition of raising two boys and two girls per family assumes a geometric rate of population

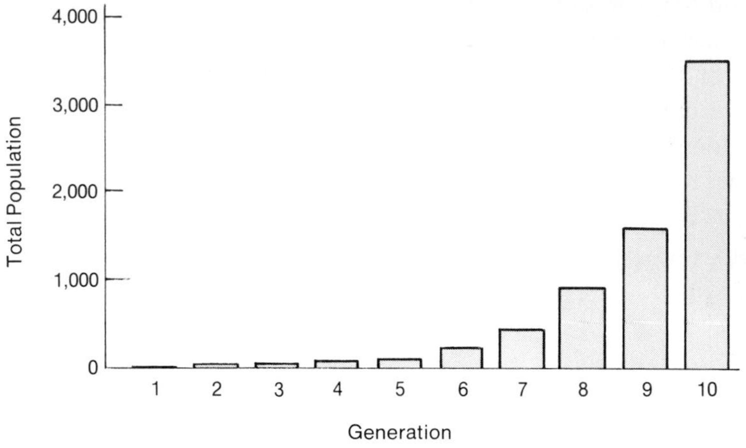

Figure 7-3. *Graph illustrating the rate of increase in the theoretical population presented in Table 7-5.* Even the medium fertility rate of 4.0 is sufficient, as can be seen, to cause a population explosion. As explained in the text, this rate is apparently still a generally *desired* value; probably also for much of the time and for a variety of reasons, it was also approximately the value of the *achieved* rate in our ancestral populations.

increase (Figure 7-3). The nature of this increase is defined by a series of parameters including birth, mortality, and natural increase rates.

BIRTH RATES

Theoretical Calculations

As defined for demographic purposes, the birth rate is calculated from the total number of births in a year divided by the total population as of the midpoint in that year, July 1, divided by 1000.

For the final generation of the hypothetical example illustrated in Table 7-5, assuming the number of births remains constant both through the year and through the 30-year generation interval, the following birth rate results:

Total number of births in 30th year = 68.3

Total population, midpoint of 30th year = 3584 − 34 (births) + 8 (deaths) ⟶ 3558

$$\text{Birth rate} = \frac{68.3}{3{,}558} \times 1000$$

which gives a birth rate per thousand of 19.8.

This figure for the birth rate is about half of what was considered even after World War II as the theoretical maximum. Demographers argued that out of 1000 head of population, 500 would be women. Of these 500, 410 would be too young, too old, unmarried (or at least unmated), or infertile.

Of the 90 remaining, 45 had just completed parturition and would have insufficient time to conceive and complete another pregnancy during the year. This left 45 in various stages of pregnancy or about to conceive, who would provide a statistic of a maximum possible birth rate of 45 per thousand per annum.

Birth Rate Statistics

In actuality a number of countries have been able within the last 20 years to surpass easily this theoretical maximum (Coale and Hoover, 1958). Dahomey holds the dubious distinction of heading this list with a 1969 figure of 54.

As already noted, comparisons of demographic statistics have to be made with caution. One reason underdeveloped countries feature so prominently in the upper portion of the contemporary selected national birth rates listed in Table 7-6 is that a high proportion of their female population is young and still nubile.

Table 7-6* ***Birth Rates from a Range of Nations About the World*** These are given per thousand of population. Many countries have now far exceeded what was until comparatively recently believed to be a theoretical maximum of 45. Belgium, with the lowest recorded birth rate, is one of the very few countries with an almost stabilized population (Table 7-8). The absence of any rates in the 30s, and few in the 20s is not fortuitous. Nations tend as a whole to adopt population control measures, in which case their birth rates fall mostly to below 20, or they have none, which leaves them up in the 40s and 50s.

Dahomey	54	Mexico	44
Sudan	52	Algeria	44
Pakistan	50	United Arab Republic	43
Ivory Coast	50	Uganda	43
Guinea	49	India	42
Tanzania	47	Hong Kong	21
Ghana	47	Australia	20
Madagascar	46	Italy	18
Guatemala	46	United States	18
Costa Rica	45	United Kingdom	17
Colombia	44	Belgium	15

* From 1970 World Population Data Sheet, Population Reference Bureau, Washington, D.C. Reprinted by permission.

Although reliable figures as to birth rates of the past are lacking, it seems reasonable to suppose this has not fluctuated by more than perhaps 50 per cent during the 2 or 3 million years of *erectus-sapiens* history. When life expectancy has been lower, there has been a correspondingly higher proportion of nubile females in the population. This circumstance has tended to maintain the level of the birth rate.

Theoretical Calculations

In much the same kind of way as in birth rates, for demographic purposes the *mortality* or *death rate* is calculated from the total number of deaths during the year divided by the total population as of the midpoint of that year, multiplied by 1000.

The hypothetical example of Table 7-6 gives:

Total number of deaths in the 30th year = 17.1
Total population, midpoint of the 30th year = 3584 − 34 + 8 = 3558

$$\text{Mortality rate} = \frac{17.1}{3{,}558} \times 1{,}000$$

which gives a mortality rate per thousand of 4.8.

Mortality Rate Statistics

There are several ways of showing mortality statistics, including age-specific death rates, expectation of life, infant mortality, and mortality rate as considered here, which is the total annual mortality rate per 1000 persons

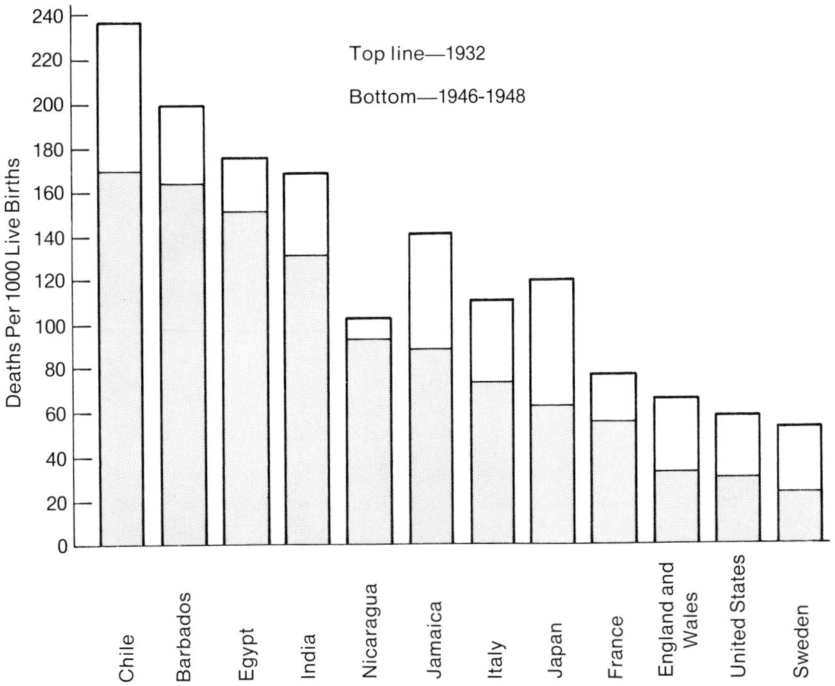

Figure 7-4. *Infant mortality* is expressed as the number of deaths of infants under 12 months of age per 1000 live births. These figures from a selection of countries illustrate that although the various disease-control measures introduced following World War II had reduced the rate in all countries, the effect was proportionally greatest in those countries with an already low mortality rate.

(Table 7-7). With regard to this last figure, records extending over two centuries suggest that in the eighteenth century this statistic, as far as can be judged, had probably not varied by a magnitude of more than one. It probably had varied by a magnitude of at most two over the whole period of *erectus-sapiens* history.

World War II focused attention on several discoveries which dramatically changed this situation on a world-wide basis. Sulfa drugs and antibiotics for the first time provided a simple but effective means of treating diseases such as dysentery, cholera, syphilis, yaws, pneumonia; DDT and other pesticides became available for widespread control of disease vectors. Their use is thought to have resulted directly or indirectly in the control of 70 diseases which include malaria. Immunization serums developed to supplement that for smallpox were individually effective against many bacterial and virus diseases such as typhoid and yellow fever.

Although these treatments were achieved in the modern industrial societies, they could readily be copied by all societies, and were. Dramatic reductions in the mortality rates resulted, the most spectacular being in some advanced agricultural societies, where these rates fell from as high as 35 or 40 in the 1930s to as low as five or six in the 1950s, as shown in Table 7-7, although the qualification in the legend of this table must be noted.

This dramatic and universal reduction in mortality rates throughout the world in the 1950s is the most significant individual causal factor of the present population explosion. The socifacts, mentifacts, and artifacts relating to public health produced by advanced industrial societies were dissemi-

Table 7-7* ***Mortality Rates from a Range of Nations About the World—per thousand of the population*** These statistics are particularly misleading, and no conclusions can be drawn from them without simultaneously taking account of *population structure*. The death rates in West African countries are high, but those in Hong Kong, Singapore, Cyprus, and Costa Rica are not necessarily low. The probability is that on examination these last countries will be found to have a very high proportion of young persons, who will not die so frequently. Belgium, with a virtually stable population, appears, because of this misleading feature of mortality rates, to have a medium-high rate.

Upper Volta	28	France	11
Guinea	26	Chile	11
Ivory Coast	25	Italy	10
Tanzania	22	United States	10
Kenya	20	Venezuela	10
Congo (Democratic Republic)	20	Australia	9
Pakistan	18	Ceylon	8
India	17	Costa Rica	8
Belgium	13	Cyprus (1969)	7
United Kingdom	12	Singapore	6
Colombia	11	Hong Kong	5

* From 1970 World Population Data Sheet, Population Reference Bureau, Washington, D.C. Reprinted by permission.

nated by cultural exchange at this time in the same manner as any other socifacts, mentifacts, and artifacts. Cultural exchange in the modern world has, however, become almost instantaneous—as rapid as the electronic waves of radio or television—and the power of modern culture to mass produce artifacts is immense. It is difficult to think of any other cultural adaptations which had such a profound effect on human populations, and certainly no other had such an immediate impact as these measures for death control. The only comparison is perhaps with the discovery of fire-making, and it seems to have taken some 300,000 years for that cultural advance to have spread to all human populations.

Although it is apparent that *erectus-sapiens* populations everywhere had gradually, over their long history, begun the processes of pollution, over-exploitation, irreversible modification of ecosystems, and annihilation of other species, the utter devastation we are now wreaking on our world will be dated by historians as effectively commencing in the decade from 1940 to 1950. This may be anticipating somewhat; first the effect of lowered mortality rates on population dynamics must be considered.

RATE OF NATURAL INCREASE

Theoretical Calculations

Subtracting for our hypothetical example the mortality rate of 4.8 from the birth rate of 19.8, 15.0 is the *rate of natural increase* for the hypothetical population in the final year considered.

The percentage rate of increase is therefore 1.5 per cent, the statistic most commonly quoted in demographic figures. When the birth rate exceeds the mortality rate, the natural increase is positive, the population is *expanding*. When the reverse holds, the increase is negative, and the population is *declining*. When birth rate equals the mortality rate, the natural increase is zero, the population growth rate zero, and the population is *stable.*

To provide some comparative figure analogous with the half-life of radioactive isotopes, demographers commonly convert the percentage rate of population increase to *population doubling time,* as illustrated in Table 7-4. This calculation involves only the standard method of calculating the rate of compound interest from a bank rate. In integers of increase, doubling rates are as follows:

Per Cent Natural Increase	*Doubling Time in Years*
1.0	70
2.0	35
3.0	24
4.0	17

For the hypothetical example in Table 7-5, with a rate of natural increase of 1.5 per cent, the doubling time is 51 years. Some current doubling time estimates are listed in Table 7-8.

Table 7-8* ***Predicted Population Doubling Rates*** Given is the year by which each country listed will have doubled its population, on the basis of present rates, starting from 1970. Costa Rica has the unenviable distinction of having led the field for a number of years and presently has an estimated doubling time of 19 years, unchallenged by any other nation except Kuwait (9 years), whose special circumstances must be regarded as making comparisons impossible. At the other end of the scale in 1969, Belgium, Luxembourg, and East Germany all tied with a doubling time of 700 years, which is a close approximation to a stabilized population. Unfortunately the latest 1970 figures indicate these three countries have been unable to hold this position.

Costa Rica	1989	Taiwan	2001
Philippines†	1991	Congo (Democratic Republic)	2002
Venezuela	1991	China (Mainland)	2009
Honduras	1991	United States†	2040
Syria	1991	Russia	2040
Mexico	1991	France	2058
Libya	1993	Italy	2058
Kenya	1993	Sweden†	2158
Swaziland	1994	United Kingdom†	2110
Ghana†	1994	Belgium	2135
Brazil	1995	Ireland	2170

* From 1970 World Population Data Sheet, Population Reference Bureau, Washington, D.C. Reprinted by permission.

† The U.N. representatives of these nations were signatories to the U.N. declaration on population in 1967 referred to at the close of Chapter 8.

Concealed Variations in Demographic Statistics

With these calculated values of birth rates, death rates, rates of natural increases, and doubling times, it might be imagined that sufficient statistics had been assembled for a valid comparison to be made between different populations, always assuming that immigration and emigration effects can be discounted. This is not the case.

For example, in the hypothetical case in Table 7-6, suppose that during the tenth generation all the mortality occurred not among the grandparents, as previously hypothesized, but entirely among infants. Without change in the number of children per nubile female, or in the number of deaths in the population, the birth rate then becomes 18.2 per thousand instead of 19.8, the mortality rate 5.1 per thousand instead of 4.8, and the rate of natural increase 13.1 instead of 15.0. Clearly, calculations of birth, mortality, and natural increase rates only have validity for purposes of comparison if they are made on populations with the same *structure* of age groups and in which mortality and natality are occurring *at the same age group levels.*

In practice, this is very far from being the case. Populations vary considerably in age structure, sex distribution, marriage age, life expectation, and differential age group mortalities and natalities. Any comparisons and predictions based on demographic statistics must make appropriate allowances for such variation.

With these theoretical calculations, figures, and qualifications in mind, it is possible to return to the 2 or 3 million years of *erectus-sapiens* history and understand how population growth remained so low for so long, and why it has suddenly moved into an explosive phase.

A nubile human female is capable of becoming pregnant and giving birth from the age of approximately 13 to 45 years. As gestation takes 9 months and conception can occur within two or three months of parturition, there is a theorctical possibility of an individual female producing some 42 offspring.

In actuality the maximum recorded number of single live births for a female is 24. There are many factors accounting, not only for the reduction of the theoretical expectation to this value, but for the usual occurrence of an even lower figure. For example, nursing an infant for a period of up to three years seems to be associated with a failure to resume ovulation following parturition. This factor alone reduces the reproductive potential from some 42 offspring to eight or nine. An average life expectancy of 30 years would halve this value, providing for a maximum number of issue per female of a mere four or five. Child mortality losses of as high as 50 per cent are not unusual, even in the contemporary world, occurring especially immediately after weaning. This could bring the maximum number of children per female down to two or three, and the birth rate would then barely suffice to maintain existing numbers.

Table 7-9 ***Variations in the Number of Live Births Per Female in Different Populations*** These fecundity figures vary considerably, depending primarily on whether the population has yet undergone the "demographic transition," the cultural adjustment of birth rate to a lowered mortality rate. The countries which are usually categorized by some such term as underdeveloped are inevitably the ones which have escaped from the cultural controls which reduced fecundity in the earliest forms of societies, and which have so far failed to complete this further cultural transition.

Cultural Category	*Live Births Per Female (to Nearest Integer)*
Hunters (category 1)	
Eskimos	3
North American Indians	3–4
Hunter-gatherers (category 1)	
Australian aborigines	5
Early agriculturalists (category 2)	
Sumatra	4
Advanced agriculturalists (category 3)	
Central Africa	circa 6
India	6–8
Advanced industrial societies (category 6)	
United States (mid-twentieth century)	3
United States (beginning of nineteenth century)	7

All these factors have operated in the past to reduce population growth. The general practice of a prolonged nursing period in many tropical African societies perhaps represents the persistence of a very ancient practice. Supposedly it accounts partly for the fact that numbers of live births per female never seem greatly to exceed nine in any contemporary society (Table 7-9). Similarly, estimates of life span at various periods of *erectus-sapiens* history suggest that until the twentieth century women died on an average some years before they had completed the menopause and become barren; even in some contemporary societies women predecease this stage.

Figures for infant mortality (Figure 7-4) show that despite the knowledge of modern hygiene and the techniques and materials available for use, some contemporary societies can still lose approximately one quarter of the children born alive before they have reached the age of 12 months.

Two of these three factors affecting the rate of natural increase, reduction in infant mortality, and a longer life expectancy are largely determined by the level of hygiene, which in turn represents the extent of health care available. This is most readily dispensed in an urban environment, which also encourages earlier weaning, because it offers both the baby food substitutes and the female employment which will induce the mother to leave her child during the day.

It is not surprising, therefore, that the massive reductions in infant mortality, the lengthening of the expectation of life to cover all the nubile years, and the shortening of the nursing period, all coincide with the industrial revolution and the greatly accelerated concentration of populations in urban centers. Nor is it surprising that both the colonial phase of society succession and the beginnings of our present population crisis have their origin in this quantum cultural advance in public health. The graphs reproduced in Figure 7-5 illustrate this coincidence between the demographic incidence of population expansion and the cultural process of industrialization.

There is a twofold reason the Western nations could undergo this industrialization and population explosion process a century ago without producing effects comparable with what happened in a parallel process in 1940 to 1960. First, the frontiers of the world were still open, and the excess populations could be accommodated in sparsely settled lands. Second, the actual proportion of the total human population of the world which these Western nations represented was low. Although their relative explosion in numbers was comparable with that which occurred a century later, absolutely their utilization of additional resources was not so extensive that the increased demands could not be met simply by overexploitation of existing supplies. We were dealing then with populations increasing by the millions, not, as now, by the billions.

One example from the many statistics which could be produced will

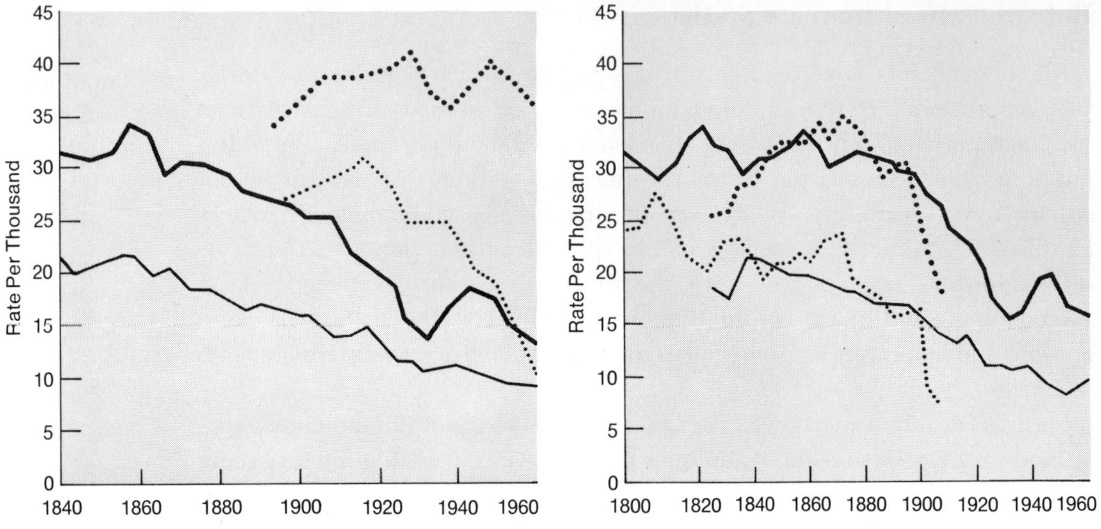

Figure 7-5. *Industrialization of societies and natural increase. A.* A comparison of birth rates and death rates between an advanced industrial society (Sweden) and an advanced agricultural society (Ceylon). Hygienic innovations improving public health following industrialization have reduced the mortality rate in both societies, allowing for the small time lag necessary for cultural exchange (outstanding in Ceylon is the resulting control of malaria, associated with a fall in the death rate from 22 in 1945 to 9 in 1963). However, the desire for fewer children or the cultural knowledge of how to achieve this, which has also depressed the birth rate in the industrialized society, has scarcely affected that of the agricultural society. In *B* which compares an advanced industrialized society (Scandinavia) with one in which succession to this stage occurred approximately half a century later (Japan), the birth rate and the mortality rate are in this instance simultaneously declining. In the year 1955, at the peak of the population decline which proceeded in Japan from 1947 until the early 1960s, some 1,200,000 legal abortions were performed (Taeuber, 1958), halving the population growth. It appears that the stimulus of succession to an advanced industrial stage is necessary to initiate a decline in the birth rate in advanced agricultural societies. (From Kingsley Davis, "Population," *Scientific American,* **209**[3]: 68, 70, 1963. Copyright © 1963 by Scientific American, Inc. All rights reserved.)

serve to illustrate the dramatic effects of the post-World War II reduction in mortality on the rate of natural increase. In Table 7-10 are shown the main population statistics for India at intervals during this century. Remarkably under the circumstances, the birth rate continues to rise. So therefore does the rate of natural increase, although the recent upward trend of the mortality rate, if real, will reduce this in future years.

The actual family size which India has to attain if it is to achieve zero population growth at present death rates may be estimated from the theoretical figures in Table 7-10 at about 2.5 children per female. This statistic, known as the *fecundity rate,* is somewhat confusing on first sight. It might be considered that a fecundity rate of precisely two would in an ideal world maintain a zero population growth; however, it will do so only in a population with a mature structure. Because of the dramatic reductions in

Table 7-10* ***Population Growth in India*** During this century, the birth rate has remained constant, fluctuating about a mean, while the death rate has fallen almost two thirds. The population growth has increased over 2000 per cent since the beginning of the century.

Census Year	*Total Population in Millions*	*Birth Rate*	*Death Rate*	*Rate of Natural Increase Percentage*
1901	236	46	44	0.1
1911	249	51	43	0.8
1921	248	49	48	0.1
1931	276	46	36	1.0
1941	313	45	31	1.4
1951	357	39	27	1.3
1961	439	40	21	1.9
1965	490	41	17	2.4
1969	537	43	18	2.5

* Partially from Makeshwari, *Science and Culture,* **32:** 104–14, 1966.

mortality rates over the past 30 years, the population in many underdeveloped nations contains a disproportionate number of young people. A birth rate based on a figure-per-thousand population is not then offset as much as it should be by a given death rate, because, being younger, many do not die when they should according to the mortality statistic. Thus India, with a death rate down to 17 or 18, should not permit a fecundity rate higher than 2.5. Hong Kong and Singapore, with death rates down to five (Table 7-7), will have to attain a fecundity rate of 0.7 to stabilize their populations at zero growth. This is tantamount to having three girls in ten remaining single while the rest get married and have one child each, and it is understandable that no society presently could contemplate discouraging child-bearing to this extent.

Table 7-11 ***Zero Population Growth in Terms of the Number of Offspring*** Assuming that in a sample population of 1000, 200 are nubile females—and making several other smaller assumptions to simplify the calculation—the following levels of fecundity would be necessary to maintain zero population growth at the given mortality rates.

When Mortality Rate Reaches This Figure	*Birth Rate to Maintain Zero Population Growth Must Be*	*Fecundity (Number of Offspring Per Female) to Provide This Birth Rate Is*
45	45	6.7
35	35	5.2
25	25	3.7
15	15	2.2
10	10	1.5
5	5	0.7

A fecundity rate of a little over two is therefore only compatible with zero population growth when the mortality rate is at least 15 per thousand. As can be seen from Table 7-7 all advanced industrialized societies are already below this figure; the others shortly will be. Very soon two will definitely *not* suffice for India and many others.

Table 7-12* ***Rate of Natural Increase from a Range of Nations About the World Together with Their Birth and Death Rates*** Countries such as the Ivory Coast with very high birth rates have an average increase because their death rate is still high. When this is drastically reduced, even a low birth rate is too much, as seen by contrasting the statistics for Ghana and Singapore, which have the same rate of increase. Belgium has achieved rates which give it virtually a stable population, but the statistics for Kuwait (52:6:4.6) are considered so exceptional it would be misleading to put them in the main body of the table.

	Birth Rate	*Death Rate*	*Natural Increase*		*Birth Rate*	*Death Rate*	*Natural Increase*
Costa Rica	45	8	3.8	Taiwan	29	6	2.3
Colombia	44	11	3.4	Australia	20	9.1	1.9
Mexico	44	10	3.4	China (Mainland)	34	1.5	1.8
Kenya	50	20	3.1	Japan	19	7	1.1
Zambia	51	20	3.0	United States	17.6	9.6	1.0
Ghana	47	20	2.9	Cyprus	25	7	0.9
United Arab Republic	43	15	2.8	Sweden	14.3	10.4	0.8
Ivory Coast	50	25	2.4	Italy	17.6	10.1	0.8
Ceylon	32	8	2.4	United Kingdom	17.1	11.9	0.5
Singapore	25	6	2.4	Belgium	14.8	12.8	0.4

From 1970 World Population Data Sheet. Population Reference Bureau, Washington, D.C. Reprinted by permission.

The rates of natural increase for a range of other countries, together with the birth and death rates, are shown in Table 7-12.

POPULATION STRUCTURE

These crude rates as explained here need further sophistication before they can be used accurately to describe a given human population. One of the obvious deficiencies is that they take no account of population structure.

In the theoretical example previously discussed, it is known that half the children produced are male, half female, and that all survive to an age of somewhere between 60 and 90 years. It is then possible to construct dia-

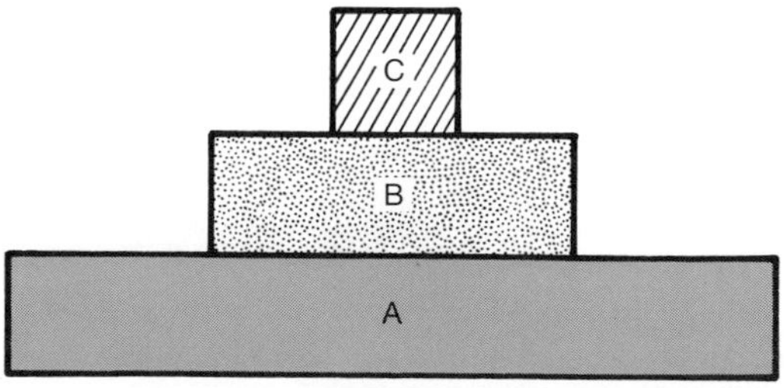

Figure 7-6. *Population structure* as developed from the theoretical example illustrated in Table 7-5 and Figure 7-3. The population is divided into three categories only: (*A*) infants and juveniles, (*B*) reproductive adults, (*C*) postreproductive adults. The numbers of the first class far exceed those of the second, so that unless a very high mortality rate occurs there, the population has to be unbalanced and experiencing a high rate of natural increase.

grams (Figure 7-6) illustrating the number of males and females in three categories as follows:

1. Children (0–13 years)—male and female
2. Adults (14–44 years)—male and female (*nubile* females)
3. Old people (45–90)—male and female

The diagram in Figure 7-6 shows what a balanced population structure looks like. If, on the other hand, one third of the old folk were to live to between 90 and 120, and as a consequence there was a reduction of one third in the birth rate for a generation, the pyramid would have the form, as shown in the illustration, of a declining population (Figure 7-7). Should all the adults die at 45, and a consequent increase occur of one third in the birth rate, the pyramid would have the form of a young and unstable population, as is also shown (Figure 7-7).

It is more usual to express such diagrams of population structure in intervals of five years, with males on the left and females on the right of the diagram. In Figure 7-7 three typical diagrams are shown, illustrating stable, expanding, and declining populations. The usefulness of this method of

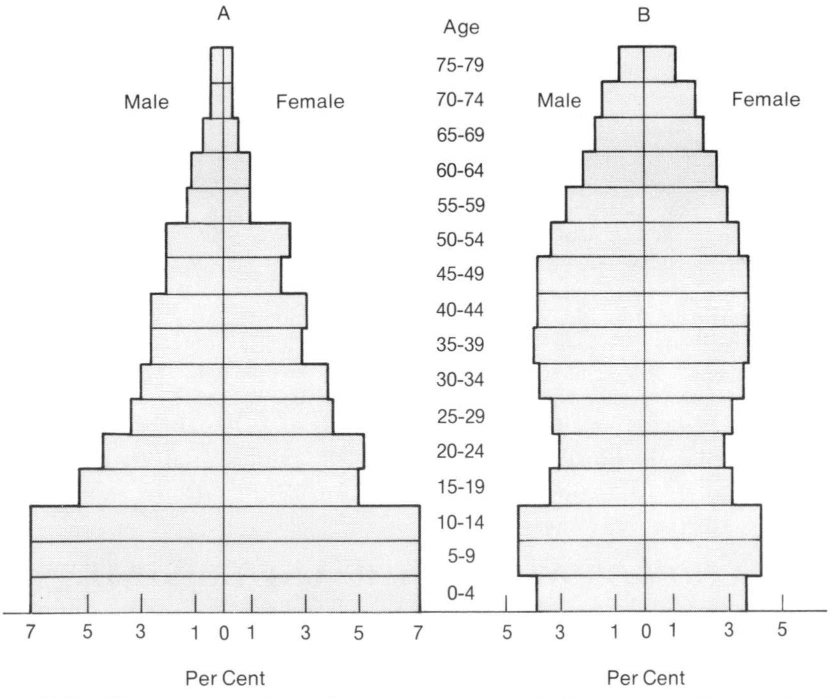

Figure 7-7. *The structure of actual populations:* that of Algeria in 1954 in *A*, Sweden in 1955 in *B*. At this time the first three age classes in the Algerian population considerably exceeded the size of the reproductive classes—this population was increasing rapidly. The Swedish population, by contrast, was declining. The first age class and also the 15–19, 20–24, and 25–29 classes were smaller than their predecessors, so that even without any mortality at all, the reproductive section of the population was being reduced in numbers. (Reproduced with the permission of the publisher from H. F. Dorn, *Science*, **135**: 288, 1962. Copyright 1962 by the American Association for the Advancement of Science.)

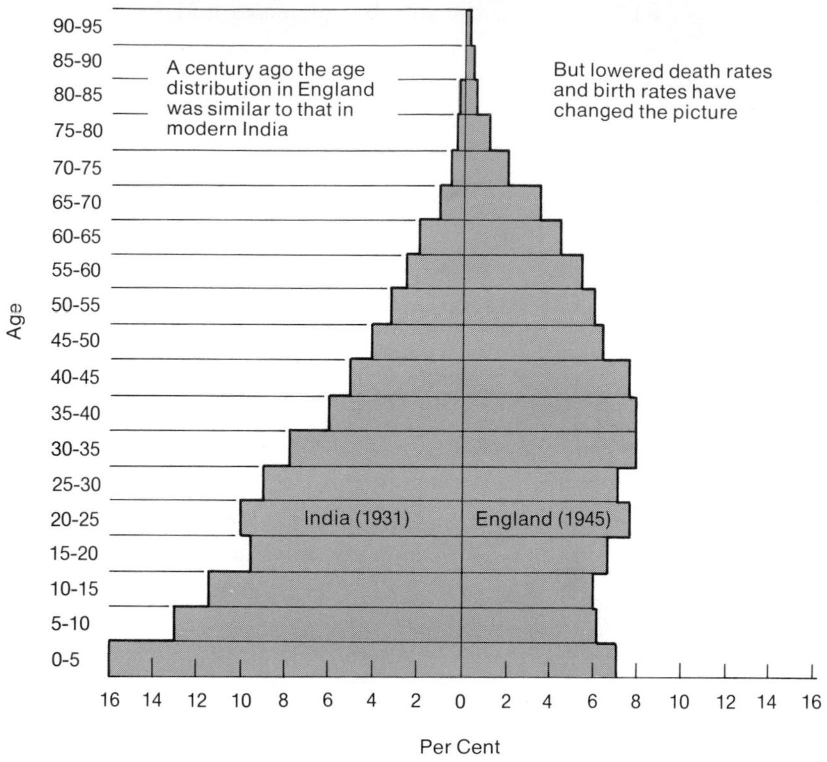

Figure 7-8. *Comparison of the population structure of an expanding population* (India—1931) *with a stabilizing one* (England—1945). Each age class in the Indian population, with one exception, so far exceeds its immediate predecessor of the previous 5-year interval that unless very considerable mortality occurs at each level, the whole population must have substantially larger numbers in 5 years' time, as indicated by the dotted line projections. The English population, by contrast, shows the effects of the declining birth rate first associated with the financial depression of the early 1930s which continued until World War II even after economic recovery had been achieved. The numbers in the younger age classes do not provide for the maintenance of the age class numbers in the middle-age classes, even when no mortality occurs in these intermediate classes. (After H. Brown, 1954, with the permission of the publisher.)

graphic display is illustrated in Figure 7-8, which analyzes further the demographic statistics for India contained in Table 7-10.

POPULATION GROWTH IN THE UNITED STATES

It is appropriate at this point to look critically at the recent demography of the United States' population. There are several reasons why this provides extremely valuable information. First, many individuals—particularly academics such as Garrett Hardin (1969), Paul Ehrlich (1968), and Georg Borgstrom (1969)—are not only publishing semipopular works dealing with the population crisis, but are also vigorously engaged in lecture and seminar programs specifically focused on the necessity of achieving world population stability. Moreover, virtually every science conference held in this country now passes resolutions urging population control. Second, and the papers about to be discussed provide evidence on this point, both birth control literature and birth control devices are more readily and universally available in the United States than in any other population of comparable size. Finally, this country's population presently forms an incompletely integrated mosaic of ethnic, religious, and economic groups, illustrating the immense complexity of demographic studies and the difficulty of summarizing observable trends in population growth and behavior on a national basis.

The Birth Rate in the United States

Every 8½ seconds a child is born in the United States; every minute a new immigrant is admitted. Every 17 seconds there is a death, and every 23 seconds an emigrant leaves. This is a somewhat flamboyant expression of the rate of population growth, which presently is very close to 1 per cent per year and provides for a doubling of the population every 70 years. The statistics are shown graphically in Figure 7-9.

Fertility Rate

Another commonly used demographic statistic should be introduced, the *fertility rate*. This is the number of live births per year occurring per 1000 females aged 15 to 44. In a detailed analytical study this provides a more reliable figure as the effects of fluctuations which confound the crude statistics, such as changes in population structure, are minimized. Recent levels of the fertility rate in the United States are illustrated in Figure 7-10.

Fluctuations in the American fertility rate in the past are illustrated in Figure 7-10. The lowest point previously recorded was in 1936, with figures of 73.3 for white, and 95.9 for nonwhite women. After rising again to a peak of 117.7 and 163.0, respectively, in 1957 the fertility rate fell to an estimated 77 and 115, respectively, in 1969. Combining both white and nonwhite, this would be a fertility rate of 123 in 1957 and 82 in 1968, very close to the figure for 1936 in the depression years.

There is yet no full explanation for these fluctuations, which contradicted all demographic forecasts. Advanced industrial societies now appear to have developed an economic feedback mechanism for population control which Boughey (1971) has called the Madison Avenue effect. This is discussed later.

Ethnic Differences in Birth Rate

The fertility rates for the United States quoted above are higher for nonwhites. Most probably economic factors are included in what is bound to be the very complex reason for these differences. These are considered further in the next two chapters. One of the few pleasures available to a woman in a miserably poor agricultural community or a desperately over-

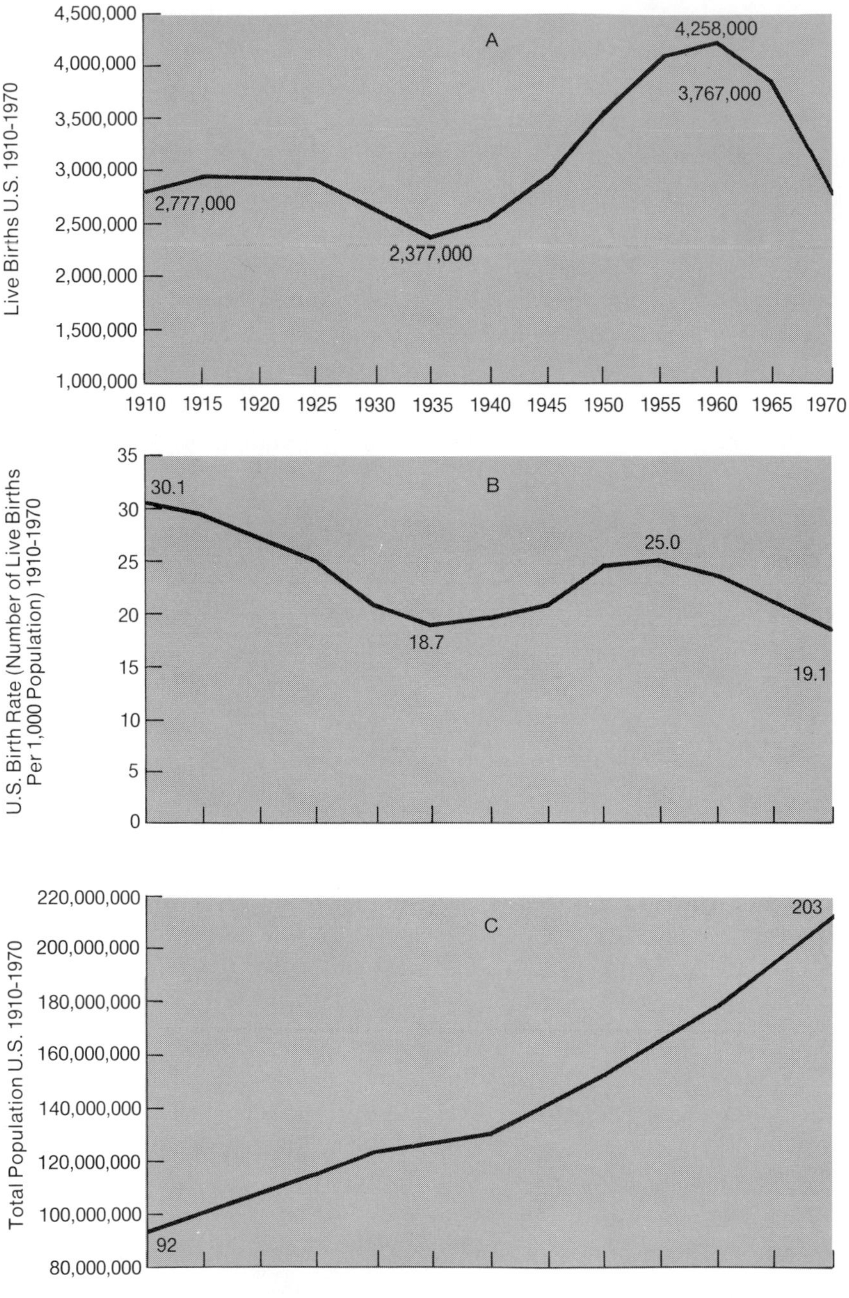

Figure 7-9. *The population of the United States.* Three ways of expressing population growth in this country projected through to 1970. In *A* are expressed the total number of live births, which has fallen since its peak in 1960, but is still well above the 1935 low. In *B* it is shown that the actual birth rate is expected to fall below the 1935 all-time low. Despite the declining number of births whichever way they are recorded, the total population size will continue to rise steeply (*C*) unless some more drastic curtailment of births occurs.

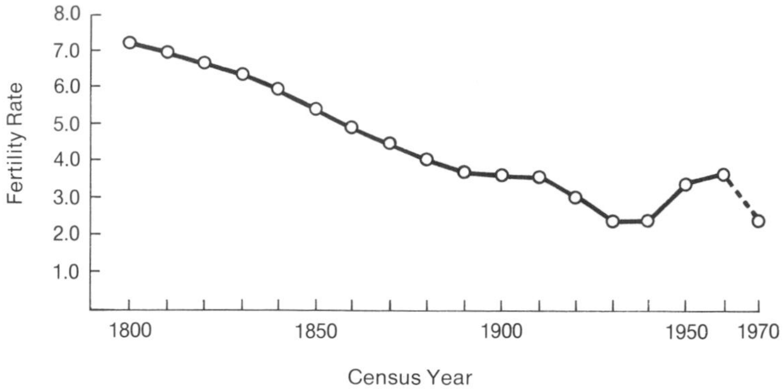

Figure 7-10. *The fertility rate in the United States.* The average number of live births occurring per female between the ages of 15 and 45 provides a more accurate statement of the amount of reproduction occurring in the population than the statistics illustrated in Figure 7-9. The fertility rate in the United States is now at an unprecedented low value and may be expected to continue to fall in response to the various socioeconomic pressures now in force, which are discussed further in the text.

crowded city ghetto appears to come through the tactile stimuli of handling her own offspring. As soon as one infant has passed beyond the fondling stage, she will get herself pregnant again to provide for this unique enjoyment. No amount of propaganda or availability of free clinics supplying contraceptive and abortion services will awaken any interest or response, and it is ludicrous under these circumstances to expect one.

The position of the United States in regard to population growth has been well expressed in the President's message on population control to Congress on July 18, 1969, the main points of which are reiterated here.

Rate of Population Growth in the United States

While the present rate of population growth of 1 per cent is the result of a decline which began in the eighteenth century (the first census in 1790 gave a figure of 3.9 million), and this rate of increase is certainly well below the world average, it is still a significant figure. Factors which tend to prevent a further decline to zero population growth include the large proportion of women of childbearing age, the desire for a particular family size, and increased longevity.

It took 300 years for the population of the United States to exceed 100 million, in 1917, but the next 100 million was added in 50 years. Even at the present declining growth rate, the third 100 million will be added by A.D. 2000 (Figure 7-11).

Location of Increased Population

Of the third 100 million, it is estimated that 75 million will live in urban areas. Reviewing this situation, the National Commission on Urban Growth

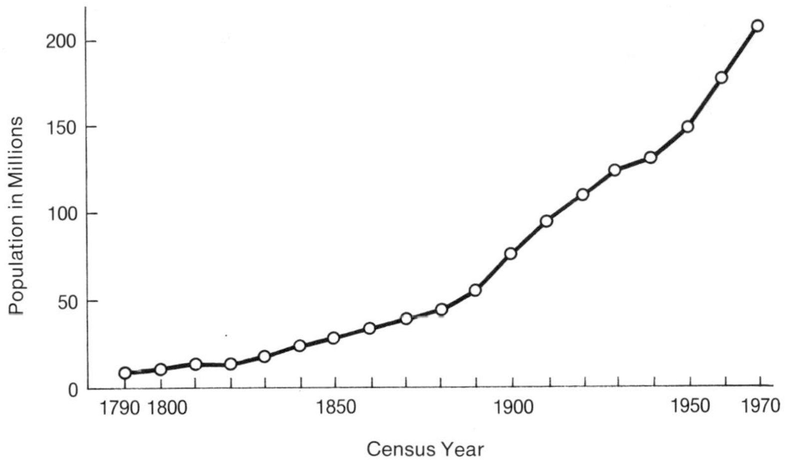

Figure 7-11. *Increase in population size in the United States* since the first census in 1790. Immigration has at times contributed significantly to the natural increase illustrated here from the 10-year census figures, more especially during the opening years of this century. If the United States were immediately to achieve zero population growth, the present maximum immigration rate would account for approximately 15 per cent of the annual additions to the population which otherwise would come from births.

has recommended the creation of 100 new towns of about 100,000 each, and 10 new cities of at least 1 million each. However, this still leaves another 55 million to be located, about the present total population of the British Isles.

Commission on Population Growth and the American Future

To meet this kind of problem, the President proposed establishment of a Commission on Population Growth and the American Future which would be charged with three main responsibilities. First, it would project population growth, internal migration, and other demographic processes up to A.D. 2000. It would be assisted in this work by the organization of census data by county in the decennial census, beginning with that of August, 1970. Computer summaries of this census should be first available by April, 1971.

The commission would also review the resources in the public sector of the economy required to deal with the estimated population increase. These include needs related to education, domestic water, recreational areas, and highways.

Third, it would survey the effect of this population growth on federal, state, and local government.

Freedom of Choice

To quote from the President's statement, none of the proposed measures would "... be allowed to infringe upon the religious convictions or personal wishes and freedom of any individual . . . ." It is with this last issue that many scientists would dissent, and problems are raised which will be discussed in Chapter 9 dealing with population control.

Bibliography

REFERENCES

Birdsell, J. B. "Some environmental and cultural factors influencing the structuring of Australian aboriginal populations," *The American Naturalist,* **87:** 171–207, 1953.

Birdsell, J. B. "On population structure in generalized hunting and collecting populations." *Evolution,* **12:** 189–205, 1958.

Borgstrom G. *Too Many,* New York: Macmillan, 1969.

Boughey, A. S. "Society succession," in preparation, 1971.

Braidwood, R. J., and Reed, C. A. "The achievement and early consequences of food production," *Cold Spring Harbor Symposia on Quantitative Biology,* **22:** 19–29, 1957.

Chevalier, A. "Le territoire geobotanique de l'Afrique tropicale Nord-occidentale et ses divisions," *Bull. Soc. Bot. de France,* **80:** 4–26, 1933.

Clarke, D. "The evolution of culture in Africa," *The American Naturalist,* **97:** 15–28, 1963.

Coale, A. J., and Hoover, E. M. *Population Growth and Economic Development in Low-Income Countries,* Princeton: Princeton University Press, 1958.

Davis, Kingsley. "Mortality decline," *Amer. Econ. Rev.,* **46:** 305–18, 1956.

Davis, Kingsley. "Population," *Scientific American,* **209**(3): 62–71, 1963.

Dorn, H. F. "World population growth: an international dilemma," *Science,* **135:** 283–90, 1962.

Ehrlich, P. R. *The Population Bomb,* San Francisco: Ballantine, 1968.

Hardin, G. "The tragedy of the commons," *Science,* **162:** 1243–46, 1968.

Harrison-Church, R. J. *West Africa,* 4th ed., New York: Wiley, 1963.

Haynes, C. V. "Elephant hunting in North America," *Scientific American,* **214**(6): 104–12, 1966.

Lee, R. B., and DeVore, I. (eds.) *Man the Hunter,* Chicago: Aldine, 1968.

Organski, H. F. K., and Organski, K. "Children become an economic liability," in A. A. Knopf (ed.), *Population and World Power,* New York: 1961.

Orians, G. H. *The Study of Life,* Boston: Allyn and Bacon, 1969.

Rappaport, R. A. *Pigs for the Ancestors,* New Haven: Yale University Press, 1967.

Sahlins, M. D. "The origin of society," *Scientific American,* **203**(3): 76–87, 1960.

Taeuber, I. B. *The Population of Japan,* Princeton: Princeton University Press, 1958.

Taeuber, I. B. "Population growth in Latin America: paradox of development., *Population Bull.,* **18:** 128, 1962.

FURTHER READINGS

Deevey, E. S. "The human population," *Scientific American,* **203**(3): 194–204, 1960.

Desmond, A. "How many people have ever lived on earth?" *Population Bull.* **18:** 1–18, 1962.

Dubos, R. *Man Adapting,* New Haven: Yale University Press, 1965.

Ehrlich, P. R., and Ehrlich, A. H. *Population Resources Environment,* San Francisco: Freeman, 1970.

Huxley, J. *The Human Crisis,* Seattle: University of Washington Press, 1963.

Keyfitz, N. *Introduction to the Mathematics of Population,* Reading, Mass.: Addison-Wesley, 1968.

Kliser, C. W., Grabill, W. D., and Campbell, A. A. *Trends and Variations in Fertility in the United States,* Cambridge: Harvard University Press, 1968.

Price, D. O. (ed.) *The 99th Hour—The Population Crisis in the United States,* Chapel Hill: University of North Carolina Press, 1967.

Rainwater, L. *Family Design, Marital Sexuality, Family Size and Contraception,* Chicago: Aldine, 1965.

Thompson, W. S. (ed.) *The Population Ahead,* Minneapolis: University of Minneapolis Press, 1958.

Thompson, W. S., and Lewis, D. T. *Population Problems,* 5th. ed., New York: McGraw-Hill, 1965.

von Foerster, H., Mora, P. M., and Amiot, L. W. "Doomsday Friday 13 November, A.D. 2026," *Science,* **132:** 1291–1305, 1960.

8 Population Fluctuation

The previous chapter considered the basic features of human population dynamics, and more especially the current population explosion which threatens to destroy most of the ecosystems we occupy. Even though the first predictions of such a situation went largely unheeded, the population explosion was not unforeseen. These early warnings were not formulated in the precise terms used today, but many writers from Greek and Roman scholars onward discussed population growth in a manner which indicates they appreciated the significance of mortality and natality rates in population growth. Terms like *teeming population* and *burdensome numbers* feature in these classical writings. During the Middle Ages the subject was apparently largely ignored, perhaps because developing urban civilizations suffered periodical checks to their population growth which prevented undue natural increase, and presented the problem of establishing sufficient numbers rather than controlling increasing ones. Not until the close of the eighteenth century was the question of the possibility of uncontrolled growth again raised in a now classical work by Thomas Malthus.

MALTHUSIAN THEORY

Thomas Robert Malthus was an English economist and demographer generally acknowledged as the founder of demography or the study of human population growth. He prepared a text entitled *An Essay on the Principle of Population as It Affects the Future Improvement of Mankind with Remarks on the Speculations of Mr. Godwin, M. Condorcet and Other Writers* which was published anonymously in London in 1798. In this work Malthus presented the inaugural essay on population growth. This recognized that all biological populations have a *potential* for increase which is larger than the *actual* rate of increase, and that the resources required for the support of increase are limited. Malthus supposed that the difference between the potential and the actual population increase resulted from this limitation, which continuously exerted pressures on the population, restricting its realization of its potential growth. Stated in modern ecological terms, increase is density-dependent; the optimum population is the maximum population.

Publication of this work by Malthus provoked violent criticism from contemporary authorities, particularly since the theory seemed to contradict the possibility of obtaining a utopia for all, and especially for the poor, which had begun to appear as one of the aims of contemporary eighteenth century society. Malthus subsequently issued a number of further publications under his own name. He modified his theory sufficiently to introduce the element of moral restraint in the procreation of children, which could perhaps act as a check to population growth.

To quote from his *Essay on the Principle of Population* (Malthus, 1816), he presents the following propositions:

1. Population is necessarily limited by the means of subsistence.
2. Population invariably increases where the means of subsistence increase, unless prevented by some very powerful and obvious checks.
3. These checks, and those which repress the superior power of population and keep its effects on a level with the means of subsistence, are all resolvable into moral restraint, vice, and misery.

Some other parts of his theory have been extensively reproduced, for example, the proposition that unchecked population increases geometrically, whereas food production can only increase arithmetically.

Much of Malthus' writing, although a little quaint in its style to twentieth century readers, contains extraordinarily acute observations. For example, in discussing population growth he supposes that ". . . the passion between the sexes is necessary and will remain in its present state." Later he states, "I do not know that any writer has supposed that on this earth man will ultimately be able to live without food. But Mr. Godwin has conjectured that the passion between the sexes may in time be extinguished. . . . But toward the extinction between the sexes, no progress whatever has hitherto been made."

Malthus also forecasts quite accurately the present rate of population growth of the United States. "In the United States of America, where the means of subsistence have been more ample, the manners of the people more pure, and consequently dejects to early marriages fewer than any modern states of Europe, the population has been found to double itself in 25 years." He goes on to predict the world population in the following terms ". . . the human species would increase as the numbers 1, 2, 4, 8, 16, 32, 64, 128, 256, 512, etc. and subsistence as 1, 2, 3, 4, 5, 6, 7, 8, 9, 10, etc. In two centuries and a quarter the population would be to the means of subsistence as 256 to 9; in three centuries as 4096 to 13, and in two thousand years the difference would be almost incalculable, the produce in that time would have increased to an immense extent."

As to checks on population, Malthus notes that "a country in pasture cannot support so many inhabitants as a country in tillage, but what renders nations of shepherds so formidable is the power which they possess of moving altogether and in the necessity they feel in exerting this power in search of fresh pasture for their herds."

He notes that "from all the accounts that we have on nations of shepherds . . . the actual population kept equal to the means of subsistence by misery and vice," and qualifies it by adding that the "commission of war is vice, and the effect of it misery, and none can doubt the misery of want of food."

MORTALITY RATES

The dire proposition of Malthus in his various works that poverty, disease, and war would be the only factors restricting the undesirable realization of the full potential growth in human population has been extensively examined during the nineteenth and twentieth centuries. A paper by Marston Bates (1955) on the role of war, famine, and disease in controlling population is representative of such definitive writings.

After reviewing the considerable evidence for universal cannibalism among hominids as established from their remains, Bates notes that the cultural evolution of *Homo sapiens* has also been characterized by intraspecific strife, which has been an important limiting factor on human population growth. He adds, however, that the period from 1650 to 1950, one in which the world population growth was quite spectacular, could hardly be called a period of peace, but rather was characterized by a succession of regional wars.

The Effect of Famine

Bates proceeds to examine the effect of famines on population growth and concludes that advanced agricultural societies are particularly susceptible to famine and malnutrition. He quotes figures for China suggesting that between 108 B.C. and A.D. 1911 there were 1828 famines, nearly one a year. The worst of these in modern times were caused by severe drought, which occurred in the years 1876 and 1897. The area affected was about the size of New England, the Middle Atlantic states, Ohio, Indiana, and Illinois, and approximately 9 to 13 million people are estimated to have died from one cause or another at this time. In 1920–1921 half a million people are believed to have died in China following a further famine.

In the Western world Bates notes that 201 famines were recorded for the British Isles between A.D. 10 and 1846, the last eight representing the Irish famine in which it is generally considered that 1 million people died, as well as 1 million people emigrating from that country. The population of the island is still only about one half that cited in the 1841 census, which estimated a population of over 8 million.

The Effect of Disease

Discussing the traditionally considered death from bubonic plague or "black death" in medieval Europe, Bates notes that this disease appeared suddenly in central Europe in 1348 and that a quarter of the population died from it. Further epidemics occurred in 1361, 1371, and 1382, but after that the plague persisted only locally, although it broke out again in 1663 and 1668. During 1664 in the first of these outbreaks, one quarter of London's population is believed to have perished. Bates observes that both plague and leprosy, which seems also to have been prevalent in Europe in medieval times, have unaccountably disappeared. He notes that the most dramatic effects on human populations are caused by the contagious diseases, of which smallpox is the most notorious. Apparently introduced by Spaniards to the New World, this disease is believed to have been as much responsible for wiping out Indian populations as their actual slaughter by the invaders. In return, the New World is thought to have contributed a more virulent form of venereal disease which at various times has been equally devastating in the Old World.

The Effect of War

Statistics generally seem to bear out these ideas presented by Marston Bates; in World War I, for example, an estimated 9 million men were killed. Despite this removal of men from society at the height of their reproductive life, the population growth of western Europe and North America does not show any significant downward trend until a decade later. Then the incidence of severe economic stress in the Western world following the Wall Street crash in 1929 appears to have had a determining effect on population growth. In World War II even more men died, but again population growth throughout the Western world shows an upward rather than a downward trend following the end of hostilities in 1945. Even global wars as they were waged in World War I and World War II would therefore appear to be without significant depressing effects on world population growth.

This has not always been the case, when more regional effects of wars are considered. The work of Rappaport (1967) in New Guinea on the warfare feedback mechanism has already been discussed. Cook (1946) has produced evidence for supposing that in pre-Columbian Central America, warfare and the human sacrifice with which it was associated effectively checked population increase and prevented overexploitation of the habitat. There is less well-documented evidence that the same ecological factors were holding West African populations in a steady state before the period in the last two centuries when captured individuals were disposed of by export as slaves instead of being immediately sacrificed.

Such local examples of past population control do not negate the assertion that modern warfare is ineffective in leading to control of population increase. If a tragic instance were needed, it is provided in the apparent ability of a small country like North Vietnam to sustain indefinitely war casualties approximately ten times those which even a large nation like the United States finds painful.

Effects of Atomic Warfare

The same ineffectiveness could not be predicted for international wars utilizing atomic as opposed to conventional weapons. It is to be fervently hoped that the utterly disastrous effects of such an outbreak can be avoided, because there is every indication that they could entirely destroy all world populations. This prospect is considered again in Chapter 10 dealing with air pollution.

EFFECTS OF DISEASE ON POPULATION GROWTH

There is ample evidence that in this century the far higher frequency of personal contacts which have developed in our essentially urban populations has considerably increased the possibility of death from infectious and contagious diseases (Armelagos and Dewey, 1970). The greater concentration of peoples in cities has presented more massive exposure to bronchial infections which are effectively spread in crowded buses, trains, stores, offices, and restaurants.

Influenza

The outbreak of influenza in 1919 following the end of World War I spread rapidly through all the cities of the world. It is very difficult to estimate the death rate from this particular epidemic, but it has been conservatively placed at from 10 to 15 million, thus considerably exceeding the number of men killed in the actual fighting. In more recent years a new form of influenza known as Asian flu spread through the whole world in 1967–1968, and again caused extensive mortalities which were estimated to be in the region of 9 million.

The molecular structure of the influenza virus is now known in detail. Each virus particle is made up of an internal ribonucleoprotein antigen, surrounded by an envelope composed of RNA coils. This envelope includes two other antigens, hemagglutinin and neuraminidase. The hemagglutinin enables the virus particles to adhere to chicken erythrocytes and cause them to agglutinate. This adherence is prevented by antibodies specific to the hemagglutinin, which is the basis for laboratory tests for particular strains of the virus.

Using this test, types A, B, and C of the virus have been distinguished. Type A is responsible for widespread and B for local epidemics; C seems not to cause influenza outbreaks at all. Strains A0, A1, and A2, which result from changes in the hemagglutinin or neuraminidase antigens, have also been detected. A0 appears presently to be dormant, A1 has caused most of the recent influenza outbreaks, and A2 produces "Asian" or "Hong Kong" flu.

The antibodies active against one influenza strain have little effect on another, so that the amount of infection developing in a community will depend on its past history of exposure. Pandemics of particular strains tend to occur in a ten-year cycle. Populations will suffer most if new strains appear for which there are neither natural antibodies in the population or antisera available. It seems that such new strains are most likely to appear after the virus has passed through other animals, especially horses or chickens. Populations living in close proximity to their chickens, as in the Far East, are therefore those in which influenza epidemics associated with new strains are most likely to start.

Whereas the contagious diseases such as smallpox, and especially those caused by microorganisms, can now be readily controlled by serum preparations, the virus diseases of the bronchial system are not yet generally controllable in this way. The concentration of people in cities is advantageous from the point of view of administering antisera to prevent disease. It does, however, make it almost impossible to control a virus infection such as influenza transmitted principally in exhaled breath droplets, unless the whole population ceases to work and the city is abandoned without any effective services.

EFFECTS OF INCREASED COMMUNICATION

Among agricultural populations, increased communications are beginning to render this section of the community as susceptible to infectious diseases as the concentrations of people in the cities. During this century, the territorial patterns which have persisted for hundreds of thousands of years, and which have probably prevented extensive contact between peoples except in market places, have begun to break down. The spread of smallpox in tropical areas was much more rapid at the beginning of this century because of the *pax Europea.* The occupation of tropical colonial areas by European powers had brought about a cessation of hostilities between the peoples of adjoining village territories and heralded an era of travel on a previously unprecedented scale. Such local travel is now a characteristic of many agricultural societies. Sleeping sickness or trypanosomiasis provides another good example of a disease whose incidence has spread with this breakdown of territoriality.

More rapid communications have also greatly increased the chances of introducing epidemic diseases such as yellow fever from one area into another presently free of the disease, but with certain conditions such as the presence of a suitable vector predisposing toward its establishment.

Vast new agricultural schemes are likely to increase the incidence of water-borne diseases such as schistomiasis, or bilharzia, which has spread widely through the continent of Africa during this century, although it had previously been endemic for 5 or 6 thousand years in Egypt.

Looking again at Malthus' three principles of war, disease, and famine, it would appear that disease will not now have any significant or immediate effect on population fluctuation, although a highly virulent form of bronchial disease would initially prove uncontrollable. War, if of a nuclear type, would undoubtedly annihilate all human populations in one generation, as well as all other higher forms of life on this planet. Famine, and its alternative expression malnutrition, remains therefore as the most urgent factor to be considered as a potential cause of major population fluctuation, as first enunciated by Malthus.

FAMINE

A recent published address by I. L. Bennett (1969), chairman of a panel of the President's Science Advisory Committee instructed to study the world food problem, competently surveys the contemporary situation relative to world food supply. From this authoritative review it is possible to assess the modern impact of Malthus' last prediction in regard to population fluctuations resulting from famine and starvation.

Bennett groups his principal conclusions under five headings:

1. *Unless the situation changes markedly* food shortage and famine are inevitable. Bennett notes that estimates of the precise date when famine will reach disaster proportions range from the mid-1970s (Paddock and Paddock, 1967) through 1980 to 1984 (U.S. Department of Agriculture); to this can be added 1985 (McElroy, 1969). These global famine disasters will occur when food transfers from "have" nations no longer compensate for the shortfalls in domestic food production of the "have-nots."

One of the earlier unequivocal statements of the lag between grain

Table 8-1* ***Indian Import of Cereal Grains*** Some variation occurs dependent on the nature of the annual Indian crop, but there is a definite upward trend which overrides this variation from year to year.

Year	*Amount in Million Tons*
1957	3.6
1958	3.2
1959	3.9
1960	5.1
1961	3.5
1962	3.6
1963	4.6
1964	6.0
1965	7.5
1966	14.0

* From Maheshwari, *Science and Culture,* **32:** 104–14, 1966.

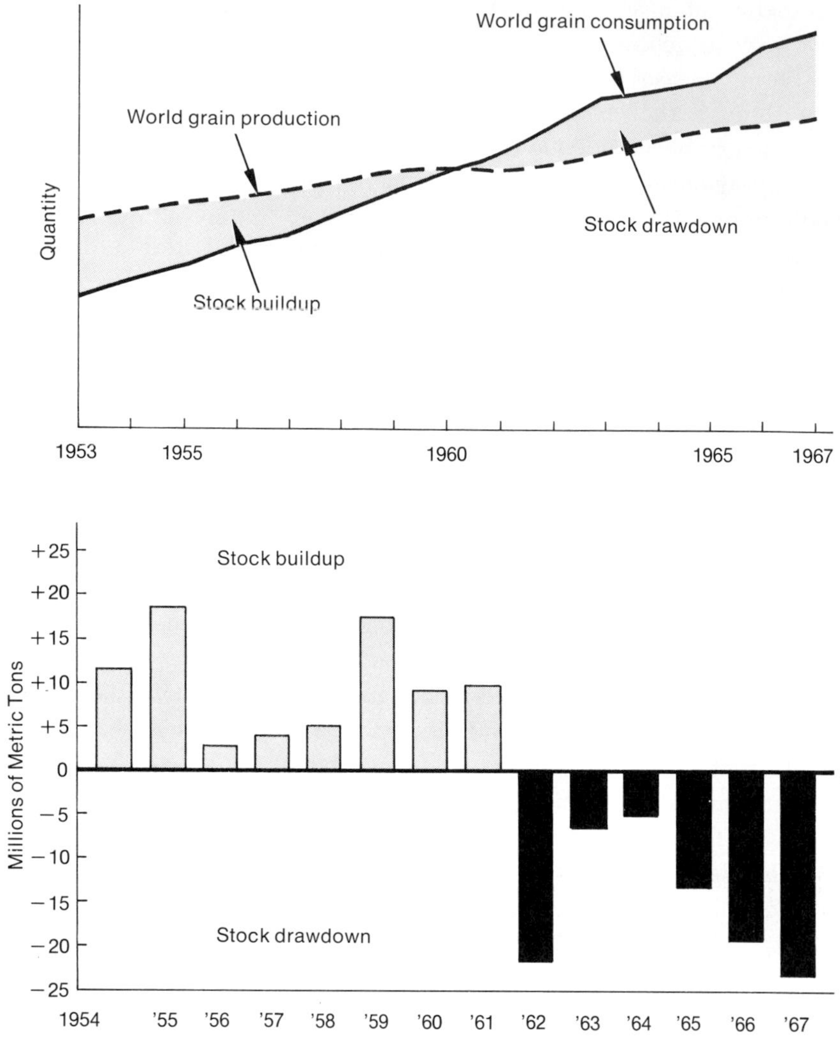

Figure 8-1. *Deficiency in world grain production as compared with world consumption.* The first graph, *A*, shows (not to scale) how increasing consumption of food by 1961 had converted a world overproduction to a world underproduction, and created a deficiency which has subsequently steadily increased each year.

Graph *B* is another way of representing the same basic figures, showing how world grain stocks are now rapidly being depleted and will shortly not be available to meet grain production shortfalls. (Reproduced by permission of the publisher from L. R. Brown, *Science,* **158:** 606, 1967. Copyright 1967 by the American Association for the Advancement of Science.)

production and consumption was prepared by Lester R. Brown. Figure 8-1, taken from a publication of his (Brown, 1967), illustrates graphically how this lag is increasing annually.

Figures such as these have prompted the current predictions of inevitable famine conditions on a catastrophic scale. While it is true that some societies do not depend on grain for their main food source, these exceptions are minor in relation to the total world population.

Additional proof to further substantiate the self-evident conclusions from such statistics can be obtained from food import figures for individual countries such as those provided in Table 8-1 for India. That country is far from moving toward independence in food production; her demands for food imports are now annually increasing and will soon attain gigantic proportions. Reference to Table 7-10, which shows the natural increase of India's population, will confirm this.

Some idea of increased food demands on a regional basis may be obtained from Table 8-2. At first sight it might appear that local improvements in yield, such as that shown for Mexico (Harrar and Wortman, 1969) and production of export surpluses in countries like the United States and Canada might cover this deficiency. However, a consideration of the figures in Tables 8-1 and 8-2 will show this is impossible. The increased food production in Mexico in the decade to 1955 actually totals less than 1 million metric tons annually. This was less than *one fourteenth* of India's shortfall in 1966. Meanwhile India has added something like another 40 million to her population. Mexico, like all Latin American countries, has also added to her population and has little good land remaining uncultivated.

These overwhelming figures can be reinforced by some crude generalizations. The total annual wheat crop of the United States is nearly 40 million metric tons. In 10 years' time the population of India will increase by about 200 million. These extra mouths will require the *total* of the current U.S. wheat production to sustain them, even if by superhuman efforts India has by then so increased her agricultural production as to be self-supporting with respect to the *present* populations. According to most authorities inside and outside India, this seems unlikely.

Table 8-2* ***Additional Food Requirements Estimated on a Regional Basis*** The first table (*A*) shows overall additional needs for 1975, based on the projected population growth. The second table (*B*) shows that for some countries, such as Mexico, conditions may permit the realization of the required increase in food. (See text for major qualifications of this statement.)

A *Region*		*Estimated Regional Population at Current Growth Rate in Millions* *1965*	*1975*	*Additional Food Production Needed 1965–1975 in Per Cent*
East Asia		876	1,040	20
South Asia		875	1,250	28
Africa		311	404	30
Latin America		248	335	35
	Total	2,400	3,000	26

B *Year*	*Cultivated Area (Hectares)*	*Yield (kg/Hectare)*	*Production (Metric Tons)*
1945	500,000	750	330,000
1955	790,000	1,100	850,000
Increase:	48 per cent	48 per cent	158 per cent

* Figures extracted from *Famine 1975! America's Decision: Who Will Survive?* Copyright © 1967 by William and Paul Paddock, p. 55. Reprinted by permission of Little, Brown and Co., Boston, Mass.

Table 8-3* ***Value of Projected Food Shortage in Less Developed Nations*** This table assumes this shortage could be made good by trading for surpluses which could be produced in developed countries. In 1960 trade balances were about to complete the change from the situation which had long prevailed, in which less developed nations had traded food surpluses to meet food deficiencies in developed nations.

	TOTAL VALUE IN BILLIONS OF DOLLARS					
	Developed Countries			*Less-Developed Countries*		
	1960	*1980*	*2000*	*1960*	*1980*	*2000*
Demand	80	113	151	47	89	179
Production	78	125	186	48	77	135

* Reprinted by permission of the publisher from T. Kristensen, *International Journal of Agrarian Affairs,* **5:** 139, 1967.

Another way of presenting the trading method of avoiding world famine has been followed by Kristensen (1967), who projects food demand and production in terms of *costs* (Table 8-3). He assumes that by the year A.D. 2000 agricultural technology in developed countries would be capable of expanding to produce annual food surpluses valued at 35 *billion* dollars (23 per cent over their needs), but it is inconceivable that the less developed nations could at that time find such an enormous annual sum of money, to purchase these surpluses. The sum indeed will represent about one twentieth of the gross national product of the United States, or *twice* what the 93 less developed nations presently spend on public health and public education. Even if these lesser developed nations gave up *entirely* their expenditure on military defense, this presently represents only one half of the 35 billion dollars needed to buy food.

2. *Present efforts will not do the job.* The scale of internationally organized assistance intended to solve food shortages is entirely inadequate, and the situation continues to deteriorate.

It is sometimes stated that introduction of new high-yielding crop varieties, increased use of fertilizers, and extension of agricultural acreages will suffice to restore the deficiency between food requirements and actual production. The statistics on which this argument is based are illustrated in Table 8-2. The average regional shortcomings are shown by such figures to vary between 20 and 35 per cent, an increase easily attained in the past, as shown by the statistics for Mexico. It must be recognized, however, that Mexico is a special case. First, as shown in Table 8-2, it was able to increase its acreage of cultivated land by 48 per cent in the decade 1945–1955. Second, it had in 1944 a cadre of trained and experienced agricultural scientists to call upon in a sophisticated program originally extensively supported by American money and skill from the Rockefeller Foundation (Harrar and Wortman, 1969). India, for example, has no such reserve of potential agricultural land; contact between village farming practice and the findings of the few sophisticated agricultural research centers she presently operates offers great logistic problems. As Paddock and Paddock (1967) relate, combined use of fertilizer, irrigation, pesticides, improved varieties, and double or triple cropping could result in fantastic increases in production of grain crops in India. However, there is not sufficient fertilizer presently produced in the whole world to permit the universal use of it in India at the same rate as in, for example, Japan. In terms of economics, such improvements have to be bought, and already, according to the Paddocks, half the rupees circulating in India are *American* rupees. India totally lacks the foreign reserve necessary to purchase the necessary supplies and equipment.

The development of "miracle rice" has been described by Chandler (1969). While average unimproved rice yields in tropical Asia are about 1500 kg/hectare, and more efficient production in Japan gives some 5000 kg/hectare, the first new rice variety, IR8, produced by the International Rice Research Institute in the Philippines, can yield over 9000 kg/hectare. Chandler states that even better varieties became available from the Institute in 1969. However, fertilizer applications are necessary to obtain the highest yields with the new varieties. Indeed, it is difficult for plant breeders to improve long-established varieties of any major crop which have been selected empirically for performance under local conditions. The mixed genotypes of these established varieties contain sufficient variation to ensure that whatever the conditions of a given season, they will be optimal for some component of the plant population. Replacing these all-purpose local varieties with a general improved one normally requires a greater degree of cultural care to ensure optimum growing conditions to meet the more exacting requirements of the new variety.

3. *Increased food must come from farming.* Although this point is reiterated by numerous agricultural authorities, the issue appears debatable. Pirie (1969), for example, has developed unconventional protein foods to the point where they have become a practicable and acceptable proposition. His work has concentrated on unconventional sources of *protein* because he maintains that shortage of protein is currently the main dietary deficiency. After noting that ruminant animals should only be utilized as a protein source when they are maintained on nonarable (noncropable) land, Pirie states that not only legumes such as soya beans but also some varieties of cereal crops contain significant amounts of protein, e.g., sorghum (3–4 per cent), wheat (3.8 per cent), and oats (4.8 per cent). There is also a new corn with increased lysine (protein) content. When leaf proteins, even of trees, are taken seriously as a food source, many crops not now thought of as food plants will come into use (Pirie, 1968).

4. *There is still hope,* but this belief is essentially based on point 3. The huge success of "miracle rice" as described by Chandler (1969) and similar improvements in wheat suitable for underdeveloped areas, appear to emphasize that this feeling of optimism is not unfounded. This question is discussed further in a later chapter.

5. *Population control alone is not a solution.* The current estimate is that food needs of "have-not" areas will double in the next 20 years. Even if

present efforts at population control are entirely successful, this will only reduce by about one fifth the increased demand for food.

Bennett illustrates the reason for this by referring to India where maintaining even the present nutritional levels *if no more children were born* in the period 1965–1975 would require 20 per cent more food. This is because more than half the population is less than 15 years old, and food requirements continue to increase approximately up to the age of 19 years. Under the same circumstances a 30 per cent increase in food supplies would be necessary to raise the level of nutrition to that recommended by the Food and Agricultural Organization of the United Nations. This increase in 10 years, Bennett notes, about equals that currently being achieved by improved agricultural practices. It is also more than twice the level of the present U.S. shipments to India, and it *allows for no reproduction whatsoever.* Unless radical action is taken, widespread famine disasters in India are inescapable *in the next decade.* Unfortunately the example of India is far from unique; it is constantly cited solely because of the immensity of its problems. The same circumstance will be found to apply to any tropical underdeveloped area. India represents only a quarter to a fifth of the third world of underdeveloped nations, depending on how these are defined.

SHORTCOMINGS IN PRESENT APPROACHES

The inevitable inadequacy of present steps to avoid world famine, which becomes apparent with even a summary review such as this, are not primarily the result of callousness or neglect of the problem. Literally billions of dollars in foreign aid are expended from both governmental and private sources in this country alone, and funded through an imposing array of international agencies—FAO, WHO, UNESCO, UNICEF, and IBRD. Again Bennett (1969) lays out the reasons for the comparative ineffectiveness of these programs. These are:

1. *The complexity of the world problem.* Hunger and malnutrition, as every agricultural scientist is aware, basically are not technological agricultural problems, but the result of inadequate economic development. The complex intricacies of the economic aspects make the appropriate solution so elusive.

2. *The real complexity is not apparent.* Solutions to the problems of hunger and malnutrition are thus almost inevitably oversimplified. Unforeseen consequences have an unfortunate habit of arising on the eve of spectacular successes. A premium is thereby placed on short-term solutions, whereas a carefully planned long-term systems approach is essential. Borgstrom (1969) describes some of the pitfalls in ignoring such a need.

3. *The problem has been stated only in generalities.* The desire to evoke humanitarian response has necessitated brief generalizations, and some kind of improvement has all too frequently lulled sympathizers into a false sense that all is now well.

4. *Food shortages and population growth are inseparable.* Solutions of the one problem will not at all automatically solve the other; both problems must be solved simultaneously.

5. *Solutions to both food shortage and population growth can only be achieved with individual cooperation.* No amount of governmental legislation will increase agricultural production and reduce population reproduction unless individuals willingly cooperate.

It is general economic experience that the supply of foodstuffs made available by farmers is closely related to the amount of attractive goods they can purchase with the cash received in return. In subsistence farming, enough is produced to meet family needs; any surpluses are commonly converted immediately into alcoholic beverages and quickly consumed in one prolonged and glorious bout of intoxication. Production over and beyond this subsistence amount has therefore to be coaxed by other attractive and economic incentives.

As will be discussed in the next chapter, these also appear the most practical incentives for obtaining the individual cooperation necessary to achieve population control.

The Demographic Transition

The question of economic incentive is the basic operative factor in models of the *demographic transition* described by Fredericksen (1969). This expression is used for the changeover which every society must now make, from a high mortality–high birth rate situation to a low mortality–low birth rate one. With the exception of Chile and Costa Rica, all countries with a preponderance of ethnic groups originating in Europe have, together with Japan, now completed this change. This process is modeled in the second scheme (*B*) in Figure 8-2; it essentially represents the process of ecological succession from an industrializing, through a colonial, to an advanced industrial society as described in Chapter 5. The first model (*A*) in Figure 8-2 is the neo-malthusian one which holds the society in an advanced agricultural society category without any possibility of further succession occurring—productivity remains too low. A number of workers have suggested that the existence of feedback mechanisms providing population control in western Europe in the eighteenth and nineteenth centuries permitted its nations to complete these final societal successional transitions.

The Triage System

The Paddock brothers (1967), who were among the first writers to present the inevitable world famine crises in a well-documented and convincing form, have suggested the triage system to cope with the problem of deciding what action developed nations can take when the famine they

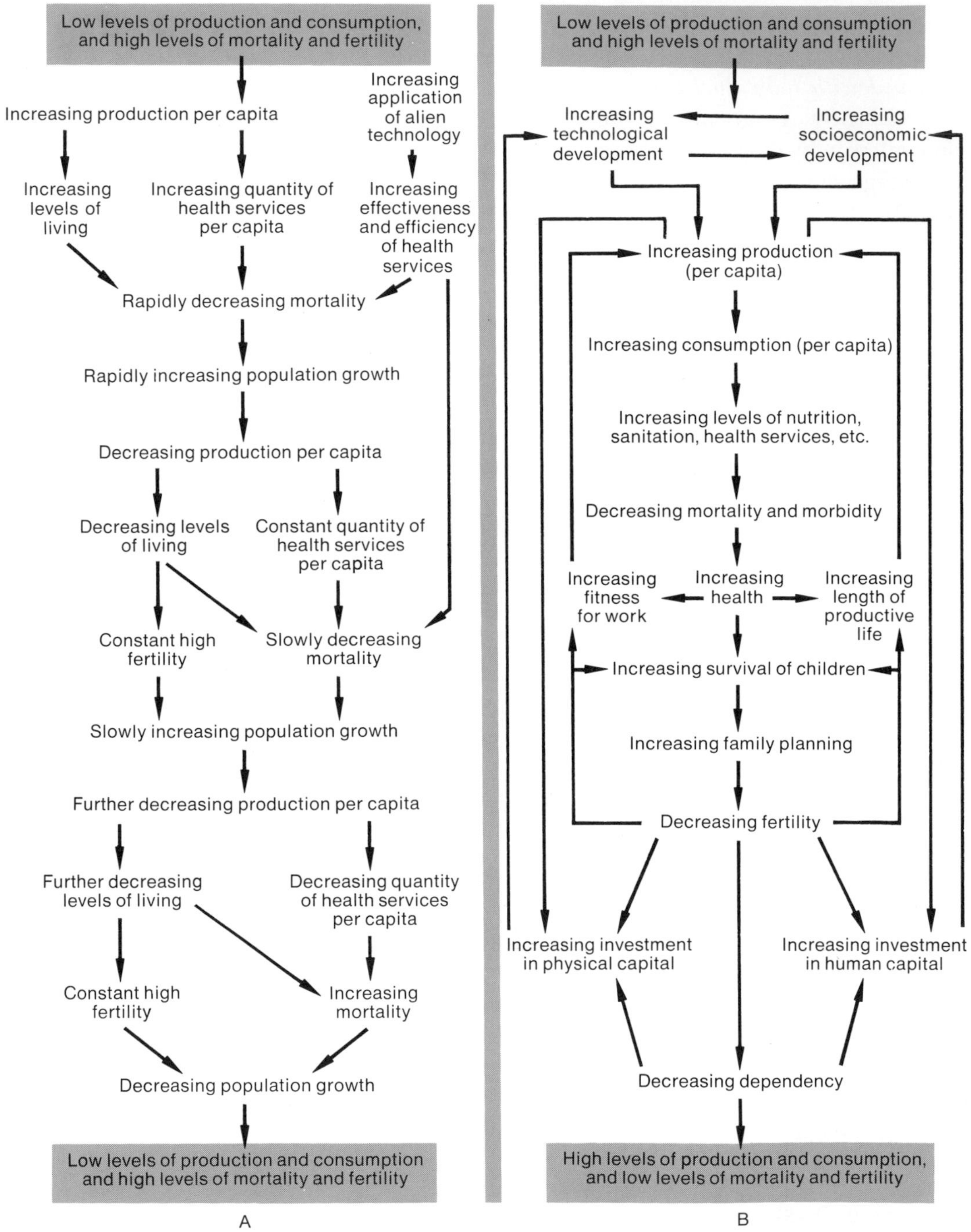

Figure 8-2. *Models of economic and demographic transition. A.* The neo-malthusian model which assumes increasing productivity is *not* accompanied by reduced fertility. *B.* A model which assumes the opposite, so that a low increasing productivity is not absorbed by increasing population growth. (Reproduced with the permission of the author and publisher from H. Frederiksen, *Science,* **166:** 839, 1969. Copyright 1969 by the American Association for the Advancement of Science.)

foresee begins to occur on a massive scale in 1975. Perhaps a little cynically, they comment that of the only four countries—Argentina, Canada, Australia, and the United States—which by that time will have any exportable food to supply, the first three will *sell* on the open market. For them there will be no problem, but for the United States, which may be expected to continue somehow to *give* surplus food away, there will be an acute problem of selecting the recipient nations.

Triage is a well-established military practice for the handling of battle casualties at saturation levels. When it becomes necessary to decide whom to treat and whom to ignore, the wounded are divided into three groups. Members of one are dying and cannot be saved; they will receive no treatment other than pain suppressants. A second group, those who can survive without immediate treatment, are held off temporarily. The third group are those likely to survive if treated right away. The limited medical resources are concentrated on these, and experience has shown that this action saves a maximum number of lives under these conditions.

Triage is not a pleasant method to apply, but it would identify the regions to receive famine assistance on the certainty that this will be in limited supply.

Nations selected to receive aid will be those in temporary imbalance where the rate of natural increase is decreasing and the food production rising, but which are too poor to purchase enough imports to meet the temporary deficiency. Some more fortunate nations may have almost closed the gap and can find the foreign exchange necessary to import food until they become self-supporting. These can make it on their own. Others in the third category will not yet have begun to reduce their population increase, or move in the right direction toward self-sufficiency in food production. They will have to be abandoned until malthusian phenomena so reduce their population size and rate of natural increase that they can become self-supporting, or nearly enough to qualify for aid.

The opportunity for political mischief-making when such a triage system has to be effected may be too good for some nations to miss. The time of famine will be most difficult for all nations, and the greatest amount of tolerance and forebearance will be needed if the world is to pull through what will be the greatest crisis it has ever faced.

The FAO Plan

For six years the Food and Agricultural Organization of the United Nations has been considering means of averting disaster in the underdeveloped world as a result of the population explosion (Chedd, 1969). This international organization has recently ratified a plan entitled "Indicative World Plan for Agricultural Development" (IWP). This analyzes the major crises facing the world in the next decade or so and makes recommendations not only as to how to solve the imminent threat of world famine, but also as to the achievement of economic and social well-being for the whole of mankind.

All projections in the plan take 1962 as the base year, with the world divided into three categories of nations. Zone A contains developed market economies like the United States and most Western countries. Zone B has "centrally planned," i.e., communist economies, and zone C "developing" economies, the underdeveloped nations.

If agriculture in a zone C country is to provide sufficient food by the end of the plan period (1985), it has to attain an annual increase which has risen from 2.8 per cent in 1962 to between 3.2 and 3.8 per cent. The difficulty of reaching this seemingly unambitious goal is illustrated by the fact that recently agricultural production in some zone C countries has not increased at all.

Chedd identifies the following five objectives of IWP:

1. Production of sufficient food to cope with 2.5 to 3 per cent natural increases in population, especially by emphasizing cereal production.
2. Producing more of the protein which rising standards and increasing urbanization demand, especially by improving the production of animal protein.
3. Strengthening the foreign exchange situation in zone C countries.
4. Increasing the number of jobs in "agro-allied" industries.
5. Intensifying agricultural production.

The plan acknowledges that zone C countries, which in 1965 totaled a population of 1.5 *billion,* will by 1985 have a combined population of 2.5 billion, requiring an 80 per cent increase in food production. IWP allows for some of this to be met from the importation of food to the value of 26 *billion* dollars (total 2 billion in 1962). The problems become more acute as they are successively considered. Provision of increased amounts of protein is difficult, and developed nations, it is suggested, can best help by providing processed milk on a massive scale. Unemployment problems have driven even the basically optimistic sponsors of IWP almost to despair. Some suggestions as to its cure seem strangely reminiscent of New Deal days in the United States, which is not surprising, for the problems are very similar.

We tend to clutch at any straw in the hope of having not to believe what we do not want to believe. A plan like IWP will not work if we use it merely to reassure ourselves. Only frenzied activity and massive sacrifice by the citizens of all zone A and many zone B countries could make it work.

It would be possible almost indefinitely to continue with opinions as to the nature of the world food crisis. This all too brief review may best be concluded by references to two recent papers. The first, by H. F. Robinson (1969), presents the findings of a Presidential committee panel on this issue, and its conclusions are worth quoting here.

1. The scale, superiority, and duration of the world food problem is so great that a massive, long-range, innovative effort unprecedented in human history will be required to master it.
2. The solution of the problem, which will exist after about 1985, demands that programs of population control be initiated now. For the immediate future, the food supply is critical.
3. Food supply is directly related to agricultural development and, in turn, agricultural development and over-all economic development are critically interdependent in hungry countries.
4. A strategy for attacking the world food problem will, of necessity, encompass the entire foreign economic assistance of the United States in concert with other developed countries, voluntary institutions, and international organizations.

The second paper is by H. D. Thurston (1969), who reviews the prospects for improvements in tropical agriculture. He concludes that the most realistic short-range solution to the world food crisis is an increase in tropical food production, necessitating a fundamental change from a previously cash crop and plantation-type agricultural economy. One of the major contributions which industrialized temperate countries can make, is by intensifying and extending the training of personnel from these tropical areas in the latest methods of tropical agricultural technology.

Nontraditional Methods

Of the nontraditional methods of increasing agricultural production, perhaps the closest approach to realization has been achieved by various techniques for desalinating salty water for irrigation or hydroponics (soilless culture) use. The economics of this process has been reviewed recently by Clawson *et al.* (1969). They conclude that the costs of desalting operations, inasmuch as it is possible to foresee these over the next 20 years, are a whole order of magnitude greater than the agricultural value of the resulting irrigation water (not fully supported by Young, 1970). This discouraging conclusion relates not only to projects for desalination of sea water, but also to desalting of drainage or underground water in such areas as the San Joaquin Valley of California, where salt accumulation may render such water resources unacceptable for agricultural purposes (Boyko, 1967).

The same kind of economic difficulties intervene whenever any other such nontraditional way of food cropping is explored, whether it is planktonic harvesting of the sea, raising fungi on petroleum or molasses, or leaf harvesting as developed by Pirie. The time required for the necessary research and development work on all such methods is quite inadequate. For this reason in particular, nontraditional cropping may find its most immediate practical application in food enrichment programs, in remedying the nutritional imbalance of much of the world's present diet.

Table 8-4 *Disparities in Protein Consumption* Mean per capita daily amount of meat, milk, and fish protein in grams in the diet in various selected countries. Advanced industrial societies generally have at least ten times the meat consumption of advanced agricultural societies. In a few of these latter protein consumption is high, just as in a few of the former (Portugal, Japan) it is low, although somewhat offset by a high fish consumption. It is tempting to conclude from such figures that a high animal protein diet is a luxury placing an unreasonable strain on ecosystem productivity. It would be less disruptive if human populations in countries in the upper section of this list functioned as primary consumers and adopted vegetarian diets.

Country	*Meat*	*Milk*	*Fish*
Australia	317	561	13
Argentina	300	394	10
New Zealand	288	724	19
United States	254	750	13
Canada	212	758	18
France	195	563	30
United Kingdom	194	591	28
Netherlands	121	776	20
Brazil	81	158	6
Mexico	65	258	13
Taiwan	50	17	56
Portugal	46	97	85
United Arab Republic	37	114	14
Turkey	36	301	7
Japan	15	50	62
Pakistan	11	114	9
Ceylon	8	32	18
India	4	130	6

Nutrition

The important subject of nutrition cannot even be adequately dismissed in one short paragraph. There are sufficient statistics to demonstrate that a high proportion of the population of underdeveloped nations is suffering from malnutrition. This contributes to a higher mortality rate, but apparently has little direct effect on the fertility rate. It restricts full physical and mental development and is a condition which exists also in impoverished pockets of developed nations such as the United States. Malnutrition is partly the result of ignorance, but mostly it is a question of economics and therefore has an economic as well as a dietary solution.

Two examples of statistics suffice to illustrate this relationship between economics and diet. Table 8-4 shows the mean amount of animal protein calculated on a national basis for selected countries at differing economic levels. Table 8-5 illustrates the proportional amounts of animal protein in the human diet on a regional basis. As Paarlberg (1967) puts it in regard to the world picture, 1 billion people in the developed countries have half again as many calories and *five times* the animal protein to eat as the 2 billion of the less-developed areas (Table 8-6). One inescapable conclusion from such statistics is that an advanced industrial society can function

Table 8-5 ***Composition of Regional Diets*** This expresses the major food elements as a percentage of the total diet and can be compared with the information expressed in Table 8-4, but regional means obscure national differences within these statistics. The same conclusion is, however, valid: a diminished exploitation of ecosystems in North America and perhaps some other areas could be attained by reducing the proportion of animal protein in the diet.

	CARBOHYDRATES			*PROTEINS*			*FATS AND OILS*
	Cereals	*Other Plant Carbo-hydrates*	*Plant Proteins*	*Meat*	*Milk*	*Fish*	*Plant Oils*
Far East	69	14	8	2	2	1	4
Near East	64	14	6	3	5	1	7
Africa	50	28	7	4	3	1	7
Latin America	40	28	7	9	6	1	9
Europe	44	22	2	8	11	1	12
North America	21	25	2	23	13	1	15
Oceania	27	23	2	24	11	1	12

without the animal protein-rich diets which presently pertain in some such nations. Another is the ecological conclusion that changing from an animal protein-rich diet to place more dependence on plant carbohydrate foods would either permit a reduced human exploitation of local ecosystems or provide a human food surplus. A new technique in plant breeding, inducing by irradiation mutant forms of crops which have a much higher protein content, offers another method of preventing malnutrition (Chedd, 1970).

DISEASE

Fluctuations in population size due to disease have already been touched upon, and some factors discussed which tend to increase any such effects. Two kinds of selection processes have tended to reduce or minimize the effects of disease on human population increase, selection of physical or biochemical characteristics which reduced the effects of the disease, and selection for culture behavior which avoided it or limited its incidence and spread.

Table 8-6* ***Comparison of the Daily Per Capita Total Calorie and Animal Protein Diet in Developed and Less-Developed Countries***

	Developed Countries	*Less-Developed Countries*
Daily calorie consumption per person	2,941	2,033
Total daily amount of protein per person in grams	84.0	52.4
Total daily amount of animal protein per person in grams	38.8	7.2
Population in millions	1,089	1,923

* From Don Paarlberg, "Food for More People and Better Nutrition," in Clifford M. Hardin (ed.), *Overcoming World Hunger.* © 1969 by The American Assembly, Columbia University. By permission of Prentice-Hall, Inc.

Disease Resistance

Using a science fiction writer's license, H. G. Wells terminated his *War of the Worlds* by having the Martian invaders succumb to bacterial infections against which human populations are protected by antibodies in their blood. In employing this idea, Wells was making use of immunological knowledge regarding the coevolution of *erectus-sapiens* populations and various parasitic diseases.

Immunological processes in the human body will produce antibodies as a defense against invasion by a wide range of microbial and viral infections. This reaction was first appreciated in the last century by Pasteur, who produced sera which would induce reactions providing immunity against infection from rabies and smallpox. Such clinical immunity can now be obtained for a wide range of diseases.

A natural immunity, which will develop phenotypically after contraction of many of these diseases, has become genetically fixed by a number of human populations.

Genetic Resistance

In all temperate zone populations, for example, there seems to be some degree of resistance to bronchial infection caused by both influenza and pneumonia. Eskimo populations, certainly isolated for 15,000 years, and perhaps longer, from temperate populations in which these diseases were endemic, apparently have not developed any resistance to them. Individual Eskimos who migrate into temperate communities not infrequently die from such bronchial infection.

Rather in the same way, early Mongoloid stocks did not apparently develop any resistance to smallpox and were decimated by this disease when it was introduced by Europeans to the New World. Europeans, in turn, have developed little or no resistance to infection by some of the tropical intestinal parasites, which apparently now cause tropical populations no inconvenience.

Dobzhansky (1960) has suggested that resistance to tuberculosis infection has been developed in some temperate zone populations (Figure 8-3). He predicts that the widespread use of antibiotic drugs to control this disease may halt the further adaptation of human populations to tuberculosis.

Cultural Avoidance

Many cultural practices through empirical selection have enabled human populations to avoid the fluctuations in number which result from disease outbreaks of epizootic proportions. May (1960) provides examples of a number of these. He cites the case of a small Chinese village in which one half of the inhabitants were decimated by a very heavy hookworm in-

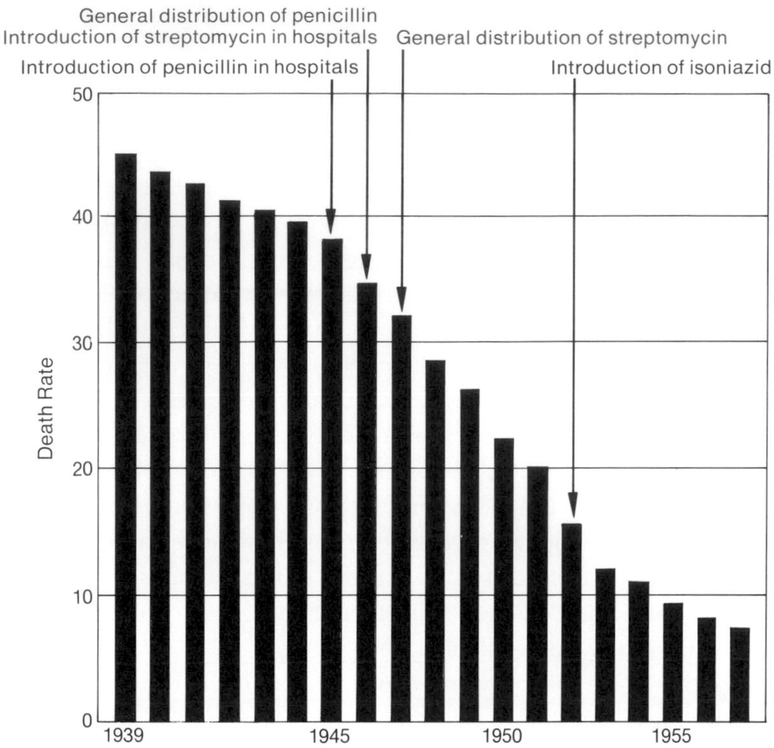

Figure 8-3. *Selection for tuberculosis resistance in a contemporary population.* The tuberculosis death rate per 100,000 persons declined dramatically with the introduction of antibiotics about the time of World War II. There is now a reduced threat to tuberculosis-susceptible individuals, and the selection pressure operating against them is greatly reduced. (From Theodosius Dobzhansky, "The present evolution of man," *Scientific American,* **203:** 208, 1960. Copyright © 1960 by Scientific American, Inc. All rights reserved.)

fection, while the other half were largely free of this disease. The infected individuals were found to be mostly rice farmers, from whom the healthy ones bought rice, with whose cultivation they were not concerned. These last were silkworm farmers, who had no need to venture into paddy fields. The rice farmers, by contrast, spent all their day in the water of the rice paddies, which had been manured with "night soil," and consequently were exposed to infection through their skin by hookworms whose eggs were introduced to the paddy in the human fertilizer.

Another example of the cultural avoidance of disease is the Islamic injunction in the Koran forbidding the consumption of pork. Around subtropical villages the pig is the universal scavenger, feeding even on human feces. Consequently its flesh contains a number of parasites which have evolved with man as an alternate host.

RECENT FLUCTUATIONS

The causes of fluctuations in population size and rate of increase so far considered are essentially malthusian; they arise from famine, war, or pestilence. It has been noted that while in the past fluctuations in numbers from these causes or combinations of them have been rather local, there is now a potential for huge variations in numbers to be associated with these factors. World famine is estimated to be certain; there remains only the question of when its intensity will reach disaster proportions, in 10, 15, 20, or 30 years. Nuclear war, it is maintained, would destroy all human populations. We risk pestilence on an ever-increasing scale because of the ever more crowded dimensions of our increasingly urban life, and our loss of genetically acquired population resistance to infectious diseases, particularly those of the respiratory and digestive systems which are the areas of our most intimate contact with the environment.

Also contributing to population fluctuation are losses due to emigration and gains due to immigration; throughout history both have significantly affected population growth. Emigration, as already noted, enabled the nations of Western Europe to undergo a population explosion without devastating their metropolitan ecosystems as they moved into the advanced industrial category of society. It permitted the Japanese to do likewise nearly a century later without drastically curtailing the rate of natural increase within their home islands.

Immigration some 20,000 years ago first populated the virgin continents of the Americas and Australia and later the equally virgin islands of Oceania. Subsequent waves of immigrants caused tremendous upsurges in the populations of these and other continents. These various effects are perhaps best exemplified by examining the greatest immigration movement of all time, that into the United States which took place during the first part of this century.

Immigration into the United States

In 1965 Congress revised the Immigration Act of 1924 to permit a total annual immigration into the United States of 290,000 persons. In 1969 demographic figures this statistic, which has to be equated to the natural increase of the population, represented 8.4 per cent of the annual United States gain in population. If this country is to achieve a zero population growth, this quota of immigrants will represent some 15 percent of the annual population gain. This appears to be a higher immigration rate than any other major developed country is now prepared to sustain. It is a figure of sufficient significance for demographic studies to have to make the necessary allowance in the statistics.

The 1924 act had established an immigration quota of a maximum of 2 per cent per year of any national group as represented in the 1890 census. This set an annual maximum of 162,000 immigrants for the United States, very different from the over 1 million annual total which had been reached for several years at the beginning of this century prior to 1913.

In 1860 foreign-born Americans represented 13.1 per cent of the population; in 1900 they accounted for 13.6 per cent. At zero population growth the present quota, if fully taken up, will result in a population which continues to have about the same level of foreign-born citizens as registered in the 1860 and 1900 statistics, a remarkable level of great biological as well as demographic significance.

Economic Influences

There are, however, other causes of population fluctuation, both negative and positive, which are little understood and which have made demographers in the past appear very bad prophets. In this century, neither the cause of the downward trend of population in most Western nations in the 1930s, nor the upward surge in many of these during the 1950s has been satisfactorily explained. A combination of economic influences which Boughey (1971) has called the *Madison Avenue effect* must be considered at least partially responsible for these fluctuations.

The Madison Avenue Effect

The Madison Avenue effect operates through interaction between the acquisitive desires of individuals as subtly exploited by selling agencies employing pressure advertising techniques through the mass media, and the complete separation between sex and reproduction which has been achieved in advanced industrial societies. Methods of birth control which have been available since at least biblical times have during the twentieth century been the subject of such intensified research that the new generation of nubile females is able to have complete control of reproduction without suffering any sexual deprivation whatsoever. The time at which a pair bond, whether sanctified by legal matrimony or not, embarks on the procreation of children can therefore be postponed, or permanently delayed, in favor of a new home, a second home, a second car, a yacht, a world cruise, or whatever glamorous alternative the advertising industry is currently promoting.

This effect has been described before, although in different terms. A. F. K. and K. Organski (1961) state: ". . . in an industrial society the family's standing depends heavily upon the occupation of the head of the household and upon the standard of living of the whole family as evidenced by the material goods it can display. A family with eight children cannot live in as good a neighborhood as a family with two; it cannot dress as well, drive as new a car, have as many conveniences and luxuries, or travel as much. The children will not receive as expensive an education, and this is particularly important in determining their social status when they become adults."

The nation in which this Madison Avenue effect had the most dramatic results is Japan. From being a colonizing society in the first half of this century, Japan has not only moved into the final category of an advanced industrial society, but has nearly stabilized its population structure and growth. A combination of legalized and readily obtained abortion, linked with extended use of contraceptive practices, has enabled young couples to respond materially to the pressure of the Madison Avenue factor. Japan, however, was not the first major national group to respond in this way; most of the industrialized nations of the New World and western Europe had shown this response, but not recognized it, following the 1929 collapse of the Wall Street stock market and the acute economic depression of the early 1930s. In these countries this was a period of a Madison Avenue factor stress operating under reinforcement from an economic crisis. Although contemporary birth control practices still involved some inconvenience and considerable restraint, in order to respond to some of the Madison Avenue pressure despite economic restriction, family size had to be drastically cut.

This was the first time in the history of the United States and other Western nations that a general voluntary reduction of the birth rate had ever occurred. No governments recognized the great prize which was then within their grasp; many actually panicked and brought in various kinds of inducements aimed at *restoring* fertility rates to their levels at the beginning of the century. This took the form mostly of income tax relief in Europe, linked often with supplementary payments for child maintenance. Many of these practices continue today.

Despite economic inducements, population growth in these countries

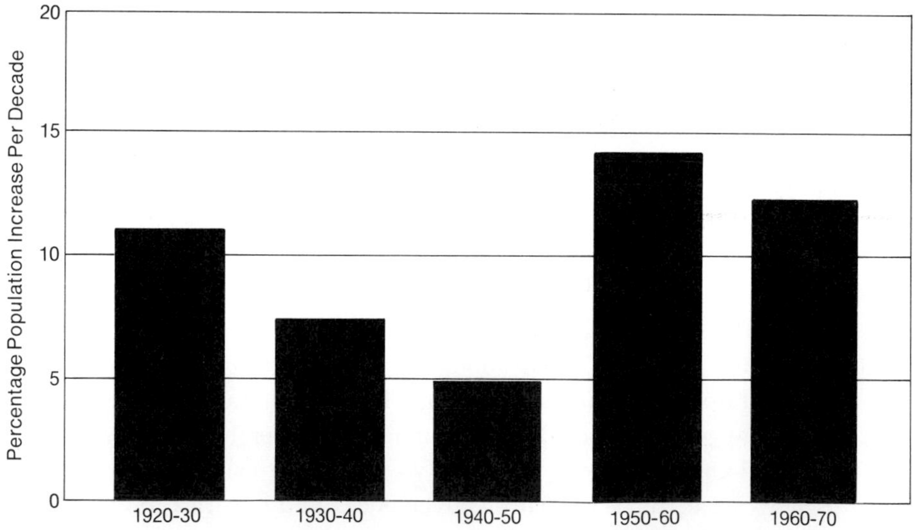

Figure 8-4. *Population growth in some western industrialized societies* during the present century. Despite various financial inducements intended to restore the falling birth rates, and a reduction in mortality rates, the rate of natural increase in industrialized societies continued to fall through this century until the early 1940s. The trend was then reversed and the rate of natural increase took an upward swing until about the middle 1950s.

continued to decline until the outbreak of World War II (Figure 8-4). From then on, international and regional war has continuously arrested and reversed the trend toward a reduced population growth in these areas. The most immediate explanation for the reversal would appear to be that surviving veterans long for a return to stability which they imagine to be a permanent and legalized pair bond with its associated home, family, and material provisions. Without such incentives, and united by a group territorial behavioral reaction, it is unlikely that men would have been willing to fight in the first place.

A general relationship between birth rates and economic factors has long been established. Galbraith and Thomas (1941) showed that United States business cycles from 1919 to 1937 affected both birth and marriage rates; Kirk (1942) demonstrated the same correlations for Germany. Spengler (1968) developed the concept that family increase was dependent on (1) the preference system, (2) the price system, and (3) income. The last two items are self-explanatory and relate to the cost of additional children relative to earnings or savings available to cover it. The preference system refers to the choice the pair bond couple makes as to whether to use

Table 8-7* ***Falling Death Rates in the Twentieth Century*** Figures per thousand persons on a regional basis (*A*) and selected national basis (*B*). The reductions obtained in individual countries of particular regions, compared with those of other national figures for the same regions, show how estimates of further extensive falls in regional death rates may well be realized. Figures in the last column of *A* are projections.

A

Region	*1935*	*1950*	*1965*	*1980*
World	25	19	16	13
Latin America	22	19	16	8
Asia	33	23	20	13
Africa	33	27	23	18

B

Region	*Selected Countries*	*Current Death Rate*
Latin America	Cuba	8
	Mexico	10
	Chile	11
	El Salvador	13
	Guatemala	16
Asia	Hong Kong	5
	Taiwan	6
	Singapore	6
	Ceylon	8
	South Korea	11
	India	17
Africa	Senegal	22
	Ivory Coast	25
	Upper Volta	25

* From *Famine 1975: America's Decision: Who Will Survive?* by William and Paul Paddock, 1967, p. 16. Reprinted by permission of Little Brown and Co., Boston, Mass. Figures from the 1970 World Population Data Sheet by permission of the Population Reference Bureau.

this money for family increase or the purchase of material possessions. Spengler's analysis approaches the Madison Avenue effect concept as defined by Boughey.

Summarizing this chapter on population fluctuation, it appears reasonable to deduce that our present culture has incidentally evolved a feedback mechanism in advanced industrial societies which has limited and may well continue to limit population fluctuation, and to contain natural increase at or below zero population growth.

For underdeveloped nations in other successional categories, and for underprivileged sections of advanced industrial societies, there is presently no such feedback mechanism operative. Among these populations, falling death rates (Table 8-7) will ensure a continuation of the high rate of natural increase which already prevails. No prospect faces such populations other than the certainty that within the present generation they will have to endure the malthusian disasters of famine, pestilence, and at least internal war. The figures for population density provided in Table 8-8 illustrate that even if there were no significant use of space other than for food cropping, none of the advanced agricultural societies has a sufficiently productive agricultural technology combined with enough land to render it self-sufficient in food production. The next chapter considers what measures can be taken to reintroduce human population control feedback mechanisms into these ecosystems which are imminently in danger of total collapse through the absence of any such cybernetic interaction.

Table 8-8* ***Per Capita Acreage of Cultivable Land*** For various countries. Japan, with the lowest acreage on this list, by enormous expenditure of individual effort contrived to become self-supporting in food. The United Kingdom has never been so in this century, nor has India, partly because of low productivity. The Soviet Union has also at times been a food importer, despite its favorable position in regard to cultivable land.

Country	*Per Capita Acreage*
United States	2.68
Soviet Union	2.59
India	0.82
China	0.50
Germany	0.48
United Kingdom	0.42
Japan	0.17

* From Maheshwari, *Science and Culture,* **32:** 104–14, 1966.

Bibliography

REFERENCES

Anonymous. *World Population Prospects, as Assessed in 1963.* United Nations Population Studies No. 41, New York: United Nations, 1966.

Armelagos, G. J., and Dewey, J. R., "Evolutionary response to human infectious disease," *Bioscience,* **20**: 271–75, 1970.

Bates, Marston. *The Prevalence of People,* New York: Scribner, 1955.

Bennett, I. L. *Problems of World Food Supply,* in XIth International Botanical Congress, Seattle, Wash., All-Congress Symposium, World Food Supply, Aug. 28, 1969.

Boughey, A. S. *The Future of Homo sapiens,* in preparation, 1971.

Boyko, H. "Salt-water agriculture," *Scientific American,* **216**(3): 89–96, 1967.

Brown, L. R. "The world outlook for conventional agriculture," *Science,* **158**: 604–11, 1967.

Chandler, R. F. *New Horizons for an Ancient Crop,* in XIth International Botanical Congress, Seattle, Wash., All-Congress Symposium, World Food Supply, Aug. 28, 1969.

Chedd, G. "Famine or sanity," *New Scientist,* **44**: 178–82, 1969.

Chedd, G. "Mutations v. malnutrition," *New Scientist,* **45**: 450–53, 1970.

Clawson, M., Landsberg, H. H., and Alexander, L. T. "Desalted seawater for agriculture: is it economic?" *Science,* **164**: 1141–48, 1969.

Cook, S. F. "Human sacrifice and warfare as factors in the demography of pre-colonial Mexico," *Human Biol.,* **18**: 81–101, 1946.

Dobzhansky, T. "The present evolution of man," *Scientific American,* **203** (3): 206–17, 1960.

Frederiksen, H. "Feedbacks in economic and demographic transition," *Science,* **166**: 837–47, 1969.

Galbraith, V., and Thomas, D. S. "Birth rates and the inter-war business cycles," *J. Amer. Statist. Ass'n.,* **36**: 465–76, 1941.

Harrar, J. G., and Wortman, S. "Expanding food production in hungry nations: the promise, the problems," in C. M. Hardin (ed.), *Overcoming World Hunger,* London: Prentice Hall, pp. 89–135, 1969.

Kirk, D. "The relation of employment levels to births in Germany," *Milbank Mem. Fund Quart.,* **28**: 126–38, 1962.

Kristensen, T. "The approaches and findings of economists," *Internat. J. Agrarian Affairs,* **5**: 139, 1967.

McElroy, W. D. "Biomedical aspects of population control," *Bioscience,* **19**: 19–23, 1969.

Malthus, T. R. *Essay on the Principle of Population,* 7th ed., London: J. M. Dent and Sons Ltd., 1816.

May, J. M. "The ecology of human disease," *Ann. N.Y. Acad. Sci.,* **84:** 789–94, 1960.

Organski, H. F. K., and Organski, K. "Children become an economic liability," in A. A. Knopf (ed.) *Population and World Power,* New York, 1961.

Paarlberg, D. "Food for more people and better nutrition," in C. M. Hardin (ed.), *Overcoming World Hunger,* London: Prentice Hall, 1967, pp. 41–87.

Paddock, W., and Paddock P. *Famine 1975,* Boston: Little, Brown, 1967.

Pirie, N. W. "Food from forests," *New Scientist,* **40:** 420, 1968.

Pirie, N. W. *"Plants as Sources of Unconventional Protein Foods,"* in XIth International Botanical Congress, Seattle, Wash., All-Congress Symposium, World Food Supply, Aug. 28, 1969.

Rappaport, R. A. *Pigs for the Ancestors,* New Haven: Yale University Press, 1967.

Robinson, H. F. "Dimensions of the world food crisis," *Bioscience,* **19:** 24–28, 1969.

Spengler, J. J. "Demographic factors and early modern economic development," *Daedalus,* **97:** 433–46, 1968.

Thurston, H. D. "Tropical agriculture: a key to the world food crises," *Bioscience,* **19:** 29–34, 1969.

Young, G. "Dry lands and desalted water," *Science,* **167:** 339–43, 1970.

FURTHER READINGS

Adams, E. S. "Unwanted births and poverty in the United States," *The Conference Board Record* 6, no. 4, pp. 10–17, 1969.

Anonymous. *Alternatives for Balancing World Food Production and Needs.* Ames, Iowa: Iowa State University Press, 1967.

Anonymous (Citizens Board of Inquiry). *Hunger, U.S.A.,* Boston: Beacon Press, 1968.

Brown, L. R. *Seeds of Change,* New York-Washington-London: Praeger, 1970.

Burnet, F. M. *The Natural History of Infectious Disease,* 3rd ed., Cambridge: Cambridge University Press, 1960.

Connell, K. H. *The Population of Ireland 1750–1845,* Oxford: Clarendon Press, 1950.

Dalrymple, D. G. "The Soviet famine of 1932–34," *Soviet Studies,* **14:** 250–84, 1964.

Davis, Kingsley. "The population impact on children in the world's agrarian countries," *Population Review,* **9:** 17–31, 1965.

Day, L. H., and Day, A. T. *Too Many Americans,* Boston: Houghton Mifflin, 1964.

Dumont, R., and Rosier, B. *The Hungry Future,* New York: Praeger, 1969.

Feiss, J. W. "Minerals," *Scientific American,* **209**(3): 128–36, 1963.

Fiennes, R. *Man, Nature and Disease,* London: Weidenfeld and Nicolson, 1964.

Freedman, R. (ed.) *Population: The Vital Revolution,* New York: Doubleday, 1965.

Hauser, P. *The Population Dilemma,* Englewood Cliffs, N.J.: Prentice Hall, 1963.

Keys, A., Brozek, J., Henschel, A., Michelson, O., and Taylor, H. L. *The Biology of Human Starvation,* Minneapolis: University of Minnesota Press, 1950.

Laffin, J. *The Hunger to Come,* New York: Abelard-Schuman Ltd., 1966.

Langer, W. L. "The black death," *Scientific American,* **210**(2): 114–21. 1964.

Lessing, L. "Power from the earth's own heat," *Fortune,* Vol. 79, Part 2, No. 7, pp. 138–41, 1969.

Lovering, T. S. "New fuel mineral resources in the next century," *Texas Quarterly,* **11:** 127–47, 1968.

Markert, C. L. "Biological limits on population growth," *Bioscience,* **16:** 859–62, 1966.

Mottram, V. H. *Human Nutrition,* London: Edward Arnold, 1963.

Osborn, F. (ed.) *Our Crowded Planet: Essays on the Pressures of Population,* New York: Doubleday, 1962.

Pirie, N. W. "Orthodox and unorthodox methods of meeting world food needs," *Scientific American,* **216**(2): 27–35, 1967.

Population Reference Bureau. "The story of Mauritius from the Dodo to the stork," *Population Bulletin,* **18:** No. 5, 1962.

President's Science Advisory Committee Panel on the World Food Supply. *The World Food Problem* (3 vols). Washington, D.C., 1967.

Revelle, R. "Water," *Scientific American,* **209**(3): 92–108, 1963.

Rhyther, J. H. "Photosynthesis and fish production in the sea," *Science,* **166:** 72–76. 1969.

Schurr, S. H. "Energy" *Scientific American,* **209**(3): 110–26, 1963.

Scrimshaw, N. S. "Food," *Scientific American,* **209**(3): 72–80, 1963.

Simpson, D. "The dimensions of the world food crisis," *Bioscience,* **19:** 24–29, 1969.

Stamp, J. D. *The Geography of Life and Death,* New York: Collins Fontana Press, 1964.

Stearn, E. W., and Stearn, A. E. *The Effect of Smallpox on the Destiny of the Amerindian,* Boston: Humphries, 1945.

Waterbolk, H. T. "Food production in prehistoric Europe," *Science,* **162:** 1093–1102, 1968.

Zinsser, H. *Rats, Lice and History,* Boston: Little, Brown, 1963.

Population Control

9

As was described in Chapter 7, human populations have the potential to achieve a geometric rate of increase. In possessing this capacity they are no different from the vast majority of plant, animal, and microbe populations inhabiting the earth. The fact that *erectus-sapiens* populations have not until the past hundred years even begun to approach realization of this potential rate of increase is because, as in all other natural populations, regulatory mechanisms of one sort or another have prevented it.

Reference has already been made to the nature of some of these regulatory mechanisms, and the reasons human populations have tended to evade such controls were discussed in the last chapter. Stated very briefly, the ability of our species to escape from limitations on natural increase is attributable especially to the unique characteristic of *erectus-sapiens* populations which permits adaptation to different environmental conditions by *cultural* rather than *physical* evolution.

EARLY METHODS OF POPULATION CONTROL

Some ecologists, notably Wynne-Edwards (1965), have developed the idea first presented by Carr-Saunders (1936) that even early *erectus-sapiens* communities possessed some form of nonmalthusian population control, either voluntarily or involuntarily practiced. Anthropologists also have considered this possibility, and Table 9-1 summarizes one such review of the extent of control through abortion and infanticide exercised by selected early groups.

In a previous chapter it was noted that hunting-gathering societies in many instances must have been regulated by density-dependent factors, and especially by the *seasonal* limitations of food and water supply imposed on such nomadic groups. It has also been observed that the early agricultural societies representing the next category of successional evolution were

Table 9-1 ***Population Control Measures Practiced by the Earliest Categories of Human Societies*** Numerous observances and taboos in such groups may be responses to feedback from density-dependent situations. Evolving cultural techniques permit later categories of societies to override these situations by achieving a greater productivity, inevitably to the detriment of ecosystem stability and diversity.

Category	*Intercourse Avoidance*	*Abortion*	*Infanticide*
1. HUNTING-GATHERING GROUPS			
Bushmen (Southern Africa)	No	No	Yes
Eskimos	No	Yes	Yes
Australian Aborigines	No	Yes	Yes
Tasmanians	No	Yes	Yes
Amerindians	Yes	Yes	Yes
2. EARLY AGRICULTURAL GROUPS			
African	Yes	Yes	Yes
Amerindians	Yes	Yes	Yes
Oceania	Yes	Yes	Yes

occasionally regulated by feedback mechanisms. These mechanisms and the responses which they triggered represented a cultural response to selection for stability in the relations between the human population and the environment. The reasons such feedback mechanisms and responses were apparently lost during the successional progress to advanced agricultural societies have been discussed, and it has been considered that in some populations of the earliest successional societies in less favorable environments, either density-dependent factors or the voluntary practice of abortion and infanticide continued to regulate population numbers.

The writings of Malthus epitomize the extent of knowledge of human population fluctuation and control which prevailed at the beginning of this century. Since that time the science of historical demography has become established. This provides more accurate and factual evidence as to the nature of control practices, some of which have persisted into modern industrial societies.

HISTORICAL DEMOGRAPHY

Absolute figures concerning the demography of populations were not generally available until periodic census-taking developed in the Western world during the nineteenth and early twentieth centuries. Before this, information had to be gleaned from such sources as parish registers and tombstones. This precensus demographic research constitutes the new science of *historical demography,* whose aims are reviewed very briefly by Revelle (1968) in introducing a volume of the periodical *Daedalus* devoted entirely to historical population studies.

In this introduction Revelle remarks on the historical variations in fecundity in the various regions of Europe at different times. He notes that even before modern population control methods became extensively utilized in this area during the present century, social customs consciously or unconsciously produced fertility control. Notably these were postponement of the time of marriage, and long-term nursing of children as opposed to early weaning. Revelle also observes that the marriage pattern of the time included within large households a considerable reservoir of unmarried individuals comprising principally servants and unmarried relatives. The European marriage pattern of this period can be regarded as a fertility control device which could respond quickly to a change in economic circumstances. A disaster such as plague could wipe out as much as one half of the population in a large city. One immediate response of the population to the need for replacing such losses was an increase in the marriage rate among this considerable reservoir of previously single individuals.

The demographic patterns of western Europe were studied in some detail by Spengler (1968), who describes the unique marriage pattern which appeared in that area during the fifteenth century and which seems to have become universal by the seventeenth century. In Western Europe during this period marriage took place at a much later age than that prevailing elsewhere, later even than that of Eastern Europe (Figure 9-1).

Associated with the large family with many unmarried relatives and servants, and the prevalence of various religious and other orders requiring celibacy, this marriage pattern resulted in a comparatively low fertility rate even before the spread of effective birth control measures. Spengler estimates that the gross reproductive rate, that is, the average number of daughters born to a woman living to the end of her reproductive life, very rarely exceeded 3.8. It resulted in a high level of per capita productivity and capital accumulation, and to some extent prevented the overexploitation of land and resources. He estimates that the resulting rises in average incomes facilitated the launching of the industrial revolution in western Europe.

Spengler points out that the age structure of modern advanced agricultural societies is far less favorable to productivity than that which existed in European countries at a comparable stage of development. Quoting 1965 figures, he notes that the fraction of the population represented by persons aged 15 to 64 years was as follows: East Asia (excepting Japan), 51.7 per cent; South Asia, 54.7 per cent; Africa, 54.2 per cent, ranging from 51.7 per cent in West Africa to 56.1 per cent in East Africa; Central America, 56 per cent; Philippines, 53 per cent. These are associated with annual natural increase rates ranging between 2.5 and 3.5 and an expectation of life at birth which is less than 40 years in Africa, 40 to 50 years in Asia, and 50 to 55 in Latin America. These high rates of population growth, according to Spengler, will absorb most of the additional capital resources which are generated and will prevent a parallel increase in per capita income.

Heer (1968) discusses fertility reduction in the populations of the Western world and illustrates this with figures for the white population

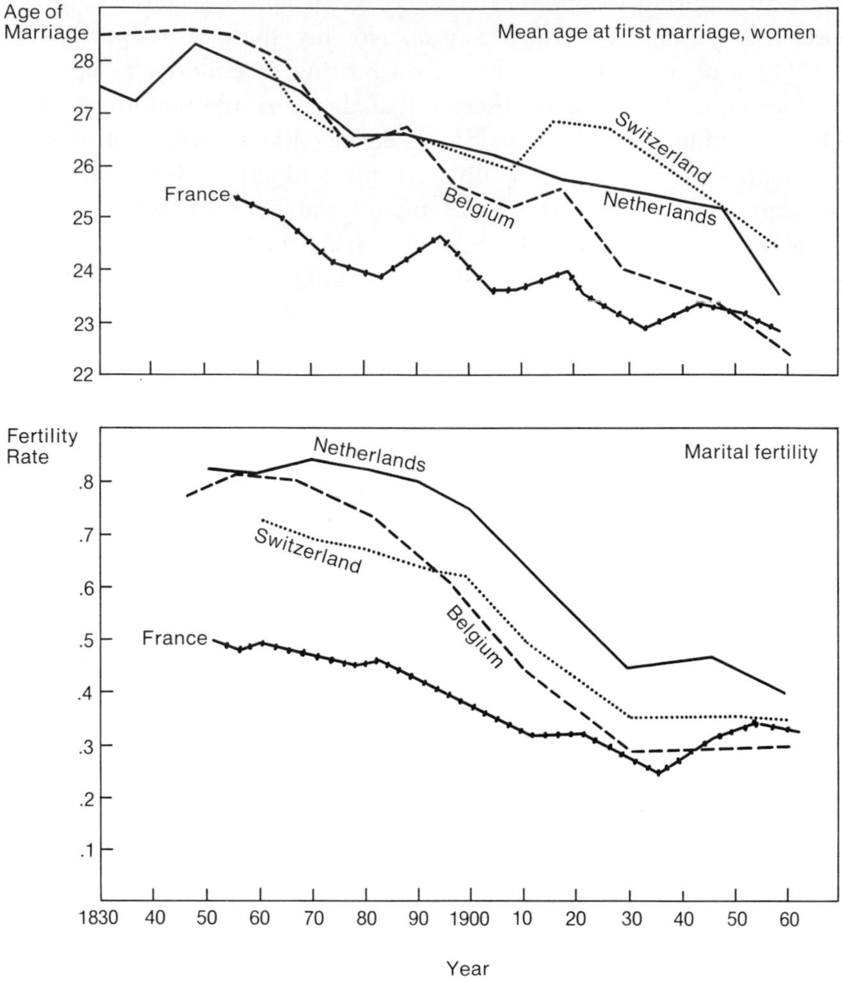

Figure 9-1. *Marriage age and fertility* in Western Europe. The lateness of marriage which characterized Western Europe in the eighteenth and nineteenth centuries was associated with a comparatively low fertility. The introduction into this area of more effective contraceptive methods permitted increasingly earlier marriage (*upper graph*) with simultaneously a decreasing fertility (*lower graph*). (Reprinted by permission of the publisher from E. Van de Walle, *Daedalus,* **97**[2]: 492, American Academy of Arts and Sciences, Cambridge, Mass.)

of the United States from 1869 to 1965 (Figure 9-2). He observes that the agricultural societies of eighteenth century America, which had an unlimited supply of land, viewed children as productive assets that could be used in working additional parcels of agricultural fields. Compulsory education laws, and a social aversion to the industrial employment of child labor, prevented a similar attitude from being generally taken toward factory work during the industrial revolution.

He also notes that from 1790 through 1960 the urban population of the United States increased from 5 to 70 per cent of the total population; without these changing attitudes toward labor, the industrial revolution

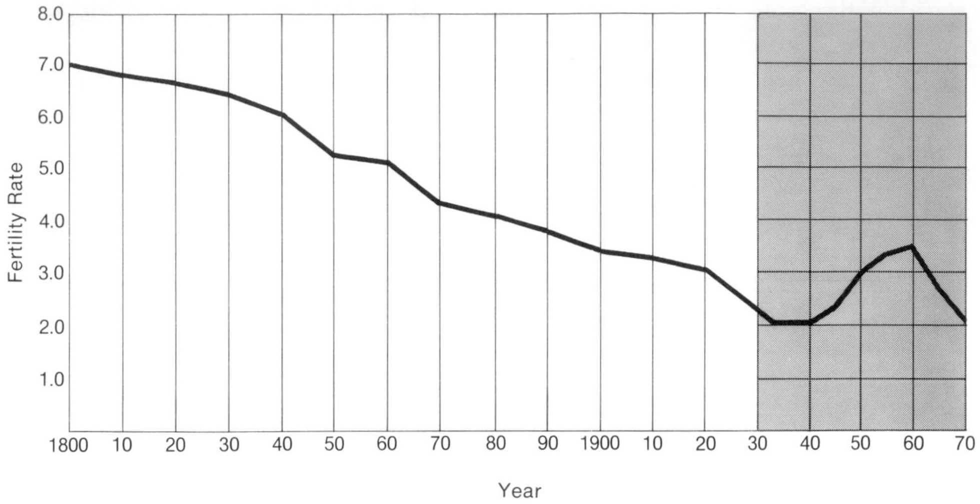

Figure 9-2. *Fertility rate for the population of the United States*—mean rate for whites. The rate declined through the demographic transition of the nineteenth century, reaching an unprecedented low in the early 1930s following the economic depression. The higher rate since, associated with a period which included three wars, has recently given way to a decline which has brought the fertility rate down to the same trough as in the 1930s. This time it may continue to fall.

would have had an even greater economic impact. Heer summarizes the factors associated with the industrial revolution which have resulted in a general downward trend in fertility rates, despite some minor reversals of a temporary nature.

These factors are institution of the social security system, suppression of child labor, compulsory education for children, changes in relative cost of living space, and increasing cost of child care, all economic features of a type discussed in the previous chapter under the heading of the "Madison Avenue effect."

It is apparent from this rapid review of early practices and factors associated with population control that there is a marked tendency in human populations, during historical times at least, for the *need* for population control to produce a *method* of control, voluntary or involuntary and however effective. Fortunately, the individual methods of control currently available are now both effective and extensively used.

PREGNANCY AVOIDANCE

All modern methods of population control in human societies basically involve the avoidance of reproduction in the individual nubile female. Many methods of pregnancy avoidance of varying degrees of efficiency have been known and practiced in human societies for a considerable period of time. Practices of earlier times now seem as amusing to us as they must have proved ineffective in our forebears. These range from pessaries of crocodile dung, honeyed tampons, potions of mule kidneys, to various superstitious acts which at least had the merit of being more sanitary.

It is easy to become involved in semantic argument as to precisely which of the many procedures since adopted can be regarded as *contraceptive,* preventing conception, and which are *abortifacient,* producing abortion. The issue for some is still a matter of conscience, religion, or philosophy. For the purposes of this work all such methods are categorized as *pregnancy control,* for pregnancy still generally takes at least days to diagnose. After this diagnosis, the artificial or natural termination of pregnancy short of parturition can be termed *abortion.*

Coitus Interruptus

Probably the oldest of the partially effective methods of pregnancy control is *coitus interruptus,* or external deposition of seminal fluid after initial intromission. Dating at least to biblical times, it is still in extensive use.

Rhythm Method

Depending on a "safe period" and avoiding coitus when ovulation is about to take place, the rhythm method may also have been practiced for a considerable time, and at least until recently was extensively recommended among some groups. It demands an accurate identification of the time of ovulation, usually the fourteenth day of the menstrual cycle, and abstinence for an appropriate time before and after this, usually the eleventh to eighteenth days. Requiring a sophisticated approach, it is unreliable; its most frequent scientific use now is in reverse. That is, subfertile couples wishing to reproduce are advised to concentrate on achieving coitus during the identified *nonsafe* period.

Condoms

The technique of using condoms is believed to have been devised in the sixteenth century by an Italian anatomist, Fallopius. The opening up of the New World had added an additional hazard to sexual intercourse in the form of syphilis, and Fallopius apparently recommended his linen sheath as a protection against venereal disease rather than pregnancy.

The invention of rubber processing by vulcanization in the mid-nineteenth century provided an eminently more satisfactory material for the manufacture of such sheaths, or condoms as they are technically described. Although no nation was at first readily willing to admit their extensive use by its own citizens (the French referred to *capots anglais* and the English to "French letters"), the use of condoms by the beginning of this century had become extensive. Lacking documentary evidence, it nevertheless seems reasonable to suppose that it was the appropriate use of condoms which greatly contributed to the unprecedented reduction in the birth rate of Western nations in the 1930s. It is estimated that presently 700 to 800 million condoms are manufactured each year in the United States (Calderone, 1964). A few simple calculations show that the impact of their use is presently of greater significance in relation to the birth rate than that of the oral contraceptive.

Spermatocides and Diaphragms

The two methods of spermatocide and diaphragms used separately or in conjunction with each other, also became popular in the twentieth century. The vaginal diaphragm had the advantage of a greater aesthetic acceptability, the spermatocidal jelly or foam of being obtainable without medical consultation. Spermatocides are sometimes also used *after* coitus as douches.

Intrauterine Devices

All the techniques mentioned so far, and several other minor ones, were based on preventing sperm from reaching an ovum by imposing a physical or chemical barrier, or both. The intrauterine device (shortened to IUD) does not prevent conception in this manner, but in some way presently unknown prevents the fertilized egg from developing into an implanted embryo in the uterus.

Various types and shapes of plastic devices which can be inserted into the uterus are now available, and they are provided with an indicator of whether "fallout" has occurred. One of the early difficulties experienced with the IUD use was detecting whether the device was still where it should be.

At first the IUD was considered, because of its cheapness, effectiveness, and simplicity, as the ideal method of pregnancy control in undeveloped areas. It may yet prove so, but some of the earlier large-scale tests suggest that women in such areas prefer the "pill."

The "Pill"

Like the IUD, oral contraceptives, which first became available in the United States in an FDA-approved commercial form in 1961, employs a different method of pregnancy control than the earlier techniques referred to here. They function by regulating reproductive hormone balance so as to prevent ovulation.

Some half million eggs are initially present in the ovaries of human females. At every ovulation each month in a mature woman only one egg is released. The mechanism which ensures this unique release and suppresses any other eggs is modified by the pill chemicals so that *all* egg release is inhibited. The various stages in this process, the chemical substances involved, and the endocrine and glandular reactions have been succinctly described by Kistner (1968) and others. Table 9-2 shows the comparative effectiveness of the pill as compared with the other methods mentioned here in preventing pregnancy.

Table 9-2* *Comparison of Various Methods of Pregnancy Avoidance* The pregnancy rate is a percentage figure expressing the number of women out of 100 who became pregnant in one year using the method stated. The more successful tests with IUD's produce a rate of 1.5 to 3.0. The relatively high rate with sequential pills here is explained by "patient failure"—forgetting to take the pills for one or two days. These figures emphasize the need for a "back-up" abortion facility. They also stress that the rhythm method is partially effective as well as free of cost and direct psychological objections. See text for further explanation.

Method	*Pregnancy Rate*
None	61
Douche	31
Rhythm	21
Jelly only	20
Coitus interruptus	18
Condom	14
Diaphragm	12
IUD	2.6
Sequential pills	2.0
Combination pills	0.1

* Figures summarize data extracted from Kourides, 1967, and Pincus, 1966.

The first pill to be mass-tested on human females, marketed as Enovid, contained the hormones norethynodrel and mestranol. Testing has been in progress since 1956 in Puerto Rico. There have been no reports from this source of serious consequences of its use during the considerable interval which has elapsed since the testing began. However, elsewhere there have been confirmed instances of blood clotting associated with the taking of some forms of oral contraceptive.

Enovid is no longer prescribed solely for purposes of pregnancy control. It has been superseded by other brands, of which there are presently approximately 30. This multiplicity of brands containing varying amounts of the hormones *progestin* and *estrogen* permits a physician to prescribe a pill which will avoid any side effects such as sore breasts, weight increase, bleeding, nausea, and diminished awareness which might arise in individual instances.

In 1969 it was estimated some 8.5 million women in the United States were using some brand of pill. Testing of Enovid, about which there is most information since it is the oldest brand marketed, shows that in 14,840 women and 116,000 cycles, only three pregnancies resulted, a pregnancy rate of 0.028 per cent (Kistner, 1968).

Pills to control male fertility have not so far received the same research attention, perhaps because of cultural factors, but doubtless also owing to the fact that a simple operation is all that is required for the temporary but complete sterilization of a male. This is achieved by tying off the vas deferens to prevent the release of sperm (vasectomy). A recent development is to form a plug in the vas deferens with silicone rubber. Both these operations are potentially reversible. The first is widely used in some countries but the second is still considered in the investigation stage. Any sperm formed after vasectomy are reabsorbed in the testes tissue, and emission of seminal fluid which is secreted by the prostate gland occurs normally. A somewhat similar and relatively minor operation in women can achieve sterilization by tying off the fallopian tubes, without affecting the menstrual cycle (bilateral tubal ligation). Other procedures are under very active investigation, including a "morning after" pill which has reached the human testing stage.

CONTROL AT THE POPULATION LEVEL

It is apparent from the review presented here and in the previous chapter that attempts at population control are presently largely but not entirely uncoordinated and essentially on an individual rather than a population basis. They are inconsistent and still place considerable emphasis on the freedom of choice. If any really effective methods of population control are to be established in time to prevent the completely disastrous onset of conditions described in the previous two chapters, it is clear that a more coordinated and consistent approach to the problem must be made on a world-wide as well as on a regional basis.

Various organizations have been working on such schemes for a number of years; a recent review by Berelson (1969) represents a detailed survey of the various approaches currently considered possible.

METHODS OF POPULATION CONTROL

The survey presented here of the various methods of population control applicable to our present stage of development largely follows the outline and subject content of Berelson's paper. He begins his account by emphasizing the four suppositions rephrased below:

1. *The population problem is among the most pressing world problems requiring immediate attention.*

2. *This problem is most urgent where population increase is hampering required social and economic development, that is, in developing countries.*

3. *Solution to the problem is vital; any postponement of action only makes an ultimate solution more difficult to achieve.*

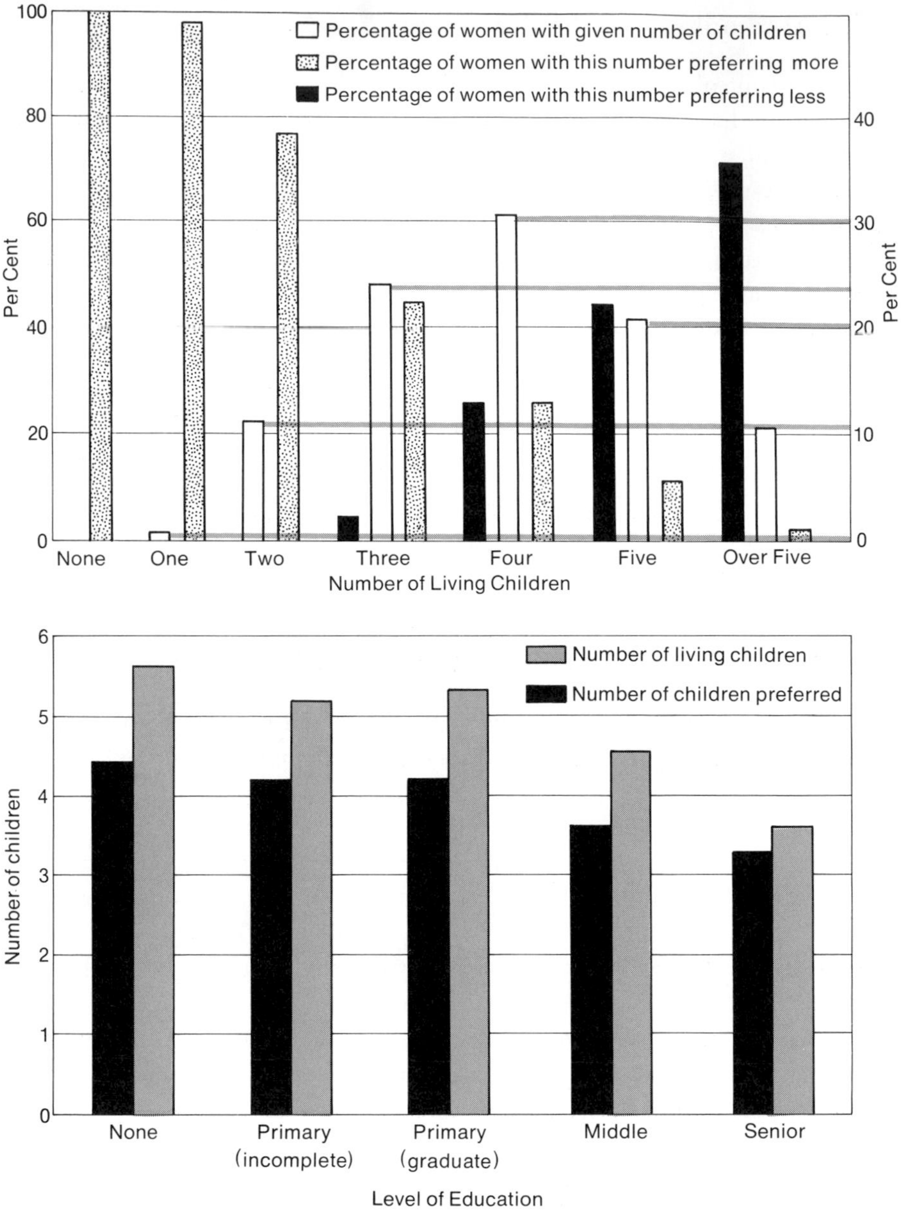

Figure 9-3. *Realized as compared with desired fecundity. Upper Figure.* An area of Taiwan, representing an underdeveloped nation. *Lower Figure.* The United States. In both cases it seems that the majority of women presently prefer a family of four children, all want some children; very few women sampled in these two societies liked having over five children.

4. *Whereas there is general agreement that population increase should be reduced, there is no consensus as to how this should be achieved.*

As Berelson remarks, family-planning programs which have been operating in most advanced societies for some years are for many reasons not applicable to the urgencies of the present population situation. The primary reason for this seems to be that these programs are concerned with the spacing of the interval between children rather than reducing the number of children. A recent report by Eisner *et al.* (1970) suggests this is true even for the most sophisticated individuals. Figure 9-3, showing statistics regarding American women on the one hand and Taiwanese on the other, indicates that many women in the population at large still desire to have an average of four children. As programs to reduce births below this figure must be developed, the various procedures which are available can, following Berelson, be categorized on the following basis:

1. INTENSIFICATION OF VOLUNTARY FERTILITY CONTROL

a. ***Extension and Legalization of Free Abortion Services to the Community as a Whole.*** Statistics from countries where abortion practices have not yet been legalized usually reveal a vast extent of illegal abortion. In a country such as Japan, where abortion has been legalized and made readily available, the results in population control have been demonstrably effective. During the period of very rapid decline in natural increase in Japan, following World War II, the annual number of abortions performed was 1,500,000. Failure to terminate these pregnancies would almost have doubled the Japanese birth rate. In the United States, current unofficial estimates put the number of illegal abortions performed at an annual figure of over a million. This is more than one quarter of the actual annual number of live births, and suggests that freely available legalized abortion might assist considerably in stablizing American population growth. Now abortion has been legalized in New York State, it is expected 100,000 operations will be carried out there annually. Table 9-2 indicate the advisability of having a backup system of legalized abortion.

b. ***Provision of Maternal Care in Village Areas.*** In developing countries three quarters or more of the population is still concentrated in villages. Maternal care there should be placed on an institutionalized basis, which makes possible the provision of both education and services in population control simultaneously with the provision of prenatal care (Taylor and Berelson, 1968).

2. INTRODUCTION OF COMPULSORY FERTILITY CONTROL

a. ***Use of a Fertility Control Agent on a Regional Basis.*** Government action in this direction is advocated by a number of writers, including Ehrlich (1968). The introduction of such group treatment would be designed to reduce fertility in the area treated to from 5 to 75 per cent below the present rate.

It is believed that a considerable range of suitable substances will be available in from 5 to 15 years as a result of present research. Such a chemosterilant substance could readily be introduced to the water supply of urban areas, where often it is especially needed. A parallel suggestion is the addition of similar temporary sterilants to staple foods such as bread or sugar, which might be more practical alternatives in some instances. The Paddocks (1967) suggest that the United Nations consider instituting a "no birth year," which would best be obtained with such mass sterilants.

b. ***Issuing "Children Licenses."*** A number of authorities have suggested that each woman be issued a license to have whatever number of children is established as necessary to maintain a population growth rate of zero in her particular community. In many areas this would be arranged so as to achieve an average of 2.2 children per female, but the actual number would vary from 7 to 0.7 (Table 7-12). These children certificates could be exchanged as gifts, or sold, and would be completely negotiable.

c. ***Temporary Sterilization of Girls by Means of Reversible Time-Capsule Contraceptives.*** The reversibility of this control device should be permitted only when the popular vote decides to permit further development of population growth.

d. ***Compulsory Sterilization of Men Having Three or More Living Children.*** This is extensively advocated as an alternative to (c). A corollary of this suggestion is not to sterilize men at this point, but to require induced

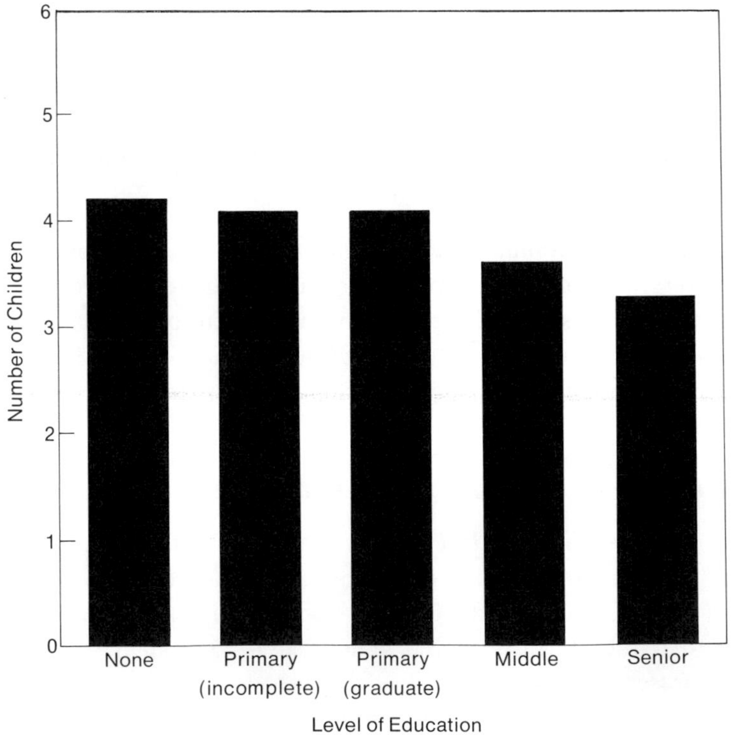

Figure 9-4. *Education and family size.* The effect of educational experience on actual fecundity among women 35–39 years old. The use of contraception most extensively by the most educated is correlated with an approximation on average to desired family size in this group. Progressively less educated women wanted more children, but progressively had more even then than they wished, correlated with a decreasing contraceptive practice.

abortion for all pregnancies resulting beyond a particular number of children.

The difficulties of enforcing such a method are quite apparent.

3. INTENSIFIED EDUCATION CAMPAIGNS

a. ***Dissemination of Education Materials on Population Control at all Primary and Secondary Levels.*** Opposition in various regions of the United States to sex education in schools illustrates the kind of difficulty which may be anticipated in a universal implementation of this suggestion, even in sophisticated societies. There appears some reason for the belief that education in general, rather than mere instruction in birth control techniques, exercises a strong controlling influence on population (Figure 9-4 and Table 9-3).

b. ***Use of Satellites for the Provision of Extensive Television Programs Disseminating Information on Population Control, Family Planning, and Attitudes Toward Population Growth.*** This is a very practical temporary measure to cover the situation where local technical facilities may be still in an early stage of development. It would need to be supplemented with a scheme for communal TV sets and could encounter the same objections as in (a) but on an international rather than a regional basis.

4. INCENTIVE PROGRAMS

a. ***Payments Made Directly to Married Couples Who Refrain from Producing Children During Particular Time Intervals.*** These would include

Table 9-3* ***Education and Fertility*** The total average number of children born to individual American white women expressed in terms of their educational exposure: figures from the 1940 census. College graduates in 1940 were beginning to approach the fertility value necessary to achieve zero population growth; all other education levels progressively exceeded this figure. The same analysis carried out on this contemporary generation might well indicate that college graduate fertility has reached the essential low figure, but would certainly reveal that in other educational classes fertility was still far too high.

Schooling Completed (Years)	*Children per Married Woman*
None	4.97
Grade school	
1–4	4.54
5–6	3.97
7–8	3.04
High school	
1–3	2.61
4	2.03
College	
1–3	2.07
4 or more	1.83

* Reprinted by permission of the publishers from Theodosius Dobzhansky, *Mankind Evolving*, New Haven: Yale University Press, 1967, p. 33.

payment for the acceptance of sterilization or for the effective employment of contraception.

b. ***Bonuses for Spacing Children or for Achieving "Nonpregnancy."*** Rewards might take the form of savings certificates for each 12-month period in which no child is born, a prize for each 5 years of childless marriage, or special lottery tickets for the childless, and so forth. If such incentive schemes designed to *increase* fertility have been successful, the reverse should apply. They should also work successfully when negative, that is, when they are the reward for nonreproduction.

5. TAX AND WELFARE BENEFITS AND PENALTIES

Such measures would represent a reversal of the present social service principles which have largely developed in many instances as a result of the previous population decline in the 1930s. These favor the production of children in that they either give cash payments in support of children, tax relief with respect to child dependents, or both. Rather than encouraging childbearing in this way, tax and welfare benefits would be reversed so as to discourage it by the following procedures:

a. ***Withdrawal of Maternity Benefits After the Birth of a Given Number of Children.***

b. ***Imposition of a Tax on Births After a Determined Number.***
Neither of these measures would be particularly helpful in industrial societies, for among them it is only the poorest element which needs to reduce its natural increase (see later in this chapter), and it is too poor to pay any further tax or sustain withdrawal of any child benefits. The same applies to (c) below.

c. ***Limitation of Governmentally Provided Medical Treatment, Housing, and Financial Aid for Schooling to Families with Fewer Than a Specific Number of Children.***

d. ***Complete Reversal of Tax Benefits.*** Instead of strongly penalizing single persons as at present, tax measures should favor the unmarried and the parents of fewer rather than more children. This is an entirely practical measure which can immediately be implemented in a society. It will considerably assist in the creation of the "uncles" and "aunts" for whom Garrett Hardin pleads (1969).

e. ***Provision by the State of a Particular Allocation of Free Schooling to Each Family.*** This free schooling could then be distributed over a family of any size as desired, giving, for example, a university education for two, or a grade school education for eight. Such a measure would only work in an undeveloped country where educational facilities were still at a premium.

f. ***Provision of Pension for Impoverished Parents Who Have Produced Fewer Than a Given Number of Children.*** This would be a form of social security for their retirement years for low income couples who decided not to have children, a measure applicable to any economically structured society.

6. SHIFTS IN SOCIAL-ECONOMIC INSTITUTIONS

This involves fundamental changes in institutional arrangements with the intention of lowering fertility. It would include:

a. ***By Legislation or Through Imposition of Effective Fees, Raising the Minimum Age for Marriage.*** This might be achieved on a voluntary basis by payment of marriage benefits only to brides and grooms over a particular age limit, or through issuing governmental loans for wedding ceremonies when the bride is over a particular age.

This is a measure with potentially disturbing social overtones, for the creation of a large group of unattached but very vigorous females could have disruptive effects on previously stable social institutions. Perhaps the measure should only be applied where it can be combined with a longer period of education for the women so released from early marriage.

b. ***Action to Require Participation of Women in the Labor Market or to Promote Their Voluntary Participation.*** This might provide other roles for women as an alternate or supplement to marriage. In effect this is what the the Madison Avenue effect referred to in earlier chapters achieves. Married couples prefer the higher standard of living which the dual income provides to the self-elected hardships of family costs.

c. ***Fundamental Restructuring of Society So As to Minimize the Social Position of the Family in Community Life.*** This proposition needs rephrasing perhaps, e.g., "so as to emphasize alternatives without denigrating the central social importance of the family."

d. ***Institution of Two Types of Marriage.*** One kind would be designed to be of a more temporary nature and not to result in the production of children. The other would be licensed to be more permanent and to be the legitimate vehicle for the production of children. In effect this is almost what we have now in some countries in the "common law marriage," but it has to be disassociated from the procreation of children.

e. ***Social Improvements of an Economic Kind.*** This could be achieved by the provision of new productive industries to encourage the employment of women and to raise their status in society, and in general to refocus attention on social contributions other than marriage. Perhaps this also could be better phrased. There is no need to destroy pair-bonding as such, but merely to demonstrate that children are not an essential feature of this association.

f. ***Strenuous Attempts to Lower Infant Mortality and Child Death Rates.*** This is considered necessary in order to obviate the feeling of the necessity for large families in order to ensure the survival of some descendants, a point well taken for many undeveloped societies with recent histories of high child mortalities.

7. POLITICAL CHANNELS AND ORGANIZATIONS

a. ***Insistence on Population Control Prior to Delivery of Famine Relief Supplies.*** This might be regarded as political blackmail, for it requires exertion of political pressure on governments before they can receive foreign aid favors. This at any rate, is not so coldly inhumane as the Paddock brothers' "triage" system, which may well have to be implemented within the next decade.

b. ***Massive Reorganization of National and International Agencies to Deal More Effectively with Population Problems.*** In the United States this would require institution of a federal department of population and environment, empowered to legislate for the establishment of a calculated and desired population size. In underdeveloped areas it supposes the creation of ministries for population control and, on an international scale, the organization of a specialized agency parallel to but larger than the World Health Organization to effectively promote family limitation techniques throughout the world, particularly in the underdeveloped areas.

c. ***Promotion of the Concept of Zero Population Growth.*** This must be considered as the aim of all human societies. Steps to achieve acceptance of this idea as of now could be taken in order to provide the necessary urge to accept even further lowered fertility measures in the present critical situation. While private enterprise and initiative have already established such organizations in this country and elsewhere, governmental attitudes have not yet been modified to any significant extent (see the end of this chapter).

8. AUGMENTED RESEARCH EFFORTS

a. ***More Sociological Research on Acceptance of Necessary Fertility Objectives***

b. ***Research on Practical Method of Sex Determination.***

c. ***Increased Research Even Beyond That Presently in Hand.*** Still mainly of a private enterprise nature, this is directed toward the improvement of contraceptive technology rather than such problems as social acceptance of zero population growth.

IMPLEMENTATION OF POPULATION CONTROL MEASURES

For reasons which have already been mentioned, and notably the difficulty in obtaining accurate census figures, it is exceedingly difficult to assess the effect of the introduction of particular population control measures, even when details of the latter are available. Kirk (1967) has nevertheless attempted a review of the prospects for reducing birth rates in underdeveloped nations. He concludes that within a decade, birth rates of 20 to 25 will be attained in the most progressive parts of East and Southeast Asia, and that the same levels may be reached in India and mainland China in two decades. By this time he expects that the whole underdeveloped world will have begun to move toward this figure, with Moslem communities bringing up the rear. Kirk also foresees an inevitable doubling, for example in the populations of most Latin American countries.

Kirk's optimistic report might be more encouraging were it not for several other considerations. First, Table 7-12 shows that with a mortality rate in most nations already fallen below 15, birth rates of 20 to 25 are not going to achieve anything approaching zero population growth. Second, and perhaps more important, powerful interests have always resisted, or are beginning again to resist the introduction of population measures. In Japan, for instance, industrial support for the fertility control program has reportedly been withdrawn, because of the mounting expense of Japanese labor compared with that of surrounding countries.

Power Politics and Population Control

The influences of sectional and national aspirations on population growth have not always been apparent, but they have never ceased to be extremely powerful. The most openly debated example has been the Roman Catholic Church, which has long been accused of seeking to maintain the numbers of its national and international congregations by promoting natural increase among Catholics.

Less obvious perhaps are minority group situations in many countries. When, as in the United States, employment of minority group personnel is based on a system of counting the number and color of noses, it would be unreasonable to expect that factional leaders would wholeheartedly support programs whose primary object if realized will remove the very source of their power.

The same is believed to apply on a national scale (Knopf, 1961; Hauser, 1958). The figures in Table 9-4 indicate the relationship which is often believed to hold between national populations and national power. France and Italy decline in the pecking order of nations as their proportional populations decline, while the United States, United Kingdom, and Germany improve their relative positions.

The lack of direct control and direct causal relationships in such interactions is stressed by Kingsley Davis (1954), who emphasizes that one of the demographic factors weakening a nation's power is a high birth rate. Before World War II, he notes, both Mussolini and Hitler were endeavoring to raise their countries' birth rates. Had they fully succeeded, their population

Table 9-4 *Correlation Between National Population Size and National Standing*
At the beginning of the nineteenth century France was a leading world power, perhaps *the* world power. She joined with Russia to resist Germany, and largely ignored Italy, the United Kingdom, and the United States. A century later France, while still allied to Russia, had to form closer ties with the United Kingdom and Italy in an endeavor, despite her weakening condition, to contain a more powerful Germany. This last country hoped, in the event of war, to keep the now powerful but isolated United States neutral.

Country	*Population** *1800*	*Country*	*Population* *1900*
Russia	37	Russia	140
France	27	United States	92
Germany	25	Germany	65
Italy	18	United Kingdom	45
United Kingdom	16	France	40
United States	5	Italy	35

* Figures in millions of population.

structures would have been loaded with noncontributing members of society, women and material resources would have had to be withdrawn from the war effort to care for them, and their chances of winning the war would have been still further reduced.

The Basic Problem

Of all the characteristics we have inherited from our ancestral populations, the demographic pattern has become the most embarrassing. It will be apparent from ideas presented in these last three chapters that during nearly 4 million years as hunting-gathering populations we adapted by natural selection to a pattern which provided a stable population level and structure with a birth rate in the region of 35 to 40, and an average fecundity level of five or six live births per female.

As cultural evolution proceeded to reduce the mortality rate, so in some circumstances did it provide for a reduction of the birth rate. Such societies remained stable and in a steady state within their ecosystems. The great majority of evolving populations, however, adapted to lower mortality rates without a parallel adaptation in birth rates. Whether this failure was unconscious or deliberate, the effect is now the same, and many societies will have to pay an appalling price for this simple demographic omission.

UNITED NATIONS DECLARATION

In order to reinforce the urgency and seriousness with which the various proposals presented in this chapter must be considered, and wherever possible implemented, the following passages are abstracted from a declaration of the United Nations on Human Rights Day, December, 1967. The italics have been inserted here for emphasis.

The peace of the world is of paramount importance. . . . But another great problem threatens the world—a problem less visible but no less immediate. That is the problem of *unplanned population growth.*

It took mankind all of recorded time until the middle of the last century to achieve a population of one billion. Yet it took less than a hundred years to add the second billion, and only thirty years to add the third. At today's rate of increase there will be four billion people by 1975 and nearly seven billion by the year 2000. *This unprecedented increase presents us with a situation unique in human affairs and a problem that grows more urgent with each passing day.*

The numbers themselves are striking, but their implications are of far greater significance. Too rapid population growth seriously hampers efforts to raise living standards, to further education, to improve health and sanitation, to provide better housing and transportation, to forward cultural and recreational opportunities, and even in some countries to assure sufficient food. In short, the human aspiration, common to men everywhere, to live a better life is being frustrated and jeopardized.

As heads of government actively concerned with the population problem, we share these convictions:

We believe that the population problem must be recognized as a principal element in long-range national planning if governments are to achieve their economic goals and fulfill the aspirations of their people.

We believe that the great majority of parents desire to have the knowledge and the means to plan their families; that the opportunity to decide the number and spacing of children is a basic human right.

We believe that the objective of family planning is the enrichment of human life, not its restriction; that family planning, by assuring greater opportunity to each person, frees man to attain his individual dignity and reach his full potential.

Recognizing that family planning is in the vital interest of both the nation and the family, we, the undersigned, earnestly hope that leaders around the world will share our views and join with us in this great challenge for the well-being and happiness of people everywhere.

This declaration was signed by the U.N. representatives of the following countries:

Australia	Finland	The Philippines
Barbados	Ghana	Singapore
Colombia	India	Sweden
Denmark	Indonesia	Thailand
Dominican Republic	Iran	Trinidad
Nepal	Japan	Tunisia
The Netherlands	Jordan	United Arab Republic
New Zealand	Korea	United Kingdom
Norway	Malaysia	United States
Pakistan	Morocco	Yugoslavia

No more critical and serious a declaration has ever been issued by such an august body in the history of this earth. It would be a very fitting note on which to close this chapter on population control, but for the fact that it hardly goes far enough to meet the extreme urgency of the situation.

It will be apparent that there is a considerable distinction between the attitude displayed in this U.N. declaration and that ascribed earlier to Berelson's population council insofar as its survey of possible control measures is concerned.

The U.N. declaration emphasizes an individual freedom of choice in the procreation of children. Faced with the population statistics presented in the last three chapters, many will consider it totally unrealistic to suggest there is still time to exercise such a freedom. There can be no question but that retention of the individual's right to decide how many children to strive for severely restricts the selection of population control measures which can quickly be brought into operation.

Nor is there any question that we have accepted other restrictions on our individual freedoms in order to achieve a betterment of social conditions for all. For example, in the vast majority of countries it is *compulsory* to pay some form of income tax. In this country we have in addition lost our right to cross the road where we please, to maintain a private army, to mint our own money, to have two or more legal wives or husbands, to send our children to work rather than to school, to visit any country we wish, to attend a state university.

It may be possible to establish the principle that to be allowed to procreate children is a *privilege, not* a right, that it is just as necessary to demonstrate a suitability for parenthood as it is to prove scholastic ability in order to enter a university.

Since social life has always entailed some obligation, it seems unrealistic to insist at this late hour that we cannot contemplate one more restriction on our liberty in such a critical cause as the survival of our species. At any rate the disastrous effects of continuing to insist on our individual rights in this matter will be made apparent to those of us living even in our own lifetimes, and our declining years could be blighted by the folly of our inaction. The future may weigh heavily on the representatives of those ninety nations who refused to respond to even this relatively innocuous U.N. declaration on population control.

POPULATION STABILIZATION IN THE UNITED STATES

The message of Hardin, Ehrlich, Borgstrom, and others—insofar as this country is concerned—is that we must take immediate steps to stabilize this nation's population by limiting to a maximum of two the number of children an individual may have. Hardin in particular stresses equally the need to adjust behavioral rituals to an acceptance of childless bachelors and spinsters as *normal* members of society.

An authoritative paper by Blake (1969) states this last need very succinctly:

Individuals who—by temperament, health, or constitution—do not fit the ideal sex-role pattern are nonetheless coerced into attempting to achieve it, at least to the extent of having demographic impact by becoming parents. . . . The rigid structuring of the wife-mother position builds into the entire motivational pattern of women's lives a tendency to want at least a moderate-size family. . . . The desired number of children relates not simply to the wish for a family of a particular size but relates as well to a need for more than one or two children if one is going to enjoy "family life" over a significant portion of one's lifetime. . . . The notion that most women will "see the error of their ways" and decide to have two-child families is naive. . . .

Table 9-5* ***Number of Children Considered Ideal by Non-Catholic Women in the United States*** Participants were arranged into four levels of economic status ranging from "high," 1, to "low," 4. The 1943 figures reflect the low fertility levels of the previous decade. From considering fewer children desirable than did more wealthy categories, the lowest income group upgraded their optimum fertility almost 50 per cent, while those in the highest category hardly varied in their opinions between 1968 and 1943.

Year	*Age Range*	*Economic Status* 1	2	3	4
1943	20–34	2.9	2.7	2.7	2.5
1952	21+	– 3.3 –		3.3	3.3
1955	18–39	3.2	3.1	3.2	3.5
1957	21+	– 3.3 –		3.2	3.5
1959	21+	– 3.5 –		3.5	3.6
1960	18–39	3.2	3.3	3.5	3.4
1963	21+	3.3	3.3	3.5	3.5
1966	21+	3.2	3.2	3.4	3.7
1967	21+	3.3	3.2	3.1	3.4
1968	21+	3.2	3.0	3.4	3.6

* Reprinted by permission of the publisher and author from J. Blake Davis, *Science*, **164:** 524, 1969. Copyright 1969 by the American Association for the Advancement of Science.

Blake addresses a considerable part of her argument to countering the popular proposition that approximately 15 per cent of the U.S. population classified as "poor" have more children per family than higher income groups, not because they desire it, but through lack of information or resources to prevent it. She presents evidence (Table 9-5) which suggests that "poor" families actually desire more children and favor birth control less (Table 9-6); and she concludes that the majority of lower-income couples already use birth control when they choose to do so.

Blake's paper evoked a strong response from Harkavy, Jaffe, and Wishik (1969). Some of their statements are extremely pertinent, not only in the context of Dr. Blake's paper, but also as they concern the efforts epitomized by Hardin, Ehrlich, and Borgstrom. They note: "There has never been official policy regarding the virtue or necessity of reducing the U.S. popula-

Table 9-6* ***Attitude Toward the Use of Birth Control*** These data are for attitudes expressed in different economic levels in the United States in polls taken between 1959 and 1966. Persons participating were aged 21 to 44 and divided into four categories of economic status, progressing from the most, 1, to the least prosperous, 4. Figures represent percentages of individuals who expressed approval of birth control.

ECONOMIC STATUS	*APPROVAL*	
	Men	*Women*
1	89	87
2	84	82
3	83	80
4	74	78

* Reprinted by permission of the publisher and author from J. Blake Davis, *Science,* **164:** 526, 1969. Copyright 1969 by the American Association for the Advancement of Science.

tion growth, much less achieving population stability," and reproduce various official pronouncements to support their contention that the federal policies in this country are directed at improvements in health and economic prosperity, *not* population control. Included in the very interesting data presented in their paper is Table 9-7.

Table 9-7* ***Relation of Poverty to Size of Family*** Figures represent the percentage of the total of all United States "poor" and "near poor" families with the number of children indicated.

Number of Children	*"Poor" Families*	*"Poor" and "Near Poor" Families*
1	9.3	14.1
2	10.2	15.6
3	12.8	21.3
4	18.6	30.9
5	27.7	42.5
6 or more	42.1	58.1

* Reprinted by permission of the publisher and author from O. Harkavy, F. S. Jaffe, and S. M. Wishik, *Science,* **165:** 372, 1969. Copyright 1969 by the American Association for the Advancement of Science.

The data presented here indicate that "poor" and "near-poor" families which represent 40 per cent of American families contain no fewer than 58 per cent of those with six or more children, but only 14 per cent of those with only one child. In an even more narrowly defined group of "poor" families constituting 26 per cent of the United States total, these included 42 per cent of the United States total with six or more children, but only 9 per cent of those with a single child.

Faced with pressures such as are being exerted by Hardin, Ehrlich, and Borgstrom, by wide divergences in specialist opinion such as exists between the authors of the two recent papers just discussed, and a general dearth of information on possible economic interactions such as the "Madison Avenue" effect postulated by Boughey, it is hardly surprising that professional politicians tread warily and appear slow to respond with positive edicts on United

States population policy. Nor are decisions any easier for the individual citizen.

There is no other way to conclude this chapter except on a somewhat ominous note; in fact, we have no real choice. The question is not if and when, but *by what means* will we elect to stabilize our individual national communities, including the population of the United States, and prevent any further increase in the size of the human global population.

Bibliography

REFERENCES

Anonymous. *Recreation in the Nation's Cities: Problems and Approaches,* National League of Cities, Dept. of Urban Studies, Dept. of the Interior, 1968.

Berelson, B., and Freedman, R. "A study in fertility control," *Scientific American,* **210**(5): 29–37, 1964.

Berelson, B. "Beyond family planning," *Science,* **163:** 533–43, 1969.

Borgstrom, G. *Too Many,* New York: Macmillan, 1969.

Boughey, A. S. "The future of *Homo sapiens,*" in preparation, 1971.

Calderone, M. S. *Manual of Contraceptive Practice,* Baltimore: Wilkins & Wilkins, 1964.

Carr-Saunders, A. M. *World Population,* Oxford: Clarendon Press, 1936.

Davis, J. Blake. "Population policy for Americans: is the government being misled?" *Science,* **164:** 522–29, 1969.

Davis, Kingsley. "The demographic foundations of national power," in M. Berger, T. Abel, and C. H. Page (eds.), *Freedom and Control in Modern Society,* New York: Van Nostrand, 1954.

Davis, Kingsley. "Population policy: will current programs succeed?" *Science,* **158:** 730–39, 1967.

Ehrlich, P. R. *The Population Bomb,* New York: Ballantyne, 1968.

Eisner, T., van Tienhoren, A., and Rosenblatt, F. "Population control, sterilization, and ignorance," *Science,* **167**, No. 3917, leader, 1970.

Hardin, G. "Not peace, but ecology," in "Diversity and stability in ecological systems," *Brookhaven Symposia in Biology* No. 22, 1969, pp. 151–61.

Harkavy, O., Jaffe, F. S., and Wishik, S. M. "Family planning and public policy: who is misleading whom?" *Science,* **165:** 367–73, 1969.

Hauser, P. M. *Population and World Politics,* New York: Free Press of Glencoe, 1958.

Heer, D. M. "Economic development and the fertility transition," *Daedalus*, **97:** 447–62, 1968.

Kirk, D. "Prospects for reducing natality in the underdeveloped world," *Ann. Amer. Acad. Pol. Soc. Sci.*, **369:** 48–60, 1967.

Kistner, R. W. *The Pill*, New York: Delacorte Press, 1968.

Knopf, A. A. (ed.) *Population and World Power*, New York: Knopf, 1961.

Kourides, I. A. "Freedom of birth," *Medical Science*, **18**(8): 25–31, 1967.

Paddock, W., and Paddock, P. *Famine—1975*, Boston: Little, Brown, 1967.

Pincus, G. "Control of conception by hormonal steroids," *Science*, **153:** 493–500.

Revelle, R. "Introduction to 'Historical Populations Studies'," *Daedalus*, **97:** 353–62, 1968.

Spengler, J. J. "Demographic factors and early modern economic development," *Daedalus*, **97:** 433–46, 1968.

Taylor, H. C., and Berelson, B. "Maternity care and family planning as a world problem," *Amer. J. Obstet. Gynecol.*, **100:** 885, 1968.

Walle, E. van de. "Marriage and marital fertility," *Daedalus*, **97:** 486–501, 1968.

Wynne-Edwards, V. C. "Self-regulating systems in populations of animals," *Science*, **147:** 1543–48, 1965.

FURTHER READINGS

Calder, R. *Common Sense About a Starving World*, New York: Macmillan, 1962.

Cook, R. C. "California after 19 million what?" *Population Bull.*, **22:** 29–57, 1966.

D'Antonio, W. V. "Birth control and coercion," *Commonweal*, Dec. 2, 1966.

Dubos, R. *The Torch of Life, Continuity in Living Experience*, New York: Simon and Schuster, 1962.

Hardin, G. *Population, Evolution and Birth Control; A Collage of Controversial Readings*, 2nd ed., San Francisco: Freeman, 1969.

Hoagland, H. "Mechanisms of population control," *Daedalus*, Summer 1964, 812–29.

Meier, R. L. *Modern Science and the Human Fertility Problem*, New York: Wiley, 1959.

Price, D. D. (ed.). *The 99th Hour—The Population Crisis in the United States*, Chapel Hill: University of North Carolina Press, 1967.

Rock, J. *The Time Has Come*, New York: Knopf, 1963.

Tietze, C., Poliakoff, S. R., and Rock, J. "The clinical effectiveness of the rhythm method of contraception," *Fertility and Sterility*, **2**(5), 1951.

Air Pollution 10

Throughout the previous chapters of this book it has been apparent that for some 4 million years, from the earliest hominids to contemporary man, one human characteristic has remained unchanged and invariable—we have always produced garbage and litter. Even on our latest adventure into space, we have sent our debris ahead of us, and we have vented it on the surface and into the atmosphere of the new world where we have landed. Indeed, without such waste we should have little record of our evolutionary past, for it is from discarded tools, unscattered remains of meals, feces, and similar artifacts or excrescences that we have been able to piece together something of our past cultural life.

Rate of Waste Accumulation

With global *erectus-sapiens* populations totaling a million individuals, all in a hunting-gathering phase, such wastes accumulated very slowly and quite locally. With a total population now estimated at 3 billion plus, the global pile of excrement increases at the rate of about 1½ *million* tons per day.

Yet this is among the least of our problems. More and more of us now live in cities, and it has been calculated that the average city dweller produces 1500 lb of garbage per year—about 5 lb per day. A garbage collectors' strike brings home to us the true significance of this rate of discarded waste.

We need no strike, however, to make us appreciate that not all this garbage is carted away for disposal and that some instead rises into the air in the form of solid pollutants. A global total of 140 million tons of solid pollutants is now emitted into the air annually. Some of this coats our buildings and soils our hands and clothes; some of it is inhaled and deposited on the tissues of our lungs. This presents us with the problem, or rather the series of allied problems, now broadly described by the term *air pollution.*

While the rate of garbage accumulation in this century may be unprecedented, the release of *particulate matter* into the air and the consequent pollution of the atmosphere is far from new. The walled cities of medieval Europe 700 years ago already had such problems with the wood smoke which belched from the chimneys of every city house. The introduction of coal as a domestic and industrial fuel in the early thirteenth century seems, however, to have really ushered in the smog era. By the middle of that century London and other British cities were said to have become almost uninhabitable. The death penalty was introduced to reinforce laws prohibiting the burning of coal in London while Parliament was in session and is believed to have been carried out on one unfortunate citizen caught burning coal while the House was sitting (Wise, 1968).

Smog and Particulate Matter

As the centuries passed, solid pollutant problems were reported from other cities. Edinburgh, Scotland, became affectionately known as "Auld Reekie"; the British industrial belt in Staffordshire and Warwickshire was called the "Black Country." London, however, remained preeminent in this notorious field. This unenviable distinction was reaffirmed in modern times during four critical days in December, 1952, when in the worst smog attack of its recorded history one out of every 2000 Londoners died, an estimated total of 4000. This does not include uncounted thousands who were made seriously ill but recovered sufficiently to live on for a considerable time—although not to their original life expectancy.

Although the term *smog* applied originally to London's special brand of "pea-soupers" such as this, it became a generic term embracing all earlier nomenclature for the condition existing when solid pollutants are visible in the air. It is also now applied to situations where *invisible* particulate matter is present which produces some visible reaction. Schaefer (1969a) remarks that particles with a cross section of less than 0.1 μ are optically invisible, but such particulates may be a major source of air pollution. An idling automobile, he notes, emits from its exhaust pipe 1×10^{11} such particles per second in a normally invisible plume.

In this text, air pollution has been given a wider definition than is sometimes employed. It is taken here to include any atmospheric disturbance resulting from human activity which has a modifying effect on the role which air plays as an abiotic element of natural ecosystems.

Smog and Toxic Elements

There have been other manifestations of air pollution not so immediately obvious as particulate matter. Some 5 per cent of U.S. soldiers stationed in the greater Tokyo area in the late 1940s developed a disorder known as "Yokohama asthma"—a breathing difficulty from which they recovered on transfer from the area. The City Health Department of New York calculates that during 15 days of heavy smog in 1963, the normal death rate was increased by 650 (Edelson and Warshofsky, 1966). In statistics gathered by a Senate committee, it is estimated that by 1960 every American city with over 1 million population had a major air pollution problem, as did to a lesser degree 64 of the smaller ones. One quarter of the United States population live in cities with a major, 30 million in areas with a moderate, and 3½ million in those with a minor problem, the report stated.

Los Angeles Smog

The city of Los Angeles has come to be synonymous with smog. Medical advisors are reported to have told at least 10,000 people to leave the city for their health's sake. Schoolchildren have been officially advised to minimize outdoor activity during smog alerts. It is no longer a question of problems with inversions in the Los Angeles basin; Ponderosa pines are dying in the San Gabriel and San Jacinto mountains at altitudes upward of 2500 m. Various species of desert plant are disappearing from as far afield as the Coachella Valley. The smog even reaches out over Palm Springs, where the affluent have fled in an attempt to preserve their lungs, or at any rate their vocal cords.

These more spectacular examples of release of garbage into our common environment illustrate the kind of problems which have arisen through overloading of the biogeochemical pathways of city ecosystems until they cease to operate effectively. The waste materials at various trophic levels accumulate in the form of garbage, instead of being broken down by decomposers and their elements recycled. In considering such ecosystem failures, it is convenient to call all such accumulations from overloaded pathways pollution, and subdivide this further both according to the nature of the environmental media polluted, that is, air and water, and to the type of pollution, noise and thermal. In this text, the term air pollution also embraces major disturbances in the proportions in which gases such as carbon dioxide, oxygen, ozone, and carbon monoxide occur in the air. A common way of classifying air pollutants is to categorize them into combustion products, radionuclides, and pesticides. The first are considered in this present chapter, the second especially in Chapter 11, and the last in Chapter 12.

ATMOSPHERIC CIRCULATION

Air masses, like water masses, are not evenly dispersed over the earth's land surfaces, but may be segmented into *air sheds* which correspond to some extent with watersheds (Figure 10-1). The composition of the air masses in these air sheds—the proportional mixture of gases, their tempera-

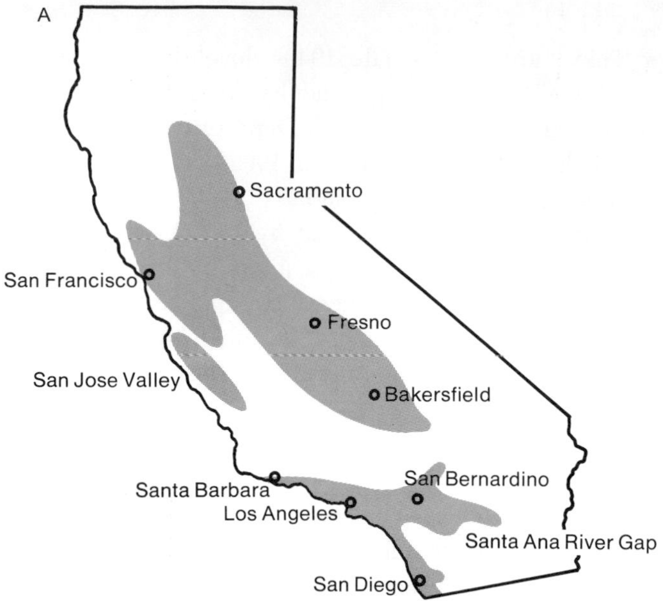
A
Sacramento
San Francisco
Fresno
San Jose Valley
Bakersfield
Santa Barbara
San Bernardino
Los Angeles
Santa Ana River Gap
San Diego

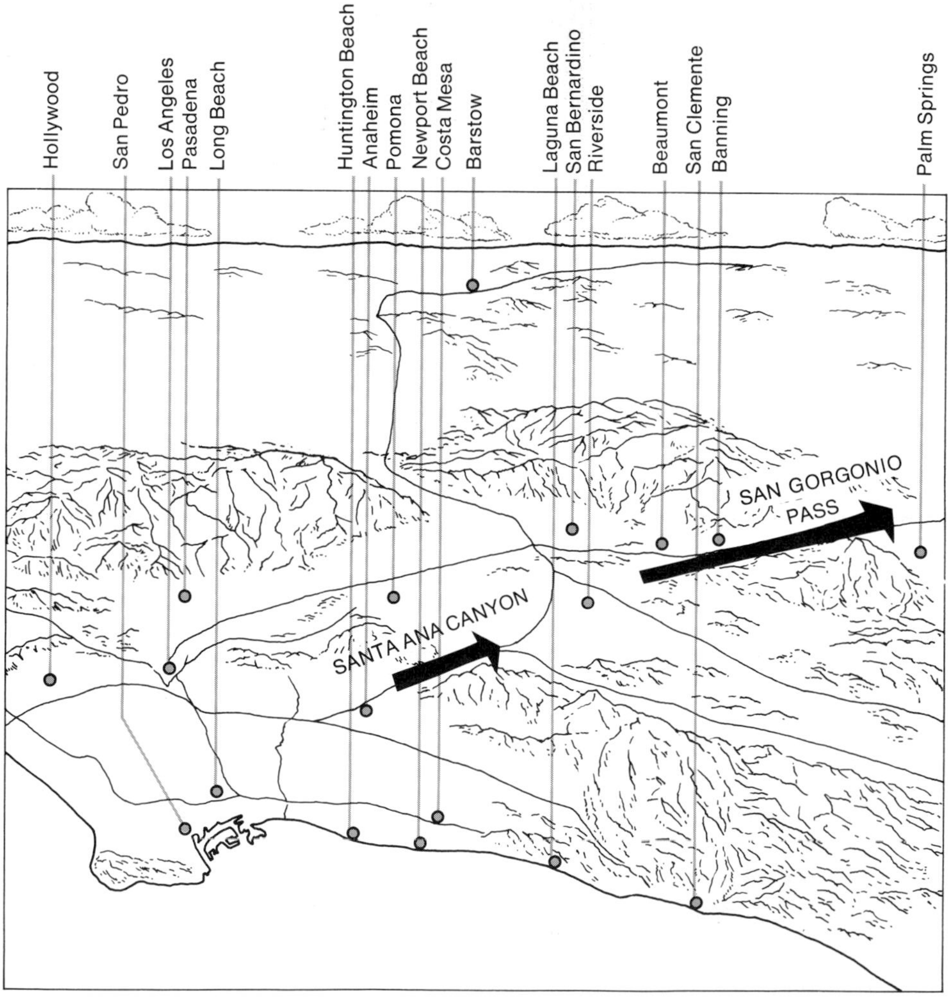
Hollywood
San Pedro
Los Angeles
Pasadena
Long Beach
Huntington Beach
Anaheim
Pomona
Newport Beach
Costa Mesa
Barstow
Laguna Beach
San Bernardino
Riverside
Beaumont
San Clemente
Banning
Palm Springs
SAN GORGONIO PASS
SANTA ANA CANYON

ture, their movement, and the solid, liquid, and gaseous pollutants they contain—depends very much on the nature of the ecosystems included within each air shed. Thus, while each human being processes perhaps 30 lb of air every 24 hours, the average car will need about *one ton* during a 200 to 300 mile run, or in using one tank of gasoline. Burning 1 lb of coal requires 14 lb of air, 1 lb of natural gas, 18 lb of air; 1 gal of fuel oil, 19 lb of air.

AIR SHED UTILIZATION

The air shed of a city of some 2 million inhabitants such as Los Angeles is obviously therefore not so much affected by the 60 thousand tons of air its citizens process a day, as by the 1 million tons which would pass through its automobiles if every citizen daily used one tank of gasoline.

The effect of the presence of these citizens is to remove some of the oxygen and to add some carbon dioxide. Even within the city's air shed, the producer populations of the local ecosystems could take care of this and restore the original balances.

The vented effluents from automobile exhausts are, however, more than any naturally occurring ecosystem can handle. Only the dispersal of air from the city air shed, and its replacement by fresh air, will remove these automobile emissions or air pollutants from the atmosphere of the city. Because of special features of meteorology and topography in Los Angeles, this air shed exchange is not always possible. When it is not, a smog attack develops.

Air Circulation

Owing to the general circulation of air masses in the northern hemisphere (Figure 10-2) these pass from one air shed to another in an easterly direction from the Pacific to the Atlantic Coast, then across the north Atlantic to Europe, across Eurasia and over the Pacific. During the ocean passages in particular it is assumed that the oxygen to carbon dioxide balance is restored through the photosynthetic activity of phytoplankton; whatever solid pollutants have been added settle out in the oceans, if fallout has not already deposited them on a land mass. Rain and snowfall considerably assist in removing particulate matter from the atmosphere.

Although very little is known about this replenishment of air sheds with clean air as a result of such atmospheric circulation, it is not unreasonable to suppose that the settling-out and gas-ratio homeostatic mechanisms of the

Figure 10-1. *Air sheds in coastal southern and central California.* The air sheds of the southern Pacific Coast commonly recognized are over the Central Valley and Bay Area, the greater Los Angeles Basin, and the San Jose Valley. This last can drain over the Outer Coast Range into the Central Valley Basin, but it is then shut in by the uninterrupted mass of the Sierra Nevada. The Los Angeles Basin drains through the Santa Ana River Gap and the San Gorgonio Pass.

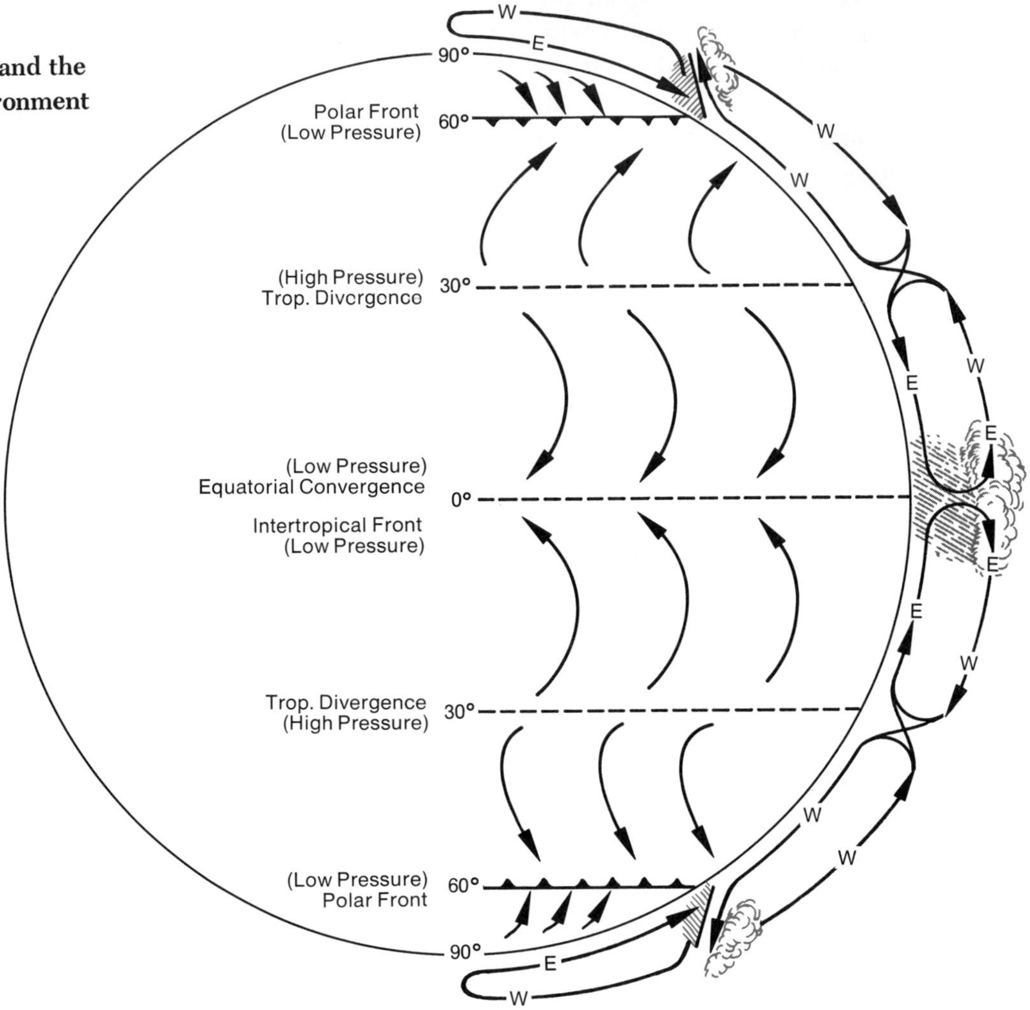

Figure 10-2. *The pattern of planetary winds* which produces prevailing westerly winds in the temperate regions of North America. Air sheds in this area therefore tend to drain toward the east. The smog generated on the Pacific Coast is drawn over the Sonoran, Mohave, and Great Basin deserts; that of the Eastern seaboard is carried out over the North Atlantic Ocean. (Reprinted by permission of the publisher from J. Gentilli, *A Geography of Climate,* Perth: University of Western Australia Textbooks Board, 1952, p. 38.)

air shed ecosystems could eventually become saturated, and that each time around the globe just a little less oxygen would be added, just a little more carbon dioxide and particulate matter left in.

Recent work by Schaefer (1967b) suggests that the process of auto-cleansing may be beginning to break down over many parts of the United States. He measured the concentration of particulates during eight trans-continental flights which included passage over most of the major polluted centers, and considered that the general fallout of pollutants had escaped beyond the limits of local air sheds.

For the present, however, a massive breakdown in the air shed replenishment occurs typically only locally, when special meteorological conditions prevail. The commonest of these is known as a *temperature inversion.*

INVERSIONS

As any jet traveler can observe by listening to the information supplied en route, air temperature in the lowest region of the earth's atmosphere, the *troposphere,* decreases with increasing distance above the ground. This temperature decrease is maintained at a steady value until a height above the surface of 8 to 18 km (the *stratosphere*) is reached.

The actual *rate* of temperature loss is known as the *lapse* rate. If the lapse rate becomes negative, *temperature inversion* occurs; instead of decreasing with increasing height, the air temperature actually *increases.* Above 8 to 18 km, where the *troposphere* is replaced by the *stratosphere,* there is a permanent inversion.

There may be a number of inversions at various heights in the troposphere, and meteorologists classify them by their various modes of origin, and the several effects they produce such as haze, fog, turbulence, fronts, and cyclones.

Characteristics of Inversions

Two conditions are especially associated with inversions. The first is the presence of a slowly moving high pressure system in the troposphere. The mass of cooler dense air in such a system prevents circulation of the surface layers of the atmosphere beyond the inversion layer, and the lack of movement produces only light winds insufficient to dissipate the air mass. Second, the topography of a particular region may tend to enclose an inversion so that when adiabatic cooling of the air included in it occurs, a balance is eventually achieved at the level of the inversion layer, where further air circulation in the air shed beyond the inversion layer is impossible. The loss of heat which occurs adiabatically as the air rises and expands causes it to cool. It then becomes denser and tends to descend again.

Topographic Contributory Factors

In a number of areas in the United States these two conditions of high atmospheric pressure and local topography are commonly met. The city which has gained most notoriety in this respect is Los Angeles. The San Gabriel and San Bernadino ranges, with peaks rising over 10,000 feet, form the boundaries of an air shed over the Los Angeles basin which in summer frequently contains cold air rolling in from the sea. As the lower layers of this cool coastal air become heated by contact with the ground, they rise, losing heat as they expand until they form a low inversion layer over the basin anywhere from several hundred to several thousand feet above sea level. High winds are needed to break up this layer, because the mountain barriers tend to stabilize the air shed and prevent its dispersal inland.

SMOG COMPOSITION

The visible material which becomes trapped in the air below an inversion layer is known as the particulate matter, as noted earlier. Not only readily visible, it is also the easiest of the smog elements to measure and was at one time known as *soot*. The U.S. Public Health Service has sampled the air sheds of various major cities in the United States to determine the amount of particulate matter present at any given time per square mile up to 100 feet. The figures are reproduced in Table 10-1.

Table 10-1* ***Amount of Particulate Matter Per Square Mile Over Various U.S. Cities*** Amounts measured over the first 100 feet of the troposphere in 1961.

City	*Tonnage*	*City*	*Tonnage*
Detroit	153	Washington	58
Chicago	124	Houston	57
Los Angeles	118	San Francisco	46
New York	108	Pittsburgh	45
Philadelphia	83	Salt Lake City	24
Atlanta	61		

* Reprinted by permission of the publisher from J. L. Bregman and S. Lenormand, *The Pollution Paradox,* New York: Spartan Books, 1966, p. 54.

Primary Pollutants

This particulate matter or soot is basically finely divided carbon particles; it is associated with a number of other substances which are less visible but constant components of all smog. A partial list of these substances includes carbon monoxide, sulfur oxides, and nitrogen oxides. The sulfur is mostly in the form of sulfur dioxide, forming sulfuric acid near the source of emission which may in its turn become converted into sulfates. The nitrogen occurs generally as nitrous oxide. Air pollutants of this kind are known as *primary pollutants;* gasoline is among them. In Los Angeles the amount of gasoline released into city air has been estimated to be 8 per cent of the quantity actually sold there (Haagen-Smit, 1967).

When an attempt is made to prepare an emissions balance for a given air shed by comparing the emissions released with the amounts actually measured, less of the first and more of the second is sometimes found (Table 10-2). The explanation advanced for this imbalance is that some of the primary pollutants have been converted to *secondary pollutants.*

The smog observed in European and eastern cities in the United States, sometimes called "London" smog, is confined to primary pollutants and is said to be of a *reducing* type. In this type the particulate matter is

Table 10-2* ***An Emissions Balance Sheet for Major Pollutants*** By calculating the amount of each pollutant released at its source, then determining the amount measurable in smog, it is possible to draw up an emissions balance sheet such as that supplied below. Primary pollutants which are observed to have values *below* those calculated are assumed to have been converted by photochemical reactions into secondary pollutants.

POLLUTANT	*PARTS PER MILLION BY VOLUME*	
	Measured	*Calculated*
Carbon monoxide	3.5	3.5
Oxides of nitrogen	0.08	0.10
Sulfur dioxide	0.05	0.08
Total hydrocarbons	0.20	0.40
Aldehydes	0.07	0.02
Organic acids	0.07	0.03

* After Haagen-Smit, 1958; reproduced with the permission of the publisher.

largely soot, and the irritating element is sulfur dioxide. In the Los Angeles type of smog there is an overriding amount of oxidizing activity. Although there is also some soot, it is not so heavy as in the reducing type of smog, and most irritation comes from the products of the interactions promoted by the oxidizing activity.

Secondary Pollutants

From the pollutant balance sheet for the Los Angeles type, or oxidizing smog, it appears that gasoline emissions only persist in smog in about one half the expected amounts, while certain acids and aldehydes appear for which there is apparently no traceable source of direct emission. Such oxidized compounds apparently have been produced from the reactive hydrocarbons in the gasoline emissions. Another feature of Los Angeles-type smog is a very high ozone level, something like thirty times that of country air. It is now considered that the London type of reducing smog, characterized by its large amounts of soot and sulfur dioxide, also contains the same types of secondary pollutants as the Los Angeles type, but their presence is masked.

PHOTOCHEMICAL REACTIONS

The knowledge of what reactions lead to the development of ozone and other secondary pollutants is based mainly on the work of A. J. Haagen-Smit (1968). He has studied Los Angeles smog from the California Institute of Technology, which is situated in one of the worst of that city's smog belts. Haagen-Smit has described the generation of ozone by photochemical reactions involving organic material and many types of hydrocarbons, oxides of nitrogen, alcohols, aldehydes, ketones, and acids. The reactions involve the formation of peroxide radicals as intermediate products and may be represented by the following equations:

$$(1)\ NO_2 \xrightarrow{\text{light}} NO + O \qquad \text{(formation of atomic oxygen)}$$
$$(2)\ O + HR \longrightarrow R + HO \qquad \text{(free radical formation)}$$
$$(3)\ R + O_2 \longrightarrow ROO \qquad \text{(peroxyl radical formation)}$$
$$(4)\ ROO + O_2 \longrightarrow O_3 + HO \qquad \text{(ozone formation)}$$
$$(5)\ ROO + NO_2 \longrightarrow ROONO_2 \qquad \text{(peracyl nitrate formation)}$$

Schematically these reactions are represented in Figure 10-3. It should be noted that they are limited to very low concentrations of reactants, which is one of the unique features of air pollution. These atmospheric reactions occur in concentrations on the order of *one millionth* of normal fast laboratory reactions. This explains why ozone and reducing agents can coexist and even free radicals can survive.

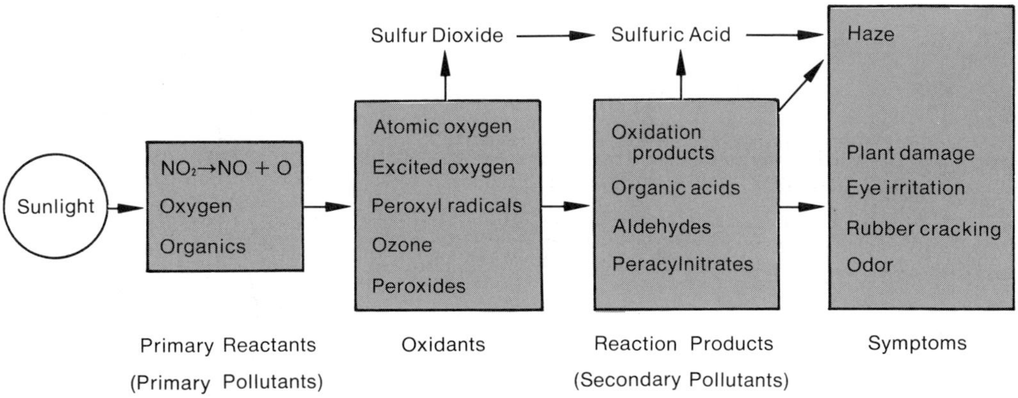

Figure 10-3. *The photochemical reactions occurring in Los Angeles type or oxidizing type smog.* These convert primary pollutants like nitrogen oxides into secondary ones such as ozone and PAN (peracyl nitrate), accounting for the differences appearing in emissions balance sheets as illustrated in Table 10-2. (After A. J. Haagen-Smit, *Scientia*, **103**[673–674]: 21, 35, 1968; reproduced with the permission of the publisher.)

The majority of organic compounds are not readily oxidized when quite pure, but in the presence of peroxides they are subject to autoxidation initiated by the removal of hydrogen from the carbon chain. Photolysis, either acting directly or on oxygen, will likewise remove hydrogen. Although most hydrocarbons lack adsorption bands in the wavelengths covered by sunlight, other substances may react photochemically and serve as oxygen donors. Nitrogen dioxides act in this way as oxidation catalysts.

SOURCES OF POLLUTION

The major sources of air pollution in the United States have been described by Haagen-Smit (Table 10-3). From this table it can be seen that dust and fumes from heavy industry, refineries, home incinerators, and public dumps contribute to smog, but they are not the major source. Automobile exhaust emissions have been held accountable for most of the organic vapors, carbon monoxide, and carbon dioxide in smog as shown in this table.

Table 10-3* *Major Air Contaminants over the United States—in millions of tons per annum.* Some of these air contaminants, such as fog or pollen, might not usually be regarded as air pollutants, but as fluctuations in their amounts can result from human activity, a pollutant budget must include them.

Natural fog (up to 25 feet high)	15
Pollen	1
Natural dust	30
Smoke (carbon)	5
Industrial dust and ash	10
Sulfur oxides	20
Nitrogen oxides	5
Miscellaneous vapors (mostly organic)	40
Carbon monoxide	50
Carbon dioxide	10,000

*After Haagen-Smit, 1968; reproduced with the permission of the publisher.

The general effect of this level of smog persistence and intensity is summarized in an extract from the Clean Air Act (88th Congress, 1963), which states:

. . . growth in the amount and complexity of air pollution brought about by urbanization, industrial development, and the increasing use of motor vehicles, has resulted in mounting dangers to the public health and welfare, including injury to agricultural crops and livestock, damage to and the deterioration of property, and hazards to air and ground transportation.

Los Angeles Smog

The special features of Los Angeles smog arise from the topographical features which limit movement in the air shed, the meterological conditions which produce a temperature inversion associated with strong sunlight, and the excessive concentration of motor vehicles—a conservative estimate of 3½ million in the greater Los Angeles area. These vehicles burn about 7 million gallons of gasoline a day (21,500 tons), emitting about 1800 tons of unburned hydrocarbons, 500 tons of oxides of nitrogen, 9000 tons of carbon monoxide (Goldsmith and Landaw, 1968). In importance they far outweigh any other source of pollutants.

Los Angeles is essentially a commuters' city, working fairly strictly on a five-day week. Through Saturday and Sunday the haze above the city slowly clears until by early Monday morning the 10,000-foot peak of the San Gabriel Mountains and the nearly 6000-foot peak of the Santa Ana Mountains are momentarily visible, only to disappear between 8 and 9 A.M. when the smog haze of the inversion layer has been reestablished. A similar but daily cycle of pollutants may also be observed (Figure 10–4).

One of the effects of smog in Los Angeles and elsewhere results from accumulation of carbon dioxide concentrations in the inversion layer in quantities much greater than that in an unpolluted air shed. This produces what is known as the *greenhouse effect*.

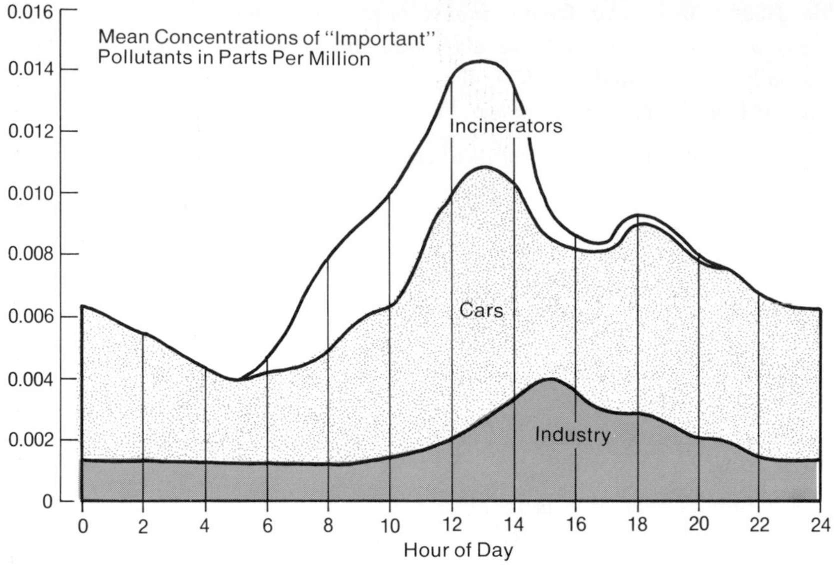

Figure 10-4. *The daily cycle of primary pollutants in Los Angeles* showing the emissions from the three principal sources in parts per million over a period of 24 hours in 1955. Although pollution from incinerators has been drastically reduced, both the number of cars and the industrial activity has greatly increased, producing a considerably higher air pollution peak in the middle of the day. (Reproduced by permission of the publisher from F. N. Frenkiel, *Scientific Monthly,* **82:** 198, 1956.)

The Greenhouse Effect

The so-called *fossil fuels*—coal, petroleum, natural gas, and lignite—are believed to have been formed during geological periods when the productivity of the producer trophic level of the totality of world ecosystems was not entirely taken up by consumers and decomposers. The amounts of atmospheric oxygen released during photosynthesis were not therefore balanced by the oxygen-utilizing processes of consumer or decomposer organisms. Likewise, the amount of carbon dioxide returned to the atmosphere during these oxidative processes would be lower, and its proportionate representation in the troposphere would fall. However, when the fossil fuels are mined and extensively burned, this reduction in the amount of carbon dioxide is abruptly reversed. The new figure can overshoot the original concentration. It is estimated that the burning of fossil fuels has increased the transfer rate of carbon dioxide to 3.5 $g/m^2/yr$, thus releasing 9×10^9 tons (2×10^{13} lb) a year into the atmosphere. This is now adding 0.23 per cent per year to the carbon dioxide content of the atmosphere; the content of this gas in air has risen from 290 to 330 parts per million (ppm) in the present century.

Carbon dioxide gas differentially absorbs the longer wavelength portion of solar radiation. Light reflected from the earth's surface, which has been converted during reflectance from shorter wavelength ultraviolet to longer wavelength infrared, is therefore absorbed instead of being reflected off

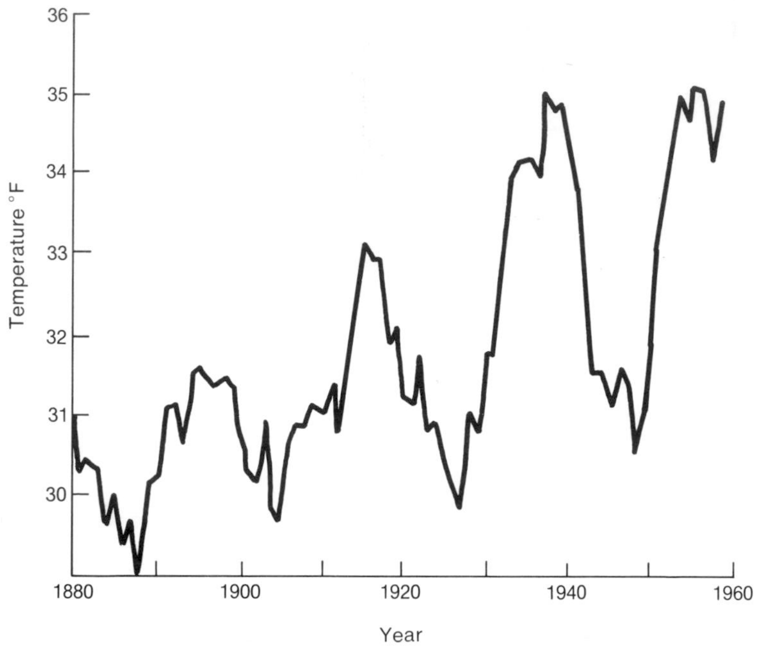

Figure 10-5. *Mean January air temperatures for New York City,* projected 1871–1958. The upward trend of the general temperature cycle during this period is commonly ascribed to the greenhouse effect. However, a contrary cooling effect may have been introduced by an increase in particulate pollutants; see text for further discussion. (Reproduced by permission of the publisher from J. Spar, *Weatherwise,* **7:** 149, 1954.)

into the stratosphere again after striking the earth. The accretions of heat energy from this longer wavelength radiation tend to raise the temperature of the lowest atmospheric layers (Figure 10-5).

It has been calculated (Aynsley, 1969) that a rise in the amount of carbon dioxide in air to 600 ppm would raise the earth's temperature by 1.5° C, although global air circulation and cloud effects might modify this figure. As the Pleistocene ice ages involved decreases of temperature in the region of 7° to 9° C, such an increase would be expected to have significant effects on all the world's ecosystems. The build-up of additional heat could be so great that the polar icecaps would begin to accelerate their rate of melting. The International Geophysical Year in 1957 to 1959 produced observations which demonstrated that, with one exception, all the glaciers of the world were now retreating. If the polar icecaps are also melting, there will soon be evidence of an extensive shift in sea levels. Countereffects are described in the next few paragraphs.

Other Meteorological Effects

It is suspected that, in addition to the greenhouse effect, air pollution has other influences on weather, more especially arising from the presence of particulate matter. Some of these may indeed modify the greenhouse effect.

Aynsley reports a number of accounts evidencing build-up of turbidity in the atmosphere, that is, an increase in atmospheric dustiness. Over Washington, D.C., this has amounted to 57 per cent, over Switzerland 88 per cent. Some estimates provide evidence of increases in particulate matter of about ten times over the last few years.

This turbidity not only reduces the amount of solar radiation reaching the earth's surface, but it may also initiate cloud condensation. Aynsley quotes figures from La Porte, Ind., some 30 miles downwind from the industrial centers of Gary and South Chicago, which indicate that since 1965, La Porte had 31 per cent more rain, 38 per cent more thunderstorms, and 245 per cent more days with hail than adjoining communities not directly downwind of a major industrial area.

In the same way, cloud cover over the North Atlantic is held to have increased by 5 to 10 per cent because of the particulate matter ejected in high flying jet aircraft vapor trails; once supersonic aircraft come into operation, an even larger effect may be anticipated. Sometimes under these circumstances "overseeding" may occur. The ice crystals which form about each nucleus may not coalesce, but will drift away to fall as precipitation elsewhere, and so *reduce* rainfall in the affected area.

Schaefer (1968), who cites automobile emissions as the most common source of nuclei for ice-crystal formation, finds that present antismog devices for cars have no effect in reducing this source. The effect of massive release of such nuclei is to condense water vapor in such small droplets that stabilized clouds are formed. He claims that such effects are already changing the weather patterns over hundreds of thousands of square miles.

Total cloud cover over the world is estimated to average about 31 per cent. An increase in only 5 per cent in this cloud cover would so drop temperatures that the earth would be plunged into a new ice age (Aynsley, 1969). For the skeptics, a dramatic demonstration of the chilling effect of cutting off even temporarily a portion of the solar radiation can be obtained from experiencing a partial eclipse of the sun. In contrast with the findings of the International Geophysical Year up to 1960, the subsequent decade is believed to have witnessed a slight *decrease* in the earth's temperature. In 1968 ice coverage in the North Atlantic was the highest recorded for this century.

EFFECTS OF SMOG ON PUBLIC HEALTH

While the greenhouse effect and other meteorological influences on the ecosphere are extremely significant in relation to stability in the earth's ecosystems, certain direct effects of pollutants of more immediate concern to us have been observed in populations. These range from inconvenient to incapacitating illnesses, and in all too many instances to fatal diseases. The particulate matter or soot component of smog is known, from extensive experimental work, to induce skin and subcutaneous cancers when painted on or injected into mice.

Lung Cancer

In England, there is a correlation between the occupation of chimney sweep and the incidence of lung and scrotal cancer. Follow-up investigations cited by Bregman and Lenormand (1966) extend this observation to all British city dwellers. Among English immigrants over 30 in New Zealand, deaths from lung cancer were 75 per cent greater than in native New Zealanders. Similar observations were made on emigrants to South Africa and the United States.

Table 10-4* ***Benzopyrene Concentration in American Cities*****—expressed in micrograms per gram of suspended particulate matter** The highest concentration found in any of the 28 nonurban areas sampled was 51 micrograms of benzopyrene per gram of particulate matter. Of the 94 urban areas sampled some were less than this; the 22 with figures greater than 100 are listed below.

City	*Micrograms Benzopyrene per Gram Suspended Particulate Matter*
1. Richmond, Virginia	410
2. Montgomery, Alabama	340
3. Charlotte, North Carolina	290
4. Hammond, Indiana	280
5. Altoona, Pennsylvania	280
6. Knoxville, Tennessee	210
7. St. Louis, Missouri	200
8. Youngstown, Ohio	190
9. Raleigh, North Carolina	180
10. Portland, Maine	180
11. Roanoke, Virginia	160
12. Des Moines, Iowa	160
13. Wheeling, West Virginia	140
14. Tampa, Florida	140
15. Flint, Michigan	140
16. Indianapolis, Indiana	120
17. Columbia, South Carolina	120
18. Chattanooga, Tennessee	120
19. Orlando, Florida	110
20. Dearborn, Michigan	110
21. Duluth, Minnesota	110
22. Cleveland, Ohio	110

* Reprinted by permission of the publisher from E. Sawicki, W. C. Elbert, T. R. Hauser, F. T. Fox, and T. W. Stanley, *American Industrial Hygiene Association Journal,* **21:** 447, 1960.

Bregman and Lenormand note that 32 polynuclear aromatic hydrocarbons have been identified in automobile emissions, including *benzopyrene.* Table 10-4 indicates the concentrations of benzopyrene in 22 heavily polluted United States cities, contrasted with nonurban areas. Benzopyrene is believed to be the primary carcinogenic agent in inhaled cigarette smoke responsible for inducing lung cancer. This respiratory disease kills 47,000 Americans a year (Edelson and Warshofsky, 1966). Its present high incidence is attributable to the habit of cigarette smoking, and correlations between death from lung cancer and the amount of cigarette smoking practiced are undeniably established.

While this correlation is indeed indisputable, the Public Health Service (Edelson and Warshofsky, 1966) has published figures from a survey which suggests that the urban resident of an average-sized American city inhales daily the same quantity of benzopyrene as would be obtained from smoking a third of a pack of cigarettes. In a city where air pollution is heavy, this amount must be raised to the equivalent of a full pack.

Emphysema

Much controversy still surrounds the precise allocation of causal factors of lung cancer, but there seem to be unequivocal correlations established for environmental effects just as there have been for cigarette smoking. To illustrate with one typical correlation, Haagen-Smit (1968)—in noting that *emphysema* is the fastest growing cause of death in the United States—observes that between 1950 and 1959 deaths among males rose from 1.5 per hundred thousand to 8 per hundred thousand.

Other Respiratory Diseases

Emphysema is, however, only one recognizable syndrome in a complex of chronic constrictive respiratory conditions which may result from breathing polluted air; Edelson and Warshofsky (1966) quote other examples. Chronic bronchitis is said to represent 10 per cent of the British Medical Health scheme's patient load. That it is not an English disease was ascertained when chronic bronchitis was diagnosed in 21 per cent of a group of men 40 to 59 years old in the United States. The added strain placed on the heart by difficulties in breathing may be fatal, and the cause of death is then recorded as cardiac failure.

In the Japanese city of Ube, which has heavy air pollution, the death rate from diphtheria was observed to be 7.8 times heavier than in a less polluted city, from lung cancer 2.4 times higher, from heart disease 2.2 times higher. In 1959 deaths recorded as resulting from pneumonia in New York City were 50.6 per 100,000 as compared with 38.6 in upstate cities and 24.2 in upstate rural areas.

Possible Synergistic Effects

One major question still unanswered regarding the effect of polluted air on human health is whether there are *synergistic* effects, that is, whether the combined effects of several pollutants are multiplied rather than simply added. As the result of animal experiments, it is suspected that pollutants act synergistically, that inhaling a mixture of two pollutants will have five or six times the effect of inhaling either one singly. One of the most interesting possibilities regarding a synergistic effect has just begun to be appreciated—tobacco smoke as a secondary pollutant.

Cigarette Smoking

The controversy over toxic effects of cigarette smoking on the individual smoker has tended to obscure possible population effects in which tobacco smoke can be regarded as another form of air pollution. Cigarette smoke is known to contain inorganic pollutants such as carbon monoxide and nitrogen dioxide, and organic ones such as phenols, aldehydes, benzopyrene, and acrolein, all of which are well-known air pollutants. It also contains some substances—for example, hydrogen cyanide—which have never been reported as general air pollutants.

The concentration of carbon monoxide in cigarette smoke has been reported as high as 42,000 ppm. Concentrations as low as 100 ppm can cause headaches and dizziness. The smoker survives supposedly because he blows away his own smoke and does not reinhale it continuously. In the same way he can avoid the full impact of the 250 ppm of nitrogen dioxide in smoke, of which 5 ppm are believed to represent a dangerous level.

The possible existence of synergistic effects when heavy air pollution is combined with cigarette smoking are suggested by such figures as those shown in Figure 10-6, where the chances of contracting lung cancer or chronic bronchitis are apparently correlated with residence in industrial cities in England and Wales. The microecosystems of large buildings must be considerably modified by the addition to their internalized and partially closed circuit ventilation systems of considerable quantities of cigarette smoke. The smoker's action therefore goes beyond the question of individual choice and may have significant population repercussions.

Schaefer (1969a) suggests one further synergistic effect of cigarette smoking. He notes that in addition to ventilating the lungs with a smoke particle concentration 10 to 100 times greater than that of badly polluted air, the smoker draws air through a burning zone in the cigarette of considerable intensity. The external air frequently contains 10,000 to 100,000 pollution particles per square centimeter. Some of these particles will be vaporized during passage through the burning zone and drawn into the lungs in highly reactable condition. Many additional chemical interactions may therefore occur in the lungs.

Some workers have proposed that the synergistic effects of pollutants are responsible for reversal of the infant mortality decline in this country, observable since 1957. Currently the United States, despite its massive hospital facilities, stands only eleventh lowest in the world among the 15

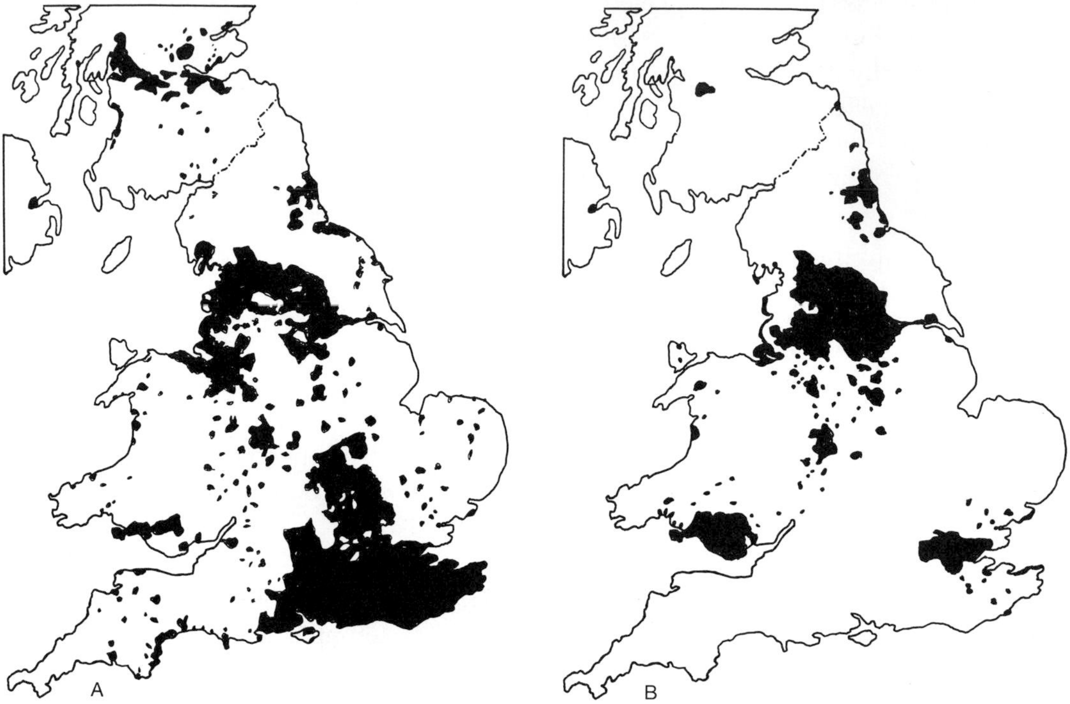

Figure 10-6. *The distribution of lung cancer and chronic bronchitis in England.* Areas in which the incidence of these diseases is above the national average are blocked in black. In the case of lung cancer (*A*) not only is the incidence of this disease above average in the major industrial centers, but many minor urban centers also appear to be affected. Chronic bronchitis (*B*), on the other hand, appears to be associated more especially with the large industrial complexes in South Wales, the Midlands, the North, and the London area. (Reproduced by permission of the publisher from L. D. Stamp, *The Geography of Life and Death,* London: Fontana Paperbacks, 1964, pp. 118 and 123, and reprinted from L. Dudley Stamp, *The Geography of Life and Death.* © L. Dudley Stamp, 1964. Used by permission of Cornell University Press.)

advanced industrial societies usually selected for comparison of infant mortality statistics.

In considering infant mortality rates it is impossible to ignore another form of air pollution which has not yet been mentioned, that arising from radioactive fallout. Hotly debated in the 1950s, this subject has again aroused considerable controversy.

RADIOACTIVE FALLOUT

A meeting of the Health Physics Society in 1969 considered new information, presented by E. J. Sternglass, indicating that at least one of three children who died before their first birthday during the 1960s may have succumbed to the effect of strontium-90 contained in the fallout from the peaceful nuclear testing carried out in America during that decade (Sternglass, 1969).

This contention was vigorously denied by the American nuclear establishment, and by a large majority of scientists (Boffey, 1969). An independent refutation was also quickly published (Stewart, 1969). Sternglass' argument is therefore not yet considered fully acceptable, but the evidence on which it is based is summarized here (Friedlander and Klarman, 1970).

Effects on Infant Mortality

Sternglass first considers an increase in the incidence of infant mortality along the path of the fallout cloud from the first atomic test in New Mexico in 1945. This was obtained from a detailed correlation of state-by-state infant mortality excesses with the early changes in strontium-90 levels in milk.

By 1963, changes in infant mortality approached one additional death in the United States per 100 live births from the release to that date of 200 megatons of fission energy. Extrapolating, he suggests the release of 20,000 megatons anywhere in the world could result in eliminating any surviving infants. This is actually the amount of fission energy needed in offensive warheads for an effective first strike of defensive ABM warheads.

From 1935 to 1950 infant mortality rates in the country showed a steady decline. After 1950 this drop, according to Sternglass, continued everywhere except in the states downwind of Alamogordo, site of the first series of atomic tests. By 1950 the infant mortality rates in Texas, Arkansas, Louisiana, Mississippi, Alabama, Georgia, and both the Carolinas showed deviations from the mathemathical model projecting the declining rates from 1935 to 1950.

More than 1000 to 1500 miles away from the test site, in Arkansas, Louisiana, and Alabama, the mortality rates of between 3 and 4.5 per hundred live births, increased by 20 to 30 per cent.

Thus the Alamogordo blast appears to have resulted in infant deaths of 1 per cent of children in the area downwind. No effect was observed in Florida, which is south of the fallout cloud path, or in any of the states to the north.

Radioactivity in Milk

During the early 1950s it was discovered that radioactive strontium became concentrated in cows' milk and was transmitted along with calcium to the bones of the developing human fetus. Such effects, however, were slow-acting, and from studies on young women working in such jobs as painting luminous watch dials, it was found that relatively large amounts of such radiation over long periods were necessary before bone cancer or leukemia could result.

Loutit and Russell (1966) estimate that during 1963 the average dosage of strontium-90 in newly formed bone in England was about 20 mrad, less than one fifth of the radiation received from the natural background. Extrap-

Table 10-5* ***Natural Radiation*** Estimates of the mean dose-rates the world population receives from natural sources, in millirads per year. These amounts should be compared with the figures supplied in Table 10-6 showing comparable fallout statistics.

	Gonads	*Cells Lining Bone Surfaces*	*Blood-Forming Cells*
EXTERNAL			
Cosmic rays	50	50	50
Terrestrial radiation	50	50	50
INTERNAL			
Potassium-40	20	15	15
Uranium and thorium series:			
Radium and decay products	1.3	14.0	1.6
Lead and polonium	0.3	3.6	0.4
Radon	3	3	3
Carbon-14	0.7	1.6	1.6
TOTAL	125	137	122

* From R. Scott Russell (ed.), *Radioactivity and Human Diet*, Oxford: Pergamon Press, 1966, p. 15.

olating to the end of this century, the accumulating dosage in bone would be about 260 mrad, the natural background amount received in about 32 months (Tables 10-5 and 10-6). Moreover, survivors of the two atomic bomb attacks at Hiroshima and Nagasaki showed no serious long-term effects from radiation. Atomic nuclear weapons were therefore tested in Nevada until 1958, and Pacific tests continued until 1963 (Figure 10-7).

Prenatal Effects

Meanwhile, observations on pregnant women who had been exposed to x-rays indicated the possibility that ova and embryos could be from 20 to

Table 10-6* ***Comparisons Between Radiation Received from Natural Radiation and Weapons Testing Fallout*** The estimated doses from A.D. 1954 to 2000 to which the world population has been committed as a result of the 1962 tests. Figures express the doses of beta and gamma radiation received in millirads.

	Gonads	*Cells Lining Bone Surfaces*	*Bone Marrow*
EXTERNAL			
From short-lived nuclides	21	21	21
From cesium-137	29	29	29
INTERNAL			
From strontium-90	—	174	87
From strontium-89	—	0.3	0.15
From cesium-137	13	13	13
From carbon-14	13	13	13
TOTAL	76	257	163
Time during which similar dose is received from natural background (months)	9	32	20

* From R. Scott Russell (ed.), *Radioactivity and the Human Diet*, Oxford: Pergamon Press, 1966, p. 20.

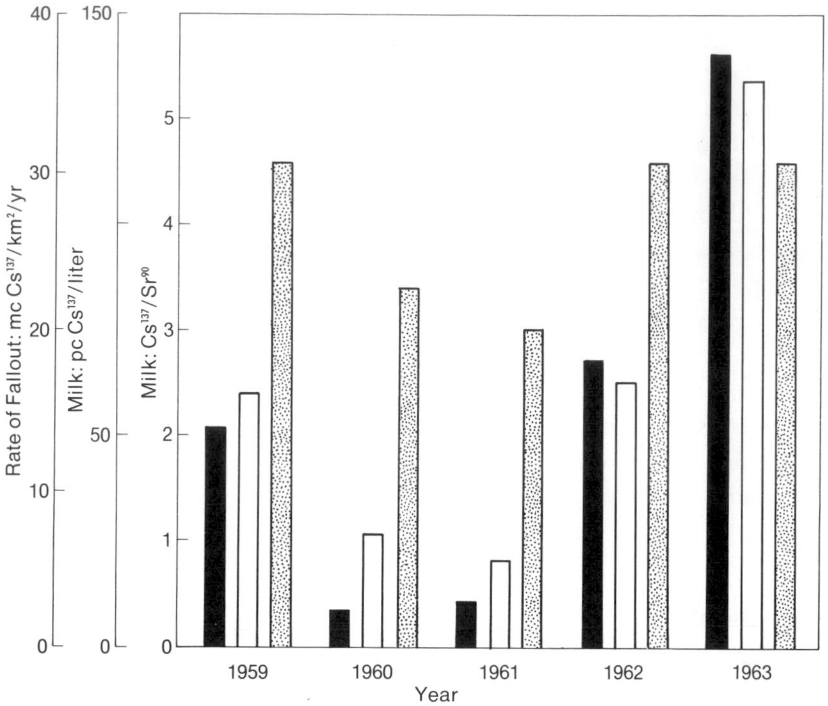

Figure 10-7. *Relationship between the amount of strontium in cow's milk and atomic test fallout.* The rate of fallout (solid ground) is determined by recording the amount of cesium-137 in soil. The amount of strontium-90 in milk is estimated by determining the amount of cesium-137 (plain ground) and the cesium-137 to strontium-90 ratio in milk (stippled ground). Although this ratio has shown little variation from 1959 through 1963, the amount of cesium and therefore of strontium has shown a strong correlation with the amount of fallout each year.

50 times more sensitive to the possible development of leukemia than the mature adult. In support of this contention Sternglass quotes from a 1958 publication by A. Stewart of Oxford University, England, showing that women who have received a series of three to five abdominal x-rays produced children nearly twice as likely to die of leukemia, or other forms of cancer, then children born from mothers who had not been x-rayed during pregnancy. This was somewhat surprising, considering that a single diagnostic exposure only provided a radiation dose of the same magnitude as that received from natural radiation such as cosmic rays (Table 10-5).

Stewart's findings, according to Sternglass, were confirmed by B. MacMahon at the Harvard School of Public Health, who examined the records of 800,000 children born in the larger New England hospitals. He found a 40 per cent increase in the cancer rate among children born from mothers who received diagnostic x-rays during pregnancy.

Leukemia and other cancers are second only to accidents as cause of death among children aged 5 to 14 years. Examination of the leukemia rate for the state of New York showed a rise and fall in this most susceptible age group from 5 to 14 years correlated with the sequence of individual test series in Nevada between 1951 and 1958. Moreover, the stillbirth rate showed an upward trend beginning within a year after testing began in Nevada in 1951. Instead of steadily declining as it had done from 1935 to 1950, from 1957 to 1963, this stillbirth rate leveled off to about 23 per thousand live births. In 1964 it rose to 27.3 per thousand only to decline again in 1965 and 1966 as the amount of fallout in milk and foods was reduced throughout the United States following the cessation of aerial tests.

By contrast, in California, which was upwind of the Nevada test site, the stillbirth rate continued a steady decline, although this decrease was less up to three years following the onset of hydrogen bomb tests in the Pacific in 1954.

The effects of fallout on the stillbirth rate, however, are more serious than the figures for childhood leukemia, because for every case reported an estimated five or six are not, and those which are recorded are more than ten times the deaths from childhood leukemia.

Correlations with Fallout in Soil

The amount of strontium-90 deposited in soil is readily recorded. Sternglass obtained the relevant statistic where this had been measured and plotted it against the excess of fetal mortality compared with expected mortality, based on the 1935 to 1950 decline.

Birth curves in New York showed a correlated decrease in rate of climb coinciding with the temporary halt of nuclear testing in 1958 to 1961, and both curves showed a sharp rise beginning with the large-scale Soviet test series in 1961. However, after the test ban agreement in 1963, both the fetal death rate and the amount of strontium-90 in soil began to decline.

Infant Mortality

Figures for infant mortality are more accurately known than those for childhood deaths from leukemia or for the number of stillbirths. Like these, according to Sternglass, infant mortality had shown a steady decline in the period from 1935 to 1950. From the onset of the Nevada test in 1951 until the test ban in 1963, however, this decline in the rate leveled off in the United States. It did not do so in other advanced industrial societies such as Sweden, Holland, and Norway, or in southern hemisphere countries like Chile and New Zealand until late in the 1950s. At this time hydrogen bomb testing in the South Pacific and Siberia began to produce world-wide fallout on a much increased scale. The United States infant mortality figures did not continue the 1935 to 1950 decline again until 1965; the observed infant mortality rate per thousand live births during the testing period was 5.4 per thousand, instead of the estimated 2.7. During the tests the rate in Sweden still declined to 2.6 per thousand.

Differential Infant Mortality Rates in the United States

Moreover, this halting of the decline in infant mortality was not universally distributed in this country. Within two years of the onset of atomic testing in Nevada in 1951, resistance to further decline in infant mortality was most marked in Eastern, Midwestern, and Southern states. This coincided with the known pattern of accumulated radioactive strontium on the ground and in the diet, as the amount carried down from the atmosphere is partly correlated with the amount of rainfall.

Clinical Effects of Radioactivity

K. G. Luning *et al.* (1963) published the results of experiments which demonstrated that small amounts of strontium-90 injected into male mice three or four weeks before mating produced an increase in fetal deaths among their offspring. The same results were not obtained with radioactive cesium-137.

Sternglass states that evidence produced in May, 1969, to an international symposium on radiation biology of the fetal and juvenile mammal demonstrated severe chromosome damage, fetal death, and congenital malformations in the offspring of female mice injected with strontium-90 before and during pregnancy. Similar effects are reported for very small quantities of tritium, which is produced by both A bombs and H bombs. In this connection Sternglass notes that, following the Hiroshima and Nagasaki bombs, the rate of death from cancer among Japanese children up to 14 years old increased by more than 200 per cent between 1949 and 1951.

To indicate the magnitude of the effects of excess infant mortality, which Sternglass associates with this air pollution by radioactivity fallout, it should be noted that in the 1950s about 3.5 to 3.0 infants of every hundred born in the United States died before attaining the age of 1 year. As about 4 million children were born each year at this time, this means that approximately 40,000 infants of up to 1 year old died as a result of the atomic testing—a total of some 375,000 by the mid-60s.

As the effects of strontium-90 appear to lie in such factors as lowered birth rate and reduced ability to resist infection, children who have received adequate medical care are more likely to survive than those who do not.

Population Effects of Fallout

Considering the probable population effects of a large nuclear war, the detonation of a single small tactical sized nuclear weapon on the ground in the Western United States appears to have led, Sternglass maintains, to one out of every 100 children born subsequently dying before reaching the age of 1 year. This nation has 8000 such tactical nuclear weapons to protect Western Europe. Obviously this protection, if used, would jeopardize all future human generations in the world.

Although admittedly controversial and disputed by several sources, this presentation by Sternglass of the projected effects of atmospheric pollution by radioactive fallout clearly demands the most serious consideration. It revives a controversy which may erroneously have been considered in these last few years less significant than other aspects of air pollution surveyed in this chapter.

OTHER EFFECTS OF AIR POLLUTION

The reducing type of air pollution, especially the sulfur dioxide portion of it, is reported as causing extensive agricultural and forestry damage. Many years ago it was necessary to remove the coniferous plantings maintained by the Royal Botanic Gardens in Kew to a country area outside London (Scurfield, 1960). More recent reports of damage are summarized by Haagen-Smit (1969). Smelters in British Columbia, emitting 600 tons of sulfur daily, almost completely destroyed firs and pines for dozens of miles around. Orange trees are reported damaged in Florida and California, spinach growing severely curtailed in California, tobacco leaves damaged in Maryland, and ponderosa pine trees killed on the San Bernardino Mountains above Los Angeles (Parmeter, *et al.*, 1962). Commercial orchid growing is now impossible in any American city, and total agricultural losses from smog damage are put at 500 million dollars annually.

Because much of the early damage of this nature was attributed to sulfur dioxide, the change from solid fuels such as coal to liquid types such as diesel oil seems to have reduced these particular effects of air pollution. The smog constituents now held responsible for most agricultural damage in the United States are ozone in the East and peroxyacetyl nitrate (peracyl nitrate, or PAN) in the West. Under smog attack metals, paper, rubber, plastics, and fabrics deteriorate, and buildings must be cleaned and restored. Expensive smog filtering devices have to be fitted to the air intakes of factories engaged in the manufacture of critical electronic components. Curiously, perhaps, such care does not seem to be taken in the preparation of oxygen cylinders. Oxygen used for the critically ill in hospitals consequently often has a higher proportion of pollutants than the air from which it was prepared.

CONTROL OF AIR POLLUTION

Action taken to restore air quality varies from none in many instances to a complete ban on the sale of internal combustion engines (as proposed in 1969 by the California State Assembly but not adopted). In between these extremes, state and federal agencies are enforcing various types of control which reduce at least partially the incidence of one pollutant or another.

"Smokeless" fuel zones in cities reduce the amount of particulate matter

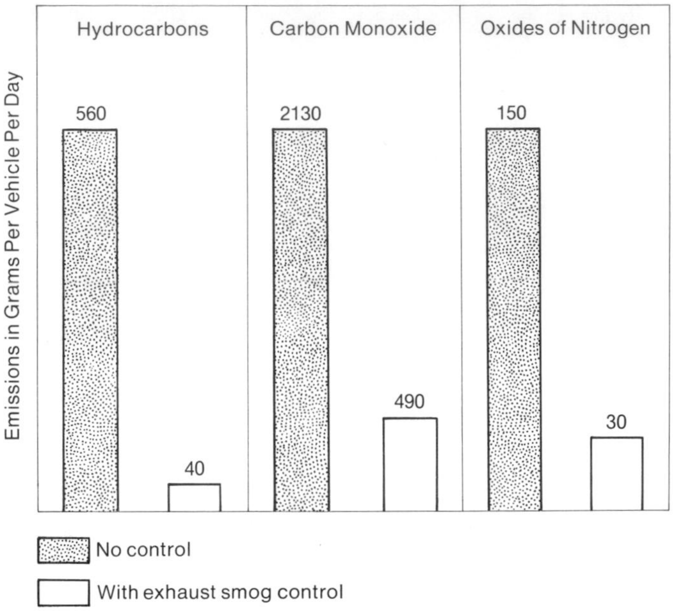

Figure 10-8. *Comparison of exhaust emissions from uncontrolled and controlled sources.* Amounts represent grams per vehicle per day as projected for 1972. The three graphs are on a different scale to reduce them to comparable size. The emission controls are those imposed by the new California emissions standards; the three major primary pollutants in smog represented here are very considerably reduced, and the secondary pollutants will likewise be affected. (Modified from Annual Report 1968, California Air Resources Board, reproduced with permission.)

and often of sulfur dioxide released. The establishment of such a zone in London following the 1952 disaster is reported to have prevented the recurrence of any of its infamous "pea-souper" fogs. In most large cities there are generally regulations concerning domestic and larger-scale burning of garbage. Natural gas and diesel oil are in any case the most common forms of fuel now used in the United States.

From 1968 all new cars sold in this country had to be fitted with exhaust emission control devices. Figure 10-8 shows the results of fitting such devices. It is estimated (Air Resources Board, 1969) that control of vehicular emissions by regulations for 1971 and 1975 could reduce emissions of hydrocarbons, carbon monoxide, and oxides of nitrogen in California to a minimum by about 1985. Moreover, these figures could be lower than at present, when there has been a reduction in 1971 models of carbon monoxide to a third, hydrocarbons to 23 per cent even allowing for an appropriate increase in the number of motor vehicles (Figure 10-9). However, taking into account imperfect function of many control devices and increases in the atmospheric load of pollutants from world-wide sources, it is uncertain that the controls will result in a reduction of urban smog in the country as a whole.

A detailed study of the literature, or a period of residence in one of the more heavily polluted cities, may persuade many people that the need for

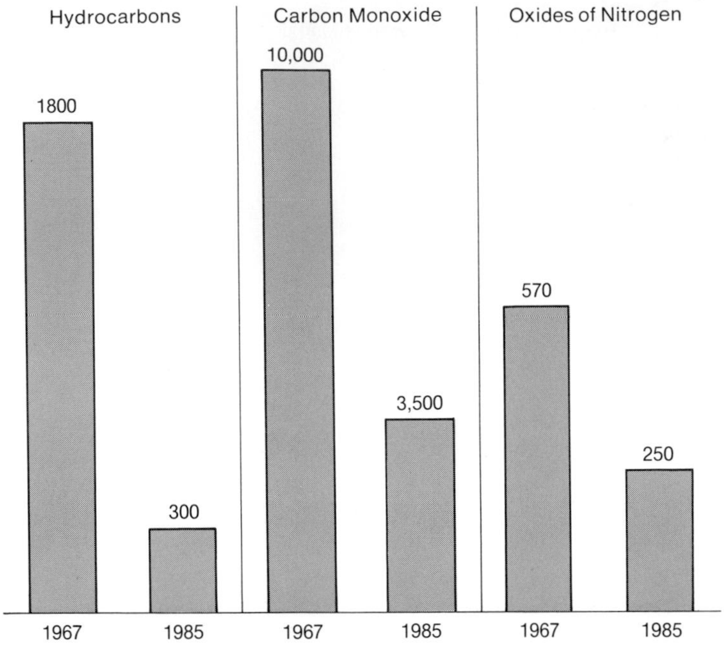

Figure 10-9. *The estimated effects of control regulations on vehicular emissions.* These are estimated figures over the 1967–85 period of vehicles registered in the Los Angeles metropolitan area, together with the extent of control established and the amount of estimated emissions. (Prepared from *1968 Annual Report on Air Pollution Control in California,* California Air Resources Board, 1969, p. 19; reproduced with permission.)

air pollution control is far more urgent than this and that to wait patiently for some reduction to reach its greatest effect in 1985 is not nearly good enough. Unfortunately, conclusions from scientific experiments or analyses on the effects of pollution are not proven; and where so many vested interests are vitally affected, it is difficult to introduce and enforce legislation on the basis of a *probable* reduction in air pollution.

NOISE POLLUTION

Because sound waves are transmitted by air, and because the internal combustion engine is simultaneously one of the main sources of both pollutants and noise, the phenomenon described as *noise pollution* is increasingly associated with urban life.

The centers of the world's great cities have in any case long been subjected to excessive noise. London, Paris, and New York, most likely sell great quantities of sedatives to permanent residents who cannot otherwise sleep.

The cacophony of sound in the modern world does not, however, emanate solely from such urban sources. The universality of public address systems, linked with the ubiquitous transistor radio, has provided a background of noise against which people everywhere must strive to communicate or concentrate. There is evidence this causes loss of efficiency (Boggs and Simon, 1968). There is also much evidence that this exposure produces irreversible deterioration of the auditory apparatus, and that many city dwellers have suffered a serious loss of auditory sensitivity by middle age, as compared with those in advanced agricultural societies, where little deterioration occurs up to or over the age of 65. Standards developed by the U.S. Air Force recommend the use of ear "defenders" if noise levels exceed 85 decibels. Unfortunately, "ordinary" noise frequently does this (Anthrop, 1969).

The effects of noise pollution on "aggression," using this term in its broadest sense, have not been extensively investigated, although in the United States there was recently a case of a man seizing an axe and dashing into the street to demolish the persistent chimes of a mobile ice cream vendor. In this country also, an appreciable percentage of neighbor dispute incidents to which the police are called are classifiable as noise pollution problems—too loud a party, excessive noise from hi-fi equipment, hammering in the late or early hours, dogs barking, and cocks crowing. Perhaps for the suburbs the most widespread source of irritation is low-flying aircraft, both commercial and private planes. There is a growing body of public opinion favoring insistence upon stricter regulations regarding jet engine noise, and abandoning of the SST project. This latter type of aircraft would benefit very few while subjecting many to shattering and frequent sonic booms (Brown, 1969; Kryter, 1969).

Problems of noise pollution are more likely to be debilitating than disastrous; the other immediately critical environmental problem which closely parallels air pollution is *water pollution.* Just as it is difficult to define air pollution precisely, so water pollution lacks any concise definition. It is best considered in relation to the function of water in the world's ecosystems, just as air pollution can be treated as a disturbance of the vital role which air plays as a major abiotic element of natural ecosystems.

Bibliography

REFERENCES

Anonymous. "Air pollution control in California," *1968 Annual Report, Air Resources Board,* State of California, 1969.

Anthrop, D. F. "Environment Noise Pollution: A New Threat to Sanity," *Bull. Atomic Scientists,* **25**(5): 11–16, 1969.

Aynsley, E. "How air pollution alters weather," *New Scientist,* **44**: 66–67, 1969.

Boffey, P. M. "Ernest J. Sternglass: Controversial prophet of doom," *Science,* **166:** 195–200, 1969.

Boggs, D. H. and Simon, J. R. "Differential effect of noise on tasks of varying complexity," *J. Appl. Psychol.,* **52:** 148–153, 1968.

Bregman, J. L., and Lenormand, S. *The Pollution Paradox,* New York and Washington: Spartan Books, 1969.

Brown, R. "Assessing damage from sonic booms," *New Scientist,* **41:** 116–17, 1969.

Edelson, E., and Warshofsky, F. *Poisons in the Air,* New York: Pocket Books, 1966.

Frenkiel, F. N. "Atmosphere pollution and zoning in an urban area," *Science Monthly,* **82:** 194–203, 1956.

Gentilli, J. *A Geography of Climate,* Perth, Western Australia: University of Western Australia Text Books Board, 1952.

Goldsmith, J. R., and Landaw, S. A. "Carbon monoxide and human health," *Science,* **162:** 1352–59, 1968.

Haagen-Smit, A. J. "The control of air pollution," *Scientific American,* **210** (1): 24–31, 1964.

Haagen-Smit, A. J. "The chemistry of air pollution," *Proc. Con. Museum Climatology, London,* 1967.

Haagen-Smit, A. J. "Reactions in the atmosphere," in A. C. Stern, (ed.), *Air Pollution,* rev. ed., Vol. 1, New York: Academic Press, 1968.

Haagen-Smit, A. J. "Air conservation," *Scientia,* **163:** 359–67, 1969.

Kryter, K. D. "Sonic booms from supersonic transport," *Science,* **163:** 359–67, 1969.

Leighton, P. A. *Photochemistry of Air Pollution,* New York: Academic Press, 1961.

Loutit, J. F., and Scott Russell, R. "Criteria for radiation protection," in R. Scott Russell (ed.), Pergamon, p. 40, 1966.

Luning, K. G., Frolen, H., Nelson, A., and Ronnback, C. "Genetic effects of strontium-90 injected into male mice," *Nature,* **197:** 304–305, 1963.

Middleton, J. T., and Haagen-Smit, A. J. "The occurrence, distribution, and significance of photochemical air pollution in the United States, Canada and Mexico," *J. Air Pollution Control Ass'n.,* 1961.

Parmeter, J. B., Bega, R. V., and Neff, T. "A chlorotic decline of Ponderosa Pine in Southern California," *U.S. Department of Agriculture Plant Disease Report,* **46:** 269–73, 1962.

Schaefer, V. J. "The nuclei from auto exhaust and organic vapors," *J. Appl. Meteorol.* **7:** 113, 1968.

Schaefer, V. J. "Some effects of air pollution on our environment," *Bioscience,* **19:** 896–97, 1969a.

Schaefer, V. J. "The inadvertent modification of the atmosphere by air pollution," *Bull. Amer. Meteorol. Soc.,* **50:** 199, 1969b.

Scurfield, G. "Air pollution and tree growth," *Forestry Abst.,* **21:** 1–20, 1960.

Spar, J. "Temperature trends in New York City," *Weatherwise*, **7**(6): 149–51, 1954.

Sternglass, E. J. "Has nuclear testing caused infant deaths?" *New Scientist*, **43**: 178–181, 1969.

Stewart, A. "The pitfalls of extrapolation," *New Scientist*, **43**: 181, 1969.

Wise, W. *Killer Smog*, New York: Rand McNally, 1968.

FURTHER READINGS

Eighty-Eighth Congress, An Act to Improve, Strengthen, and Accelerate Programs for the Prevention and Abatement of Air Pollution. Public Law 88-206, 88 Congress, H.R. 6518, 1963.

Frankenberg, T. T. "Air pollution from power plants and its control," *Combustion*, **34**: 28–31, 1963.

Green, H. L., and Lane, W. R. *Particulate Clouds, Dusts, Smokes and Mists*, Princeton, N.J.: Van Nostrand, 1964.

Haagen-Smit, A. J. "Carbon monoxide levels in city driving," *Arch. Env. Health*, **12**: 548–50, 1966.

Hepting, G. H. "Damage to forests from air pollution," *J. Forestry*, **62**: 630–34, 1964.

Hohonemser, K. "Onward and upward," *Environment*, **12**(4): 22–27, 1970.

Miller, M. E., and Holzworth, G. C. "An atmospheric diffusion model for metropolitan areas," *J. Air Pollution Control Ass'n. Amer.* **17**: 46–50, 1967.

Miller, P. R., Parmeter, J. R., Taylor, O. C. and Cardiff, E. A. "Ozone injury to the foliage of Pinus ponderosa" *Phytopathology*, **53**: 1072–76, 1963.

Miller, R. W. "Delayed radiation effects in atomic-bomb survivors," *Science*, **166**: 569–74, 1969.

Scott Russell, R. (ed.) *Radioactivity and Human Diet*, Oxford: Pergamon Press, 1966.

Stern, A. C. (ed.) *Air Pollution*, 2nd ed., New York: Academic Press, 1968.

Sternglass, E. J. "Infant mortality," *Environment*, **11**(10): 9–13, 1969.

U.S. Public Health Service, *Proceedings of the National Conference on Air Pollution of 1962*, 1963.

Weinstock, B. "Carbon monoxide: residue time in the atmosphere," *Science*, **169**: 224–25, 1969.

Woodwell, G. M. "Radioactivity and fallout: the model pollution," *Bioscience*, **19**: 884–87, 1969.

World Health Organization, *Air Pollution*, Monogr. Series 46, 1961.

Water Pollution 11

Chapter 10 considered the problems which confront us because industrial societies dump into air sheds a heavier load of waste products than the reducing and recycling processes of their ecosystems can handle. It is entirely arbitrary and purely for convenience that the process of *air pollution* is separated in this text from *water pollution*. Radioactive fallout in the air sooner or later contaminates all natural waters. Disturbance of gas ratios in the atmosphere affects their concentrations in the water of lakes, rivers, and oceans. Particulate matter released into the atmosphere must eventually settle or be washed down on to water as well as land surfaces.

There are, however, certain differences between air and water pollution which provide some substance as well as convenience to the distinction, not the least of which is that they are investigated by somewhat different techniques. Thus, separate research groups conventionally handle these two interrelated aspects of environmental pollution.

RECYCLING PROCESSES

In any ecosystem water is essentially the vehicle through which a recycling of nutrients is achieved. While it is also necessary in some form or another for the continued existence of most of the producer, consumer, and reducer populations of all ecosystems, it is especially with respect to this recycling process that the water transport of essential substances is most critical for the continued functioning of a given ecosystem.

The two substances most critical in recycling processes are *nitrates* and *phosphates*, both of which limit the productivity of most natural ecosystems.

Any disturbance of the process of recycling nitrates and phosphates through an ecosystem will therefore generally have most critical effects upon it.

Decomposers in aquatic ecosystems usually release the more soluble nitrates quicker than the less soluble phosphates. This is readily observable in lake ecosystems.

LAKE ECOSYSTEMS

Most lakes are comparatively short-lived, at least in a geological sense. During the Pleistocene there were extensive lake systems extending over much of North America, but these are now represented by only a few reduced water surfaces together with an impressive system of fossil lake beds. About the world the majority of lakes are of Holocene or recent date; shallow cyclic bodies of water, they appear, mature, silt up, and disappear in a matter of centuries rather than millennia.

If the drainage basin of any of these various lakes is infertile and supplies few nutrients, it is said to be *oligotrophic.* On the other hand, when it is located in an area of readily weathered rocks, which release considerable amounts of nutrients, the lake ecosystem productivity is high, and it is said to be of a *eutrophic* type.

Oligotrophy and eutrophy are really two extremes of a continuous range. Because available nutrients in a lake accumulate with time, even an oligo-

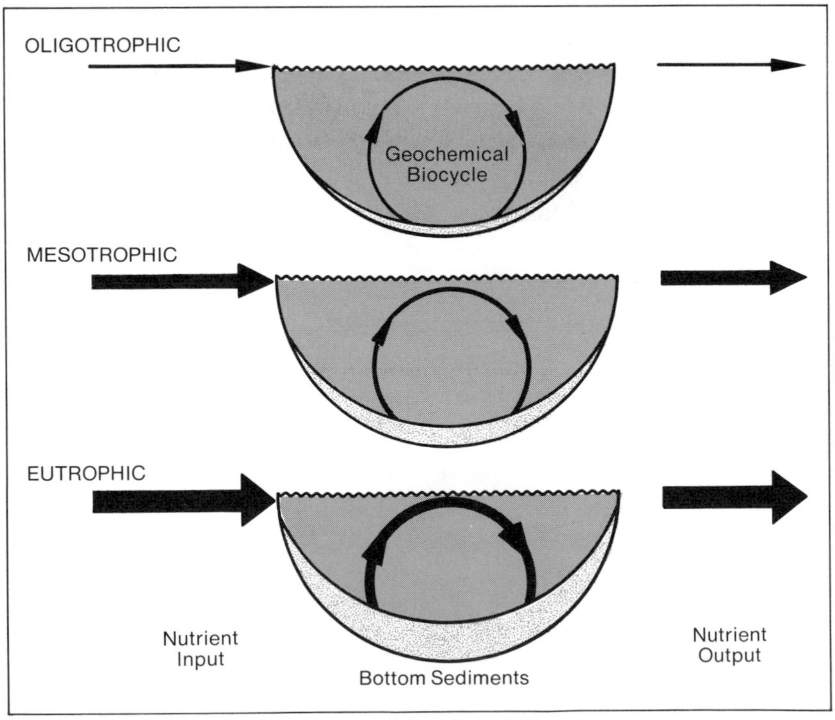

Figure 11-1. *The natural process of ecological evolution of a lake, or eutrophication.* This leads through a series of successional stages, from oligotrophic through mesotrophic to eutrophic in nature, in which the amount of nutrients recycled and the biomass which accumulates in bottom sediments gradually increase, eventually completely filling in the lake. (Based on Sawyer, 1966.)

trophic lake eventually becomes eutrophic; that is, it undergoes a successional ecological process of *eutrophication* (Figure 11-1). It does so because the biomass or organic matter produced at various trophic levels, if not consumed by organisms of higher trophic level, sinks to the bottom of the lake where decomposers reduce it, eventually releasing inorganic nutrients. The more soluble nitrates are rapidly carried away in any outflow; the phosphates tend to be lost more slowly, as already noted.

At the bottom of the lake the decomposer organisms may be limited in their activity by one or more ecological factors, such as low oxygen pressure or low temperature. The organic matter then tends to accumulate instead of being broken down immediately. This, as was observed in an earlier chapter, is the main source of fossil fuels, if bottom deposits in lakes are included with those in marine basins and river systems.

DISPOSAL OF WASTE

Until human populations reached the size and densities achieved following the industrial revolution, the amount of supplemental organic matter added to the larger bodies of water reached only local significance. Human excrement indeed was very often simply thrown into the streets. The invention of the indoor toilet in the early part of the nineteenth century changed this situation, for sewage was then flushed untreated into the nearest watercourse. It is estimated that 20 per cent of U.S. sewage is still handled in this way. In addition, many waterways and marine basins lack laws or enforcement of laws forbidding the use of open toilets on boats.

Adding untreated sewage to an aquatic ecosystem seriously disturbs its process of biogeochemical circulation by vastly increasing the accumulation of organic matter and the demand for oxygen. Sewage treatment does not prevent this, for while *primary* treatment consists of the removal of solid matter, *secondary* treatment is essentially a fermentation process in which nitrates and phosphates are released in large quantity. The oxidation which results considerably reduces the "biochemical oxygen demand." In either case, the maturation from an oligotrophic to a eutrophic stage is greatly accelerated, and the process of *eutrophication* proceeds so fast that the normal successional phases are shortened and bypassed.

Waste production by animals in the United States has been estimated as approximately ten times that of the human population, attaining a figure in the region of 2 billion tons annually. Large increases in domestic animals coupled with a modern tendency toward "factory" production result in such dense concentrations that their waste products also cause serious eutrophication problems.

EUTROPHICATION

The addition of organic matter in the form of untreated human or animal excrement or outflow from a treated sewage plant rich in phosphates and nitrates, thus results in accelerated eutrophication of the body of water into which the effluents drain. On a smaller scale, individual septic tanks produce a similar effect, for the nitrates and phosphates they release find their way first to the water table, then to stream and river drainage systems.

Table 11-1 ***Estimated Amounts of Nitrogen and Phosphorus Reaching Wisconsin Surface Waters from Various Urban and Rural Sources*****—figures expressed in 1000 lb per annum.** These illustrate a number of points which occur repeatedly in such figures—e.g., the high phosphate content of sewage plant effluents (from detergents) and the high nitrogen content leached to ground water tables—but are low for this comparatively rural state in some features, such as those for industrial wastes.

	NITROGEN		*PHOSPHATE*	
Source	*Actual Amount*	*Percentage Figure*	*Actual Amount*	*Percentage Figure*
URBAN				
Municipal sewage treatment installations	20,000	24.5	7,000	55.7
Private sewage systems	4,800	5.9	280	2.2
Industrial wastes	1,500	1.8	100	0.8
Urban run-off	4,450	5.5	1,250	10.0
Subtotal	30,750	37.7	8,630	68.7
RURAL				
Manured lands	8,110	9.9	2,700	21.5
Other cropland	576	0.7	384	3.1
Forest land	435	0.5	0.43	0.3
Pasture, woodlot, and other lands	540	0.7	360	2.9
Ground water	34,300	42.0	285	2.3
Precipitation on surface of water areas	6,950	8.5	155	1.2
Subtotal	50,911	62.3	3,927	31.3
Grand total	81,661		12,557	

Another cause of accelerated eutrophication is the large amount of soluble fertilizers now applied to most agricultural and horticultural crops in an attempt to boost yields. When organic manure was the sole fertilizer used by farmers, release of inorganic nutrients was relatively slow, and they were mostly taken up by the soil and plants, rather than leached into the water table or carried off in flood waters. he liberal use of such compounds as ammonium sulfate and potassium phosphate now results in as much as one half of the added nutrients being lost in drainage water (Table 11-1). The nitrate and phosphate pollution of natural waters by such agricultural drainage may entirely disturb the balance of populations in an aquatic ecosystem. Although these would usually eventually evolve to a more eutrophic state, the term *eutrophication* has now come to be applied to the accelerated rather than the natural successional process (Figure 11-2).

While the effluent from sewage plants may be treated further to remove particularly the nitrates and phosphates (Eliassen and Tohabanoglous,

1969), it is more difficult and even more expensive to control water pollution from agricultural sources, and little attempt is presently made to try.

Rate of Eutrophication

While all natural waters thus age and undergo a process of succession from an oligotrophic to a eutrophic state, a great acceleration of the rate of this process can be very disturbing (Figure 11-3). It is likely to result in a number of highly undesirable primary consequences such as depletion of oxygen, increased turbidity of the water, accumulation of organic matter, and blooms of toxic algae, together with a wide range of secondary consequences such as elimination of many fish species.

Accelerated aging or eutrophication has been observed in various lakes throughout the world (Hasler, 1947). The first to be investigated was Lake Zurich in Switzerland. Fure Lake in Denmark and Lake Washington in the

Figure 11-2. *Production of carbon by algal photosynthesis in four Swiss alpine lakes.* A. Millstatter. *B.* Klopeiner. *C.* Worther. *D.* Constance (lower part). These lakes show progressively higher levels of eutrophication, as indicated by their increased production in mg C/m³ per day. In *D*, however, the increased algal biomass restricts light penetration in depth into the lake, so that algal growth as measured by mg C/m³ per day production is virtually restricted to the surface 3m. (Reproduced with the permission of the author and publisher from A. D. Hasler, *Bioscience,* **19**[5]: 427, 1969.)

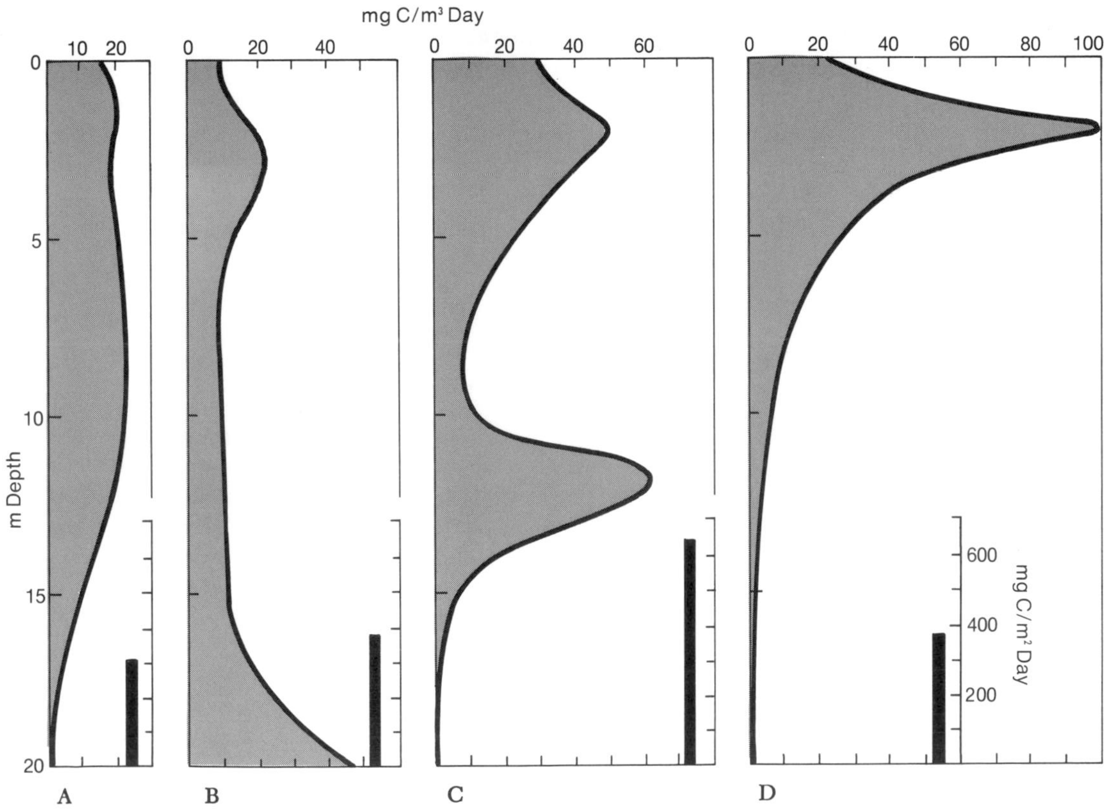

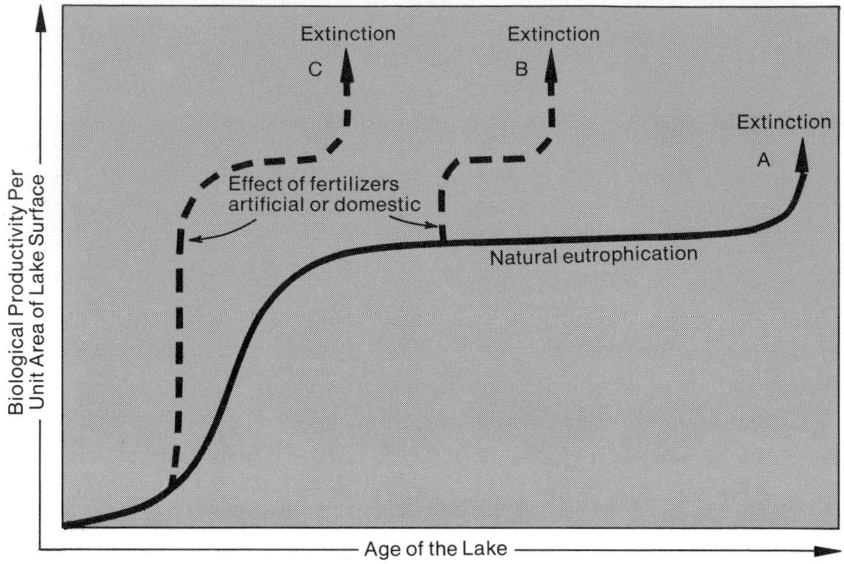

Figure 11-3. *Accelerated eutrophication in a lake.* The curve *A* represents the slow process of ecological succession from an oligotrophic to a eutrophic condition illustrated in Figure 11-1. Curve *B* shows the effect when the increase in net primary productivity is advanced by the addition of nitrates and phosphates into the biochemical cycling processes of the natural ecosystem. Curve *C* represents even heavier dosages of such additions. (Based on Hasler, 1947.)

Table 11-2* ***Physicochemical Characteristics of the St. Lawrence Great Lakes*** Lakes Erie and Ontario, into which the St. Lawrence drains, have a low concentration of oxygen in the hypolimnion, a characteristic of accelerated eutrophication. These two lakes also have high amounts of dissolved solids, which similarly characterize this condition.

Lake	*Mean Depth (m)*	*Transparency (Average Secchi Disc Depth, m)*	*Total Dissolved Solids (ppm)*	*Specific Conductance (μmhos at 18°C)*	*Dissolved Oxygen*
Oligotrophic	>20	High	Low: around 100 ppm or less	<200	High, all depths all year
Superior	148.4	10	60	78.7	Saturated, all depths
Huron	59.4	9.5	110	168.3	Saturated, all depths
Michigan	84.1	6	150	225.8	Near saturation, all depths
Eutrophic	<20	Low	High: >100	>200	Depletion in hypolimnion <70% saturation
Ontario	86.3	5.5	185	272.3	50 to 60% saturation in deep water in winter
Erie, average for lake	17.7	4.5	180	241.8	
Central basin	18.5	5.0	—	—	<10% saturation, hypolimnion
Eastern basin	24.4	5.7	—	—	40 to 50% saturation, hypolimnion

* Reprinted by permission of the publisher from A. M. Beeton, *Limnology and Oceanography*, **10:** 241, 1965.

Pacific Northwest are two other early examples. The most extensive, in terms of surface area at least, are the American Great Lakes (Beeton, 1965).

Detection of Eutrophication

As eutrophication is basically an accelerated rate of increase in net primary productivity, it may be detected by any method which measures the rate of net primary productivity. Sometimes the change of rates is so obvious that it can be seen or smelled; it is expressed in the following features:

1. *Increased amounts of standing crop.* In particular the amount of algal growth is greatly increased (Figure 11-4); sometimes toxic species become dominant. A thick algal mat frequently fills stream beds in areas where the septic tanks of vacation homes drain down from a watershed area.
2. *Diminished transparency*—as measured with a standard Secchi disc. One of the early signs that the accelerated eutrophication of Lake Washington was being slowed was the realization that the beer cans on the bottom of the lake had become visible again. The increasing turbidity localizes algal growth in the surface layers of water (Figure 11-2), and utilization of food materials becomes restricted to near-surface water.
3. *Oxygen production*—measured scientifically by a dark and light

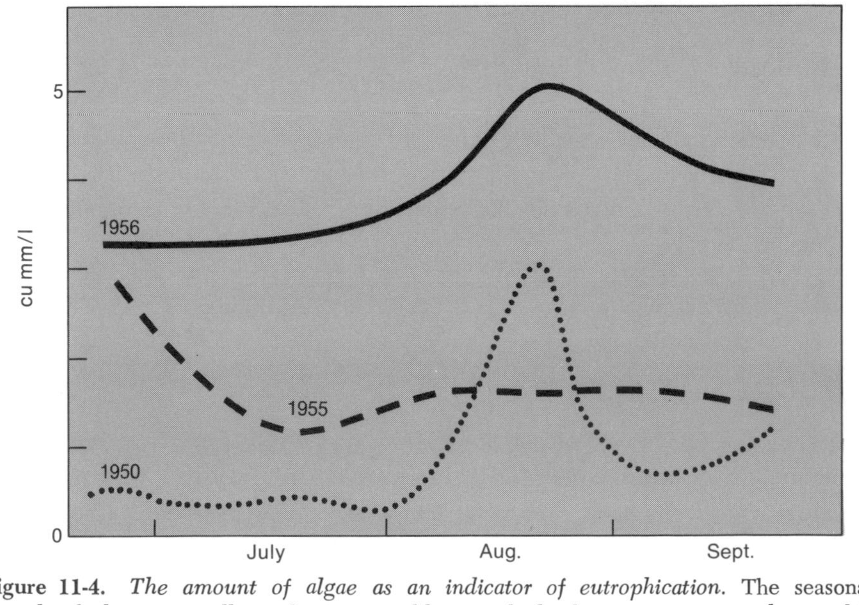

Figure 11-4. *The amount of algae as an indicator of eutrophication.* The seasonal growth of algae, typically with a spring bloom, which characterizes even oligotrophic lakes, occurred in Lake Washington (near Seattle, Wash.) in 1950 and began to persist throughout the year as eutrophication developed, until the volume of algae in 1956 persisted at a level higher than the seasonal level of the unpolluted lake. (From G. C. Anderson, Trans. 1960 Seminar, R. A. Taft San. Eng. Center, U.S.P.H.S., Cincinnati, Ohio, p. 63, 1960; reproduced with permission of the publisher.)

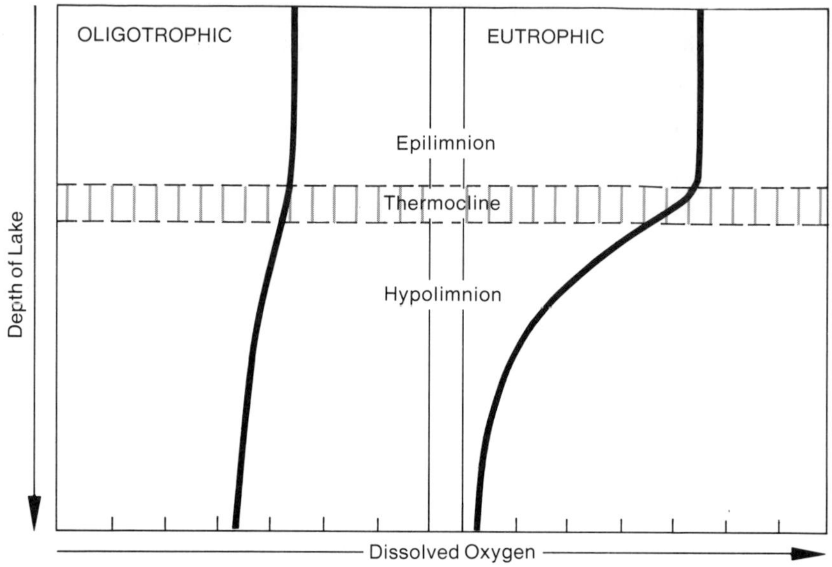

Figure 11-5. *Summer stagnation in a lake through oxygen depletion.* The thermocline which forms in summer, separating water circulation in the warmer upper section of the lake from that in the cooler deeper portion, acts as a barrier to rapid gas exchange. The oxygen content of the water below the thermocline becomes very low because of the activity of decomposer organisms which are reducing the increased amounts of organic matter settling out from the higher productivity of a eutrophic condition in the lake.

In winter the surface layers of water are cooled and become more dense; overturn occurs, the thermocline disappears, a single water circulation develops in the lake, and the resulting enhanced gaseous exchange restores normal oxygen levels throughout the water depth. (Based on Sawyer, 1966.)

bottle technique. Lack of oxygen may become obvious by the smell when anaerobic processes in the deoxygenated lake result in the formation of odoriferous gases (Figure 11-5). Hydrogen sulfide in particular tends to accumulate in toxic concentrations when biochemical oxygen demands from untreated biological wastes significantly deoxygenate lake waters.

4. *Nutrient levels*—particularly of nitrates and phosphates, which become higher as eutrophication proceeds.

THE GREAT LAKES

In considering the rate of eutrophication, limnologists are by no means in agreement as to recognizable stages. It is convenient, however, to distinguish between *physicochemical biological* conditions. The physicochemical conditions of a lake include water transparency, amounts of dissolved solids, electrical conductivity, and quantity of dissolved oxygen.

Physicochemical Conditions

Table 11-2 lists measurements of physicochemical values for the Great Lakes. It can be seen from this table that Erie and Ontario have a low concentration of oxygen in the *hypolimnion,* the water below the *thermocline,* which is characteristic of eutrophic conditions. The high total of dissolved solids and conductance values for these two lakes also indicate eutrophic conditions.

Biological Characteristics

The biological features of the Great Lakes, summarized in Table 11-3, indicate that all except Lake Erie are in an oligotrophic state as far as the biological characteristics listed in the table as typifying oligotrophy are concerned. This is evidenced by the dominance of salmonids—salmon, trout, and char—in the fish populations.

Although species of these salmonid fish groups may still be present in the eutrophic conditions of Lake Erie they have been extensively replaced by perch, bass, smelt, and dorem.

Degree of Eutrophication

Combining this physicochemical and biological information, Beeton (1965) considers that Huron and Superior are definitely oligotrophic, Michigan and Ontario, mesotrophic. Since the water of the clearly eutrophic Lake Erie flows on into Lake Ontario via the Niagara Falls, it is not surprising that the dissolved solid content of this last lake is also typical of eutrophic conditions.

Supporting evidence for these conclusions regarding the St. Lawrence Great Lakes is sometimes confused and is drawn mostly from studies on the behavior of much smaller bodies of water. In regard to the chemical characteristics which Beeton summarizes, Erie and Ontario alone show significant increases in calcium and chloride while sulfates have increased in all except Superior (Figure 11-6). Chlorides and sulfates are major components of domestic and industrial waste.

Some workers identify blooms of the blue-green planktonic alga *Oscillatoria rubescens* with later stages of eutrophication. Such indicator blooms occurred in various European lakes, but planktonic studies on the Great Lakes were at first too inadequate to provide any useful evidence as to the occurrence of this alga. Subsequent research, however, suggests that certain planktonic changes are taking place uniquely in Lake Erie.

Lake Erie

Since eutrophication appears to have proceeded furthest in Lake Erie of all the Great Lakes, attention has been focused there on the causes of this accelerated maturation. As in all five lakes, the change seems to have occurred during the past half century. During this time the population of the northeast central states has grown from approximately 16 million in 1900 to

Table 11-3* ***Biological Characteristics of the St. Lawrence Great Lakes*** All except Lake Erie on this biological basis are still in an oligotrophic condition.

Lake	*Bottom Fauna and Dominant Midges*	*Dominant Fishes*	*Plankton Abundance*	*Dominant Phytoplankton*
Oligotrophic	*Orthocladius-Tanytarsus* type (*Hydrobaenus-Calopsectra*)	Salmonids	Low	*Asterionella formosa* *Melosira islandica* *Tabellaria fenestreta* *Tabelleria flocculosa* *Dinobryon divergens* *Fragilaria capucina*
Superior	*Pontoporeia affinis* *Mysis relicta* *Hydrobaenus*	Salmonids	Very low	*Asterionella formosa* *Dinobryon* *Synedra acus* *Cyclotella* *Tabellaria fenestrata* *Melosira granulata* *Fragilaria crotonensis*
Huron	*Pontoporeia affinis* *Mysis relicta* *Hydrobaenus* *Calopsectra*	Salmonids	Low	*Tabellaria fenestrata* *Fragilaria construens* *Fragilaria pinnata* *Cyclotella kutzingiana* *Fragilaria capucina*
Michigan	*Pontoporeia affinis* *Mysis relicta* *Hydrobaenus*	Salmonids	Low	*Fragilaria crotonensis* *Melosira islandica* *Tabellaria fenestrata* *Asterionella formosa* *Fragilaria capucina*
Ontario	*Pontoporeia affinis* *Mysis relicta*	Salmonids, ictalurids, percids	——	——
Eutrophic	*Tendipes plumosus* type	Yellow perch, pike, black bass	High	*Microcystis aeruginosa* *Aphanizomenon* *Anabaena*
Erie				
Central basin	*Tendipes plumosus*	Yellow perch, smelt, freshwater drum	High	*Melosira binderana* *Stephanodiscus* *Cyclotella* *Fragilaris crotonensis*
Eastern basin	*Pontoporeia affinis* few *Calopsectra*	Yellow perch, smelt, few salmonids	High	*Microcystis* *Aphenizomenon*

* Reprinted by permission of the publisher from A. M. Beeton, *Limnology and Oceanography*, **10:** 242, 1965.

some 36 million in 1960. Twenty-five million people are now estimated to be living in the communities around the shores of the Great Lakes; approximately 11 million of them—about one-twentieth of the whole United States population—are concentrated on Lake Erie. The changes which have occurred in Lake Erie have gone much beyond mere eutrophication, owing to excessive release into it of phosphates and nitrates. The dumping of wastes and garbage of all kinds, combined with the discharge of domestic and industrial effluents, has given the lake the unenviable distinction of being the most polluted large body of water in the world.

THE DYING LAKE

To many, what has befallen Lake Erie is the first (and perhaps last) large-scale warning that we are now destroying by industrial exploitation the habitability of this earth for humans. There can be no doubt that it is a massive commentary on our loss of environmental quality.

The western end of the lake is dead, with no sign of life above or below the water. Patches of oil, trash, and sewage float on the surface; foul-smelling scum mixed with the bodies of waterfowl, fish, and assorted jetsam, among which scuttles an occasional rat, now line the shore. The Cuyahoga

Figure 11-6. *Changes in chemical characteristics of the St. Lawrence Great Lakes.* All except Lake Superior show chemical changes indicative of accelerated eutrophication. In Erie, and Ontario into which it drains, this affects the levels of all the nutrients recorded; in Michigan it affects all except calcium levels, in Huron all except calcium and sodium + potassium. (Reproduced by permission of the publisher from A. M. Beeton, *Limnology and Oceanography,* **10:** 247, 1965.)

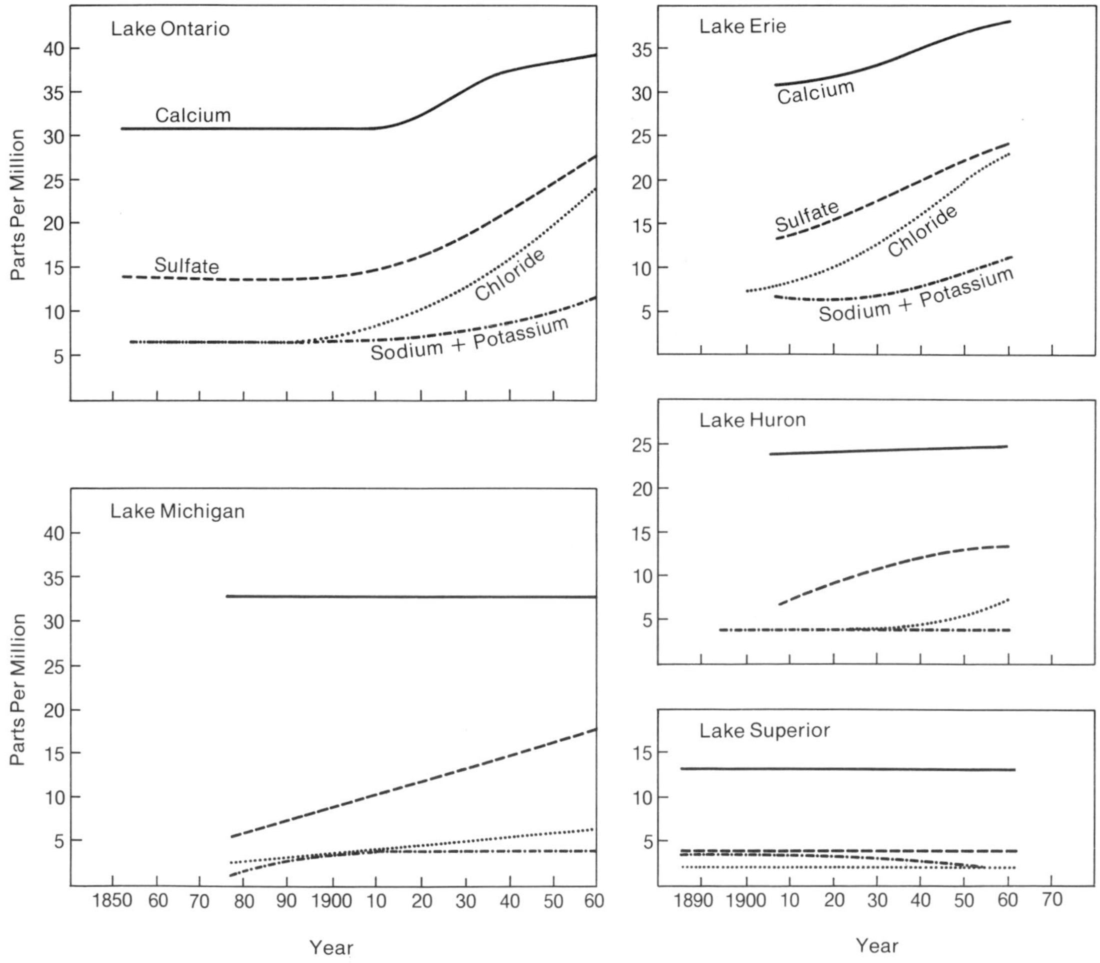

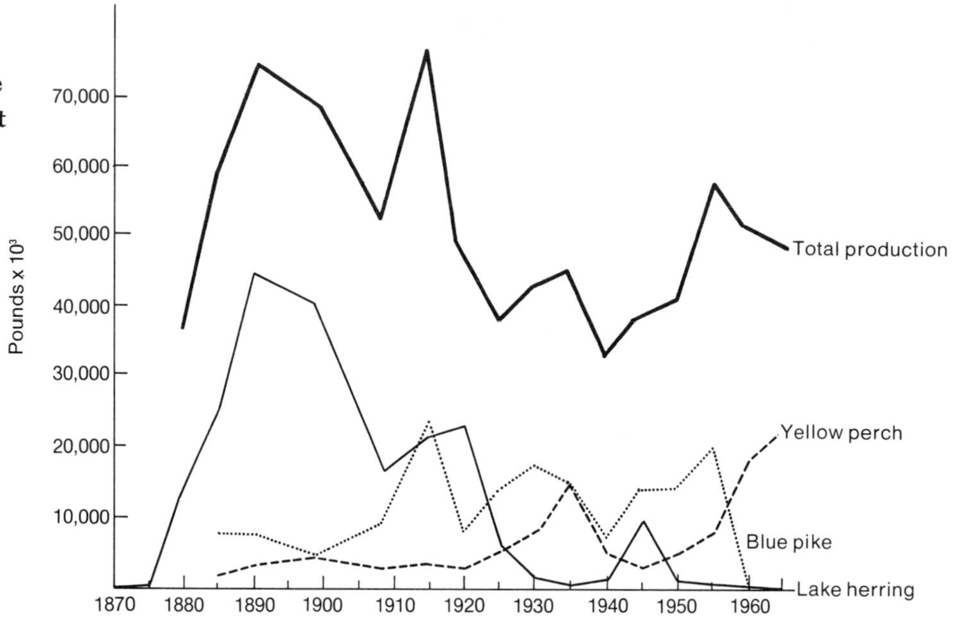

Figure 11-7. *Changes during the past century in the fish population of Lake Erie.* The catch of the two predators, blue pike and lake herring, has fallen to nil, whereas in their absence, the numbers of the herbivorous yellow perch, and therefore the catch, have risen considerably. (From N. S. Baldwin and R. W. Saalfied, Great Lakes Fisheries Commission Technical Report No. 3 plus supplement, 1962, p. 37; reproduced with the permission of the publisher.)

and Buffalo rivers have been declared *fire hazards,* and recently the former, which flows into the lake at Cleveland, actually burned.

The somewhat spectacular estimate has been made that the lake now contains a billion tons of algae—enough to fill a freight train 40,000 miles long. The western quarter of the lake is becoming an algae marsh. Variations over recent years in number of algae, oxygen content of the water, and amount of pollution are shown in Figure 11-7.

FISHING AND HUNTING

Commercial fishing, once a thriving industry on Lake Erie, has declined and almost disappeared with the loss of such species as whitefish, pickerel, sauger, perch, and sturgeon. One fishing group on the Vermillion River, which once employed over 200 men, now has only nine or ten. An estimated 12,000 ducks were recently reported killed on the Detroit River by oily pollutants, and in many areas the only animals left to hunt are rats. The colonies of snowy egrets which nest on the islands in the Detroit River diminish each year.

FALL IN WATER LEVEL

Associated with this pollution is a lowering of the water level of this shallow lake, which is mostly only about 15 m deep, little over 50 m at its deepest point. The Army Corps of Engineers dredged 3 million cubic yards of spoil, at a cost of 1 million dollars, and dumped this pollution-laden material back into Lake Erie. This is the traditional way of handling materials dredged to keep open the waterways to the big lakeshore cities.

Increased run-off from the surrounding rivers, bringing silt, pesticides, and fertilizers, has accelerated the rate at which the shipping channels fill.

CAUSES OF POLLUTION OF LAKE ERIE

Approximately 2 per cent of the sewage disposal plants in the country are considered adequate to deal with the living and household wastes they should handle. The great majority, and those around Lake Erie are no exception, are at most 50 per cent efficient. Their effluents contain not only the phosphates and nitrates released from living matter but also the very high levels of phosphates which modern detergents release. The states of Pennsylvania, New York, Indiana, Michigan, and Ohio discharge an estimated 1,500,000 gallons of sewage into Lake Erie every day. The lakeshore communities themselves pour in an estimated 18,000 tons daily of sewage, sediments, and fertilizers, including detergents. During rainstorms some 39 principal sewage overflow pipes release an estimated 50 million gallons of raw sewage into the lake.

The nearly 400 major industrial plants contribute an additional 10 million gallons of waste materials. Detroit provides wastes from its automotive, steel, chemical, paper, and petroleum industries. Toledo dumps the waste products from automotive, steel, petroleum, and glass factories; Cleveland from oil, cyanide, steel, automotive, chemical, phenol, and paper industries; and Buffalo from steel, chemical, and cement industries and from flour mills.

CONTROL OF POLLUTION IN LAKE ERIE

Problems created by technology (as in the case of water pollution), whether in Lake Erie or elsewhere, have technological solutions. An issue which has already been raised in this text several times, it will appear again. Briefly, it is a matter of *internalizing* costs instead of *externalizing* them from a particular industry to the community as a whole.

Antipollution regulations have already been established for the industries in the Great Lakes region; some few factories have shut down or moved elsewhere because of the added cost of conforming to the required measures. It is unlikely that more than one quarter of the industries and one half of the cities will be able to accommodate to newly introduced antipollution requirements, estimated to require a capital expenditure of one-third billion dollars for full implementation.

Against this expenditure should be set for comparison the value of the estimated 17 *billion* dollars' worth of cars, steel, chemicals, rubber, paper, and petroleum products which the Great Lakes region is estimated to produce annually. It is projected that this will increase up to five times in the next half century. So will the pollution; what price are we willing to pay to prevent it? There is no doubt about who eventually has to pay, so it should not be difficult to identify where the decision must be taken. Concerning Lake Erie, its "flushing time" is such that it would take an estimated 20 years to restore the lake to something approaching the unpolluted, mesotrophic state which natural succession would be expected to have attained at this period of its history, even if all recommended controls were immediately implemented.

Lake Washington

To provide some contrast to this appalling story of Lake Erie, the recent history of Lake Washington illustrates what can be done to reverse changes in eutrophication and pollution processes if they are vigorously pursued.

The case of Lake Washington is somewhat simpler than that of the Great Lakes for three reasons. First, industrial pollution was never a significant compounding factor. Second, surrounding activities in the Pacific Northwest are essentially of a forestry rather than an agricultural nature: run-off of pesticides and fertilizers is consequently minimal. The third reason is that a convenient emptying ground, Puget Sound, is available to take treated sewage effluent.

Nevertheless, the operations necessary to clear up Lake Washington and reverse the accelerated eutrophication there cost in excess of $120 million. This money seems to be regarded by the people of the Pacific Northwest, who provided most of it, as having been well spent.

An account of the earlier part of the Lake Washington story has been published by Edmondson (1961, 1968), and completed by him with an address given in September, 1969, at the 11th International Botanical Congress in Seattle. The lake has had two episodes of pollution by sewage. In the first, which reached a maximum just before the depression of the 1930s, pollution by raw sewage became so extensive that in 1926 this was diverted instead into Puget Sound. This diversion ensured that by the mid-1930s the lake was back in good condition.

However, further human population growth in the area led to the erection of sewage plants releasing *treated* sewage effluent into the lake. By 1956 there were ten such plants handling 20 million gallons of raw sewage daily. Accelerated eutrophication from the added phosphates and nitrates showed up in the usual way with depleted oxygen contents in the deep water, and summer phytoplankton populations persisting at values as high as previous spring blooms (Figure 11-4). In 1955 *Oscillatoria rubescens,* which was associated with the eutrophication occurring in European waters such as Lake Zurich, appeared also in Lake Washington.

As a result of public alarm at this increasing pollution of Lake Washington, legislation was introduced in the State of Washington (instigated by the mayor of Seattle and a committee he formed to deal with waste disposal) which permitted a concerted effort to be made to halt this accelerated eutrophication. In 1963 work was begun on two main sewage lines, completed in 1968, which pick up all wastes from the area and deliver them to a main sewage treatment plant on Puget Sound. The treated effluent from this plant, which also handles the raw sewage previously dumped into the Sound, is released some distance offshore in an area of strong tidal flow at a depth of about 75 m.

This is not just an externalization of the problem into a marine instead of a fresh-water ecosystem, for because of an upwelling situation, Puget Sound is a nutrient-rich habitat. The nutrient levels where the treated effluents are released are about the same for nitrates and phosphates as Lake Washington had at the point of maximum pollution.

The nutrient status of Lake Washington has now almost returned to the 1933 level, at least with regard to phosphates. Nitrates are reacting somewhat more slowly. The water is clear again, and the bottom has once more become visible near the shore. By 1971 the lake will probably be completely restored to its nutrient status of 1933. Similar action to lower biochemical oxygen demand, phosphate content, and coliform bacteria contamination will probably save another famous beauty spot, Lake Tahoe (Culp, 1969). Agricultural use of treated effluents is also possible (Kardos, 1970).

Pollution of Coastal Waters

The discharge of sewage effluent into coastal waters is not always accompanied by so little ecological disturbance as has resulted from the example just described for Puget Sound. Further south along the Pacific Coast, in Southern California, the explosive reproduction of sea urchins around sewage outfalls has been described by W. S. North and others. Here sea urchins can utilize the high concentrations of organic materials because of their apparent ability to absorb amino acids directly through their spines and tube feet. Their numbers increase enormously as a result, and they destroy kelp beds through their habit of gnawing away the holdfast, thus releasing the massive kelp fronds. Following destruction of the kelp beds, the urchins turn to destroying other marine invertebrates in the area of the sewage outfall.

North has pioneered a method of controlling such sea urchins outbreaks with the use of quicklime, which selectively kills the urchins, after which the kelp beds and their invertebrate populations become reestablished.

It has been estimated that in Pacific coastal waters in 1967, some 12 million fish were killed by pollution; moreover, reports of abnormalities in species such as flatfish and bass are constantly received. A recent note (Valentine and Bridges, 1969) reports as many as 56 per cent abnormal individuals in a marine fish population off the California coast.

In an endeavor to facilitate a systems approach to the study of such marine pollution effects, D. L. Mayer (Sawbridge and Bell, 1969) has presented a "waste impact index." This is derived by the following equation:

Waste impact index $= \triangle P_p + \triangle B_p + \triangle D$
where $\triangle P_p =$ Primary productivity water (determined by the chlorophyll method)
$\triangle B_p = O_2$ consumption surface sediments (an estimate of benthic productivity)
$\triangle D =$ Index of diversity of Foraminifera populations.

Such quantitative approaches are clearly necessary both for pursuing fundamental studies of marine pollution and for any necessary enforcement of antipollution legislation.

OTHER FORMS OF WATER POLLUTION

Apart from sewage and fertilizer pollution, modern industry has succeeded in dumping virtually every imaginable waste product into natural waters. Indeed the economic terms *externalization* and *internalization* have now been extensively applied by ecologists to this dumping process. Instead of going to the trouble and expense of removing all harmful substances from an industrial effluent by internalized processes, industry dumps its effluent, externalizing the problem on society at large, and saving itself much cost. This is happening in Lake Erie.

These externalized waste substances are sometimes grouped for convenience of discussion. One particularly dangerous group are the radioactive isotopes. As an example the amount of radioactivity in the discharged water from a nuclear power station is listed in Table 11-4. The question of absorption of radioactive isotopes has already been examined in the previous chapter.

Table 11-4* ***Radioactivity Discharge in Waste Water from a British Nuclear Power Plant*** The figures indicate the mean monthly discharge in curies of beta emitters in 1962. Besides these elements, a further 34 radionuclides have been detected in the outflow from nuclear power stations in amounts varying from 200 curies monthly to traces only.

A tightening of the United States regulations regarding waste discharge of radioisotopes was apparently responsible for reducing the number of new nuclear power stations ordered from 17 in 1968 to 3 in 1969. Up to the end of 1968, 88 nuclear power stations had been ordered for the United States of which 12 were operative.

Ruthenium-106	1916
Cerium-144	200
Ruthenium-103	153
Yttrium	125
Cesium-137	92
Strontium-9	85
Zirconium-95	78
Strontium-89	42

* Reprinted by permission of the publisher from H. J. Dunster, R. J. Garner, H. Howells, and L. F. U. Wix, *Health Physics*, **10:** 361, 1964.

Radioactive Isotopes

Along with two other groups of pollutants, actual poisons and pesticides, the most serious aspect of radioactive isotope discharge is that once introduced into an aquatic ecosystem, they may be selectively absorbed. In other words some populations of one trophic level or another may concentrate them in a particular portion of the bodies of the organisms which form the population. While continual monitoring of the concentration of the isotope, poison, or pesticide in the *water* may indicate that this remains well below tolerance levels, selective absorption may be passing on from one trophic level to other quite toxic concentrations of the substance. There are many examples of the occurrence of this selective concentration, and the subject will be considered again in the next chapter when problems of pesticide and poison absorption are examined further. Some comment, however, must be made at this stage (Aberg and Hungate, 1966).

Radioactive effluents from nuclear power plants are, together with fallout from atomic tests, one of the main sources of artificially produced radioactive contamination of marine waters. The nuclear reactor at Stanford in the Pacific Northwest discharges effluents which have been measured as reaching 1000 millicuries a day in the Columbia River estuary 350 miles downstream (Figure 11-8). Some of the isotopes present are of little significance because of short half-lives or poor absorption characteristics. Others, however, such as chromium-51 and zinc-65 have been detected in pelagic organisms some distance out in the Pacific Ocean.

An indication of the general contamination of marine waters on a worldwide basis resulting from atomic testing may be obtained from Table 11-5. The extent to which radioactive contamination of sea water from this, as from any other source, may be selectively concentrated in marine ecosystems is indicated in Table 11-6.

Mercury

In addition to general forms of water pollution such as eutrophication and contamination with radionuclides and other substances which are selectively absorbed as they pass through ecosystems, serious concern is being expressed regarding the dispersal and distribution of specific elements, one of which is mercury. Some of the most striking evidence as to occurrence of this element in various ecosystems has been provided from Sweden (Löfroth and Duffy, 1969). Since the 1930s mercury compounds have been used in that country for dusting the seeds of many agricultural crops in order to suppress seed-borne diseases, and in some instances to provide protection against fungal attack during seed germination.

During World War II Swedish farmers extended this practice and used liquid preparations of mercury in a commercial form known as Panogen for such crops as wheat, oats, and barley. The actual form of mercury in this

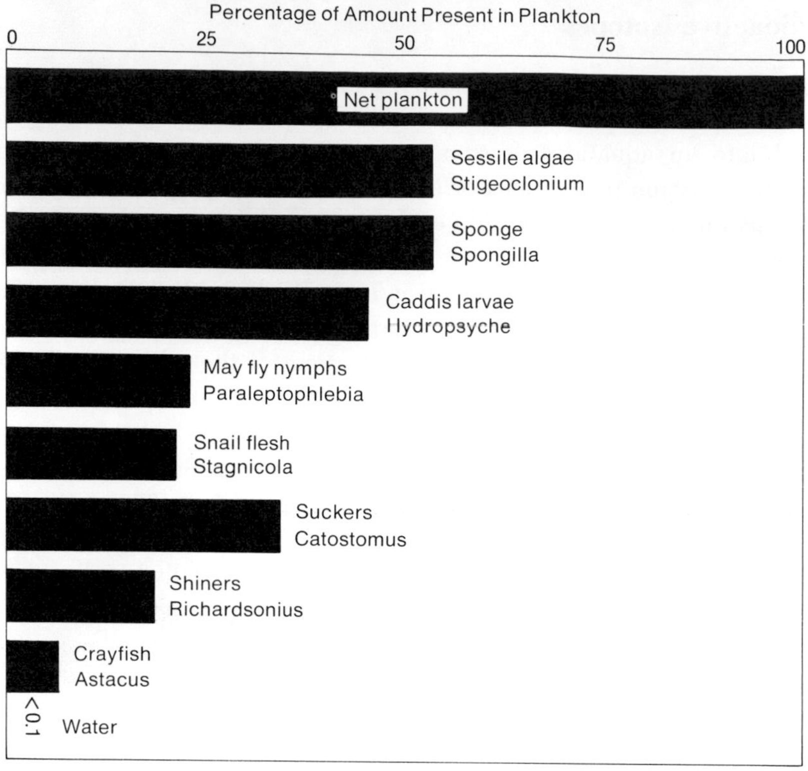

Figure 11-8. *Amounts of radioactivity present in various organisms at different trophic levels in the Columbia River.* The relative amounts of beta-emitting radioisotopes have never been recorded as reaching hazardous proportions in any organism. Fish collected downstream of the reactors have, however, 100 times the dose of control fish, while bottom animals, especially herbivorous insect larvae, may be even more radioactive. (Reproduced with the permission of the publisher from J. J. Davis and R. F. Foster, *Ecology,* **39:** 531, 1958.)

Table 11-5 ***Concentration in Surface Layers of Sea Water of Some Radioactive Isotopes*** Figures expressed in microcuries per gram of sea water $(\mu c/l)_s$ representing the effects of estimated world-wide fallout into the oceans. The only isotope occurring in significant concentrations in marine waters is potassium-40, which represents over 90 per cent of marine radioactivity. Contamination of sea water in general with artificially produced radioisotopes appears slight, but see Table 11-6 for the effects of selective concentration in marine ecosystems.

NATURAL (cosmic-ray produced)	
Carbon-14	—0.1
Tritium (radioactive hydrogen)	—4.0
Uranium-238	—1.0
Rubidium-87	—3.0
Potassium-40	—277.0
WEAPON-TESTING FALLOUT	
Cesium-137	—0.1
Strontium-90	—1.0
Carbon-14	—0.001
Tritium	—1.0 to 10.0

Table 11-6* ***Selective Concentration of Radioactive Isotopes in Marine Ecosystems*** The concentration factor at various trophic levels: producer (algae), primary consumer (mollusk), secondary consumer (crustacean), and tertiary consumer (fish). For some isotopes the insignificant concentrations in sea water (Table 11-4) are concentrated by a magnitude of four and can have significant effects.

	PRODUCERS	*CONSUMERS*		
Isotope	*Edible Red Algae*	*Primary Mollusks*	*Secondary Crustaceans*	*Tertiary Fish*
FISSION PRODUCTS				
Strontium-90	10^{-1}–1	10^{-1}–1	10^{-1}–1	10^{-1}–1
Cesium-137	1–10	10–10^{2}	10–10^{2}	10–10^{2}
Cerium-144	10^{2}	10^{2}	10^{2}	10–10^{2}
Zirconium-95	10^{2}–10^{3}	10–10^{2}	10^{2}	1–10
Niobium-95	10^{2}–10^{3}	10^{2}	10^{2}	1–10
Ruthenium-106	10^{3}	1–10^{3}	1–10^{3}	1–10
INDUCED ACTIVITIES				
Zinc-65	10^{2}	10^{3}–10^{5}	10–10^{4}	10^{3}–10^{4}
Iron-55	10^{3}–10^{4}	10^{2}–10^{4}	10^{2}–10^{4}	10^{2}–10^{4}
Cobalt-60	10^{2}	10–10^{3}	10–10^{3}	10–10^{2}
Manganese-54	10^{3}	10^{3}–10^{4}	10^{2}–10^{4}	10^{2}–10^{3}
Chromium-51	10–10^{3}	10^{3}	10^{3}	10^{2}–10^{3}

* From R. Scott Russell (ed.), *Radioactivity and the Human Diet,* Oxford: Pergamon Press, 1966, p. 436.

commercial preparation is methyl mercury dicyandiamide. Extremely toxic to all vertebrates, such methyl mercury compounds are effectively absorbed through the skin or by inhalation. They accumulate in the body because they are only slowly excreted.

The first concern over methyl mercury poisoning in Sweden was with possible effects on wildlife, but attention soon became focused on agricultural products. According to Löfroth and Duffy, in 1964 Swedish hens' eggs averaged 0.029 ppm of mercury, whereas those from six other continental countries averaged 0.007 ppm. An examination of other farm products provided the results shown in Table 11-7.

These findings in Scandinavia were confirmed by investigations on the

Table 11-7 ***Amounts of Mercury in Scandinavian Meat Products in Parts Per Million*** An analysis carried out in 1965 of the following agricultural products in Sweden and Denmark revealed there is serious contamination with methyl mercury.

RAW PRODUCT	*MERCURY (in parts per million)*	
	Swedish	*Danish*
Pork chops	0.030	0.003
Beef	0.012	0.003
Bacon	0.018	0.004
Pig's liver	0.060	0.009
Ox liver	0.016	0.005

From G. Westoo, *Nord Hyg. Tidskr.,* 1969; reproduced with the permission of the publisher.

use of mercurial fungicides in Japan. Further research there, and subsequently in Sweden, revealed, however, that the main source of the introduction of methyl mercury into agricultural ecosystems was industrial discharge rather than its agricultural use as a fungicide. Pulp factories use a mercury compound (phenyl mercury acetate) to discourage fungal growth on their machinery. Chlorine factories using mercury electrodes release mercury into both air and water, as do some sections of the electrical industry. Certain fossil fuels when burned release small quantities of mercury compounds; even the sludge from sewage plants may contain sufficient mercury to make it unsuitable for use as a soil fertilizer.

In the United States, although the pattern of use of mercury compounds in agriculture and industry is similar to what has been described for Sweden and Japan, comparatively little is known about the circulation of mercury compounds in American ecosystems. A large additional use in this country is in paints, to prevent the development of mildew, and especially in antifouling paints used on boats and in other damp environments. Acrylic paints, according to Novick (1969), may contain up to 1 per cent mercury fungicide. These are also used in making paper, and Novick states that it is difficult to obtain figures on the extent of this use in the paint industry.

Control of mercury pollution in industrial waste water is difficult; the selective absorption of mercury compounds and their passage through the trophic levels of natural and agricultural ecosystems provide for their persistence from 10 to 100 years in toxic concentrations affecting particularly the top carnivores in these systems. The most that presently can be done within the range of practical possibilities is to hold the mercury contamination levels of our local and global ecosystems as low as possible, and to carefully monitor the results of long-term exposure to specific low levels of mercury contamination.

Lead

Very similar problems are presented by lead, which, because of its growing use as a gasoline additive, is increasingly being introduced into not only the air sheds but also the watersheds of the total global system. At one time lead entered human ecosystems as a water pollutant because of the extensive use of lead pipes for water transport. Like mercury, it is only slowly excreted from the human body; even small amounts of contamination from this source could therefore eventually reach toxic concentrations. Water pollution by lead seems likely, however, to have rather different but even more serious ecological consequences. Concentrations of lead in sea water are believed to be increasing until they are now approaching levels at which they may possibly have toxic effects on phytoplankton, particularly on diatoms, which represent a significant proportion of the phytoplankton of marine ecosystems in the open sea. As the phytoplankton constitute by far the largest element of the producer trophic level in the world's ecosystem, any reduction in their activity through water pollution by lead compounds could result in reduced carbon dioxide absorption and oxygen restoration in the atmosphere. The proportions of oxygen and carbon dioxide in the earth's atmosphere are well buffered against change, but the ultimate result of the lead poisoning of a major group of marine producer populations would be disastrous for all aerobic organisms on this globe.

THERMAL POLLUTION

Pollutants affect aquatic ecosystems through modification of chemical processes which control productivity. Another form of water pollution becoming more prominent is *thermal* pollution, a physical modification in the form of increased temperatures. This is perhaps somewhat analogous to noise pollution and its significance in relation to air pollution, but with quite different results.

Water, extensively used as a *coolant* in machines ranging from internal combustion engines to thermal power plants, is the standard medium for the dispersal of unutilized heat in nuclear power stations. Temperature rises in the effluent water of such installations range generally from a low of 2° C to 10° C (Environment Staff Report, 1970).

The last figure is known from van Hoff's work to double the rate of any chemical reaction involved and obviously will cause profound disturbances to an aquatic ecosystem. Even as low a variation as 2° C may be critical and could raise sea water, for example, beyond the temperature tolerance limits for establishment of giant kelp beds. A possible means of utilizing the heat load has been discussed by Carter (1969), who describes experiments on warm-water irrigation of agricultural crops.

Air pollution is forcing attention on a need to change from thermal to nuclear power stations for the production of electricity. At the same time, the large volume of cooling water required for a nuclear power station may generate new problems. One of them is thermal pollution, which may threaten the survival of aquatic ecosystems long regarded as part of a regional heritage.

BIOLOGICAL POLLUTION

All forms of pollution represent some kind of disturbance to the continuing function of a naturally occurring ecosystem. Air and water pollution operate through physical, chemical, or biological disturbance of productivity, either directly or indirectly. *Biological pollution* causes disturbance to an ecosystem by directly influencing the relationship between component species populations.

The classical case resulted from the opening of the Welland Canal during construction of the St. Lawrence Seaway. This permitted the penetration of sea lampreys from Lake Ontario, with a balanced parasite-host relationship, to lakes Erie, Huron, and Michigan, where trout—one of two predators in the lake ecosystem—had no such evolutionary relationship with the parasitic lampreys.

The resultant decrease in numbers of trout in the last three lakes had effects over and beyond a disastrous decline in commercial fishing in those regions. The reduction in population numbers of a top predator lessened the extent of cropping of primary consumers such as alewives. Numbers of these primary consumers rose very rapidly, and occasionally great quantities of these commercially undesirable fish are cast up to rot on the lake shores.

Construction of the Suez Canal might have resulted in similar ecosystem disturbance through mixing of the populations of the Mediterranean and Red Sea ecosystems, had the Bitter Lakes not continued to act as a barrier. The Bitter Lakes are a series of shallow lakes part way along the Canal, where water evaporation results in a salinity appreciably higher than that of sea water; it is so high that few marine organisms can survive long enough to move through them from one region to another. The prolonged closure of the canal is believed to be modifying the effectiveness of this barrier.

Proposals to blast a new Panama canal operating entirely at sea level now threaten to mix the Pacific and Atlantic marine ecosystems. If the canal is built, it appears certain that almost half of the combined marine

Plate 8. *The Kariba Dam* constructed on the lower reaches of the Zambezi River on the frontier between Zambia and Rhodesia, and first operative in 1958. The next year biological pollution by a small introduced water fern, *Salvinia auriculata,* was reported, and within a year 10 per cent of the water surface was covered by this weed.

Plate 9. *Biological pollution:* a bay of the developing young Lake Kariba in 1961 covered from shore to shore with a floating *Salvinia* mat on which both indigenous and introduced plant species have become established to form impenetrable floating colonies of "sudd."

Salvinia auriculata is a South and Central American species apparently introduced into the Zambezi system during the 1950 or 1940 decade. Mats of this floating weed disrupt aquatic ecosystems in the lake and impede navigation; no satisfactory control has yet been discovered.

species populations will disappear, because extensive competition will arise between ecological equivalents in the two oceans.

The disturbance to the tropical marine ecosystems of these two major oceans, which have evolved in complete independence for many millennia, would have extensive and harsh effects on their productivity for many years. It could also lead to extinction of numerous interesting and valuable species populations (Topp, 1969). The insertion of a fresh-water lake somewhere along the new canal would effectively prevent this mixing of the two marine ecosystems.

Such examples could be cited almost indefinitely. Holm *et al.* (1969) have recently surveyed major outbreaks of aquatic weeds, including water hyacinth (*Eichornia crassipes*), which has now entered virtually every major tropical and subtropical ecosystem in the world. Boughey (1963) describes how a previously insignificant water fern (*Salvinia auriculata*) assumed disaster proportions when allowed to pollute a new aquatic environment. The effects of a number of other such typical instances of biological pollution are cited in the discussion of conservation in Chapter 13.

One last aspect of biological pollution must be mentioned: as in the case of an air or water pollutant, a biological pollutant does not need to be introduced from one ecosystem into another. It can develop by a disturbance to the steady state reached within one particular ecosystem. A dramatic example of this is provided by the recent explosive development of a giant starfish which predates coral. A general account of this disturbance which threatens to become a major catastrophe for many small tropical islands has been provided by Dixon (1969), and a more specialized account by Chesher (1969).

The giant venomous starfish, *Acanthaster planci,* occurs in all tropical waters where coral is found. Although adult starfish are predated in their turn by the giant triton snail *Charonia tritenis,* a more significant predation is believed to be that of the larval stages of the starfish by coral polyps.

The most plausible hypothesis yet presented for this starfish "explosion," which has been noticed since 1963, is that destruction of large areas of coral by blasting and other means during harbor development created for the first time considerable areas of dead coral surfaces. In the shelter of these, starfish larvae could develop without being regulated by coral predation. The resulting mass of adults would then attack areas of coral adjoining the dead surfaces and thereby extend the dead areas in a continuing vicious circle. As one adult giant starfish is believed to be able to kill 1 square meter of coral per month, it can be imagined it will not take long to destroy a coral reef completely.

It is estimated that 30 to 40 per cent of the Pacific coral reefs have already succumbed to starfish attack. Fish quickly desert such dead reefs, so that the many small coral islands of Oceania are threatened with loss of their major source of protein food. Moreover, if the dead reefs break up under wave erosion, the small islands previously sheltered by them will eventually go too. This will provide one more unfortunate illustration of the dangers inherent in human disturbance of regulatory feedback mechanisms in natural ecosystems.

WASTE DISPOSAL

Aside from the pollutant effects of pesticides and accidental pollution—like the Santa Barbara channel oil spillage or the several oil tanker disasters (Holcomb, 1969; McCaull, 1969)—air and water pollution are essentially externalization and internalization problems whose control may be achieved by suitable techniques of environmental engineering. Given the appropriate economic stimulus, there are no obvious technological difficulties involved in solving any pollution problem. The release of hydrocarbons from internal combustion engines is preventable if electrically powered cars are used, provided the electricity generating stations are not themselves sources of pollution. Eutrophication is avoidable if nitrates and phosphates are first removed from sewage effluents and then applied to crop plants in such a manner that they are not immediately drained off.

Industrial wastes almost always contain recoverable substances. If an economically feasible recovery method can be technologically applied, this will be developed with alacrity. Even garbage can, in principle, be sorted and recycled.

It is all a question of regarding human byproducts as an inseparable element of one ecosystem or another, and of ensuring that recycling of materials continues and the essential balance of particular ecosystems is not destroyed. For some time to come the energy which drives all our ecosystems will continue to originate as solar energy. The environments in which these ecosystems operate are the air, soil, and water of this planet. Over geological time, feedback mechanisms have developed in all natural ecosystems which permit effective exploitation of the available energy. Pollution of one form or another—air, water, thermal, noise, biological—is threatening to impose sufficient change on activities of these ecosystems of a kind that will effectively destroy many and disrupt the rest. It will also cause the rapid extinction of numerous species which have slowly evolved over the last 3½ to 4 billion years.

FOOD ADDITIVES

Human populations must always have sought means to arrest the biogeochemical processes which, through the activities of microbial populations, cycle elements through ecosystems. Various attempts have been made to preserve food for subsequent use after a period of days, weeks, or even years. With the development of urban ecosystems, this need for food preservation became even more urgent, and many substances were employed in an attempt to delay the inevitable reduction of food substances to their basic nutrient elements by reducer organisms.

Food pollutants, however, include an even wider range of substances than those which are added to improve the taste, color, appearance, and consistency of various consumable products. The total of such alien substances is immense (there may well be nearly one half million), and it is almost impossible to investigate their possible deleterious effects. While it was relatively simple to legislate, for example, against the use of formalin for the preservation of food, a demonstration that monosodium glutamate is ultimately harmful to the human system is exceedingly difficult. The recent outlawing of cyclamates as food and drink sweeteners illustrates how minimal experimental work on animals has to be extrapolated into possible human effects, and action taken even before any of these effects can be directly and positively demonstrated. It is possible that many food additives of a preservative or of an improving kind now widely employed are having both long- and short-term effects which increase the risk of our developing abnormal metabolism, abnormal offspring, or abnormal mortality. As many of these substances are utilized because of the disruptive effects they have on organisms involved in ecological recycling, it can be anticipated that their effects on these microbial reducer organisms may also be duplicated to some extent on organisms in other trophic levels.

Bibliography

REFERENCES

Aberg, B., and Hungate, F. P. (eds.) *Radiological Concentration Processes,* London: Pergamon Press, 1966.

Baldwin, N. S., and Saalfield, R. W. "Commercial fish production in the Great Lakes 1867–1960," *Great Lakes Fish. Comm.,* Techn. Rept. No. 3, 1962.

Beeton, A. M. "Eutrophication of the St. Lawrence Great Lakes," *Limnology and Oceanography,* **10:** 240–54, 1965.

Boughey, A. S. "The explosive development of a floating weed vegetation on Lake Kariba," *Adansonia,* 3(1): 49–61, 1963.

Carter, L. J. "Warm-water irrigation: an answer to thermal pollution," *Science,* **165:** 478–80, 1969.

Chesher, R. H. "Destruction of Pacific corals by the sea star *Acanthaster planci,*" *Science,* **165:** 280–83, 1969.

Culp, R. "Water reclamation at South Tahoe," *Water and Wastes Engineering,* (April): 36–39, 1969.

Davis, J. I., and Foster, R. F. "Bioaccumulation of radioisotopes through aquatic food chains," *Ecology,* **39:** 530–35, 1958.

Dixon, B. "Domesday for coral?" *New Scientist,* **44:** 226–27, 1969.

Edmondson, W. T. "Changes in Lake Washington following an increase in the nutrent income," *Proc. Intl. Ass'n Theoret. Appl. Limnol.,* **14:** 167, 1961.

Edmondson, W. T. "Water-quality management and lake eutrophication. The Lake Washington case," in T. H. Campbell and R. O. Sylvester (eds.), *Water Resource Management and Public Policy,* Seattle: University of Washington Press, 1968, pp. 139–78.

Edmondson, W. T., Anderson, G. C., and Peterson, D. R. "Artificial eutrophication of Lake Washington," *Limnology and Oceanography,* **1:** 47–53, 1956.

Eliassen, R., and Tohabanoglous, G. "Removal of nitrogen and phosphorus from waste water," *Environmental Science & Technology,* **3:** 536–41, 1969.

Environment Staff Report "A new river," *Environment,* **12**(1): 36–41, 1970.

Gatz, D. F., and Dingle, A. N. "Air cleansing by corrective storms," in A. W. Klement (ed.), *Radioactive Fallout from Nuclear Weapon Tests,* Oak Ridge, Tenn.: Div. Tech. Information, 1965, pp. 566–81.

Hasler, A. D. "Eutrophication of lakes by domestic drainage," *Ecology,* **28:** 383–95, 1947.

Hasler, A. D. "Cultural eutrophication is reversible," *Bioscience,* **19:** 425–31, 1969.

Holcomb, R. W. "Oil in the ecosystem," *Science,* **166:** 204–206, 1969.

Holm, L. G., Weldon, L. W., and Blackburn, R. D. "Aquatic weeds," *Science,* **166:** 699–709, 1969.

Kardos, L. T. "A new prospect," *Environment,* **12**(2): 10–21, 27, 1970.

Löfroth, G., and Duffy, M. E. "Birds give warning," *Environment,* **11**(4): 10–17, 1969.

McCaull, J. "The black tide," *Environment,* **11**(9): 2–16, 1969.

Novick, S. "A new pollution problem," *Environment,* **11**(4): 2–9, 1969.

Rawson, D. S. "Algal indicators of trophic lake types," *Limnology and Oceanography,* **1:** 18–25, 1956.

Rohlich, G. A., and Stewart, K. "Eutrophication—a review," *California State Water Quality Control Board,* Publ. No. 34, 1967.

Sawbridge, D. F., and Bell, M. A. M. "Pacific shores," *Science,* **164:** 1089, 1969.

Sawyer, C. N. "Basic concepts of eutrophication," *J. Water Pollution Control Federation,* **38:** 737–44, 1966.

Smith, S. H. "Status of the deepwater cisco population of Lake Michigan," *Trans. Ann. Fisheries Soc.,* **93:** 209–30, 1964.

Topp, R. W. "Interoceanic sea-level canal: effects on the fish faunas," *Science,* **165:** 1324–27, 1969.

Valentine, D. W., and Bridges, K. W. "High incidence of deformities in the serranid fish *Paralabrax nebulifer* from Southern California," *Copeia,* **3:** 637–38, 1969.

Wilson, B. R. (ed.) *Environmental Problems: Pesticides, Thermal Pollution, and Environmental Synergisms.* Philadelphia and Toronto: Lippincott, 1968.

Woodwell, G. M. "Radioactivity and fallout: the model pollution," *Bioscience,* **19:** 884–87, 1969.

FURTHER READINGS

Ayres, J. C., Kraft, A. A., Snyder, H. E., and Walker, H. W. *Chemical and Biological Hazards in Food,* Ames, Iowa: Iowa State University Press, 1962.

Clark, J. R. "Thermal pollution and aquatic life," *Scientific American,* **220** (3): 18–27, 1969..

Cole, La Mont, C. "Thermal pollution," *Bioscience,* **19:** 989–92, 1969.

Goldman, M. I. (ed.) *Controlling Pollution. The Economics of a Cleaner America,* Englewood Cliffs, N.J.: Prentice-Hall, 1967.

Grant, N. "The legacy of the Mad Hatter," *Environment,* **11**(4): 18–23, 43–44, 1969.

Hennigan, R. D. "Water pollution," *Bioscience,* **19:** 976–78, 1969.

Lotspeich, F. B. "Water pollution in Alaska: present and future," *Science,* **166:** 1239–45, 1969.

Lowman, F. G. "Radionuclides of interest in the specific activity approach, *Bioscience,* **19:** 993–999, 1005, 1969.

Oberle, M. W. "Lead poisoning: a preventable childhood disease of the slums," *Science,* **165:** 991–92, 1969.

Rutzler, K., and Sterrer, W. "Oil pollution," *Bioscience,* **20:** 222–24, 226, 1970.

Task Force on Environmental Health and Related Problems. A Report to the Secretary of Health, Education, and Welfare. U.S. Government Printing Office, Washington, D.C., 1969.

Toms, R. "Monitoring river pollution," *New Scientist,* **43:** 595–96, 1969.

Williamson, S. L. "Population pollution," *Bioscience,* **19:** 979–83, 1969.

Pesticides 12

The various kinds of pollution discussed in the previous two chapters involved the incidental introduction of toxic or waste substances into the air sheds or watersheds of particular ecosystems. Except that industry has purposely externalized the elimination of waste products on human societies, the release of such pollutants has not been deliberate. In the case of pesticides, however, highly toxic substances are intentionally introduced into given ecosystems in order to reduce the population growth of particular species believed responsible for certain plant and animal diseases, spoilage, or wastage.

Whereas atmospheric and water pollution by various forms of human waste have existed for several millennia—and are probably as old as the urban societies with which they are associated—pollution by pesticides dates essentially from World War II. A new human generation will soon be entering middle age which, for the first time in history, will have been continuously exposed to the effects of pesticide pollution. If these effects are anything approaching the magnitude and expression of those observed in other animals, this generation will be extremely resentful of what its predecessors have allowed to occur.

CLASSES OF PESTICIDE

It is now usual to include under the heading pesticide any form of chemical substance used for the regulation of population growth, whether it is technically for the control of herbaceous plants (herbicides), woody plants (arboricides), insects (insecticides), or has biocidal activity affecting rodents, arachnids, or any other population.

Before World War II, only "natural" pesticides were in common use, apart from specific application of poisons such as sodium arsenite, several forms of sulfur, and various mercurial salts for particular and limited purposes. These latter inorganic substances were not used on a sufficient scale to become widespread pollutants; the principal organic substances used were derris powder, nicotine, and pyrethrum powder. Interest in these has revived now that it is apparent the chlorinated hydrocarbons will be phased out by legislative action.

These earliest pesticides are occasionally classified in two groups, stomach poisons and contact poisons. The former included sodium arsenite (Paris green), lead arsenate, and nicotine; contact poisons were notably pyrethrum, derris, and certain nicotine preparations.

Contact Poisons

These organic poisons were naturally occurring substances. Derris and other rotenones in particular had a rather widespread distribution in various plant groups and were the active agents in a number of fish poisons traditionally used for stunning fish in confined waters. It was used especially as a dust on agricultural crops. Pyrethrum, obtained from the flowers of a daisy-like genus, *Pyrethrum,* was mostly used in suspension as a knockdown spray for killing household insects such as flies and mosquitoes.

Neither of these organic substances was considered very satisfactory, for their effect was immediate and temporary; their pesticide activity did not persist more than a few hours. Use of them did, however, suggest the idea of more persistent substances, if these could be found or synthesized. During World War II the first of this new class of synthetic insecticides, DDT, was developed.

CHLORINATED HYDROCARBONS

DDT (1,1,1-trichloro-2,2-bis[p-chlorophenyl]-ethane or *di*chloro*di*phenyl*tri*chloroethane, hence DDT) was first synthesized in 1874, but its insecticidal properties were not realized until 1939. The first large-scale demonstration of its efficiency as an insecticide came in 1943, when it prevented an epidemic of typhus in Naples, Italy. The Neapolitan population was dusted with DDT to control lice, the vector of typhus, an often fatal human disease.

During the past two decades the use of DDT as a pesticide has become immensely diversified. Its success has prompted the introduction of a number of new compounds in this same class of *chlorinated hydrocarbons.* Although some amounts of these may be carried away in drainage waters, mostly they are distributed to ecosystems other than the one intended by evaporation and subsequent fallout in rain or snow. England, for example, is estimated to receive 40 tons of chlorinated hydrocarbons annually as fallout.

DDT, like all the chlorinated hydrocarbons presently in use, is not readily decomposed by the reducer organisms in natural ecosystems. It persists for many years, either unchanged or modified to degraded substances of similar chemical structure and activity such as DDD and DDE. This is not unexpected, for the reducer organisms of natural ecosystems have had no prior exposure to this synthetic organic chemical, and there has been no selection for populations able to utilize it in their metabolism. By contrast, an extensively used herbicide, 2,4-D, is broken down in soil in a matter of days. 2,4-D is a synthetic compound whose chemical structure closely resembles naturally occurring growth-promoting plant hormones, or *auxins*. There has been adequate evolutionary time for some reducer populations to be adapted to utilize this substance, and no fundamental difficulty in overriding the comparatively minor chemical difference.

The first major attempt to describe possible irreversible changes which were resulting from the massive application of DDT and other *broad-spectrum* persistent chlorinated hydrocarbons came with the publication in 1962 of *Silent Spring* by Rachel Carson. This sparked a violent controversy, but was essentially responsible for initiating the public reaction which has culminated in the prohibition of DDT use from 1969 in certain American states, in Sweden, and some other countries. Another result was the shift in emphasis from broad-spectrum types of pesticides to *integrated control.*

Since 1962 it has been repeatedly established that DDT residues have become incorporated in all naturally occurring ecosystems (Egler, 1964; Woodwell, 1967). Their presence as pollutants can be demonstrated in soil (Edwards, 1966); water (Weaver *et al.*, 1965); air (Antommaria *et al.*, 1967); and man (Quinby *et al.*, 1965). Recently reported effects on various marine phytoplankton (Menzel *et al.*, 1970) suggest the proportion of oxygen in the atmosphere could be affected.

SELECTIVE CONCENTRATION

Although DDT may be introduced directly into the soil, water, or air of a particular ecosystem, it is relatively insoluble (1 to 2 parts per billion) and is most commonly distributed through ecosystems by *selective concentration* as it passes unchanged along the successive population elements of food chains and food webs, much in the manner previously described for radioactive elements. Thus in Lake Michigan, for example, the concentration of DDT in lake sediments was found to be 0.0085 ppm. Invertebrate primary consumers selectively concentrated this to 0.41 ppm, their fish predators to 3 to 8 ppm; the fatty tissues of herring gulls predating the fish were discovered to have no less than 3177 ppm. Essentially similar findings are reported from marine ecosystems, as illustrated in Table 12-1.

As might be anticipated from theoretical considerations, the effect of this selective concentration of such a persistent substance with this broad general toxicity is readily noticeable in top carnivores. The group of this class most susceptible appears to be the carnivorous birds, whose fate is

Table 12-1* ***Pesticides in a Marine Ecosystem*** Residues in parts per million in order of magnitude concentrations to the nearest multiple of 10. The amounts of residues show a progressive increase at each successive trophic level.

Trophic Level	*Species Involved*	*DDD (Including DDE and TDE)*	*Dieldrin*
Tertiary consumers	Dolphin	1.0	1.0
(top carnivores)	Seal	0.1	0.1
	Duck		
	Gull		
	Shag	0.1 to 1.0	0.1 to 1.0
	Cormorant		
	Gannet		
		0.01 to .1	0.01
	Plaice		
Secondary consumers	Herring		
(general carnivores)	Sand eel		
	Cod		
	Whiting		
Primary consumers	Microzooplankton	0.01	0.01
(herbivores)			
Producers	*Fucus*	0.001	0.001
(plants)	*Laminaria*		

* Reprinted by permission of the publisher from J. Robinson, A. Richardson, A. N. Crabtree, J. C. Couldon, and G. R. Potts, *Nature,* **214:** 1308, 1967.

relevant to human ecology in several ways. *Homo sapiens* also often behaves as a top carnivore of this type, as when eating tuna or salmon.

The destruction of top carnivores causes serious imbalance in the ecosystem involved. In a less material sense, the presence of top carnivores, such as the bald eagle, represents part of the indefinable "quality of environment" in terms of human interest and excitement. In regard to other carnivorous birds affected, Ames (1966) has recently described correlations between the nesting success of ospreys and the presence of DDT residues in the eggs.

Osprey Populations

Ospreys (*Pandion haliaetus*) are large, widely distributed fish eating birds usually associated with extensive stretches of inland or coastal waters. It is estimated that their numbers have declined during this century by 2 to 3 per cent per year, but recently this rate of decline has greatly increased to about 30 per cent annually.

In 1960 Ames observed in a large breeding colony in Long Island Sound only seven fledglings from 71 active nests. This is a reproductive rate of less than 0.1 young per nest.

By 1965 this colony was down to 12 pairs from an estimated 200 pairs of breeding birds in 1938. Significant amounts of DDT and its derivatives were found in the osprey eggs and also in the fish which formed the osprey diet.

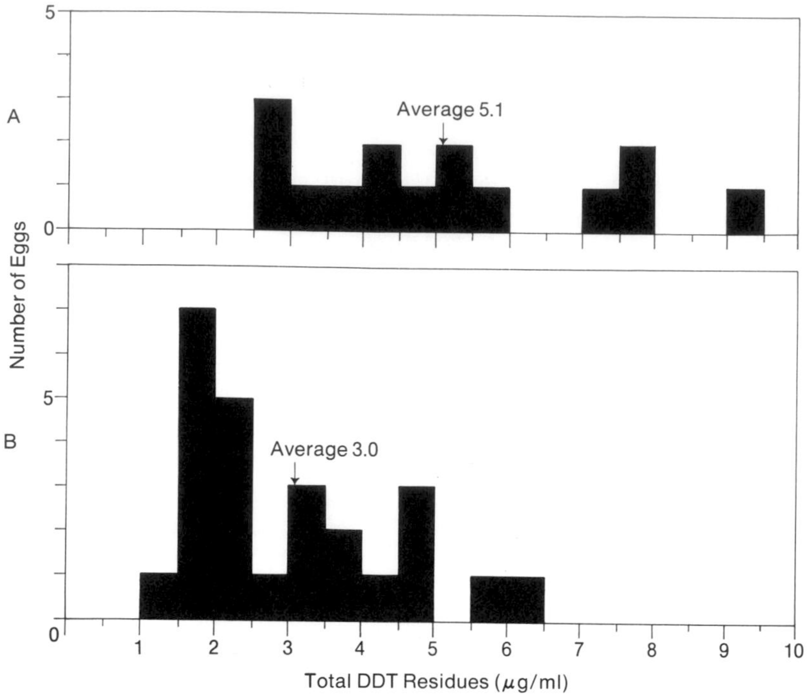

Figure 12-1. *Comparison of DDT residue levels in eggs of osprey populations.* Sample *A* is from a site in the Connecticut River where from 1957 to 1961 the osprey population underwent a very severe decline. Sample *B* is from a population on the lower Potomac River on the western edge of Chesapeake Bay, where ospreys seemed to be maintaining their numbers. Both samples were examined in 1963. Although the Maryland birds were about 2–2.5 times as successful in hatching their eggs as the Connecticut birds, whose eggs, as seen from the graphs, contained nearly twice as much DDT residue, when compared with vigorously reproducing osprey colonies, it would seem that even the lower level of DDT in their eggs is having some effect on their reproductive rate. (Reproduced with the permission of the publisher from P. L. Ames, *Journal of Applied Ecology,* 3[Suppl]: 92, 1966.)

While no direct evidence on this point was obtained, it can be presumed that pollution of the coastal waters of Long Island Sound with DDT and its derivatives introduced these substances to the marine ecosystem, where they became concentrated first in fish, then in osprey eggs. There, selective concentration has raised the DDT content sufficiently for it to be fatal to chick embryos, although not to adult birds (Figure 12-1).

Causes of Population Declines Among Predatory Birds

The first specific evidence as to the causes of population decline in predatory birds is provided in a paper by Ratcliffe (1967). British ornithologists had become concerned by falling population numbers in peregrine falcons, sparrow hawks, and golden eagles, beginning in the early 1950s. It was noted that of 109 peregrine falcon nests recorded as examined in Britain in the period 1904 to 1950, only three contained eggs broken before hatching. During the period 1951 to 1966, 47 of the 168 nests examined contained eggs prematurely broken.

Attempting to link this significant increase in egg breakage in a causal relationship with the decline in predatory bird populations and the extended use of chlorinated hydrocarbon pesticides, Ratcliffe measured eggshell thickness in peregrines, sparrow hawks, and golden eagles using egg collections dating back sometimes to the beginning of this century. In the peregrine he found a 20 per cent decrease in thickness from 1947, in sparrow hawks, 24 per cent, in golden eagles, 8 per cent.

In the United States, Hickey and Anderson (1968) reported a 26 per cent decrease in the egshell thickness of the East Coast peregrine, 25 per cent in ospreys from New Jersey, and 19 per cent in bald eagles from Florida. They also showed a correlation in herring gull eggs between the decrease in thickness and the amount of chlorinated hydrocarbon residue in the eggs. Enderson and Berger (1970) established a correlation between chlorinated hydrocarbon residues in prairie falcons, thin eggshells, and poor hatching success.

Chlorinated hydrocarbons dissolve in fatty animal tissues. This was one factor leading to their use as pesticides, for they must be absorbed through the fatty chitinous exoskeleton of insects in order to be effective. Kuntzman (1964) reported that drug-metabolizing liver enzymes in rats attained a significantly higher rate of activity after receiving nontoxic doses of chlordane. Because of the continuing effect, he concluded this chlorinated hydrocarbon was stored in fatty tissues in the rats and slowly released into the circulatory system. Peakall (1967) showed that in birds given DDT, dieldrin, or both of these chlorinated hydrocarbons, there was an increase in the breakdown rate of the sex hormones, testosterone in the males, progesterone in the females. As a consequence of these experimental results, it is hypothesized that excess enzyme activity due to ingestion of a chlorinated hydrocarbon breaks down estrogen, producing inadequate calcium mobilization during eggshell formation and producing thinner eggshells. Moreover, the eggshell effect is only one of a number of metabolic disturbances initiated by the presence of a chlorinated hydrocarbon in the tissues of mammals and birds. The others are still largely obscure.

SECONDARY EFFECTS OF PESTICIDES

Besides having the direct effect on individual organisms at various trophic levels as indicated above, pesticide pollution may also seriously disturb natural ecosystems through selective absorption.

A dramatic example of this has been described by Hunt and Bischoff (1960). They investigated the effect of the chlorinated hydrocarbon DDD (dichlorodiphenyl dichloroethane) on gnat (*Chaoburus asticiopus*) control programs at Clear Lake in northern California. It is rather ironic that these gnats, although somewhat resembling mosquitoes in appearance, are not bloodsuckers, and it appears unlikely the adults feed at all. They were nevertheless considered a nuisance in this highly popular scenic area, and it was decided to eliminate them.

The first DDD treatment in Clear Lake was carried out in 1949, and the estimated concentration in lake water was one part in 70 million parts of water. A second treatment was made in 1954, with concentrations reaching one part in 50 million parts of water. In December, 1954, 3 months after the second treatment, 100 western grebes were reported dead; in 1955 more dead birds were found.

As gnat populations still increased despite these two pesticide applications, a third DDD treatment was made in 1957, at the same dosage as the second. Three months later 75 dead grebes were reported. Examination of several revealed that DDD was present at the extremely high concentration of 1600 parts per million in their fatty tissue, a concentration ratio over 100,000 times that of the lake water.

Subsequent examination of fish from Clear Lake revealed DDD concentrations ranging from 40 ppm in carp to 2500 ppm in brown bullhead, in all cases far over the maximum tolerance level for human consumption of 7 ppm set by the Food and Drug Administration. Generally speaking, smaller fish picked up less DDD than larger, and plankton feeders less than carnivorous fish. The general disturbance to consumer trophic levels in the lake which these pesticides produced caused eutrophication, and Clear Lake became anything but clear. The gnats remained.

Port Clinton Experiment

The effects of treatment of Clear Lake with chlorinated hydrocarbon were duplicated experimentally on a marsh near Port Clinton, Ohio, by T. J. Peterle (1969). In 1964 this marsh was sprayed with a known amount of DDT into which chlorine-36 had been incorporated to serve as a radioactive tracer to simplify detection of residual pesticide.

The highest level of DDT in surface water was reached about one hour after spraying, and at the end of two weeks no residues were detectable there. In bottom sediments, however, residue levels remained constant from about six weeks after spraying to more than 15 months after. The levels of residual pesticide in marsh populations at various trophic levels during this experiment are summarized in Table 12-2.

Antarctica

That no ecosystem is immune from the insertion of organochloride pollutants is evidenced in a paper by Tatton and Ruzicka (1967) dealing with DDT and its derivatives in Antarctica, where there is no agriculture, no insect life, and no use of such pesticides. Penguins and their eggs, skua, shags, and fish from Antarctica were examined. All were found to have

Table 12-2* ***Application of DDT to a Marsh*** Concentrations in parts per million of the pesticide subsequently found at various trophic levels. The temporarily very high pesticide concentrations in water following spraying quite soon disappear and are never reflected in the herbivore populations. Selective absorption occurs in the carnivorous trophic levels and persists there at a high level longest.

Trophic Level	*Name of Species*	*Time and Level of Maximum Residues*	*Time and Level of Residuals at Last Observation*
Tertiary consumers (top carnivores)	Carp	1 month (10)	2nd year (1)
	Snapping turtle		15 months (16)
Secondary consumers (general carnivores)	Red leech (*Erpobdella*)	7 days (13)	2nd year (1.5)
	Crayfish	——	2nd year (<1)
	Leopard frog (tadpole)	4 hours (42)	——
			13 months (42)
	Water snake	——	
Primary consumers (herbivores)	Muskrat	(<1)	
Producers (plants)	Alga (*Cladophora*)	3 days (218)	——
	Rooted plants	——	2nd year (about 1)
	Floating plants	——	2nd year (nil)

* Table prepared from figures extracted from Peterle, 1969.

significant quantities of various pesticide residues in their bodies, including DDT and its derivatives.

DDT in Fish Populations

The occurrence of DDT in fish populations is not always the result of selective concentration through successive trophic levels after contamination of water. Cope (1961), who studied the effect of DDT spraying in the Yellowstone River system for spruce bud-worm control, concluded that the DDT found in fish there was incorporated by the ingestion of dead and dying insects contaminated with the insecticide.

Human Milk

In the case of human populations, while accidental contamination may likewise result in direct intake of pesticides, more commonly and more insiduously it usually results from selective concentration of residues along a food chain. Löfroth (1968) reports that in areas where use of DDT is widespread, average amounts of DDT in fatty human tissues are 5 to 27 ppm. Such levels are known to result from a daily intake of less than .001 mg DDT per kilogram body weight, which is ten times less than the highest permissible tolerance level recommended by the United Nations.

Work in Sweden cited by Löfroth shows human milk there contains an average .117 ppm DDT. This means nursing babies take in .017 mg DDT per day per kilogram body weight. That is some 70 per cent over the United Nations' recommended tolerance level. Löfroth considers breast-fed babies in the United Kingdom have a similar level of intake, and nursed babies in the United States perhaps an even higher one. Comparisons between DDT residues in human and in cows' milk are shown in Table 12-3, which illustrates the concentration factor operating with a carnivore as compared with a herbivore.

Table 12-3* ***Pesticide Residues in Human Milk*** Contrasted with those in cows' milk from the same locality in England.

	DDT	*DDE*	*Total DDT Equivalent*	*Total BHC*	*Dieldrin*
Cows' milk	0.002	0.002	0.004	0.003	0.003
Human milk	0.045	0.073	0.128	0.013	0.006

* Reprinted by permission of the publisher from H. Egan *et al.*, *British Medical Journal*, **2:** 68, 1965.

As regards dieldrin, the situation is equally disturbing. British and American nursing babies consume about ten times the recommended maximum (Egan *et al.*, 1965). In Western Australia Löfroth states breast-fed babies have an intake of .67 ppm dieldrin daily, thirty times the maximally acceptable dosage. The implications of this observation, if it can be confirmed by further and more extensive studies, are quite simply shattering.

Tolerance Levels

One of the acute difficulties in attempting to decide what a *safe* use of DDT would be, if indeed there is such a thing, is determining the *tolerance levels*. Actual lethal effects on mammals appear to require higher dosages than in the case of birds. At the same time very serious effects can occur before such lethal dosages are reached. In mammals these effects appear to be especially associated with the motor controls of the central nervous system.

Anderson and Peterson (1969) reported on a disturbing effect of DDT on the nervous system of brook trout (*Salvelinus fontinalis*). It has been known for some time that fish exhibit behavioral changes following exposure to sublethal levels of pesticides. These two workers have shown that modifications of two specific responses in fish, the thermal acclimation mechanism and establishment of a visual conditional avoidance response, may result from exposure to sublethal dosages of DDT.

ACCUMULATION OF DDT IN THE ATMOSPHERE

If DDT is being concentrated in the biomass of producer organisms in the ecosphere, it will become ever more concentrated as it passes in succession to the progressively smaller biomasses of primary, secondary, and tertiary consumers (Tables 12-1 and 12-2).

Table 12-4* ***Human Residual Pesticide Loads*** In parts per million of DDT/DDE. United States citizens eating three meals per day in 1964–1966 had an average daily pesticide intake of 0.08 to 0.12 mg, of which some three quarters was DDT. A steady state was reached at this level, the excretion rate balancing the intake rate, with residual accumulations in the body fat of from 5 to 20 ppm, that is from average to high on the national figures quoted above.

India	26	Canada	5
Hungary	12	Germany	4
United States	12	England	3
France	9	Alaska	3

* Reprinted by permission of the publisher from H. Egan, R. Goulding, J. Roburn, and J. O'G. Tatton, *British Medical Journal,* **2:** 68, 1965.

Concentrations of pesticide pollutants might be expected to be greatest in estuarine situations and over the continental shelf, where polluted drainage systems discharge into the ocean. These are precisely the sections of the ecosphere where human marine food is especially harvested.

As if these various concentration factors were not enough, DDT and other chlorinated hydrocarbons are stored in the human body particularly in the fatty tissues (Table 12-4). A period of prolonged physical stress, which utilizes an extensive amount of these fatty food reserves, could therefore bring the levels of pesticide circulating in the body well above tolerable acceptances. The more serious illnesses, a deliberate fast, or drastic diet could all prove fatal.

CIRCULATION OF CHLORINATED HYDROCARBONS

The detection of chlorinated hydrocarbons in Antarctica, far from any known source of contamination, was explained when it was realized that pesticides are part of the general atmospheric circulation and are carried as air pollutants for thousands of miles. A recent paper (Risebrough

Table 12-5* ***Pesticides in Rainwater*** A comparison of remote, agricultural, urban, and industrial areas in the United Kingdom and United States. Figures express mean monthly concentration in parts per trillion in the rainfall 1966–1967, those for DDT include DDD and DDE.

Location	*BHC*	*Dieldrin*	*DDT*
UNITED KINGDOM			
Lerwick (far north)	145	11	73
Sheffield (industrial)	87	6	87
London (urban)	88	16	93
Maidstone (horticultural)	103	2	97
Camborne (far south)	48	6	115
UNITED STATES			
Ripley, Ohio (agricultural)	50	—	180
Coshocton, Ohio (agricultural)	6	—	75
Cincinnati, Ohio (urban)	20	—	360

* Reproduced with permission of the publisher from K. R. Tarrant and J. O'G. Tatton, *Nature,* **219:** 726, 1968, and J. M. Cohen and C. Pinkerton, *Advances in Chemistry,* **60:** 163–67, 1966.

et al., 1969) described how dust particles carried 3000 miles across the North Atlantic by northeasterly trade winds, transferred DDT, DDE, and DDD from Africa or Europe to the Caribbean island of Barbados. The pesticides had apparently been absorbed in vapor form on the dust particles, which had an annual fallout rate over the Atlantic of approximately two thirds of a ton.

Tarrant and Tatton (1968) estimated fallout from atmospheric circulation over Britain by determining the amount of DDT, dieldrin, BHC, DDE, and DDD residues in rain water. Their results are summarized in Table 12-5 together with comparable figures for the United States. The British results confirm that pesticides are in general circulation in the atmosphere and provide an average figure of one ton of pesticide in every inch of rainfall. This amounts to a pesticide fallout four times greater than that which the Mississippi River annually carries out into the Gulf of Mexico. This magnitude of fallout pattern would appear to be characteristic of the North Atlantic (Figure 12-2). This massive distribution of pesticides would alone account for their universal appearance in all global ecosystems, but

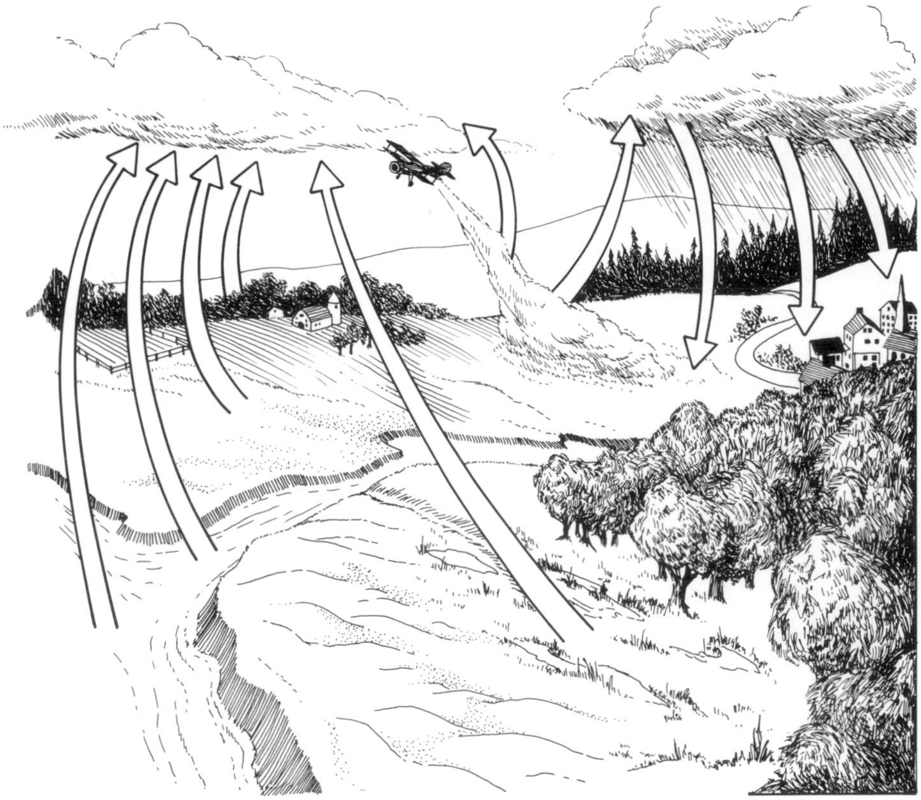

Figure 12-2. *Global circulation patterns of pesticides.* Although some local concentration of pesticides occurs near the point of application, and in estuarine and coastal waters, the global circulation is more related to the atmospheric circulation and to the amount of precipitation, that is, rainfall or snow, which will carry particulate matter with vaporized absorbed pesticides to the ground.

Table 12-6* *Annual Amounts of Chlorinated Hydrocarbons Produced in the United States During the Last Decade* Figures shown are rounded to the nearest 1000 tons: those in parentheses for 1964 indicate the amount believed to have been used by United States farmers (see Table 12-7). It is predicted that agricultural needs in underdeveloped areas (which took the major portion of the remaining production) will increase their pesticide applications by six times their use at the end of the last decade.

	1960	*1964*	*1967*
DDT	102,000	124,000 (27%)	103,000
Aldrin-toxaphene group†	85,000	103,000 (52%)	120,000

† Includes aldrin, chlordane, dieldrin, endrin, heptachlor, and toxaphene.
* Figures compiled from U.S. Tariff Commission Pub. 295, 1969, and U.S. Department of Interior, Agric. Econ. Rpt. No. 131, 1968.

it is probably repeated over other continental masses and related ocean basins. Tables 12-6 and 12-7 show the amounts of pesticides used in the United States and exported, which provides some idea of how the global fallout system is being constantly replenished.

Various experimental determinations suggest that only one half to one third of the pesticide applied actually reaches the ground. The rest volatilizes before the spray droplets fall on their terrestrial target or the soil. From leaf or land surfaces volatilization will in any case usually occur within a few weeks, depending partly on ambient temperatures. Concentrations of pesticides in the atmosphere will tend to be highest over agricultural areas, as shown in Table 12-8. However, once the amount vaporized reaches a steady state with the amount of fallout, updrafts of air from cold fronts, mountain masses, and other mixing mechanisms can carry the pesticides up into the troposphere. There, the temperate westerlies and the tropical easterlies, together with their north-south polar eddies, will carry the pesticides in a global pattern. As Frost (1969) states, the 10 parts per trillion of pesticide residues in the atmosphere over London,

Table 12-7* *Amounts of Chlorinated Hydrocarbons Used Annually by Farmers in the United States* **(in Tons, Figures Rounded)**

Toxaphene	39,000
DDT	37,000
Aldrin	11,000
Strobane	2,700
Endrin	2,200
Methoxychlor	1,400
Lindane	1,000
Dieldrin	900
Chlordane	500
BHC	300
Other	800
Total	96,800

* Figures from Agric. Econ. Rpt. No. 131. Reproduced with permission of the Economic Research Service, U.S. Department of Agriculture.

Table 12-8* ***Pesticides in the Air over Various Cities and Regions*** Expressed in parts per trillion by weight; sampled at different times between 1963 and 1967. Districts like La Jolla, where the prevailing winds are landward, with an unknown admixture of air from neighboring agricultural areas, can have a total pesticide content in the air 1000 that of marine air remote from sites of application as in Barbados.

LOCALITY	*PESTICIDE CONCENTRATION*			
	DDT	*Dieldrin (HEOD)*	*BHC*	*Total*
United States				
Pittsburgh (heavily industrialized)	.177	—	—	
La Jolla, Calif.				.07
Mean of agricultural areas	5	—	—	
Caribbean				
Barbados	.00006	.000001	—	.000078
Europe				
London (urban)	10	18	6	

* *Sources:* P. Antommaria, M. Corn, and L. DeMaio, *Science,* **150:** 1476, 1965. R. W. Risebrough, R. J. Huggett, J. J. Griffin, and E. D. Goldberg, *Science,* **159:** 1233, 1968. D. C. Abbott, R. B. Harrison, J. O'G. Tatton, and J. Thomson, *Nature,* **211:** 259, 1966.

England (Table 12-8), can be extrapolated to give a total global figure of 5700 tons in the atmosphere. This is one tenth the amount of pesticide sold annually in the United States, more than one half of this total amount finding its way into the atmospheric circulation. This latter reservoir might continue to support the atmospheric circulation of pesticides at present levels for a number of years even if the use of pesticides were to be entirely prohibited on a world-wide scale.

Other Chlorinated Hydrocarbons

Other chlorinated hydrocarbons are now marketed under a variety of names; dieldrin, endrin, and heptachlor, together with DDT, are the most commonly used. These and all others of this group listed in Table 12-7 are *persistent pesticides,* not readily broken down in any ecosystem by the decomposer organisms of the reducer trophic level. Eventually microorganisms might be evolved which would cause more rapid breakdown of these substances. Their success as pesticides, however, must especially be due to their novelty in the ecosphere. If organisms at various trophic levels had been long exposed to this group of compounds they would by now have *adapted* to them.

OTHER PESTICIDES

The other main group of pesticides are the *organophosphates,* of which parathion and malathion are the best known; others like phosdrin and chlorthion are quite widely used. These are highly toxic to human beings, and their application in agriculture invariably requires the wearing of special protective clothing (Petty, 1957). Some of these organophosphates find their way into domestic use and, despite the required printed warnings on the container, are indiscriminately sprayed around the home.

One particular feature of this group is their frequent use as systemic insecticides, as substances which can be taken up into and circulated through plant tissues where they remain toxic for a length of time to any animals consuming these tissues. As a group organophosphate pesticides are *biodegradable.* They are readily broken down by reducer organisms in natural ecosystems so that they are not long persistent and do not present the same problems as chlorinated hydrocarbons.

Nerve Gases

The main component of many nerve gases is the group of organic phosphorus compounds known as anticholinesterases. They are also the active agents in a number of pesticides, including parathion. These compounds inhibit the activity of cholinesterase, which causes an accumulation of acetylcholine at mammalian nerve endings. Normally the enzymatic breakdown of acetylcholine by cholinesterase occurs almost instantly, so that a nerve impulse for which acetylcholine serves as a chemical messenger has only a momentary effect. When it accumulates instead, the muscle cells are either constantly stimulated or become paralyzed. This is expressed by nausea and vomiting, or staggering and twitching in the affected animal.

On March 4, 1968, sheep grazing through the snow near the U.S. Army Chemical and Biological Weapons Testing Center at Dugway near Salt Lake City were stricken with a "staggering" disease. After a day or so more than 6000 of them had died, together with rabbits, deer, and some other wildlife. The U.S. Department of Agriculture and Public Health Service determined that these animals died as a result of exposure to nerve gas released during what the Army described as a routine weekly demonstration test on the previous day, March 3. The Army denied that their test had caused the sheep deaths. The civilian agencies also concluded that sheep rather than other animals had died because sheep have a habit of obtaining their water requirements by eating snow. In the affected area snow was indeed found to be contaminated with nerve gas.

The possible accidental release of this type of colorless and odorless nerve gas, during testing, transport, manufacture, or storage has since been regarded with considerable public misgiving, and assurances regarding an overhaul of safety precautions have been sought (Marwick, 1968).

RESISTANT STRAINS

Even as early as 1946 some housefly populations in Sweden had been reported as resistant to DDT. By 1948 there were 12 such species, and by

1957, 76. In 1969 apparently 224 insect pests were resistant to one pesticide form or another. Some (Table 12-9) are even resistant to both chlorinated hydrocarbons and organophosphates.

Table 12-9 ***Some Insect Pests in Which Strains Have Evolved Resistant to Both Chlorinated Hydrocarbon and Organophosphate Types of Pesticides***

FLIES
Chrysomyia putoris
Musca domestica (housefly)
TICKS
Boophilus micropus (southern cattle tick)
BEDBUGS
Cimex lectularis (common bedbug)
COCKROACHES
Blattella germanica (German cockroach)
MOSQUITOES
Aedes melanimon
Aedes nigromaculis
Aedes taeniorhynchus (black salt-marsh mosquito)
Culex pipiens (southern house mosquito)
Culex quinquefasciatus
Culex tarsalis
MOTHS
Epiphyas postrittana
Heliothis virescens (tobacco budworm)
Trichoplusia ni (cabbage looper)
HEMIPTERA (bugs and aphids)
Erythroneura lawsoniana
Myzus persicae (green peach aphid)

There appear to be two principal ways in which insect populations adapt to pesticides, one physiological, the other behavioral. The physiological adaptation occurs when races of the insect species population which can destroy or detoxify the pesticide are selected. This selection for genotypes which contain genes producing detoxifying enzymes is quite common. From laboratory experiments with the fruit fly, *Drosophila,* it has even been possible to determine the locus of the genes responsible.

The selection of races possessing such enzyme systems is greatly favored by current pesticide application techniques. The spraying of a broad-spectrum insecticide over an extensive area removes not only most competing species, but also most predatory and parasitic insect species. The few individuals which survive because they possess a particular genotype are then quickly able to increase to form resistant races without either competition or predation. Some economic pests such as the salt marsh sandfly are reported to have evolved pesticide-resistant races in this way after only three pesticide applications. The more quickly one generation replaces another, the earlier resistant races appear.

Increasing the dosage rate of the pesticide merely delays somewhat the evolution of resistant races. The massive pesticide applications now being used for this reason in the cotton-growing parts of the United States and other western hemisphere countries constitute what must be regarded as a major threat to national as well as global health.

The other form of insect pesticide resistance is developed by behavioral avoidance. Just as selection for individuals with particular enzyme systems occurs, so selection for individuals whose behavioral ecology takes them outside the area of contact with the pesticide will produce resistant races. Thus mosquito populations, which originally were primarily house feeders, will now bite only outside houses; those which enter houses alight on DDT-sprayed walls and are killed.

This could be called selection for pesticide avoidance, and it has developed in a number of tropical species of *Aedes* and *Culex* (Table 12-9). Only careful development of schemes for *integrated control,* as discussed below, will prevent the appearance of many further races or strains of pesticide-resistant insects of a behavioral or any other type.

BIOLOGICAL CONTROL

In any ecosystem there is a considerable amount of production, i.e., producer biomass, removed by primary consumers in the form of herbivorous insects or related forms. This is most obvious when a swarm of locusts visits a corn or millet field and removes the *total* aboveground biomass accumulated by producer organisms. Less conspicuous cropping activities may nevertheless reach formidable dimensions.

Borgstrom (1969) estimates that if the insects of tropical Africa, which compete in herbivorous activity with human food production could be controlled, it would be possible to feed two billion people, eight times as many at present on that continent.

Figures of similar magnitude are produced by the agricultural industry wherever and whenever measures are proposed for prohibiting the use of particular pesticides. A total prohibition of their use, effected immediately, would obviously result inevitably in local if not global famine, as well as in widespread insect-transmitted disease epidemics.

There are several ways in which the use of persistent broad-spectrum pesticides may eventually be superseded with less drastic consequences. One is by development of *selective* pesticides, of which a most promising group is the *ecdysones.* These are the substances which initiate ecdysis or metamorphosis from one stage to another in the larval development of insects. Overstimulation with ecdysones results in repeated metamorphosis without sufficient time for the accumulation of food reserves, so that eventually the larva becomes exhausted and dies. Many plants apparently contain ecdysones or ecdysone analogues in sufficient amount to provide them with immunity from insect attack.

There are also many other insect-plant relationships which provide a balance between herbivore and producer populations. If such relationships had not evolved, the herbivores would literally have consumed the producer populations into extinction. Proper understanding of such steady-state relationships will almost certainly provide new approaches in the search for selective pesticides.

Another aspect of *biological control* is the location and introduction of secondary consumers which prey on herbivorous pests.

Introduction of Predators and Parasites

The earliest application of the principle of biological control by introducing a predator or parasite to regulate the numbers of a herbivore population came long before the development of pesticides. Toward the end of the last century, the citrus industry in California was suffering a massive infestation of a mealy bug, cottony cushion-scale (*Icerya purchasi*), introduced from Australia on acacia in 1868. The introduction of two Australian species, the ladybirds *Radola cardinalis* (vedalia ladybird) and *Cryptochetum iceryae,* provided the necessary predator-prey regulation and reduced the mealy bug populations to levels at which they no longer constituted a major pest infestation. Unfortunately, however, as is shown in Figure 12-3, cottony cushion-scale again reached the major pest popu-

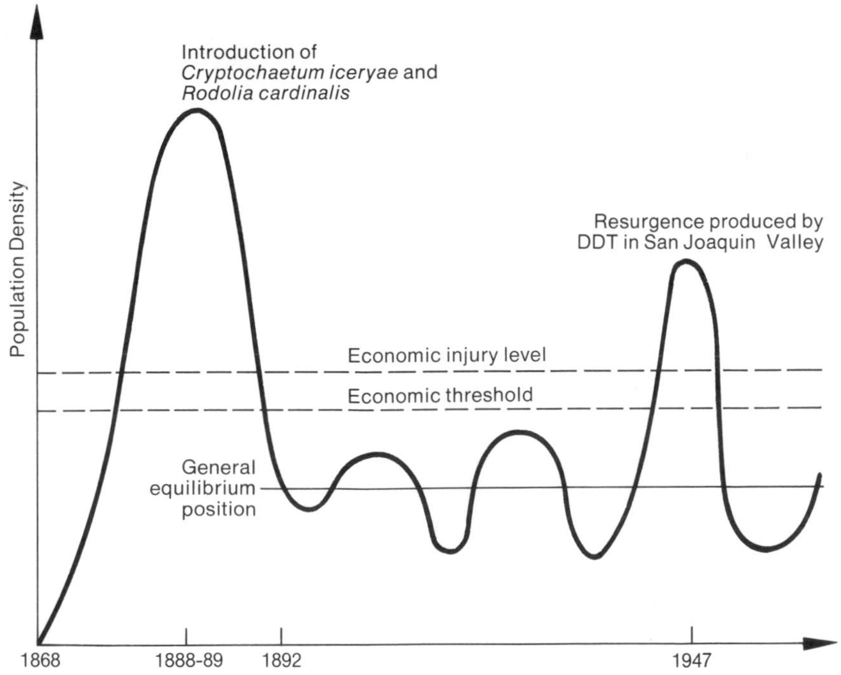

Figure 12-3. *Cottony cushion-scale* (Icerya purchasi) *incidence on citrus in California.* Introduced in 1868, this pest increased rapidly until two of its ladybird predators were obtained and released in 1889. A resurgence of this pest occurred in 1947 following the use of DDT sprays on citrus, which caused a reduction of the predator populations of ladybirds. (From V. M. Stern *et al., Hilgardia,* **29:** 93, 1959, reproduced by permission of the publisher.)

lation levels in California when extensive use of DDT for citrus spraying eliminated the vedalia ladybird locally (Ewart and DeBach, 1947).

This recurrence emphasized the danger of indiscriminate use of pesticides, which are likely to have a catastrophic effect on the population regulatory mechanisms which have held pests below the economic threshold in agricultural microecosystems. While they momentarily diminish the numbers of a particular pest, the pesticides commonly also reduce the numbers of natural enemies in the form of insect predators and parasites. The pest then undergoes a population explosion before population numbers in the natural enemies can recover.

Subsequent to the successful introduction of a biological control measure for cottony cushion-scale, further introductions were made to control other introduced pests, including gypsy moths, Japanese beetles, and European corn borers.

The Sterile Male Technique

A different technique of biological control was introduced in the early 1950's to control the screw-worm fly (*Callitroga hominivorax*), whose larval stage infests sheep. Male flies were rendered sterile by exposure to gamma radiation which did not, however, reduce their vitality or sexual aggression. The sterilized males were then released in numbers larger than those of males in the natural populations, so that females copulating with them proceeded to lay unfertilized eggs (Baumhover *et al.*, 1955).

Using this technique the screw-worm had been eliminated by 1958 from the island of Curacao and from the southeastern states, the only part of the continental United States in which this pest can overwinter. Further applications of the same technique are now being tried with other pests, combined with the use of chemosterilants and genetic male sterile forms.

Integrated Control

The most useful mode of attack for the present, however, would appear to be *integrated control,* which combines several methods in a unified attempt to control a particular pest. The total effect of these combined methods tends to be *synergistic* rather than additive; not only does it reduce the pesticide pollution problem, but the control obtained is more effective.

One of the earliest applications of integrated control was reported from California (Schlinger and Dietrick, 1960). The practice there of mowing alfalfa over a large acreage in a single operation was shown to cause serious disturbance to the predator-prey balance between spotted alfalfa aphid and its natural enemies. By adopting successive strip cutting over a period of time, parasites and predators of the aphid were maintained at an average of 56 per square foot instead of the 14 per square foot in fields with single-operation cutting.

Also in California, integrated control was applied to the treatment of grape leafhopper after this pest was found to have developed resistance to organophosphate pesticides. It was discovered that the leafhopper was heavily attacked by a wasp (*Anagrus*), which overwinters on blackberry. By interplanting blackberry vines in the vineyards, it is possible to combine the predatory attacks by wasps on the leafhoppers with limited use of new and selective insecticides.

The concept of integrated control has been fully discussed in a paper by Stern *et al.* (1959). It includes not only appropriate combinations of pesticides, natural enemies, and cultural treatments, but also the use of insect pathogens (Steinhaus, 1957).

Bibliography

REFERENCES

Ames, P. L. "DDT residues in the eggs of the osprey in the northeastern United States and their relation to nesting success," *J. Appl. Ecol.* 3(suppl.): 87–97, 1966.

Antommaria, P., Corn, M., and Demaio, L. "Airborne particulates in Pittsburgh; association with PIP-DDT," *Science,* **150:** 1476–79, 1965.

Baumhover, A. H., Graham, A. J., Bitter, B. A., Hopkins, D. E., New, W. D., Dudley, F. H., and Bushland, R. C. "Screw-worm control through the release of sterilised flies," *J. Econ. Entomol.,* **48:** 462–66, 1955.

Cope, O. B. "Effects of DDT spraying for spruce budworn on fish in Yellowstone River system," *Trans. Amer. Fish. Soc.* **90:** 239–51, 1961

Edwards C. D. "Insecticide residues in soils," *Residue Reviews,* **13:** 83–132, 1966.

Egan, H., Goulding, R., Roburn, J., and Tatton, J. O'G. "Organo-chlorine pesticide residues in human fat and human milk," *British Med. J.,* **2:** 66–69, 1965.

Egler, F. E. "Pesticides in our ecosystem," *American Scientist,* **52:** 110–36, 1964.

Enderson, J. H., and Berger, D. D. "Pesticides: eggshell thinning and lowered production of young in prairie falcons," *Bioscience,* **20:** 355–56, 1970.

Ewart, W. H., and De Bach, P. "DDT for control of citrus thrips and citricola scale," *California Citrog.*, **32:** 242–45, 1947.

Frost, J. "Earth, air, water," *Environment,* **11**(6): 15–25, 1969.

Gould, R. F. *Organic Pesticides in the Environment,* Washington, D.C.: Advances in Chemistry Series No. 60, American Chemical Society, 1966.

Hammerstrom, R. J. "Insect resistance to insecticides," *Public Health Reports,* **73**(No. 12): 1126–31, 1958.

Hickey, J. J., and Anderson, D. W. "Chlorinated hydrocarbons and eggshell changes in raptorial and fish-eating birds," *Science,* **152:** 271–72, 1968.

Hunt, E. G., and Bischoff, A. I. "Inimical effects on wildlife of periodic DDT applications to Clear Lake," *Calif. Fish and Game Bull.,* **46:** 91–96, 1960.

Kuntzman, R. "Similarities between oxidative drug-metabolizing enzymes and steroid hydroxylases in liver microsomes," *Pharmacol. Exper. Therap.,* **146:** 280–85, 1964.

Löfroth, G. "Pesticides and catastrophe," *New Scientist,* **38:** 166–67, 1968.

Marwick, C. "Death in Skull Valley," *New Scientist,* **38:** 166–67, 1969.

Menzel, D. W., Anderson, J., and Randtke, A. "Marine phytoplankton vary in their response to chlorinated hydrocarbons," *Science,* **167:** 1724–26, 1970.

Peakall, D. B. "Pesticide-induced breakdown of steroids in birds," *Nature,* **216:** 505–506, 1967.

Peakall, D. B. "Pesticides and the reproduction of birds," *Scientific American,* **222**(4): 73–78, 1970.

Peterle, T. J. "Pyramiding damage," *Environment,* **11**(6): 34–40, 1969.

Petty, C. S. "Organic phosphate insecticide poisoning: an agricultural occupational hazard," *Louisiana Med. J.,* **109**(5): 158–64,1957.

Ratcliffe, D. "Decrease in eggshell weight in certain birds of prey," *Nature,* **215:** 208–10, 1967.

Risebrough, R. W., Hugget, R. J., Griffin, J. J., and Goldberg, E. D. "Pesticide Transatlantic movements in the Northeast Trades," *Science,* **159**: 1233–36, 1968.

Schlinger, E. I., and Dietrick, E. J. "Biological control of insects aided by strip-farming alfalfa in experimental program," *Calif. Agriculture,* **14:** 8–9, 1960.

Steinhaus, E. A. "Concerning the harmlessness of insect pathogens and the standardization of microbial control products," *J. Econ. Entomol.,* **50:** 715–20, 1957.

Stern, V. H., Smith, R. F., van den Bosch, R., and Hagen, K. S. "The integrated control concept," *Hilgardia,* **29:** 81–101, 1959.

Tatton, J. O'G., and Ruzicka, J. H. A. "Organochlorine pesticides in Antarctica," *Nature,* **215:** 346–48, 1967.

Pesticides

Anderson, J. M., and Peterson, M. R. "DDT: sublethal effects on brook trout nervous system," *Science,* **164:** 440–41, 1969.

Bitman, J., *et al.* "Estrogenic activity of O.P'-DDT in the mammalian uterus and avian oviduct," *Science,* **162:** 371–72, 1968.

Brown, A. W. A. "Insecticide resistance comes of age," *Bull. Entomol. Soc.,* **14:** 3–9, 1968.

Burdick, G. E., *et al.* "Accumulation of DDT in Lake Trout," *Trans. Amer. Fish. Soc.,* **93:** 127–29, 1964.

Butler, P. A., and Spruger, P. T. "Pesticides—a new factor in coastal environments," *Trans. 28th N. American Wildlife and Natural Resources Conference,* 1963, pp. 378–90.

Cottam, C. "The ecologist's role in problems of pesticide pollution," *Bioscience,* **15:** 457–63, 1965.

Curley, A., and Kembrough, R. "Chlorinated hydrocarbon insecticides in plasma and milk of pregnant and lactating women," *Arch. Environ. Health,* **18:** 156–64, 1969.

Diamond, J. B., and Sherbourn, J. A. "Persistence of DDT in wild animals," *Nature,* **221:** 486–87, 1969.

Duggan, R. E., and Weatherwax, J. R. "Dietary intake of pesticide chemical," *Science,* **157:** 1006–10, 1967.

Edwards, C. A. "Insecticide residues in soils," *Residue Reviews,* **13:** 83–132, 1966.

Edwards, C. A. "Soil pollutants and soil animals," *Scientific American,* **220** (4): 88–99, 1969.

Falk, H. L., Thompson, S. J., and Koten, P. "Carcinogenic potential of pesticides," *Arch. Environ. Health,* **10:** 848–58, 1965.

Fiserova-Bergerova, V., Radomski, J. L., Davies, J. E., and Davies, J. H. "Levels of chlorinated hydrocarbon pesticides in human tissues," *Industr. Med. Surg.,* **36**(1): 65–70, 1967.

George, J. L., and Frear, D. E. H. "Pesticides in the Antarctic," *J. App. Ecol.,* 3(suppl.): 155–67, 1966.

Gunther, F. A., Westlake, W. E., and Jaglan, P. S. "Reported solubilities of 738 chemicals in water," *Residue Reviews,* **20:** 1–148, 1968.

Hickey, J. H. (ed.) *Peregrine Falcon Populations,* Madison: University of Wisconsin Press, 1969.

Hunt, E. G. "Biological magnification of pesticides," *Symp. on Scientific Aspects of Pest Control, Nat. Acad. Sci.–Natural Res. Council,* 1966, pp. 252–61.

Jeffries, D. J. "The delay in ovulation produced by p,p'-DDT and its possible significance in the field," *Proc. Soc. Exper. Biol. Med.,* **109:** 266–71, 1966.

Jones, F. J. S., and Summers, D. D. B. "Relation between DDT in diets of laying birds and viability of their eggs," *Nature,* **217:** 1162–63, 1968.

Laws, E. R., Curley, A., and Biros, E. F. "Men with intensive occupational exposure to DDT," *Arch. Environ. Health,* **15:** 766–75, 1967.

Lichtenstein, E. P., Shulz, K. R., Fuhrmann, T. W., and Liang, T. T. "Biological interaction between plastecizers and insecticides," *J. Econ. Entomol.* **62:** 761–65, 1969.

Meeks, R. L. "The accumulation of CI-36 ring-labelled DDT in a freshwater marsh," *J. Wildlife Management,* **32:** 376–98, 1968.

Mellanby, K. *Pesticides and Pollution,* London: Collins, 1967.

Messenger, P. S. "Utilisation of native natural enemies in integrated control," *Ann. Appl. Biol.* **56:** 328–30, 1965.

Moore, N. W. "A synopsis of the pesticide problem," *Adv. Ecol. Res.,* **4:** 75–129, 1967.

Nash, R. G., and Woolson, E. A. "Persistence of chlorinated hydrocarbon insecticides in soils," *Science,* **157:** 924–27, 1967.

Radomski, J. L. *et al.* "Pesticide concentrations in the liver, brain, and adipose tissues of terminal hospital patients," *Food and Cosmetic Toxicology,* **6:** 209–20, 1968.

Risebrough, R. W., Menzel, D. B., Martin, D. J., and Olcott, H. S. "DDT residues in Pacific sea birds: a persistent insecticide in marine food chains," *Nature,* **216:** 589–90, 1967.

Robinson, J., Richardson, A., Crabtree, A. N., Couldon, J. C., and Potts, G. R. "Organochloride residues in marine organisms," *Nature,* **214:** 1307–11, 1967.

Rudd, R. L. *Pesticides and the Living Landscape,* Madison: University of Wisconsin, 1964.

Ruzicka, J. H. A., Simmons, J. H., and Tatton, J. O'G. "Pesticide residues in foodstuffs in Great Britain: IV, organochlorine pesticide residues in welfare foods," *J. Sci. Food and Agricul.,* **18:** 579–82, 1967.

Shepard, H. H. *Methods of Testing Chemicals on Insects,* Minneapolis: Burgess, 1968.

Smith, R. F., and van den Bosch, R. "Integrated control," in Kilgore, W. W. (ed.), *Pest Control,* New York, Academic Press, 1967, pp. 295–328.

Sparr, B. I., Appleby, W. G., DeVries, D. M., Osmun, J. V., McBride, J. M., and Foster, G. L. "Insecticide residues in waterways from agricultural use," *Adv. Chem.,* **60:** 146–62, 1966.

Tatton, J. O'G,, and Ruzicka, J. H. A. "Organochlorine pesticides in Antarctica," *Nature,* **215:** 346–48, 1967.

Whittes, J. L. *That We May Live,* Princeton, N.J.: Van Nostrand, 1966.

Williams, C. M. "Third-generation pesticides," *Scientific American,* **217**(1): 13–17, 1967.

Wilson, B. R. (ed.) *Environmental Problems: Pesticides, Thermal Pollution and Environmental Synergisms,* Philadelphia and Toronto: Lippincott, 1968.

Winter, R. *Poisons in Your Food,* New York: Crown, 1969.

Woodwell, G. M. "Toxic substances and ecological cycles," *Scientific American,* **216**(3): 24–31, 1967.

Woodwell, G. M., Wurster, C. F., and Isaacson, P. A. "DDT residues in an East Coast estuary: a case of biological concentration of a persistent insecticide," *Science,* **156:** 821–24, 1967.

Wurster, C. F. "DDT reduces photosynthesis in marine phytoplankton," *Science,* **159:** 1474–75, 1968.

Wurster, C. F., and Wingate, D. B. "DDT residues and declining reproduction in the Bermuda petrel," *Science,* **159:** 979–81, 1968.

Conservation 13

This survey of the evolution of human populations, their ecological relationships and environmental confrontations, would be incomplete without an attempt to review both what man has achieved so far, and what will be his eventual fate. Whatever view is taken of the nature of man, there is one overriding ecological principle that can be neither denied nor ignored: the pattern of human behavior is relevant only to one time and one place. Change there always has been, change there always must be if extinction is to be avoided. The uniqueness of human populations lies in their capacity to adapt to this change and in the speed of their response. Within a period of 3 to 4 million years, *erectus-sapiens* populations have provided a striking demonstration of this remarkable adaptability by escaping from the ecosphere of one planet to invade that of its satellite. They have also inserted artifacts into the biospheres of other planets of the solar system which could irreversibly change ecosystems which may have evolved there.

GENERAL CONSIDERATIONS

There are several implications of this remarkable capacity which are relevant to the ideas which have been considered in this text, but first human ecology must be provided with a time dimension by setting it against estimates of a universal chronology. Several estimates now place the origin of the universe at 10 billion years ago. There is increasing evidence, as was considered in the opening chapter, that life on this planet began somewhere between 3½ and 4 billion years ago. *Erectus-sapiens* populations have been recognizable for about 3 to 4 million years; the present cultural patterns which we refer to as *urban civilization,* for about 10,000 years.

In the whole universe what is the chance of similar cultural levels having evolved elsewhere, even in this last *one millionth* of universal time? We know from astronomical studies that the evolution from hydrogen and helium of the more than 100 different chemical elements appears to have occurred in every part of the universe which we examine. Could evolutionary response to similar physical environments in other ecospheres prescribe that living systems also had to evolve toward a dominant cultural creature wherever life arose?

We can be fairly confident that if it were so, these other cultural creatures would be totally different from any of the multitude of life forms which have appeared at one time or another on this planet—different in morphology, anatomy, physiology, chemical nature, and genetic processes. All that can be said with any degree of certainty is that if there were dominant cultural forms in other parts of the universe, they would necessarily have evolved some kind of social communication. This would have to be of a form which our own culture could detect either by our bodily senses or through our mechanical sensors, for sound, light, or some other form of electromagnetic waves would be the most likely transmission medium.

If during our future space travels we were to encounter such other cultural forms of life, it is likely that our senses or our sensors would record the encounter. Such a meeting would be a momentous event, for it would again herald competition for the same ecological niche—that of the dominant social heterotroph—but this time on a universal scale. Only cultural displacement could save one or the other of us from extinction.

Extinction Times

In considering the future in such universal ecological terms, we should recall that no dominant form of higher organism has survived more than a short 250 million years on our own planet. We are presently a mere 10 to 30,000 years into the latest 250 million-year interval which can be expected to elapse before the next cataclysmic series of ice ages. Yet we have contrived in this brief moment of universal time to exploit and destroy most of this planet's resources, without so far achieving any stability in its human populations or any adequate system for recycling its finite resources. This is poor ecological practice indeed, and it is small wonder that we are now confronted with so many environmental crises.

Resource Exploitation

Through having failed to achieve a proper understanding of territoriality, we are forced to devote huge allotments from our current productivity to defending the regional boundaries of the national subdivisions of our global population. On an even more parochial scale, territoriality is a constant cause of personal frictions, extensively violated even to the extreme of mayhem and murder wreaked on our own kind.

In our social evolution we have as yet evolved no better means of developing initiative and encouraging efficiency than the fratricidal struggle which is called "private enterprise." In the resulting rat-race no holds are barred; all resources are up for grabs. No serious attempt is made to conserve these resources and establish and maintain stability in the ecosystems we occupy at a level which will ensure the preservation of a maximum diversity in these systems.

Territorial Dissociation

At the same time the feeling of isolation which human populations have always contrived to adopt in regard to the fate of populations in other territories has intensified. "This is America," or Vietnam, or France, or Costa Rica; "things like that could not happen here." The ruthless slaughter of Watusi, Ibos, Salvadorans, and Hondurans; Chinese-Russian fighting; Arab-Jew killings; famine in India or Pakistan; illiteracy in South America—are all images on a television screen which can be turned off or ignored like the commercials and appear to most viewers to be just as fantastic and unreal.

Technological Consequences

Our technological advances in a mere two centuries since the Industrial Revolution began have brought some of the populations in our global ecosystem within reach of the utopian dreams of leisure, health, and bounty. But these advances have also brought the capacity to destroy all life in the ecosphere. This can be done catastrophically by an atomic holocaust; or the same result can be achieved more slowly and more insidiously, but certainly as effectively, by permitting pollution of one form or another at such a level as to prevent the continuing reproduction of our species.

With all our technological advances we have failed utterly to provide the socioeconomic measures necessary to avoid the threatened onset of a malthusian phase of famine and pestilence which may shortly devastate some of the world's societies if desperate action is not taken. As a great American conservationist stated over 30 years ago (Leopold, 1933), "*Human ecology has now become a matter of ethics.*"

CARRYING CAPACITY

The reason this chapter has been headed "Conservation" is because the level at which carrying capacity is placed will determine what can be conserved. There is no doubt that in advanced industrial societies the carrying capacity in terms of human populations could be set much higher than with present population sizes. The ecosystems of these areas still include many animal and plant populations which are not contributing to human food chains, many in fact which, directly or indirectly, compete with them. Wilderness areas are still permitted to exist. Populations of inedible birds and insects abound and utilize considerable amounts of energy at one trophic level or another. The case for the conservation in these industrial societies of evolutionary diversity has already been eloquently presented by Hutchinson (1961).

By contrast, human population pressures in some of the advanced agricultural societies have caused the whole landscape to be reduced to basic ecosystems which relate exclusively to human productivity. Paddy rice fields can cover the whole land, and all surface water is turned on to these fields. No plants but rice grow in the paddies, other than microscopic and planktonic forms. No animals but buffalo and chickens are allowed to exist. The food web is simply expressed as:

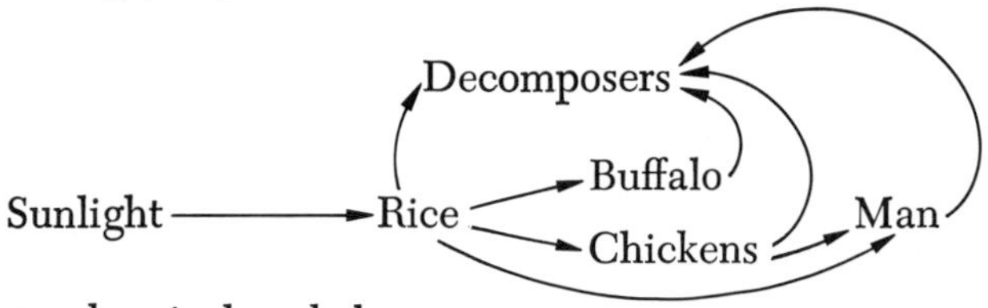

The biogeochemical cycle becomes:

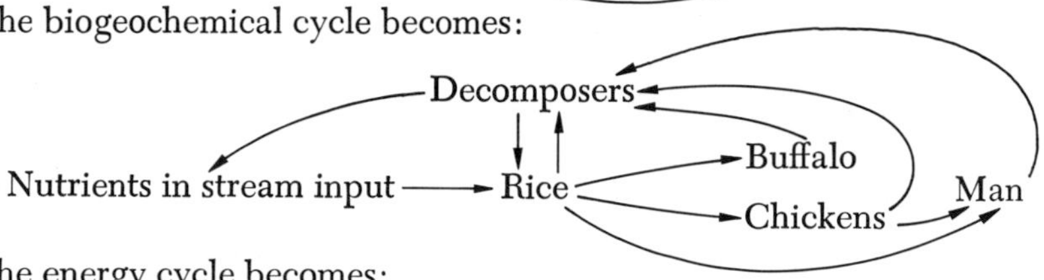

The energy cycle becomes:

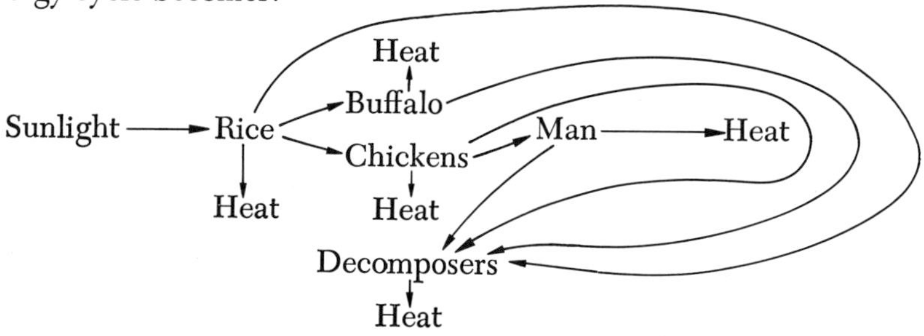

Obviously these simple diagrams understate ecosystem reality. A few egrets will probably also be included, as well as flies, a few human parasites such as hookworm, a few rats or mice. But the human society in such an ecosystem is unlikely to devote much time to worrying about wilderness conservation.

Water Requirements

Carrying capacity is a complex quantity related to many factors, some of which will have additive, and others synergistic effects. Regarding limiting factors to any further increase in carrying capacity for human populations, water is of primary importance outside the polar regions, where temperature becomes a more restrictive factor.

Water requirements of the human population in the United States were considered by Bradley (1962). Although, as he observes, a mere 2 quarts of water daily suffices for drinking purposes, between 300 and 2500 gallons a day are required to raise the various other necessary consumables. This includes evapotranspiration from the plants consumed, water losses during breadmaking, losses from animal feed, utilization by domestic animals, and so forth.

If all Americans consumed nothing but a minimal vegetarian diet, 300 gallons of water per individual daily would support a population, according to Bradley, of about 17 billion, 85 times the present United States population. However, an advanced industrial society has additional water needs; industry uses about 1400 gallons a day per person. In addition, of the total rainfall over the country, about one quarter is lost in run-off. The rest allows about 13,800 gallons of water per person daily, thus giving a total use of about 15,200 gallons per person per day.

With the present United States population and a rainfall of about 5000 billion gallons per day, the daily individual allowance may be estimated at 25,000 gallons. As we are already using over 60 per cent of this, this country's population obviously could not even be doubled without suffering some reduction in the standard of living, or finding some water supply other than rainfall.

Bradley, on a basis of water requirements, places the carrying capacity of the United States at 230 million—very close to the population it has already attained. His calculations ignore water supplies from desalination plants and Canadian rivers; nor do they take into account the presently

Plate 10. *The economic advantages of monoculture tend to concentrate the cultivation of single crops in increasingly large areas,* as illustrated from this view of the Paarl Valley in South Africa. The vineyards of this valley are said to produce more sherry than any other region in the world. This concentration of grapes, while convenient for many management purposes, provides ideal conditions for the spread of insect pests and diseases.

Plate 11. *Glacier National Park, Montana.* The effect of human occupation of this ecosystem has been so slight, as yet, that not only mountain sheep and mountain goat populations survive, but also grizzly bears, although these latter may be removed.

necessary use of water in flushing sewage, cooling industrial plants, and certain other such uses from which water could potentially be reclaimed.

Other Limiting Resources

The relation between carrying capacity and water requirements is singularly clear-cut and factual. So is that of food requirements. The huge food surpluses which the United States produces, and the considerable agricultural subsidies which are paid to farmers so they do *not* produce certain items, illustrate that food is much less a limiting factor on carrying capacity in this country than water. Its distribution, nevertheless, still obviously leaves much to be desired, and the situation is even less favorable than it appears because food production must compete for space with other ecosystem activities such as cities, recreation lands, roads, and wilderness areas.

The same unevenness applies also to space where, for many districts in the great cities, we appear to have already reached or even exceeded the carrying capacity.

SPACE REQUIREMENTS

Space requirements involve many factors. Individual *local* space requirements, for living, are one thing; allocation of *regional* or *national* space—for highways, cities, airports, etc.—is another.

In terms of land use, Landsberg (1967) estimates that cities, for example, presently occupy less than 1.5 per cent of the area of the United States. This modest figure suggests that the number of cities could be increased considerably before, in terms of regional space, they approached any carrying capacity.

Likewise, highways, railroads, and airports together still occupy a mere 3 per cent of the area of the country.

Recreational Land

In contrast, as Landsberg remarks, by 1980 it is estimated there will be a need for an estimated 76 million acres of recreational land, rising to 134 million acres by the year 2000. Only 44 million acres are presently available (about 2.5 per cent of the total land area) in the form of national and state parks, monuments, national forests, and other such areas. Because the allocation of 5 to 6 per cent *more* land suitable for recreational purposes may pose a serious problem, in terms of the availability of such space, the United States may also be approaching its carrying capacity.

Comparison with Other Countries

On the other hand, population density in the United States is still far below that of other advanced industrial societies. European population densities are 5 to 15 times higher, as shown in Table 13-1. In Japan they are higher still, and in certain tropical advanced agricultural societies they are highest of all. Carrying capacity in terms of population density is

Table 13-1 ***Natural Population Densities*** Expressed in persons per square kilometer estimated from the total population and the total area of the nation for a selection of countries, these can be extremely misleading. No one would have any difficulty appreciating that the top six countries on the list are quite crowded. So also are at least five of the six at the bottom of the list, because extensive mountainous or desert terrain within the national borders permits only the sparsest settlement. However, in terms of conservation there may still be relatively undisturbed ecosystems in these inhospitable areas of such countries which can be selected for preservation. In densely settled countries such as those at the head of the list, significant areas of natural ecosystems have long since disappeared.

Holland	333	Guatemala	39
Hong Kong	308	Uganda	34
Belgium	301	United States	29
Japan	263	Ghana	28
United Kingdom	215	Costa Rica	26
Italy	172	United Arab Republic	26
India	136	Mexico	18
Pakistan	100	Madagascar	9
South Vietnam	80	Venezuela	8
		Australia	1

clearly relative, and it is partly a question of what standards a particular population demands.

In regard to space, most societies lie in some kind of intermediate position between the two extremes just quoted. While schemes have been presented for locating cities underground, or even under the sea, when we run out of space above ground, the time when we have to resort to such edifices is still well ahead. The time for conservation action is, however, already upon us everywhere, as has been admirably expressed by Whyte (1968): "*The land that is still to be saved will have to be saved in the next few years.* We have no luxury of choice. We must make our commitments now and look to this landscape as the last one. For us, it will be."

Levels of Conservation

Clearly, individual concepts of the extent to which the diversity of our ecosystems should be conserved will vary with personal experience. Someone raised in a city might readily understand and support a proposal to institute a world gene pool for the preservation of existing variations in the many breeds of dogs; but he might fail to appreciate why small isolated herds of mustangs which have managed to survive into this century should not disappear into cans of dog food. Organizations such as the Sierra Club will fight hard to preserve certain wilderness areas, but largely ignore the circumstance that the ecosystems included in such areas have frequently reached a steady state in balance with certain human operations such as burning, which are necessary to prevent change.

It is not really sufficient, therefore, to clamor for a reduction of all human family size to a maximum of two children in order to avoid further encroachment on the finite resources and limited diversity of our ecosystems. There must initially be some determination of acceptable carrying capacities for each ecosystem. This is exceedingly difficult to obtain and probably has to be arrived at by a compromise representing a majority agreement. This dilemma has already been discussed in Chapter 9 when the problem of deciding upon the optimum population was considered.

In achieving such a compromise decision about the size of an optimum human population for a particular ecosystem, certain guiding principles can be followed. This problem was considered several years ago by Kramer (1964), who suggested a logical procedure which can be summarized as follows:

1. Method of population control at desired density
2. Resource management to provide for population
3. Pollution control

WILDERNESS RESERVES

Rephrased and slightly reoriented, these basic requirements can form the principles on which land-use plans may be based and areas for conservation

Plate 12. *Joshua Tree National Monument, California.* Although this appears to be still a natural ecosystem, this is not so. The only animals known to eat the joshua tree (*Yucca microflora*), the ground sloths, became extinct about 12,000 BP, along with many other larger animals of the Rancho La Brea fauna (see page 124). Sloth dung, with interwoven yucca fibers, can still be found in fossil form in the Mohave Desert.

selected. Viable examples of all major naturally occurring ecosystems within a given region should be conserved in order to maintain some portion of the diversity which evolutionary processes have already produced, and in which diversity may be expected to continue to develop. By the same token, all species populations which have evolved should be maintained wherever feasible in such a way as to include the whole range of their variation.

Stone (1965) has discussed many of the problems involved in the selection and management of such reserves illustrating ecosystem diversity. He emphasizes the inevitability of change and the necessity for management to adjust the rate or direction of such change. As to the selection of the ecosystems to be preserved, and particular sites which are suitable for this, he recommends the use of university groups from campuses with strong ecological and resource management interests. Norris (1968) described one such system for site selection and management instituted by the state university in California. This university organized a "Natural Land and Water Reserve System" which is examining some 80 proposed reserve areas typifying the extremely rich ecosystem diversity of that state. When approved, sites are incorporated in the system and maintained by appropriate management as teaching and research reserves, which also fulfill the need to preserve adequate samples of California's ecosystem diversity. Probably

Plate 13. *Cape Buffalo* (*Syncerus caffer*) in the Wankie National Park, Rhodesia. The seral communities which this species favors in this area are shrub savannas in the final stages of degradation to grassland through the action of grass fires and grazing. Such seral communities are ephemeral; management practices for the maintenance of a mosaic including this type of community require close control of the buffalo population.

Plate 14. *Greater Kudu* (*Strepsiceros strepsiceros*) in the Wankie National Park, Rhodesia. This species, like the Cape Buffalo, feeds in shrub savannas. Being a less aggressive species, the greater kudu, however, prefers a savanna with a much taller woody growth in which it is partially concealed. Unlike the buffalo, its numbers are not sufficient to affect successional processes in this community significantly. Management plans for the preservation of this animal species do not therefore at present involve limitation of the density of this species by culling.

about 40 of the proposed areas will eventually be incorporated in the system. Twelve reserves have already been established.

The International Union for the Conservation of Nature is cooperating with the Conservation of Terrestrial Communities section of the International Biological Program to initiate measures to preserve examples of ecosystem diversity viewed on a global basis.

SYNTHETIC ECOSYSTEMS

The value of reserves as described in the last section will be greatly enhanced if they can be surrounded by "synthetic ecosystems." This is a new name for a concept which foresters and resource management groups have been investigating for a number of years with varying degrees of intensity. The synthetic ecosystem concept envisages that an area has been completely planned for maximum and continuing *production* without regard to the maintenance of existing ecosystems, populations, or diversity. Stability and diversity in this instance can be ignored because high productivity can be maintained only if stability and diversity are secured.

The nearest approach to this concept is what was previously known as "multiple land use." Thus, for example, an imaginative scheme in Wisconsin designates land as "recreational, industrial, or residential in the hope that it might be used for these designated purposes. In the way multiple land use has often developed, however, it has tended to continue the domination of one preexisting use—e.g., forestry—while adding other activities which do not seriously interfere with this main purpose.

A synthetic ecosystem can be developed after an analysis of all possible activities and their potential productivity, with consideration given to both additive and synergistic effects. This would involve cost-benefit analyses, which might well stress, for example, recreational activities, rather than more traditional commercial operations.

Buffer Zones

It is likely that buffer zones of synthetic ecosystems created around reserves, thus separating them from direct contact with agricultural and urban areas, would be extremely beneficial. It would prevent marauding invasions of the agricultural areas by cougars, coyotes, bobcats, racoons, and opossums. It would also discourage drastic changes in the behavioral patterns of these animals and a marked tendency for them to become scavengers and scroungers when in direct contact with "civilization."

Range of Activity

It is possible to imagine a reserve area which has fine stands of Douglas fir surrounded by a synthetic ecosystem. This would have a mosaic pattern of rotational clear-felled plantation lumber which would tend to break up manmade wildfires. Open rides would form ski runs in the winter and serve as additional fire-breaks in the summer. These grassy areas would be grazed by feral sheep, which could be hunted under license with bow and arrow, while seasonal shotgun hunting of several introduced game birds like the Himalayan partridge would be permitted.

Thinnings in replanted areas would be marketed for Christmas trees, an already existing practice. Dams scattered through the area could be used for recreational fishing, water reservoirs for fire-fighting, and centers for duck and geese shoots. Backpacking trails would be provided with rest-camp stops in which timber trash would be stacked for camp fires. Limited trailer parks would be available on the perimeter. Berry crops such as loganberry, blackberry, and raspberry would be cultivated at particular stages of regrowth after clear felling of lumber, and beehives would be seasonably moved into the area. Firing ranges and skeet shooting areas could be located in isolated positions, with hill climbs for cars, buggies, and cycles similarly provided.

The planning of such a synthetic ecosystem and its management would need careful control and monitoring, but there is no theoretical reason why such buffer zones should not provide diversified recreational and commercial activities, while maintaining productivity and some semblance of the kind of landscape characterizing the less disturbed parts of the region.

Synthetic Ecosystems Elsewhere

In advanced agricultural societies which still retain some desirable vestiges of undisturbed ecosystems, buffer zones of such synthetic ecosystems are both feasible and desirable. Africa, for example, contains the richest surviving Pleistocene megafaunas of game animals. Some years ago, and with varying success, limited hunting zones were created around some of the game reserves established to preserve examples of this megafauna. Many of these reserves are running into management problems and a review of them should obviously include the practicability and desirability of surrounding them with synthetic ecosystem buffer zones. A French and Belgian colonial concept once applied in tropical Africa was to have each *réserve intégrale* buffered by reserves permitting a limited measure of exploitation.

RARE SPECIES

Many biological forms are rare in naturally occurring ecosystems and are especially vulnerable if they are either new or relict populations. These rare populations will often have to be removed and maintained in zoological or botanical gardens if they are to be preserved. An interesting example of individual enterprise in this direction was described in the *New Scientist* (Anon., 1969). Quoting various publications, this essay provided examples of how living material from various colonies of comparatively rare British plants which are about to be destroyed by one form or another of development, were transplanted to safer areas. Similar activities could be cited from many countries in both the Old and New Worlds. It is now a well-established policy of all the world's larger zoological gardens to include a breeding program for one or more endangered animal species.

Endangered Species

The question of the extinction of species by human interference, either by direct reduction of population size or by disturbance of ecosystem steady state, has been considered earlier in this text in relation to *Pleistocene overkill.* In recent years attention has again been focused on the possible accelerated disappearance rate of larger animal species from basically the same kind of interference, and "red book" and "black book" lists have been prepared. The first names the species—more especially of mammals, such as the giant panda, or larger birds, like the Californian condor—whose population size is so reduced the species is unlikely to persist unless special measures are taken to preserve it. The "black book" names those species which have been lost since 1600.

These lists have been drawn up by the Survival Service Commission of the International Union for the Conservation of Nature and Natural Resources, which has its headquarters at Morges, Switzerland. The year 1600 was selected as the starting date for these lists because from that time decriptions of animals were usually adequate, especially in reference to color, to permit a diagnosis of the taxonomic entity to which they referred. Moreover, specimen skins began to become available at this time.

It is estimated there were, in 1600, 4226 living species of mammals, 36 of which (0.85 per cent) have now become extinct; 120 (2.84 per cent) are in some danger of extinction. The corresponding figures for birds are 94 extinct out of 8684 species in 1600 (1.09 per cent), 187 (2.16 per cent) now threatened. These figures are further illustrated in Figures 13-1 and 13-2, which are taken from a recent work by Fisher, Simon, and Vincent (1969), the source for much of this information on endangered species. Other recent figures are cited by Talbot (1970).

Clearly, before these lists in the red and black books become even longer, some kind of policy must be adopted as to the extent and nature of the measures we adopt to maintain the present diversity in the larger mammalian and bird groups. The analysis of probable causes of extinction included in Table 13-2 suggests that hunting and ecosystem disturbance between them have been responsible for over three quarters of the losses and reductions. Hunting has become much more effective with the introduction of high velocity rifles and telescopic sights. Ecosystem disturbance takes the form of interference with the predator-prey balance, and with the other consumer and producer populations—or abiotic elements—of the ecosystem, like clearing a forest.

Table 13-2 *Analysis of Causal Factors Leading to the Extinction or Endangering of Bird and Mammal Species Since 1600*

	BIRDS			*MAMMALS*
	Nonpasserine (Large) Per Cent	*Passerine (Small) Per Cent*	*Total Per Cent*	*Per Cent*
CAUSE OF EXTINCTION				
Natural	26	20	24	25
Human	74	80	76	67
Hunting	54	13	42	33
Introduced predators	13	21	15	17
Other introduction	—	14	4	6
Habitat disruption	7	32	15	19
	100	100	100	100
CAUSE OF PRESENT RARITY				
Natural	31	32	32	14
Human	69	68	68	86
Hunting	32	10	24	43
Introduced predators	9	15	11	8
Other introductions	2	5	3	6
Habitat disruption	26	38	30	29
	100	100	100	100

From J. Fisher *et al. The Red Book: Wildlife in Danger,* New York: Viking Press. © IUCN 1969.

Comparison of Extinction Rates

It is interesting to compare the extinction rate of species recorded in the red and black books with postulated rates of Pleistocene overkill. As was discussed earlier in this text, this last seems to have proceeded between 11,000 and 8,000 BP. During this time Fisher *et al.* (1969) estimate that approximately 50 mammal and 40 bird species disappeared. This represents a rate of about three species a century.

Because since 1600, some 36 species of mammals and 94 species of birds have gone, the extinction rate is now beginning to approach 50 per century. This far higher rate of "kill" suggests that Pleistocene *erectus-sapiens* populations were not very effective hunters, or that they evolved totem and taboo rituals against killing of particular species, or both. The comparison serves to emphasize that we shall extensively limit the diversity of all our remaining ecosystems if we make no immediate and deliberate further effort to maintain this still rich diversity.

Figure 13-1. *Threatened species of mammals.* Each number on this map corresponds with a mammalian species or recognized infraspecific mammalian category which is considered so imminently threatened with extinction as to justify its inclusion in the Red Data Book prepared by the Survival Service Commission of the International Union for the Conservation of Nature and Natural Resources. No area of the globe is immune from the threat of extinction of some mammalian form among the populations of its natural ecosystems. Data on whales are not included in this diagram. (After J. Fisher *et al., The Red Book: Wildlife in Danger,* New York: Viking Press. © IUCN 1969.)

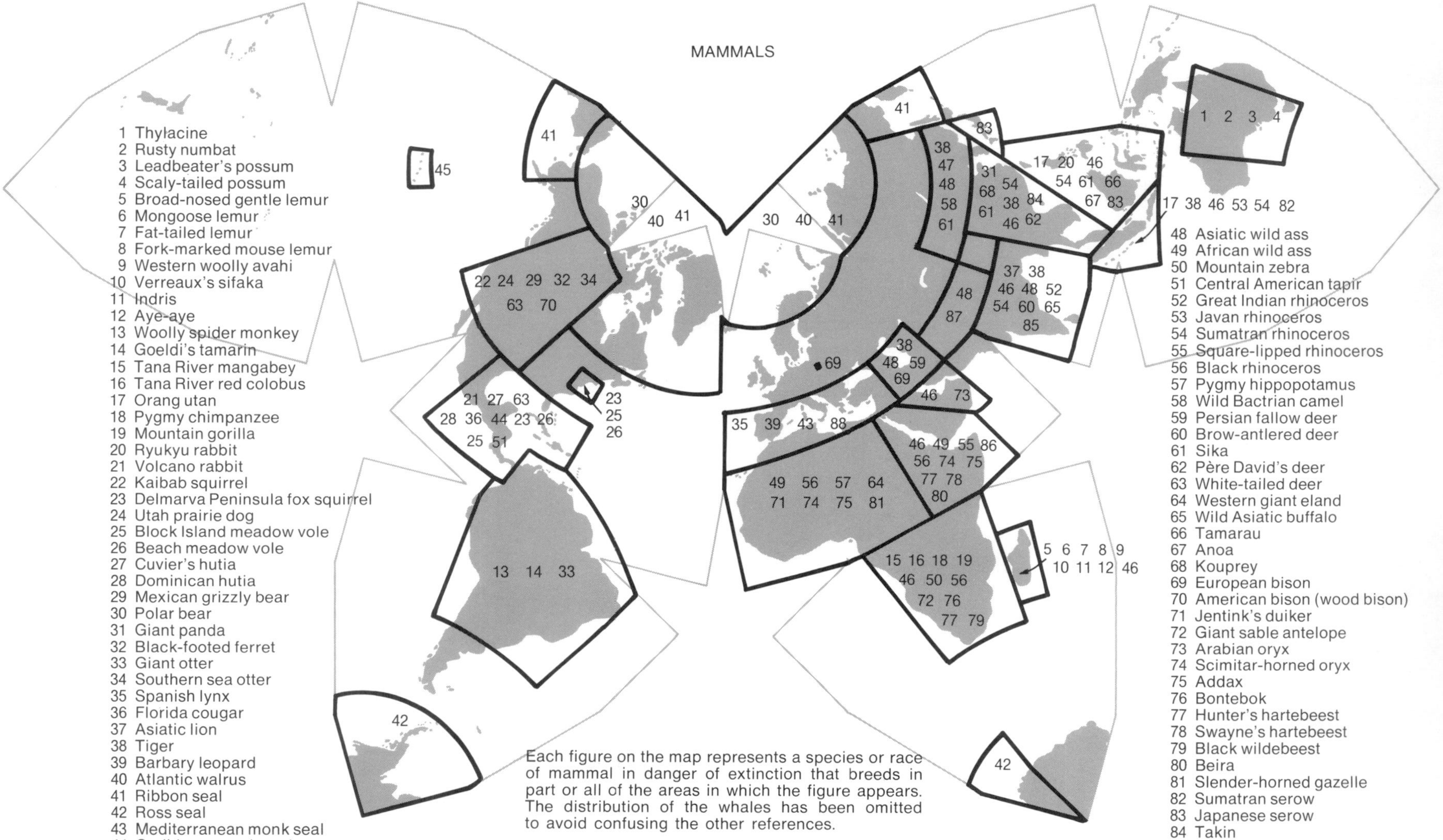

Each figure on the map represents a species or race of mammal in danger of extinction that breeds in part or all of the areas in which the figure appears. The distribution of the whales has been omitted to avoid confusing the other references.

1 Thylacine
2 Rusty numbat
3 Leadbeater's possum
4 Scaly-tailed possum
5 Broad-nosed gentle lemur
6 Mongoose lemur
7 Fat-tailed lemur
8 Fork-marked mouse lemur
9 Western woolly avahi
10 Verreaux's sifaka
11 Indris
12 Aye-aye
13 Woolly spider monkey
14 Goeldi's tamarin
15 Tana River mangabey
16 Tana River red colobus
17 Orang utan
18 Pygmy chimpanzee
19 Mountain gorilla
20 Ryukyu rabbit
21 Volcano rabbit
22 Kaibab squirrel
23 Delmarva Peninsula fox squirrel
24 Utah prairie dog
25 Block Island meadow vole
26 Beach meadow vole
27 Cuvier's hutia
28 Dominican hutia
29 Mexican grizzly bear
30 Polar bear
31 Giant panda
32 Black-footed ferret
33 Giant otter
34 Southern sea otter
35 Spanish lynx
36 Florida cougar
37 Asiatic lion
38 Tiger
39 Barbary leopard
40 Atlantic walrus
41 Ribbon seal
42 Ross seal
43 Mediterranean monk seal
44 Caribbean monk seal
45 Hawaiian monk seal
46 Dugong
47 Przewalski's horse
48 Asiatic wild ass
49 African wild ass
50 Mountain zebra
51 Central American tapir
52 Great Indian rhinoceros
53 Javan rhinoceros
54 Sumatran rhinoceros
55 Square-lipped rhinoceros
56 Black rhinoceros
57 Pygmy hippopotamus
58 Wild Bactrian camel
59 Persian fallow deer
60 Brow-antlered deer
61 Sika
62 Père David's deer
63 White-tailed deer
64 Western giant eland
65 Wild Asiatic buffalo
66 Tamarau
67 Anoa
68 Kouprey
69 European bison
70 American bison (wood bison)
71 Jentink's duiker
72 Giant sable antelope
73 Arabian oryx
74 Scimitar-horned oryx
75 Addax
76 Bontebok
77 Hunter's hartebeest
78 Swayne's hartebeest
79 Black wildebeest
80 Beira
81 Slender-horned gazelle
82 Sumatran serow
83 Japanese serow
84 Takin
85 Nilgiri tahr
86 Walia ibex
87 Markhor
88 Cyprian mouflon

Zoo Banks

As mentioned earlier, all major zoological gardens in the world are now cooperating in a plan to breed in captivity populations of endangered animal species. These are known as *zoo banks.*

Two examples will serve to illustrate how effective such zoo banks can be, the cases of the European bison and the Hawaiian goose. The story of the European bison in this century has been described by Fisher *et al.* (1969). The European bison (*Bison bonasus*) is regarded as a separate species from the American bison (*B. bison*) although they are probably both recent geographical populations descended directly from some Pleistocene ancestor which evolved into the geographical groups known as *B. antiquus* in North America and *B. priscus* in Eurasia (Figure 13-3). *B. antiquus* co-existed in North America with three other glacial bison populations, *B. latifrons, B. alleni,* and *B. crassicornis,* and survived them to persist into the Wisconsin glaciation, when it was hunted by the early Mongoloid Paleo-Indians. The wood bison (*B. bison athabascae*) and plains bison (*B. bison bison*) appear to have developed directly from it as geographically and ecologically distinct populations.

European Bison

The European bison, or wissent, likewise evolved apparently into two separate populations, usually described as subspecies—the Lithuanian or lowland bison (*B. bonasus bonasus,* Figure 13-3) and the Caucasian or mountain bison (*B. bonasus caucasius*). Both of these, like the wood bison, were browsers, thus contrasting with the plains bison (Figure 13-3), which is a grazer.

At the beginning of this century the lowland bison, whose areas had originally included western and southern Europe, survived only in the wild as a single herd in the Bialowieza Forest in Poland, under the personal care of the Russian Imperial family. In 1914 there were 737 animals in this herd; all disappeared during World War I. However, 45 animals which had been distributed from this herd survived in various European zoos, and there was also from this same source a semiwild herd in the Pszcyna forest

Figure 13-2. *Threatened species of birds.* Each number on this map corresponds with a bird species or recognized infraspecific bird category which is considered so imminently threatened with extinction as to justify its inclusion in the Red Data Book prepared by the Survival Service Commission of the International Union for the Conservation of Nature and Natural Resources. The key figure on the map is located in the breeding area or part of this area. It should be noted that it is more particularly those bird species that breed on islands that are especially endangered. (After J. Fisher *et al. The Red Book: Wildlife in Danger,* New York: Viking Press. IUCN 1969.)

BIRDS

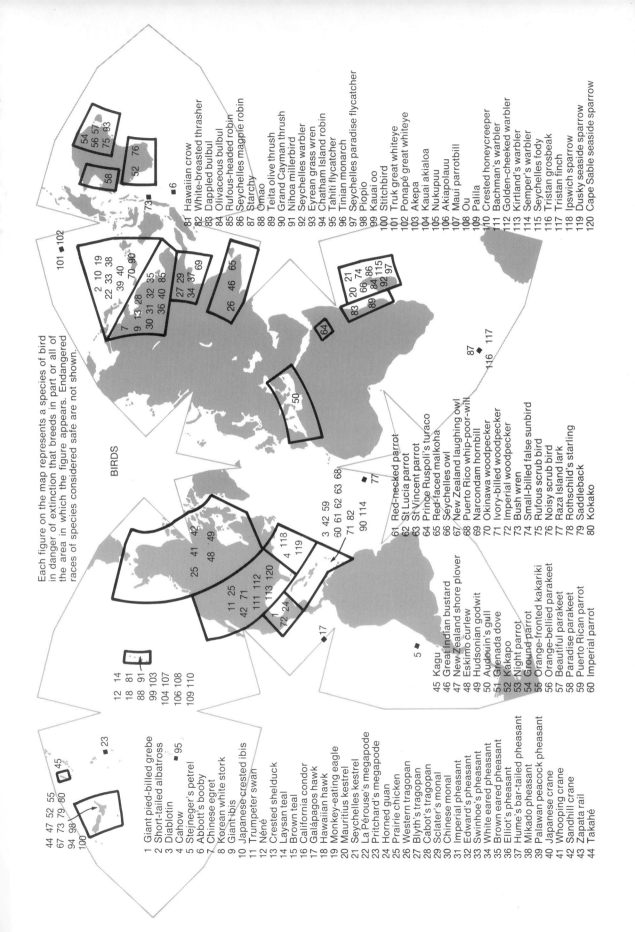

Each figure on the map represents a species of bird in danger of extinction that breeds in part or all of the area in which the figure appears. Endangered races of species considered safe are not shown.

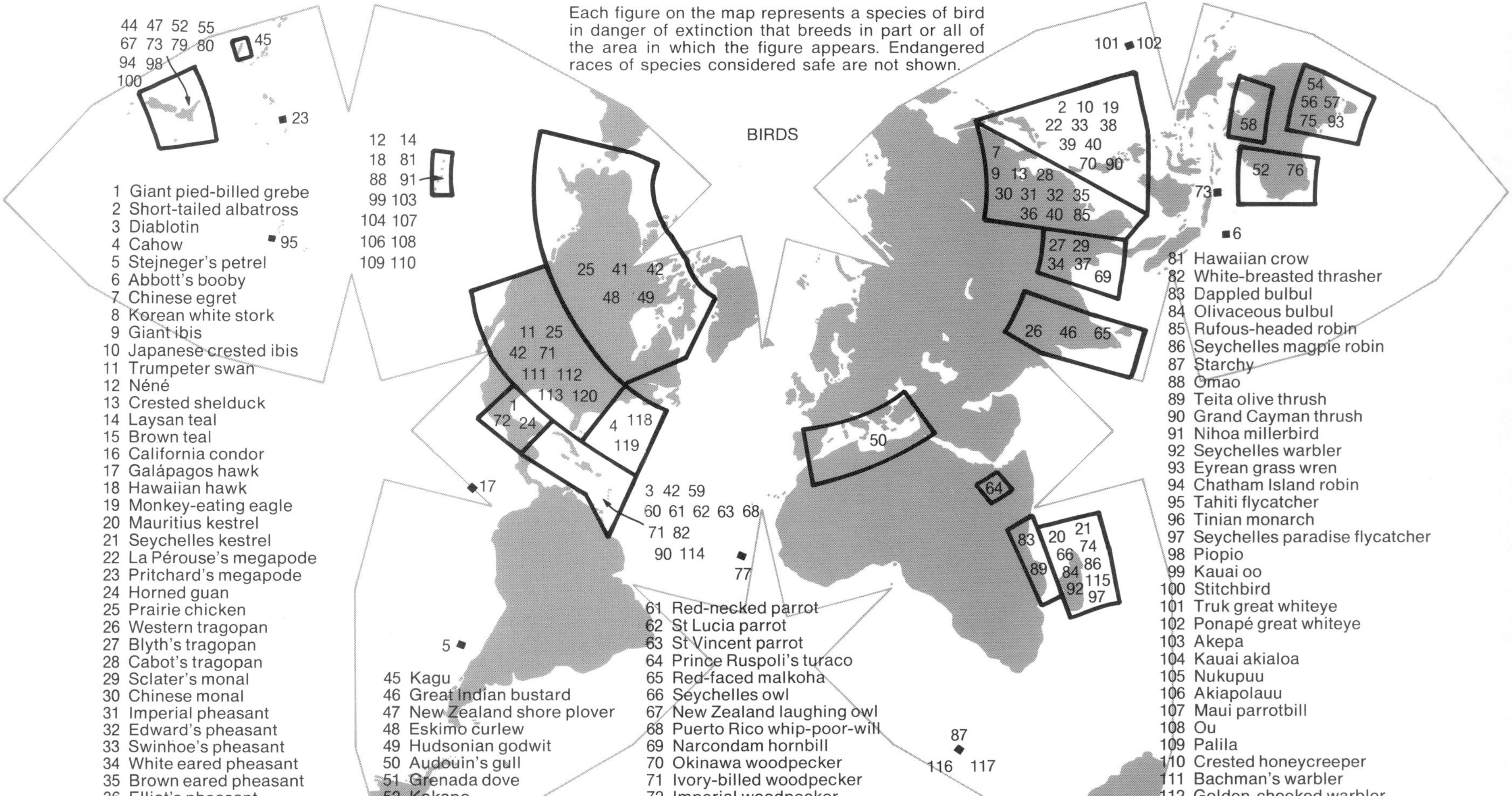

1 Giant pied-billed grebe
2 Short-tailed albatross
3 Diablotin
4 Cahow
5 Stejneger's petrel
6 Abbott's booby
7 Chinese egret
8 Korean white stork
9 Giant ibis
10 Japanese crested ibis
11 Trumpeter swan
12 Néné
13 Crested shelduck
14 Laysan teal
15 Brown teal
16 California condor
17 Galápagos hawk
18 Hawaiian hawk
19 Monkey-eating eagle
20 Mauritius kestrel
21 Seychelles kestrel
22 La Pérouse's megapode
23 Pritchard's megapode
24 Horned guan
25 Prairie chicken
26 Western tragopan
27 Blyth's tragopan
28 Cabot's tragopan
29 Sclater's monal
30 Chinese monal
31 Imperial pheasant
32 Edward's pheasant
33 Swinhoe's pheasant
34 White eared pheasant
35 Brown eared pheasant
36 Elliot's pheasant
37 Hume's bar-tailed pheasant
38 Mikado pheasant
39 Palawan peacock pheasant
40 Japanese crane
41 Whooping crane
42 Sandhill crane
43 Zapata rail
44 Takahé
45 Kagu
46 Great Indian bustard
47 New Zealand shore plover
48 Eskimo curlew
49 Hudsonian godwit
50 Audouin's gull
51 Grenada dove
52 Kakapo
53 Night parrot
54 Ground parrot
55 Orange-fronted kakariki
56 Orange-bellied parakeet
57 Beautiful parakeet
58 Paradise parakeet
59 Puerto Rican parrot
60 Imperial parrot
61 Red-necked parrot
62 St Lucia parrot
63 St Vincent parrot
64 Prince Ruspoli's turaco
65 Red-faced malkoha
66 Seychelles owl
67 New Zealand laughing owl
68 Puerto Rico whip-poor-will
69 Narcondam hornbill
70 Okinawa woodpecker
71 Ivory-billed woodpecker
72 Imperial woodpecker
73 Bush wren
74 Small-billed false sunbird
75 Rufous scrub bird
76 Noisy scrub bird
77 Raza Island lark
78 Rothschild's starling
79 Saddleback
80 Kokako
81 Hawaiian crow
82 White-breasted thrasher
83 Dappled bulbul
84 Olivaceous bulbul
85 Rufous-headed robin
86 Seychelles magpie robin
87 Starchy
88 Omao
89 Teita olive thrush
90 Grand Cayman thrush
91 Nihoa millerbird
92 Seychelles warbler
93 Eyrean grass wren
94 Chatham Island robin
95 Tahiti flycatcher
96 Tinian monarch
97 Seychelles paradise flycatcher
98 Piopio
99 Kauai oo
100 Stitchbird
101 Truk great whiteye
102 Ponapé great whiteye
103 Akepa
104 Kauai akialoa
105 Nukupuu
106 Akiapolauu
107 Maui parrotbill
108 Ou
109 Palila
110 Crested honeycreeper
111 Bachman's warbler
112 Golden-cheeked warbler
113 Kirtland's warbler
114 Semper's warbler
115 Seychelles fody
116 Tristan grosbeak
117 Tristan finch
118 Ipswich sparrow
119 Dusky seaside sparrow
120 Cape Sable seaside sparrow

Figure 13-3. *Bison species. B.* The lowland form of European bison (*B. bonasus bonasus*) was released into the wild again in 1956 after a number of generations had been maintained in semicaptivity. A wild herd established from these in the Bialowieza Forest in Poland numbered 57 head in 1962. *A.* The wood bison (*B. bison athabascae*) was unfortunately interbred with (*D*) the plains bison (*B. bison bison*) during earlier conservation operations. An isolated wild herd of about 200 head was located in 1957 in Wainwright Buffalo Park in Alberta, but suffered disease losses. This subspecies, which resembles the European bison, is now preserved in three separate wilderness areas in Canada and, like the plains bison, should survive in its various preserve areas. The bison in *C* is *B. antiquus,* which is very commonly represented among the Rancho La Brea fossils. It is the probable ancestral form of the plains bison. Although this ancestral form therefore survived until the early Wisconsin, it may have been one of the earliest of the La Brea species to become extinct.

in Upper Silesia, totaling over 70 animals in 1921. By the end of 1921 only a cow and two bulls were left undestroyed from the Pszcyna herd.

These three animals, together with two cows and another bull purchased from the remaining zoo-bank animals under semidomesticated conditions, were used to reestablish the Bialowieza herd. In 1930 a stud book was published, and this included by 1949 nine purebred cows at Pszcyna, three at Bialowieza. In 1956 there were enough bison for some to be released in the Bialowieza forest; this "wild" herd numbered 57 in 1962. This forest is believed to have a carrying capacity for 100 to 115 bison under wild steady-state conditions. Other breeding centers have been established in Poland, and there are still animals in the zoo bank, so that the lowland bison now appears safe from extinction.

The Caucasian bison subspecies was less fortunate. This had also been under the personal protection of the Czar of Russia, but in 1924 after the Russian Revolution, only about 15 to 20 animals were estimated to be alive, partly because of destruction by local herdsmen. By 1925 even these animals had apparently gone, but a bull presented as a yearling in 1908 survived to this same year and sired a number of calves from lowland bison. The Polish Ministry of Forestry is reportedly attempting to reconstitute the Caucasian bison by selecting for its characters from among the fourth and fifth generation descendants of these hybrid calves.

The Hawaiian Goose

The Hawaiian goose (*Branta sandvicensis,* Figure 13-4) has a similar history, and again the present account is essentially derived from Fisher *et al.* (1969). This goose is estimated to have maintained a population of about 25,000 birds after Polynesian occupation of the Hawaiian islands, and until Europeans arrived following Cook's visit in 1770. By 1850 it occurred only in wilder mountainous areas, and in 1900 it was rare even there. However, from the time of the first recorded breeding in the London Zoo in 1834, a number of zoos had maintained breeding flocks in captivity.

Despite these captive flocks, by 1947 there were only an estimated 50 Hawaiian geese left in the world, and these were on Hawaii, either wild or in captivity.

The Hawaiian Board of Agriculture promptly started a breeding program with two captive pairs and a gander, together with a captured wild goose. In 1950 the Board flew two geese from a captive flock on Hawaii back to England and mated them with a gander from the same source. When this gander died in 1963, his progeny had reached more than 230 birds, 50 of which had been released on the Hawaiian island of Maui. By 1964 the total wild and captive birds were estimated as numbering over 500, and the population is doubling every three or four years. Free birds are again occupying the mountainous areas of Hawaii and Maui, where some sanctuaries have been established. The future of the Hawaiian goose, official bird of the fiftieth state, thus seems to have become assured again, partly because of the captive stocks held in aviculture banks.

Other Zoo Banks

Successful attempts have been made to breed in captivity other animals on the red book list of endangered species. These include such mammals as orangutan (*Pongo pygmaeus*), pygmy chimpanzee (*Pan pumiscus*),

Figure 13-4. *Three threatened species of birds in the Red Data Book. A.* The New Zealand Takahe (*Notornis mantelli*) is a large flightless gallinule, once widespread in both north and south islands as judged from fossil remains. A sanctuary some 200 square miles in extent in a wild and remote area has been established where the main population of 200–300 birds of this relict species have survived. *B.* The Great Indian Bustard (*Choriotis nigriceps*), probably the largest flying bird which alights on land, has become rare over all of its previously wide area of distribution in India and is believed to be extinct over much of this former range. Creation of a preserve presents many problems, and perhaps this species will be best maintained, for the present at least, in an aviculture bank. *C.* Hawaiian goose (*Branta sandvicensis*), male on right, female left; this species is now re-established in part of its former range on mountainous areas in Hawaii and Maui, by the release of birds from captive flocks. (Adapted from J. Fisher *et al. The Red Book: Wildlife in Danger,* New York: Viking Press. © IUCN 1969.)

mountain gorilla (*Gorilla gorilla beringei*), giant panda (*Ailuropoda melanoleuca*), Przewalskis horse (*Equus prezewalskii*), pygmy hippopotamus (*Choeropsis liberiensis*), Pere David's deer (*Elaphurus davidianus*), and birds like the whooping crane (*Grus americana*) and great Indian bustard (*Choriotis nigriceps*). Increasing attention is being given to the establishment of zoo banks for species of other major groups of animals which have been successfully bred in captivity, including reptiles such as the Galapagos giant tortoise (*Testudo elephantopus*).

Treatment of Endangered Species

For any threatened species, there is now a fairly well-established procedure. First, its autecology and distribution range are determined. If a preserve area can be set aside for it in which it appears likely that the species can maintain a viable population, this is the principal action taken, as with the large flightless New Zealand Takahe (*Notornis mantelli*) (Figure 13-4).

Sometimes areas from which the animal has disappeared are restocked from surplus breeding areas, as is being done for the Kruger National Park in South Africa from the Umfolozi and Hlwehlwe Game Reserve stocks of the white rhino (*Ceratotherium simum*). Unfortunately, where localized geographic forms of a species had evolved, this does not restore them unless adaptation subsequently occurs in the same directions as in the original geographic form. Sometimes the species has become extinct in the wild, as with the European bison, or the South African bontebok (*Damaliscus dorcus dorcus*), which also has been reestablished in a National Park in a portion of its former distribution area from captive animals. Another alternative is to capture wild animals in areas where eventual extinction is inevitable, and translocate them to a new preserve area, as was done in the case of the Persian fallow deer (*Dama mesopotamica*).

Some animal species unfortunately cannot be handled in any of these ways; whales form the best-known example. In such cases the only possible approach is to limit catches, or prohibit them altogether, and hope that the species survives. For several whale species this international action may be too late (McVay, 1966).

RARE PLANTS

With plants the problem of conservation is similar in some ways to that of animals, but in other ways it is very different and fortunately easier. It is similar in that an *ecosystem* rather than a species must be conserved. It is different in that many plants can be propagated by vegetative means, and more or less indefinitely because plant tissues do not age. This circumstance has permitted an almost world-wide distribution of a famous rare plant once believed to be extinct, the Dawn Redwood, *Metasequoia glyptostroboides.*

Metasequoia

The coniferous tree genus, *Metasequoia* was originally described as a fossil plant from Pliocene beds in Japan and was subsequently found in

Plate 15. *Botanic gardens* are commonly stocked with rare or endangered plant species having curious or incompletely understood features. This is the case on both counts with this species of *Leucospermum* (family Proteaceae) growing in the Kirstenbosch Gardens in South Africa.

Plate 16. *Botanic gardens* can be developed for other functions than those shown in Plate 15, for example, the maintenance and display of the range of variation in cultivated plants, as in this bed of lettuce varieties in the Montreal Botanical Garden. This imaginatively planned garden facility well illustrates the potential for conservation of genetic diversity, as well as the display, research, and educational aspects of botanical garden functions.

Cretaceous rocks. The genus was therefore at least 60 million years old and was not thought to have any living species. However, about 30 years ago Elmer Merrill, then director of the Arnold Arboretum at Harvard and an authority on Pacific plants, heard rumors of the existence of a rare tree in China. He succeeded in obtaining seed of what proved to be a *Metasequoia* and raised some plants.

In 1948 Ralph Chaney visited the Chinese locality in Szechuan and Hupeh where *Metasequoia* was reported to grow; he found a valley in which the tree was not uncommon and collected seed from it. From this seed many plants were grown throughout the world. They were further propagated by cuttings, so that the tree is now established in many official gardens. Nevertheless it will probably suffer the same fate as the almost equally extensively grown Maidenhair tree (*Ginkgo biloba*), which belongs to a genus which geologically is even older. In this instance, the sole surviving species of the genus no longer occurs naturally.

Anomalous Distributions

In the case of a number of rare plants it is not sufficient, however, merely to ensure their survival under cultivation. Their scientific interest essentially lies in accounting for their occurrence in the particular ecosystems of specific areas. Hepper (1969) mentions a number of such rare plants, including *Pitcairnia feliciana* and *Vateria seychellarum.* The *Pitcairnia,* which occurs on rocks in Guinea in West Africa, represents the only known occurrence of a member of the family Bromeliaceae outside tropical America. The bromeliads are characteristic epiphytic plants of the tropical forest throughout Central and South America, and it is an unexplained phytogeographical enigma why one species alone should be found across the other side of the Atlantic in the Old World.

Likewise, *Vateria,* of which only half a dozen specimens survive in the Seychelle Islands off the east coast of Africa, is the only member of a flowering plant subfamily, Dipterocarpoideae, to be encountered outside the Indo-Malaysia area.

In both examples, and in many similar ones which could be cited, research needs to be done on the biology of the *whole* relict population in order to be able to offer explanations for these apparent anomalies. Cultivated material propagated from a small sample of the population will not suffice.

WEED SPECIES

The problem of ecosystem conservation when considering individual plant species' survival is greater than that regarding animals. Many of the unique island floras of the world—Juan Fernandez, St. Helena, Madagascar, New Zealand, and Hawaii, to mention only a few—are disappearing before invading species of cosmopolitan *weeds*. Not only are these unique island floras exposed to such invasion, but many continental areas as well.

For example, in the small coastal county of Orange in the Pacific Southwest, out of a total of 778 flowering plant taxa at the species or infraspecific level recorded for the county, no fewer than 191 (or 25 per cent) are introductions, mostly from Eurasia (Boughey, 1968). Such replacement of native by introduced weed floras is accelerated by development. Agricultural clearings not only destroy the plant populations of natural ecosystems, but also provide the synthetic ecosystems to whose environmental conditions weeds are specifically adapted. The opening up of communication systems, roads, railroads, waterways, and airports also increases the rate of long-distance dispersal of various invading species. The biology of such colonizing species has been extensively treated in a symposium volume edited by Baker and Stebbins (1965).

The same kind of thing happens in the case of faunas, where certain "weed" animals follow close behind urban development. The English sparrow (*Passer domesticus*) and the common starling (*Sturnus vulgaris*) had spread through most of the world by the beginning of this century, as had the common or Norway rat (*Rattus norvegicus*), house mouse (*Mus musculus*), housefly (*Musca domestica*), flea (*Pulex irritans*), louse (*Pediculus humanus*), and common bedbug (*Cimex lectularis*). In some instances the introduction of such weed animals poses a serious threat to the persistence of natural ecosystems; in all cases they are responsible, directly or indirectly, for ecosystem change.

Migration of the House Mouse

A recent paper by Fertig and Edmonds (1969) describes the particular features which make one such animal weed species, the feral house mouse, so successful a competitor and colonizer of new ecosystems. These include its unobtrusiveness owing to its small size and nocturnal habit; omnivorous diet of, if necessary, dry food; ability to exist on metabolic water alone or on sea water; aggressiveness within its own ecological niche; and breeding potential, including its capacity for continuous inbreeding.

Direct consumption of human food by the house mouse, or direct damage to stored materials, results in annual losses running into millions of dollars. Indirectly, its effects are equally serious as a potential vector for plague, tularemia, food poisoning, and other human disorders.

The ancestral form of the house mouse is believed to be a central Asian subspecies, *Mus musculus wagneri,* a wild grass seedeater still including in its area of distribution the fertile crescent where Neolithic agricultural settlements first appeared (as described in Chapter 5). Starting from the fertile crescent it has been possible to trace the historic migration of the house mouse through the world (Figure 13-5). It would similarly be possible to account for all the familiar animal weed species.

NECESSARY LIMITATIONS ON CONSERVATION ACTIVITIES

Much of this chapter has been devoted to the issue of deciding what is to be conserved. Having determined what this is, there is then a question of determining the land use of the rest of a particular region under a multiple land-use scheme. Consideration must be given to the extent to which externalization and internalization can be permitted in relation to other such regional units. While it is essential that development master plans meet all these requirements, inevitably they impose drastic restrictions on both economic growth and private enterprise in the conventional speculative meaning of the term. There will have to be other restrictions, such as limiting population migration into an area already exceeding its carrying capacity. Such restrictions are naturally opposed by the individual and sectional interests which stand to lose most from their introduction. One major aspect of conservation is not even considered here, *soil con-*

Figure 13-5. *Migration of the house mouse* from its adaptation as a commensal of agricultural ecosystems in neolithic settlements of the fertile crescent to its present worldwide distribution. The parent subspecies *Mus musculus wagneri* (bold lines) still occurs wild in west central Asia. Two other subspecies, *M. m. praetextus* and *M. m. domesticus* out of a further four known, have traveled, supposedly by boat, to the New World, where they have met and interbred in the central United States. (From D. S. Fertig and V. W. Edmonds, "The physiology of the house mouse," *Scientific American,* **221**[4]: 110, 1969. Copyright © 1969 by Scientific American, Inc. All rights reserved.)

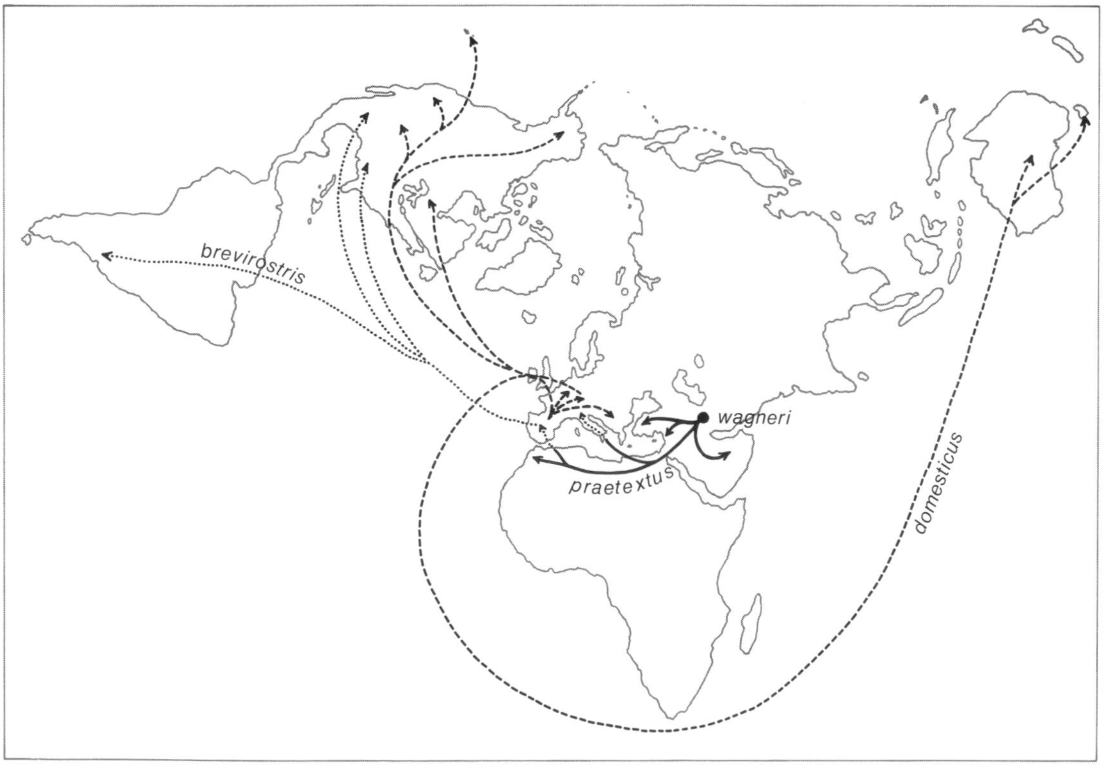

servation. This has already been extensively investigated, and restrictive legislation in many countries ensures conformation with basic soil conservation practice, even if it ignores more insidious problems (Waller, 1970).

Many nations are fiercely independent. This is understandable, considering that they have often paid an extreme price to win their independence. Attempts to plan their behavior, let alone attempt to condition it artificially, are certain to be strongly resisted. Many such feelings of independence are associated with individual territorial patterns which Ardrey (1968) and others have discussed in detail. Not enough is known about territorial behavior in human populations. It may be that it could be just as much a matter of conditioning as is, apparently, social morality. If this is so, some might consider that an element of territoriality could with advantage be added to our training in early infancy, as advocated by Eysenck (1969). This would possibly prevent further gross misuse and plundering of the natural ecosystems which survive today despite all our past exploitation and neglect.

Ecological Land Use

Thus far, we have been concerned with carrying capacity in terms of living standards, and with the conservation of portions of ecosystems as extensive and representative samples of existing biological diversity. A complementary but different approach is to view human land use as an integral function of a given ecosystem, which is accommodated within its structure and processes without irreversibly changing their nature.

Landscape Development on an Ecological Basis

The leading protagonist and most eloquent spokesman for this approach is Ian McHarg (1967), who has developed an internationally recognized school of landscape architecture based on this philosophy at the University of Pennsylvania. If such an approach had always been adopted in regional land-use planning, America would now be a much more pleasant and interesting place in which to live. It would also of necessity be carrying either a lower population, or a more extensively distributed one.

As with all conservation issues, it is necessary at some stage to reach a quite arbitrary decision, even with the McHarg philosophy. Human occupation, even the mere human visitation of an area, inevitably imposes some changes in its ecosystems. What can be conserved then, or what degree of diversity and stability can be maintained, must always be a matter of degree.

Future Environments

In 1965 the Conservation Foundation organized an international conference to consider the future environments of North America. The papers presented at this conference and the discussions following their presentation have subsequently been published (Darling and Milton, 1969). They represent a valuable compendium of conservation thought and provide interesting background to any consideration of conservation problems. If such an extensive and exhaustive series can be said to express any common views, there are two. First, conservation is basically a matter of economics. Second, as Lewis Mumford emphasized in the closing address at this conference, conservation must start from a study of urban man.

One of the premises developed early in this text was that urban settlements *preceded* the agricultural revolution, and therefore their inception marks the turning point when *erectus-sapiens* populations began for the first time extensively to destroy natural ecosystems. We are committed irrevocably to an urban civilization. As it was the urban revolution which launched the first wholesale attack on our natural ecosystems, so it must now initiate the task of conserving that which remains.

Bibliography

REFERENCES

Anonymous. "Blasphemy with a trowel," *New Scientist,* **42:** 676–77, 1969.

Anonymous. "The solar system may be giving birth to a new planet," *New Scientist,* **42:** 679, 1969.

Ardrey, R. *The Territorial Imperative,* New York: Delta, 1966.

Baker, H. G., and Stebbins, G. L. (eds.) *The Genetics of Colonising Species,* New York, Academic Press, 1965.

Boughey, A. S. *A Checklist of Orange County Flowering Plants,* Museum of Systematic Biology, University of California, Irvine, Res. Ser. No 1, 1968.

Bradley, C. C. "Human water needs and water use in America," *Science,* **138:** 489–91, 1962.

Darling, F. Fraser, and Milton, J. P. (eds.) *Future Environments of North America,* New York: The Natural History Press, 1966.

Eysenck, H. "The technology of consent," *New Scientist,* **42:** 688–90, 1969.

Fertig, D. S., and Edmonds, V. W. "The physiology of the house mouse," *Scientific American,* **221**(4): 103–10, 1969.

Fisher, J., Simon, N., and Vincent, J. *Wildlife in Danger,* New York: Viking Press, 1969.

Hepper, F. N. "Plants," in J. Fisher, *et al.* (eds.), *Wildlife in Danger,* New York: Viking Press, 1969, pp. 353–60.

Hutchinson, G. E. "Fifty years of man in the zoo," *The Yale Review,* **51**(91): 58–68, 1964.

Kramer, R. J. "Strengthening the biological foundations of resource management," *Trans. N. Amer. Wildlife and Nat. Resources Conf.,* **29:** 58–68, 1964.

Landsberg, H. H. "The U.S. resource outlook: quantity and quality," *Daedalus,* **96:** 1034–57, 1967.

Leopold, Aldo. "Conservation ethic," *J. Forestry,* **31:** 634–43, 1933.

McHarg, I. L. "An ecological method for landscape architecture," *Landscape Architecture,* Jan., 1967, pp. 105–107.

McVay, S. "The last of the great whales," *Scientific American,* **215**(2): 13–21, 1966.

Norris, K. S. "California's natural land and water reserve system," *Bioscience,* **18:** 415–17, 1968.

Stone, E. C. "Preserving vegetation in parks and wilderness," *Science,* **150:** 1261–67, 1965.

Talbot, L. M. "Endangered species," *Bioscience,* **20:** 331, 1970.

Waller, R. "Modern husbandry and soil deterioration," *New Scientist,* **45:** 262–64, 1970.

Whyte, W. H. *The Last Landscape,* New York: Doubleday, 1968.

FURTHER READINGS

Aubréville, A. *Climats, Forêts et Desertification de l'Afrique Tropicale,* Paris: Muséum d'Histoire Naturelle, 1949.

Boughey, A. S. "Man and the African environment," *Proc. Trans. Rhodesia Sci. Ass.,* **48:** 8–18, 1960.

Cerowsky, J., "Conservation in East Europe," *New Scientist,* **46**(697): 122–26, 1970.

Charter, S. P. R. "Why preserve nature?" *Man on Earth,* **1**(2): 1–8, 1965.

Ciriacy-Wantrup. S. V., and Parsons, J. J. (eds.) *Natural Resources—Quality and Quantity,* Berkeley: University of California Press, 1967.

Committee on Resources and Man, *Resources and Man,* San Francisco: Freeman, 1969.

Commoner, B. *Science and Survival,* New York: Viking, 1966.

Conway, W. G. "Zoos: their changing roles," *Science,* **163:** 48–52, 1969.

Darling, F. Fraser. "Conservation and ecological theory," *J. Ecology,* **52**(suppl.): 39–45, 1964.

Dassman, R. F. *Environmental Conservation,* New York: Wiley, 1959.

Egler, F. E. "Wildlife habitat measurement for the citizen," *Atlantic Naturalist,* **22:** 166–69, 1967.

Elton, C. S. "The reasons for conservation," in *The Ecology of Invasions by Animals and Plants,* London: Methuen, 1958, pp. 143–52.

Hediger, H. "Man as a social partner of animals and vice-versa," *Symp. Zoological Society of London,* **14:** 291–300, 1965.

Henning, D. H. "Comments on an interdisciplinary social science approach for conservation administration," *Bioscience,* **20**(1): 11–16, 1970.

Hickey, J. J. (ed.) *Peregrine Falcon Populations,* Madison: University of Wisconsin Press, 1969.

Hoffman, L. "Saving Europe's wetlands," *New Scientist,* **46**(697): 120–22, 1970.

Iltis, H. H. "To the taxonomist and ecologist—whose fight is the preservation of nature?" *Bioscience,* **17:** 886–90, 1967.

Jarret, H. (ed.) *Environmental Quality in a Growing Economy,* Baltimore: Johns Hopkins University Press, 1966.

Leopold, A. S., Cain, S. A., Cottam, C. H., Gabrielson, I. N., and Kimball, T. L. "Wildlife management in the national parks," *American Forests,* **69:** 32–35, 61–63, 1963

Love, R. M. "The rangelands of the western U.S.," *Scientific American,* **222**(2): 89–96, 1970.

McHarg, I. L. *Design with Nature,* New York: Natural History Press, 1969.

Sears, P. B. "The inexorable problem of space," *Science,* **127:** 9–16, 1958.

Shepard, P. *Man in the Landscape,* New York: Knopf, 1967.

Spurr, S. H. "Wilderness management," *The Horace M. Albright Conservation Lectureship,* Berkeley: University of California, School of Forestry, 1966.

Westhoff, V. "New criteria for nature reserves," *New Scientist,* **46**(697): 108–13, 1970.

The Future 14

For many centuries writers have attempted to describe the future of human civilization. The credibility gap between these fictional presentations and reality diminishes with each new development as we achieve further long-predicted goals. Recently, however, the auguries have tended to become not only more realistic, but more bleak. Ranging from the undogmatic, carefully weighed considerations of *Mankind 2000* (Jungk and Galtung, 1969) to the deliberately provocative doomsday threat of Ehrlich (1968), such authors are consistently if varyingly pessimistic. A foreboding of environmental disaster hovers over the bright promise of the future.

There is no shortage of prophets, or of prophecies. In medicine we are promised banks of spare body parts, chemical correction of defective genotypes, larger brains, a delayed aging, test-tube births, brain transplants, electronically controlled behavior, and even immortality by freezing (Taylor, 1968; Rosenfeld, 1969). Education offers college training for all, sleep learning, instruction by injection, a computer terminal in the "education room" of every home, and computers that think and reproduce themselves.

In the socioeconomic field labor will be minimized and leisure maximized; a new boom is promised for the "surging seventies." Equality of the sexes in reality as well as theory is projected as producing a less inhibited, more fancy-free society. Redundancy and unemployment disappear because continuing education copes with problems of obsolescence. Everything is disposable—clothes, linen, carpets, walls, houses—or automatic—cooking, correspondence, financing, vehicles, travel.

IMPLEMENTAL FAILURES

In the harsh light of reality some of these possibilities are no nearer achievement than when the ideas were first presented decades or even centuries ago. The recent heart transplants emphasize how far we still remain from technological perfection. Our fumbling techniques may buy a little time, and for this individuals are grateful. They are willing to be used as pioneers in areas where we can only advance from actual human experience.

Yet, before we progress into these new dream worlds, there is the stark question of how our global population survives even through the remaining three decades of this second millennium A.D. The brief review of environmental crises presented here has suggested some choices we must make, urgently and immediately. As several authors have recently remarked (Michael, 1968), scientific information is becoming increasingly used as a political shuttlecock, volleyed around in an ever more partisan world. The concerned individual is confronted by opposed factions plausibly arguing the immediate adoption of diametrically opposite courses. The hypotheses presented in these pages, taken together with the experimental evidence on which they are based, should, however, provide inescapable argument for the necessity of immediate positive action to avoid the otherwise certain ecological disasters which may now be identified. The difficulty of obtaining any consensus as to priority of needs in technological invention and innovation is well exemplified by the report of a National Academy of Science panel formed to make recommendations on such requirements (Brooks and Bowers, 1970). Two of the four objectives considered as soon realizable are concerned with death control, none with population control. The same emphasis continues into the 1980's according to this report.

Population Ecology: The Problem

As emphasized repeatedly in this text, by far the most critical of our present major environmental crises is *population control.* This is one problem which has been with us in an acute form for a mere 20 years, for reasons discussed in earlier chapters. Every country in the world now needs to take *immediate* steps to ensure that *no later than the end of this millennium* its population growth has been reduced to zero. For not a few areas this will still be too great a population size, and additional measures will have to be taken to bring the population closer to an estimated carrying capacity.

The information presented in Chapters 7 through 9 is intended to show both why this must be done and how it can be done. *All other developments for the future are contingent on immediate population control action in all nations and all segments of nations.*

RESOURCE MODELING

In outlining these prospects for the future, it might appear that pragmatic political considerations override any biological ones, but this is not the case. Such political decisions must ultimately be taken, but they must be based on ecologically determined criteria. Application of systems analysis techniques to the study of the causal relationships of environmental crises should prove extremely illuminating. As Waterman (1968) has recently expressed, this "systems analysis may be defined quite generally as the application of organized analytical and modelling techniques appropriate to explaining complex multivariate systems, many of whose functional components may be initially quite imperfectly measured or even largely unidentified." As a result of such research it should be possible to prepare models of given environmental situations. Predictive simulation models are truly the only logical basis on which all political decisions can be founded.

The primary need is to create predictive simulation models for population growth. Demographic data entered into these will provide reliable estimates, within specified limits, of the manner of growth of the population, its changing age structure, predictable mortalities, sex distribution, and other required information. In this century demographic projections have provided inadequate warning of both downward and upward population trends. This is because the forecasts were based on simple mathematical models rather than more complex, multivariate forms which can now be constructed with computing facilities.

To these predictive population simulation models, once they have been prepared, can be added the various resource limitations and requirements. These further simulations will then provide the first real estimates of national needs in terms of limited resources such as food, fuel, minerals, education, and space.

No simulation model will provide anything but partial information, however, unless it is related to contemporary ecosystems. The ecosystem is indeed the ultimate conceptual reality against which all predictive models have to be measured. As an objective, society has to strive for the maintenance of stability and diversity in all the ecosystems which it occupies, or with which it is in contact. Only in this way can we avoid repeated environmental crises, and the externalization of our problems in time and space. Utilization of resources and discharge of wastes must become internalized procedures which cannot be allowed to extend from one ecosystem into the resources of another. Nor should the producer segment of the population always transfer the cost of internalization to the consumer segments. The problem of waste discharge is solved by ensuring that biogeochemical cycling returns all material resources for reuse without creating any spin-off wastes.

René Dubos (1969) has recently expressed this need to internalize our economies in the following passage:

> . . . all ecological systems, whether manmade or natural, must in the long run achieve a state of equilibrium for several decades. Furthermore, ecological instability is increasing at such an accelerated rate that disasters are inevitable if the trend continues. We cannot afford to delay much longer the development of a nearly "closed" system in which materials will retain their values throughout the system, by being recycled instead of discarded. . . .

This in essence is the message this book is intended to convey, for it would be immoral to present such a work on human ecology at this time which left unstated the ecological conclusions to be drawn from our critical situation.

INTERNATIONAL OBLIGATIONS

Earlier chapters have discussed how societies have evolved—in a way comparable with an ecological succession—through various ecological stages, one of which has involved population explosion followed by colonization of other territories.

With the world now totally segmented into a mosaic of national territories, the last frontier has gone, and there is no further possibility of colonization without displacing some previous human occupants of the territory. The first international freedom which has to be relinguished is therefore the right of a nation to expand its boundaries by force. This might seem an elementary assumption, but during the 12 months in 1968–69 when this text was being prepared, there were at least four separate and major examples of occupation by one nation of territory of another. These were an attempted invasion on the Chinese-Russian frontier, another of Honduras by El Salvador, and continuing occupation of the Sinai Peninsula by Israel and of South Vietnam by North Vietnam. However arbitrary the methods by which the present international boundaries were achieved, unless they can be readjusted in free negotiations there can be no change. Time may require some modifications, and negotiation should make these possible.

With the removal of the need to defend international frontiers, the tremendous resources which were previously deflected to their defense would be released for other enterprises. There is already a world forum for discussion, negotiation, and law enforcement—the United Nations—and a judiciary body, the International Court of Justice. These could provide all the international law and law enforcement necessary to maintain international accord.

A United Nations conference on the human environment has been arranged for 1972 in Sweden. At this conference plans will be presented for the International Council of Scientific Unions (ICSU), which draws its membership from all the international unions of chemists, biologists, astronomers, and other scientists, to create an environmental committee with the (unfortunate) acronym of SCOPE (Scientific Committee on the Problems of the Environment). This committee will establish ICE (International Center for the Environment), charged with investigating any scheme appearing likely to cause environmental degradation and attacking such long-range problems as atmospheric and water pollution. It is hoped to have prototypes of both SCOPE and ICE operating even before the formal presentation of this idea to the Swedish conference.

Construction of computer simulation models of populations and resources, and predicting the dimensions of internalized processes, will make possible an estimation of the *carrying capacity* of particular regions in terms of human populations, the optimum population.

The carrying capacity or optimum population is a somewhat indefinable concept (Hulett, 1970). Unless it is matched against other features of the ecosystem, such as the degree of diversity which it is desirable to maintain, its estimation will be quite arbitrary. Obviously there must be some compromise between conservation and utilization, and the carrying capacity of a given area must be arrived at after some political decision has been taken as to the extent of diversity which it is agreed should be conserved. This involves economic land-use planning, and the acceptance by the whole community of the restrictions which this imposes on freedom of choice.

Many national territories have already far exceeded the carrying capacity which simultaneously permits the conservation of a wide diversity. Others may well do so in the near future, or may wish to do so rather than too rigidly restrict population growth at this stage. Internationally provided incentives must be offered where nations are urged to set a low carrying capacity in order to conserve particular diversity, e.g., a surviving megafauna of game animals. By the same token, economic incentives may be offered to the individual or group within the national territory to achieve this same object.

TECHNOLOGICAL REQUIREMENTS

The last quantum step in the ecological evolution of human societies was the urban revolution and the concentration of populations in cities. The particular features of urban societies are *specialization, interaction,* and *innovation.* Our urban society must have these ecological characteristics if it is to progress; they are inseparable from urban ecosystems.

These urban ecosystems must, however, be more rationally constructed, and not left to chance. Cities need to be analyzed in terms of their purposes and their needs, so that their structures can conform more readily to desirable plans for urban living. Land-use planning operations must start from the cities and reach outward. As Ian McHarg has eloquently emphasized, we need to estimate the carrying capacity of a given region in terms of its limited resources, and contrast this with what we require in the form of "environmental quality." A city or cities are then constructed in situations which provide for the optimum attractions for a population at this carrying capacity. To provide the necessary support for this population, industries are finally brought in which can be based on internalized practice without having to externalize any problems on surrounding ecosystems or communities except by mutual arrangement.

This is the exact reverse of what has traditionally been the practice in our industrial societies. Industries have grown up where there have been exploitable resources. People have moved to the industry without reference to their needs in terms of outdoor recreation and other living requirements such as education, shopping, entertainment, and public health. By relating carrying capacity to resources in terms of food and water, and services such as health and education, it is possible to avoid externalizing industrial problems. In this way water and air pollution, poisoning of the ecosystem, and overexploitation of resources are entirely avoided.

Exhaustion of Resources

With the exception of advanced industrial societies, where incidental factors operate to reduce population growth, many existing social groups left to themselves may be expected to ignore such advice and continue unchecked the evolution of their population growth rates until they completely exhaust their environmental resources. The U.S. National Policy Panel of the U.N. Association, in a recent report entitled "World Population," stated that high fertility and high population rates in developing countries can mean widespread famine, increased illiteracy, unemployment, squalor, and unrest threatening the very foundations of public order.

While the mounting external pressures and propaganda to which earlier successional societies are now beginning to be exposed might cause some to reduce this fatal rate of population growth, the exhaustion of resources they have already sustained will still inhibit industrialization. No net primary production will be available for the continuation of ecological society succession. The life-support systems of such depleted societies entirely absorb whatever limited gross productivity they can develop.

NATIONAL OBLIGATIONS

Within nations themselves, considerable sacrifices will have to be made by various segments of the population. For example, as stressed at the beginning of this chapter, all societies will have to reduce their population growth at least to zero, and for many it will be desirable to run at a negative population growth until the population has been reduced to a more realistic size.

To achieve this low level of population growth, it will be necessary to ask the youth of each country to restrict their ambitions as to family size. This should not be done without some equally restrictive contribution from the middle-aged and the elderly. The most obvious form of their contribution is in taxation, which is the very burden this segment of the population in many advanced industrial societies is now unwilling to contribute. This is especially unreasonable when it is precisely the uncontrolled self-propagation indulged in by the older generations which has placed modern youth in the situation where it has to severely limit its own reproduction.

Many catchwords have been bandied about in this century such as socialism, fascism, and communism. Without applying such words, it is obvious that many societies in the world have to go much further than they have at present in resource sharing within their populations. The distribution of wealth is very spotty, and in many instances hereditary cliques are still privileged and provided with opportunities in great excess, as compared with the less wealthy members of society.

It will be apparent from even the brief treatment of this subject which has been possible in this text that we are seriously lacking in fundamental knowledge of social behavior in human populations. Indeed, it is only in recent years that we have even initiated such experimental studies in other social primates. We therefore have little understanding of our own behavioral needs and responses in such ecological areas as territoriality, group identity, group defense, pair-bonding, social learning, social hierarchies, and aggression. We are quite unable as yet to separate our responses in these areas into phenotypic and genotypic classes, the cultural reactions resulting from or modified by our earlier conditioning, and the behavioral reactions which develop from our genetic inheritance. Perhaps our contemporary advertising media have come closest to obtaining some understanding of certain aspects of these ecological relationships, through an essentially empirical process of trial and error in perfecting selling techniques. Likewise great orators throughout history have happily (or unhappily, in some instances) hit upon the right combination of verbal stimuli required to trigger desired ecological responses.

RELIGIOUS BELIEFS

We are still unwilling to face many philosophical conclusions and deductions which may be made from our examination of ecological evolution. The most restrictive aspect of this refusal is undoubtedly the tenacious persistence of *doctrinaire* religious beliefs. Religious organizations, with their well-structured and often tightly disciplined hierarchies, retain a firm hold on many of the resources as well as some of the beliefs of many of the world's societies.

The reason strong efforts are not made to disprove such doctrinaire beliefs may well reside in the fact that few scientists are nihilists. They are hesitant to destroy an old hypothesis before they have what they regard as a more tenable substitute. Toward this end Julian Huxley (1958) has been striving with his "religion without revelation," which he intends to contain enough verisimilitude to be scientifically acceptable, but remain sufficiently flexible to permit periodic reconciliation with new discoveries. Even Huxley, however, as is apparent from his *The Humanist Frame* (1961), cannot avoid the implication of a "human destiny." Few scientists presently care to go into print on such issues. One of the few (Goldstein, 1969) stated recently when discussing exemption of churches from taxation in the United States: "This kind of discrimination is particularly offensive for nonbelievers (a group to which most biologists probably belong) . . ." Such statements have a high emotion content and are likely to provoke strong reactions.

Some nevertheless will consider that the lingering persistence of doctrinaire religious belief represents an impediment to the introduction of any realistic philosophy of life that would provide an acceptable motivation for future societies. Proper motivation can only be achieved when we are sufficiently honest with ourselves to acknowledge that, despite our unique cultural development, there is no more *raison d'être* for our species than there is for any other plant, animal, or microbial population on this planet.

We enjoy living, and the vast majority of us wish to continue living, because over many millennia we have been selected for genotypes which produce phenotypes with such feelings. If they did not, they would have been automatically eliminated from the gene pool of future generations.

There is no justification for the persistence of our human population other than its representation as an extremely interesting development among the diversity of populations which have survived in our contemporary world following selection by ecological evolutionary processes. Even were we to learn how to control the universe, this would not be fulfilling any divine purpose or realizing any predestined universal plan. We have no preordained function, either on this planet or in the universe, and the choice is entirely ours as to whether we continue or discontinue the propagation of our particular species.

Concerning the individual, there are patently personal feelings both of well-being and of discomfort which are unique to each of us. Partly genetically determined, they seem mostly the result of conditioning in the very early months of life. These feelngs, like all those expressed as human cultural behavior, are exceedingly complex and still only imperfectly analyzed and understood. For the moment perhaps all that can be said is that in order to ensure continuation of the species, the individual should feel "good!" If the future of further generations of our species is to be assured, this will have to be associated with improved conditions over those that we ourselves have known, so that the good feeling persists. This oversimplification presents us with the only rational philosophy of life presently conceivable: enlarge our territorial concepts to encompass all mankind and improve conditions for the next generation without simultaneously making ourselves too utterly miserable.

To effect such a philosophy, we are immediately faced with a number of pragmatic decisions. These invariably impose some loss of individual freedom. As long as man has been a social animal he has been selected to concede some measure of individual loss of freedom in return for the benefits of social life, the ecological process of "group selection."

There are many modern examples which could be cited of loss of freedom which we take for granted, even though it has not always been so, even when the privileges we have lost pertained until, say, 10 years ago, or even last year. Some of these have been mentioned in the chapter on population control. We cannot in this country run away if ordered to stop by a police officer, whether he is immediately identifiable as such or not, and we may be shot dead if we ignore such a request. We cannot, if we are young, fit, and male, avoid being directed to fight and kill other individuals of our species if we are so instructed, without incurring social censure and/or physical imprisonment. We cannot venture onto a substantial portion of the land of these United States which is in military hands. Nor can we walk over much of the rest which is in private hands. We cannot, at least in America, legally practice polygamy, even if it is a tenet of our religious belief as it was for Mormons and is for Moslems.

Such a list of restrictions on freedom, serious or otherwise, could be extended. In view of the many limits which we already accept or take for granted, it is interesting to look at the kind of further restrictions which would need to be imposed here, for example, to obtain more peaceful social arrangements and a world which had some chance of survival without catastrophic ecological change. These rights which would have to be conceded include:

1. The right to have as many children as we wish.
2. The right to have any children at all by mates with particular genotypes.
3. The right to keep pets which consume food which could directly or indirectly be used for human purposes while populations and individuals elsewhere are stunted from malnutrition or dying from starvation.
4. The right to externalize our labor problems by strikes which dislocate societal facilities.
5. The right to reside in any locality of our own choice in these United States.
6. The right to accumulate wealth entirely disparate with basic needs while many elsewhere still cannot satisfy these, or to transfer inherited wealth without reduction to an indefinite number of descendant generations.
7. The right to monopolize what would otherwise be community facilities.
8. The right to exploit national resources to the public detriment.
9. The right to possess lethal weapons.
10. The right to discharge wastes into the environment.

If we fail to recognize that it is ecologically unsound to permit individual members of our population to remain unregulated in regard to the above "rights," we can never achieve the necessary steady-state stability in our human ecosystems. It is hoped that the presentations in this text demonstrate that it is ecologically impossible to avoid population regulation (items 1 and 2), to permit resource depletion (3, 4, 5, 6, 7, 8), to allow factional and individual strife (4, 9), and to sanction pollution and contamination (10). We must calmly and rationally prepare a master simulation model of our global ecosystems which will include ecological feedback mechanisms involving at least the periodic or temporary denial of all these ten aspects of our culture which we have traditionally regarded as "inalienable rights." The ecological unsoundness of such an assumption should now be apparent, and the reasons this monumental task must be completed within the next decade ought to be equally clear.

ECOLOGICAL EVOLUTION

Until we learn to alter the chemistry of genes in an extensive and generally applicable manner, further evolution of our population will occur by the same processes which have determined it over the past 4 million years. Even without chemical control of genes we can apply artificial selection to human genotypes; this is still another political decision which we must eventually make. Much progress could be made in avoiding "disadvantaged" homozygous genotypes if tests for heterozygosity for these "deleterious" traits could be universally applied to prospective parents, or similar tests applied to embryos. Positive selection could be made, and has indeed been recommended, by many respected authorities for such features as intelligence and creativity. The comparative frequency with which genius occurs, i.e., the number of times we encounter individuals with I.Q.'s measured in the region of 200 to 250 or higher, indicates that we could considerably improve on the general level of intelligence by artificial selection, because to an appreciable extent intelligence is hereditarily controlled. Julian Huxley (1957) has presented proposals relevant to this issue.

There would be some substance to an argument that in order to cope with our increasingly complex technology—particularly as computers evolve from peripheral information retrieval and auxiliary calculating devices to decision-making innovators (Wooldridge, 1968)—the general level of intelligence should be raised. It is more difficult to argue a case for longevity, although by storing the germ plasm of individuals while they were progeny-tested for longevity, it would be relatively simple artificially to select for longevity and produce a population with a longer life span. In a technological society which seems increasingly to favor built-in obsolescence, it is possible there would be some resistance to built-in longevity being made the object of artificial selection at this stage of our population's development.

Negative selection is an even more difficult matter to legislate, although simulation models will provide predictions of the rate of spread through the population of genes presently considered detrimental to individuals.

Most people would agree, for example, that mutants which resulted in limbless individuals were not desirable, unless some important compensatory genetic feature were associated with them which could only be maintained in the human gene pool by continuing to propagate genotypes resulting in such a drastic variation. Even this bizarre possibility cannot be entirely ruled out, for as J. B. S. Haldane (1963) quite seriously commented, legless astronauts would be more effective for the initial series of space probes.

When we come down the scale to congenital diabetics, it is more difficult to obtain a majority for a political decision against continuing procreation from genotypes known to produce this disturbance. Finally we have minor features, such as insensitivity to musical tones or color blindness, which only slightly impair the individual's full appreciation of particular behavioral rituals. Where should negative eugenics stop, or rather, where could it begin?

It seems doubtful whether the predictions of any computer simulation model will require that immediate decisions be made on such choices. In view of the vital decisions on major restrictions which we must immediately make in terms of population growth and resource exploitation, it would appear advisable to postpone such eugenic decisions for some time, especially as each decade brings us closer to the possibility of chemical adjustment of "undesirable" genetic material.

This availability of the power of chemical modification of genes, when it is realized, will pose still more political problems. Not only will it offer also the possibility of increasing the rate of natural mutations, but it will provide the opportunity to produce entirely new mutant forms.

EMIGRATION AND IMMIGRATION

Although national boundaries have been more rigidly maintained from the beginning of the twentieth century, movement across them has always been restricted. There seems no justification for entirely stopping these movements to prevent some measure of emigration and immigration. An exchange of genic material is biologically desirable if further cultural evolution of the *Homo sapiens* grade and the spread of any further grades which evolve such as *H. innovatus* is not to remain restricted. The concentration of particularly innovative, inventive, and creative groups in certain centers may lead, by assortative mating, to the evolution of new forms of our genus. Provided no barriers to gene flow are artificially erected, this kind of concentration and rediffusion is necessary for continuing cultural evolution.

The need to permit the concentration of innovative individuals from many countries in areas which facilitate their free expression is illustrated by the national origins of U.S. Nobel laureates. Of those awarded the Nobel prize for medicine or for science 25 per cent of the Americans have been foreign born, a far greater proportion than is present in the population at large.

While territorial aggression in terms of international wars may soon be effectively discouraged, aggression and the associated phenomenon of territoriality on a personal basis will be much more difficult to control. In the so-called advanced industrial societies, crime and mayhem flourish alongside a general decline in social morality. This decline is especially dangerous because individuals are externalizing their difficulties on society at large, a process Hardin (1968) has described as the "tragedy of the commons." Individual pilfering from stores and supermarkets is paid for not by the owner, but by the more honest customers. They also pay for the towels which are removed from hotels and motels, the insurance to cover theft, the security measures to guard against robbery, the policing of areas to protect life and property. Finally there is the game which no one group can ever finally win, the walkout strike, which again is basically almost always an externalization of particular problems on society at large.

INDUSTRIALIZED SOCIETIES

The advanced industrial nations, contrasted with less evolved societies, may be expected to enter a phase of selection pressure for particular behavioral patterns such as they have never previously experienced and whose intensity has not yet been calculated. These pressures will tend to reproduce specifically those genes which favor "parental" characteristics against the "swinging" life, or against forms of deviant behavior which are unlikely to arouse a need for self-propagation aside from sexual activities. There will also be a contrasting selection for group "service" genes which act against the individual but favor reproduction of the group.

For a number of generations extensive genetic evolution will be proceeding simultaneously with cultural evolution. This circumstance, which has not applied to human populations for many millennia, will arise from the almost complete separation of sex and reproduction which population control will require and which modern techniques permit. Whereas previously many individuals or couples contributed to the human gene pool whether they really wanted to or not, now only those whose genetic characteristics have disposed them toward parenthood will reproduce. The corollary of such genetic selection is that parental gene frequencies will increase, as will resistance to compulsory population control measures (Clarkson *et al.*, 1970).

This will not necessarily produce a more moral age; in fact it might be much the opposite. While actual criminal activity will be subject to negative selection by a reduced tendency to reproduce such genotypes, because of isolation in corrective institutions, social competition could sharpen to the point where malpractice and manipulations still permitted within the law are fully exploited. The offspring of these more parental parents will not all breed true, but the gene frequencies expressing these characteristics must steadily increase in the population.

It would seem advisable to direct some of this heightened social competitive drive into some different form of challenge. Athletic competition is as old a sublimation technique as history; it has served the older nations of Europe well. We must, however, turn to the possibilities of other areas of enterprise. Intellectual problem-solving is the most promising, but with it must come a new social hierarchy. There is already, as Eric Hoffer observes (1967), a possible conflict between those who work with their hands, producing artifacts, and those who employ mainly their minds, developing mentifacts. These are separated somewhat along the lines of C. P. Snow's *Two Cultures* (1963). There is no need for stress to arise from such cleavage, provided each type of citizen is content that his constructive cultural opportunities are not restricted by the social hierarchy. Jacobs (1969) envisages the possibility that significant new industries can and will develop even from such "lowly" occupations as janitorial work.

The Creative Society

The political concept of the "creative society" is, perhaps unconsciously, an approximation of this ideal social structure, at least in its aims (Johnson, 1968). The pursuit of new knowledge (mentifacts), the fashioning of new tools (artifacts), and the performance of new activity (socifacts) are the features which have always characterized our populations and for which we have been subject to selection pressures over perhaps 4 million years. We cannot simply lose these characteristics unless we deliberately select eugenically for the indolent and the unimaginative. Some means of achieving the essential social structure needed for a peaceful society must be evolved. Perhaps it would suffice if all elected representatives remained honest, unbiased, and nonpartisan (Pearson and Anderson, 1968).

Brain Drain Effects

We may expect that particular regions of rapid technological advance will continue to exert an irresistible attraction for phenotypes in which enterprise and initiative—and intelligence—are highly developed These are self-perpetuating characteristics (Dobzhansky, 1960); selection pressures may well continue to operate until these phenotypes have little or no reproductive contact with the parent gene pool from which they were originally selected.

This preferential association of reproducing individuals in relation to the characters their genes determine in them is what geneticists term *assortative mating*. As Mather relates (1964), its chief effect in human populations is to associate genes of similar effect but at different loci. With some measure of reproductive isolation, it is certain that individuals possessing these unique associations will be the founders of a new species grade very different from our own in its social hierarchy, reproductive characteristics, intelligence, and harnessing of aggression. Evolution in the several species grades of the genus *Homo* has characteristically taken this form of cultural speciation"; for this latest species grade of our human populations the name *Homo innovatus* has been suggested as most appropriate.

Homo innovatus

We could expect *Homo innovatus* grade populations to appear first in the megalopoli. In the United States this means the three burgeoning metropolitan areas around the Northeastern seaboard ("Boswash"), the Great Lakes ("Chipitts"), and the southern Pacific Coast ("Sag"). Because it probably already contains higher gene frequencies for the particular characters involved, the West may well prove to be the center of origin of this new species grade; perhaps individual clans of *H. innovatus* grade are already established there. Occupied initially by Causcasoid and Mongoloid stocks partially selected in advance for aggressive characteristics, the West has continued this selective attraction for aggression as it is expressed in the forms of enterprise and initiative.

Of Lynn's (1969) estimated 5000 persons with an I.Q. of 130 to 150 annually leaving Britain for the United States, and his 23 per cent of the annual university scientific output which emigrated, a considerable proportion migrate to the Amercan West. They are often accompanied by mates and offspring. Similar disproportionate selective immigration occurs from other countries and from other states (Nussenzweig, 1969).

Price and Bass (1969) have recently considered the relationship among innovation, invention, and basic research and conclude that the process of change requires an effective coupling of scientific and technological communities. Nowhere is this better exemplified than in the synthetic and essentially immigrant societies of the Western megalopolis.

Spread of *H. innovatus*

Slightly varying geographical populations of *H. innovatus* grade may appear later in the other two American megalopoli, also around Moscow, Peiping, Tokyo-Osaka-Yokahama, and possibly Sydney, Australia, where similar selection pressures prevail. It is clear that *H. innovatus* everywhere will have multiethnic origins, as did the *H. sapiens* grade. All human groups have contained at some frequency level genes which when combined can produce a Cetawayo, a Genghis Khan, or a Napoleon.

Because no two populations with even partially distinct breeding systems can coexist in the same ecological niche, not only will the populations of *H. innovatus* grade increase in size until they exclusively occupy their centers of origin, but their selected recombinant gene characteristics could slowly introgress into the surviving populations of *H. sapiens* grade until the genotypes of this species have been largely replaced and it has passed to extinction, as did the *H. erectus* grade populations.

Economic Considerations

If we look around us, certain features of the nightmare world of George Orwell's *1984* are already beginning to come about. The "haves" and "have-nots" are already divided by natural fences through which movement is severely restricted. Unless an entirely new economic approach such as that presented by Jacobs (1969) is immediately and successfully instigated, the condition of the "have-nots" must inevitably deteriorate still further until we reach the world famine years of the 1970s (Paddock and Paddock, 1967).

While the "haves" are increasingly made aware of many of the distressing circumstances of the "have-nots," they as yet contribute little of their abundant resources to alleviate these dire needs. Desultory and often disorganized efforts are occasionally made by private enterprise and officially through international agencies to bring about some improvement in the condition of these underprivileged world citizens.

Meanwhile, the steady drain of the genotypes which produce a fitter phenotype is allowed to continue, and further progress of the "have-not" population is impeded by this genetic depauperization, coupled with the general lowering of intelligence through early malnutrition (Eichenwald and Fry, 1969). The computer revolution has led to a quantum advance in the industrial progress of the "have" nations, as Hardin (1969) has stressed in a recent paper. The operation of sophisticated computer-based techniques is entirely beyond the present ability of the advanced agricultural societies, whose *per capita* resources providing food, education, medical attention, and communication for their citizens are rapidly becoming less as their population growth continues unabated.

Precisely what kind of effort would be needed in an advanced agricultural society to achieve some progress has been estimated by Enke (1969). He calculates that about one quarter of the population aged 15 through 49 would have to practice contraception to halve the gross reproductive rate in 30 years. In terms of economic welfare this would provide an increase in income per head of 3.0 per cent a year instead of 1.7 per cent and a third more capital per worker after 30 years.

Viewed in isolation, these calculations might be encouraging, but contrasted with estimated material progress in a "have" nation over a comparable period, this is still a depressing picture. Although it may be a source of self-congratulation that some elements of the world population of our present species grade may evolve into a form with greater intelligence, increased aggression, and a greater identity with a more effective social order, this is little consolation for the apparent certainty that for billions

Taylor, G. R. *The Biological Time Bomb,* Cleveland: World Publishing, 1968.

Waterman, T. H. "Systems theory and biology—view of a biologist," in M. D. Mesarovic (ed.), *Systems Theory and Biology,* New York: Springer-Verlag, 1968, p. 4.

Woolridge, D. E. *Mechanical Man: The Physical Basis of Intelligent Life,* New York: McGraw-Hill, 1968.

FURTHER READINGS

Allen, G. E. "Science and society in the eugenic thought of H. J. Muller," *Bioscience,* **20:** 346–53, 1970.

Beadle, G. V., and Beadle M. *The Language of Life,* New York: Doubleday, 1966.

Boulding, K. E. *The Meaning of the Twentieth Century,* New York: Harper & Row, 1964.

Bronowski, J. *The Identity of Man,* New York: The Natural History Press, 1965.

Clarke, A. C. *Profiles of the Future,* New York: Harper & Row, 1962.

Cloud, P. E. "Realities of mineral distribution," *Texas Quarterly,* **11:** 103–26, 1968.

Comfort, A. *The Nature of Human Nature,* New York: Harper & Row, 1966.

Dubos, R. *Man Adapting,* New Haven: Yale University Press, 1965.

Dubos, R. *Man, Medicine, and Environment,* New York: New American Library, 1968.

Ehrlich, P. R., and Ehrlich, A. H. *Population, Resources, Environment: Issues in Human Ecology,* San Francisco: Freeman, 1970.

Enke, S., and Zind, R. G. "Effects of fewer births on average income," *J. Biol. Sci.,* **1:** 41–55, 1969.

Fermi, L. *Illustrious Immigrants,* Chicago: University of Chicago Press, 1965.

Foerster, H. von, Mora, P. M., and Amiot, L. W. "Doomsday: Friday 13, November A.D. 2026," *Science,* **132:** 1291–95, 1960.

Glass, H. Bentley. *Science and Ethical Values,* Chapel Hill: University of North Carolina Press, 1965.

Haller, M. H. *Eugenics: Hereditarian Attitudes in American Thought,* New Brunswick: Rutgers University Press, 1963.

Kahn, H., and Wiener, A. J. *The Year 2000: A Framework for Speculation on the Next Thirty-three Years,* New York & London: Macmillan, 1967.

King-Hele, D. *The End of the Twentieth Century,* New York: Macmillan, 1970.

Kyllonen, R. L. "Crime rate vs. population density in United States cities: a model," *Yearbook of the Society for General Systems Research,* **12:** 137–45, 1967.

Lerner, M. I. *Heredity, Evolution, and Society,* San Francisco: W. H. Freeman, 1968.

Medawar, P. B. *The Future of Man,* New York: New American Library, 1961.

Peterson, M. L. "The space available," *Environment,* **12**(2): 1–9, 1970.

Pincus, G. *The Control of Fertility,* New York: Academic Press, 1965.

Platt, J. "What we must do," *Science,* **166:** 1115–21, 1969.

Roslansky, J. D. (ed.) *Genetics and the Future of Man,* New York: Appleton-Century-Crofts, 1965.

Shepard, P. "Introduction: ecology and man—a viewpoint," in P. Shepard and D. McKinley (eds.) *The Subversive Science,* Boston: Houghton Mifflin, 1969, pp. 1–10.

Sonneborn, T. M. (ed.) *The Control of Human Heredity and Evolution,* New York: Macmillan, 1965.

Teilhard, P. *The Future of Man,* New York: Harper & Row, 1964.

White, L. "The historic roots of our ecologic crisis," *Science,* **155:** 1203–1207, 1967.

Glossary

Abductor Muscles which move the upper or lower limbs away from the line of the body, see Figure III-2.

Acetabulum Cup-shaped depression on the pelvis into which the head of the femur fits, see Appendix III.

Adductor Muscles which oppose the abductor muscles, see Figure III-2, Appendix III.

Agglutination Clumping of cells normally dispersed individually.

Aldehyde Organic compound with a terminal carbonyl group ($C=O$) on the carbon chain.

Allele One of the two or more forms of a gene.

Allopatric Having a different dispersal area.

Amino acid An organic carbon chain or ring compound with both *amine* (NH_2) and *carboxyl* ($COOH$) groups, bonding with other amino acids to form proteins.

Aneuploid Karyotypical variant having more or less than the normal number of chromosomes for one or several homologous sets.

Anthropocentric Considering the world only from a human standpoint.

Anthropoid (noun or adjective) Belonging to a suborder of Primates containing monkeys, apes, and men.

Antibody Proteins in mammalian blood which react with specific antigens and neutralize them.

Antigen An organic substance introduced into an animal body and generally toxic to it.

Arboreal Occupying a tree habitat.

Assortative mating Pair-bonding between individuals of largely similar phenotypes.

Autocleansing Self-cleaning by internalized processes.

Autoxidation Self-oxidation, without any external interaction.

Autosome Chromosome not directly involved in sex determination.

Autotoxic Toxic to the life processes which produced it.

Autotroph (**adjective, autotrophic**) An organism which synthesizes its food from inorganic substances.

Auxin One of a universal group of growth-promoting plant hormones.

Biome A regional category of related ecosystems, e.g., tundra, grassland, rain forest.

Biosphere The totality of the world populations, and the materials and factors with which they interact.

Biota The totality of organisms in one place or time.

Bipedal Locomotion solely by means of the two hind limbs.

Brachiation Arboreal locomotion using the upper limbs only, as in gibbons.

Carcinogenic Cancer-inducing.

Cerebellum The portion of the brain controlling muscular coordination.

Cerebrum The portion of the brain in which ideas are coordinated.

Chaparral Vegetation dominated by small-leaved evergreen shrubs, characterizing the Pacific Southwest.

Clavicle The collar bone, controlling articulation between the scapula and the forelimb.

Cline A directional change in gene frequencies in a population along a gradient of continuous variation in some abiotic factor.

Coitus Sexual intercourse resulting in the deposition of sperm in the vagina.

Coprolite Fossilized feces.

Cultigen A cultivated plant species.

Cultivar An individual variety of a cultivated plant species, often identified by a common name.

Cusp A projection above the upper surface of molar or premolar teeth in primates.

Dominant In a bioenergetic sense, the particular species of plant, animal, or microbe at each trophic level through which the major portion of energy transfer in a given ecosystem occurs.

Dominance (**social**) The acceptance of a subordinate social role by all individuals of an animal population except the dominant individual or clique.

Deme A local, freely interbreeding population.

Dimorphic Having two forms.

Dentition The number, form, and arrangement of teeth in an animal.

Diversification The range of variation in characters exhibited within a species, community, or ecological niche.

Down's syndrome Trisomic 21; three homologous chromosomes instead of two in set number 21 in a human karyotype, resulting in mental and physical deformity, mongolism.

Ecological niche The totality of biotic and abiotic factors to which a given species is exposed.

Electrophoresis A chemical technique which separates compounds according to their different rates of migration in an electric field.

Epoch A major division of geological time less than a *period* and greater than an *age*.

Era The first major division of geological time, greater than a *period.*

Estrus The stage of the reproductive cycle in female primates when ovulation, release of one or more eggs from the ovary, occurs.

Eutrophic Adjective applied to a body of water rich in mineral nutrients.

Exogamy Outbreeding: mating which involves no intersibling or parent-offspring crosses.

Extractive efficiency A measurement used in anthropology to quantify the ability of a social group to obtain food from a given ecosystem.

Fallopian tubes Paired tubes carrying eggs from the ovary to the uterus.

Femur The principal thigh bone.

Gene A portion of a DNA molecule in a chromosome which determines one or more characters.

Genotype The genetic inheritance of an organism as represented by the particular assemblage of genes present in its nuclei.

Geophytic refers to plants which perennate by means of underground food storage organs, e.g., tubers, rhizomes, corms.

Gestation The pregnancy period, beginning with implantation and ending with parturition.

Gluten A protein which has the property of increasing cohesiveness in wheat dough.

Hafting The attachment of a previously exclusively hand-held tool or weapon to a wooden shaft.

Hemoglobin The reddish protein pigment in blood cells of higher animals which is involved in oxygen transport.

Heterotroph (adjective, heterotrophic) An organism which obtains its organic food from other organisms.

Heterozygote (adjective, heterozygous) An organism whose genotype has different alleles at the same locus on each homologous chromosome pair. The character for which the organism is heterozygous is usually stated or inferred.

Homoiotherm Endothermic, regulating body heat essentially by *physiological* mechanisms.

Hominid The "man-ape" group embracing all forms included in the genera *Ramapithecus, Paranthropus, Homo,* and synonymous taxa.

Homozygote (adjective, homozygous) An organism whose genotype has identical alleles on each homologous chromosome pair. The character for which the organism is homozygous is usually stated or inferred.

Implantation Inserting of the fertilized mammalial ovum in the uterus lining.

Infancy In a mammal commonly taken to mean the period between weaning and the attainment of sexual maturity.

Insectivora A mammalian order often placed with the Primates, containing small insectivores like shrews and hedgehogs.

Karyotype The chromosome set characterizing the cells of a particular species.

Keratin A fibrous protein which may be incorporated in epidermal tissues.

Lipid Any kind of fat or wax compound.

Locus The position on a chromosome at which a particular gene is located.

Mandible The lower jaw.

Marsupial Primitive subclass of mammals in which the young complete their development in a pouch provided with mammae.

Melanin A dark pigment present in the skin of many animals.

Mesotrophic Adjective applied to a body of water containing an average amount of mineral nutrients.

Mongolism See Down's syndrome.

Mutualism An association or symbiosis between two organisms of different species which appears mutually advantageous.

Niche See Ecological niche.

Nubile Applied to the potentially fertile stage of a woman's life, often taken as 15 to 45 years.

Nuchal Muscles at the back of the neck which hold back the head; see Figure III-1.

Oligotrophic Adjective applied to a body of water poor in mineral nutrients.

Orogeny Mountain chain formation and uplift.

Parturition Childbirth.

Peptide An organic compound formed from two or more amino acids.

Period A major division of geological time, less than an *era* and greater than an *epoch.*

Phenotype Character expression in an organism resulting from the interaction between its genotype and the environment during development.

Photolysis Chemical reaction promoted by light.

Photosynthesis The process of conversion of light energy to chemical energy in green plants by synthesizing various carbon compounds from atmospheric carbon dioxide, releasing oxygen.

Poikilotherm (adjective, poikilothermous) An exothermic animal, regulating body heat essentially by behavioral mechanisms.

Polygenic Several genes acting in a complementary manner on the same character.

Polymorphic Having two or more forms of expression of the same character.

Polyploid Organism with more than two sets of chromosomes in its cells.

Pongid (noun or adjective) Fossil or living ape; a tailless anthropoid with canines projecting beyond the general surface of the teeth.

Prosimian Primate at a level of organization below the monkey grade;

living forms are usually taken to include tree-shrews, tarsiers, lorises, and lemurs.

Respiration The aerobic oxidation of food substances releasing utilizable energy and carbon dioxide.

Speciation The evolutionary development of new species.

Steroid A chemical compound having a basic structure of four rings of carbon atoms; vitamin D is an example.

Stratosphere Second region of the atmosphere, above the troposphere and below the mesophere and the ionosphere.

Sympatric Having an overlapping dispersal area.

Taiga Arctic ecosystem dominated by coniferous trees.

Taxon (pl., taxa) A taxonomic group of unspecified rank.

Trait The particular phenotypic character expression produced by the presence of a given allele in the genotype.

Trisomy Three instead of two homologous chromosomes in one pair of the karyotype.

Troposphere Region of the atmosphere closest to the ground, varying in height according to the season and latitude.

Tundra An Arctic ecosystem dominated by low shrubby plants or herbs.

Vas deferens Paired tube carrying sperm from the testes to the penis.

Volcanism Volcanic eruptions and activity.

Appendix I

U.S. ADMINISTRATIVE AND REGULATORY BODIES INVOLVED WITH ENVIRONMENTAL PROBLEMS*

1. Federal Agencies

DEPARTMENT OF AGRICULTURE

Agricultural Stabilization and Conservation Service
Rural Community Development Service
Forest Service
Soil Conservation Service
Agricultural Research Service
Cooperative State Research Service

DEPARTMENT OF COMMERCE

Environmental Protection Agency
Environmental Science Service Administration
  Environmental Data Service
  Weather Bureau
  Institutes for Environmental Research
  National Environmental Satellite Center
  Coast and Geodetic Survey

DEPARTMENT OF DEFENSE

Corps of Engineers

* I am indebted to Dr. I. Clark for this list. A comment on this situation has recently been published by A. Baker, "Policies for the environment: too many cooks?" *Bioscience*, 19:457–58, 1969. The Federal Administration has recently taken several steps intended to improve matters. The latest is the formation of an independent Environmental Protection Agency, plus a National Oceanic and Atmospheric Administration in the Commerce Department.

DEPARTMENT OF HEALTH, EDUCATION, AND WELFARE

- Public Health Service
  - Bureau of Disease Prevention and Environmental Control
  - National Center for Air Pollution Control
  - National Center for Urban and Industrial Waste
  - National Environmental Sciences Center
- Food and Drug Administration

DEPARTMENT OF HOUSING AND URBAN DEVELOPMENT

- Land and Facilities Development Administration
- Office of Planning Standards and Coordination

DEPARTMENT OF THE INTERIOR

- Office of the Science Adviser
  - Office of Ecology
- Office of Water Resources Research
  - Fish and Wildlife and Parks
  - Commissioner of Fish and Wildlife
    - Bureau of Commercial Fisheries
    - Bureau of Sport Fisheries and Wildlife
    - National Park Service
- Office of Mineral Resources
  - Office of Oil and Gas
  - Office of Mineral and Solid Fuels
  - Office of Coal Research
  - Bureau of Mines
  - Geological Survey
- Office of Public Land Management
  - Bureau of Indian Affairs
  - Bureau of Land Management
  - Bureau of Outdoor Recreation
- Office of Water and Power Development
- Bureau of Reclamation
  - Bonneville Power Administration
  - Southeastern Power Administration
  - Southwestern Power Administration
- Office of Water Pollution Control
- Office of Saline Water
- Federal Water Pollution Control Administration

DEPARTMENT OF JUSTICE

- Land and Natural Resources Division

DEPARTMENT OF STATE

- International Boundary and Water Commission—U.S. and Mexico

International Scientific and Technical Affairs
International Joint Commission—U.S. and Canada

EXECUTIVE OFFICE OF THE PRESIDENT

Council of Economic Advisers
  Federal Committee on the Economic Impact of Pollution Abatement
Office of Science and Technology
  President's Science Advisory Committee Panel on the Environment
  Federal Council for Science and Technology
    Committee on Water Resources Research
  President's Council on Recreation and Natural Beauty
  National Council on Marine Resources and Engineering Development

2. Independent Agencies

ATOMIC ENERGY COMMISSION

NATIONAL SCIENCE FOUNDATION

TENNESSEE VALLEY AUTHORITY

WATER RESOURCES COUNCIL

APPALACHIAN REGIONAL COMMISSION

DELAWARE RIVER BASIN COMMISSION

SMITHSONIAN INSTITUTION

3. Quasigovernmental Organizations

NATIONAL ACADEMY OF SCIENCES, NATIONAL ACADEMY OF ENGINEERING, NATIONAL RESEARCH COUNCIL

Environmental Studies Board
Committee on Persistent Pesticides
Committee on Resources and Man
Committee on Agricultural Land Use and Wildlife Resources
U.S. National Committee for the International Biological Program
Agricultural Board
Committee on Solid Wastes Management
Committee on Air Pollution
Committee on Water Quality Management
Committee on Remote Sensing of the Environment
Committee Advisory to the Environmental Science Service Administration
Committee on Environmental Physiology

Committee on Water
Advisory Committee to the Federal Radiation Council
Committee on SST-Sonic Boom
Committee on Ocean Engineering
Committee on Geography
Committee on Toxicology and the Advisory Center on Toxicology
Committee on Hazardous Materials
Ad Hoc Committee on Human Factors in Environmental Change
Committee on Urban Technology and Committee on Social and Behavioral Urban Research
Committee on Hearing, Bioacoustics, and Biomechanics

4. Government Interagency Committees

FEDERAL COUNCIL ON SCIENCE AND TECHNOLOGY

Interdepartmental Committee for Atmospheric Sciences
Committee on Environmental Quality
Committee on Scientific and Technical Information
Committee on Solid Earth Sciences
Committee on Water Resources Research
Interagency Committee on Meteorological Services and Interagency Committee on Applied Meteorological Research
Federal Committee on Pest Control
Armed Forces Pest Control Board
Interagency Aircraft Noise Abatement Advisory Committee
Federal Advisory Committee on Water Data
Interagency Committee on Coordination of Sewer and Water Programs
Steering Committee: U.S.-German Cooperative Program in Natural Resources, Pollution Control, and Urban Development.

Appendix II

GEOLOGICAL DATING

Until this century the age of rocks and their contained fossils was determined in most instances solely by their position relative to a base series. The study of this base complement, the science of *stratigraphy,* had no absolute reference points, except in the Quaternary Period. Two procedures, *dendrochronology,* and observations on *varved clays,* provided these absolute dates, reaching back some 20–30,000 years BP. The first depends on the fact that many trees, especially temperate coniferous species, produce distinct annual growth rings in their wood. Moreover, the rings vary in size according to the particular growing season. The rings of long-dead trees can thus be matched where they overlap the ring pattern of younger specimens. This permits the backward extension of the dendrological time scale for wood incorporated in domestic articles or buildings to about 10,000 BP.

Varved clays are fresh-water sediments, more especially those produced in glacial lakes. During the summer the less turbid water produces fine sediments. In the spring thaw, coarse sediments carried into the lake settle in a distinct layer. Again, the alternating layers of coarse and fine sediments provide a recognizable patterning which can be matched when one alluvial deposit is compared with another.

Such absolute dating methods as these were useful in archeological studies and in Quaternary geology, but the real breakthrough in dating came with the appreciation of the significance of the rate of decay of radioactive isotopes. Calculations based on the rate of change of radium provided the first absolute (but inaccurate) estimation of the age of the earth. It was then discerned by an American chemist, William Libby, how the radioactive isotope of carbon (C-14) could be used for absolute dating of the age of organic material.

Carbon-14

Libby (1952) proposed that events in the Holocene and late Pleistocene could be given an absolute date by utilizing C-14.

This isotope is created when cosmic rays from the sun strike atoms of nitrogen in the earth's stratosphere. C-14 has a half-life of over 5000 years, but its concentration in atmospheric air is only about one part in a trillion. So, although it becomes incorporated in plant tissues by photosynthesis just as do atoms of the commonest carbon isotope C-12, its radioactivity is not easy to record on a geiger counter, and an extremely sensitive instrument is required. Because radioactive decay commences the moment the C-14 is incorporated by photosynthesis into a living plant, a comparison of the C-12/C-14 ratio in dead organic matter with that of the atmosphere will provide an absolute estimate of its age.

After Libby's ideas on C-14 dating had been confirmed, the 1950s and 1960s saw the technique extensively applied to material dated between 300 and 50,000 BP. Beyond these limits it is experimentally impossible to establish significant differences between the ratios of C-12 and C-14. Any producer and any consumer organism, each of which must directly or indirectly receive a mixture of C-12/C-14, therefore leave organic carbon remains which can be dated by this method when their ages fall between these limits.

Potassium/Argon

Other radiometric techniques have been developed to cover periods between the relatively recent interval to which C-14 dating can be applied and the extended time period of radium. For the purposes of hominid dating the most serviceable of these is potassium/argon dating.

The element potassium occurs naturally as a mixture of the isotopes K-39, K-41, and K-40. The last is radioactive and decays to form calcium-40 and argon-40. K-40, which occurs as about 0.0118 per cent of the mixture, has a half-life of 1.30×10^9 years. All organisms contain potassium, so do many rocks. The age of a fossil or rock can therefore be determined by a calculation which is based on the relative amounts of A-40 and K-40 it contains (Carr and Kulp, 1957). Igneous rocks are particularly suitable for dating by the potassium/argon method, because all the argon gas they might previously have contained has been driven off by the heating during their molten stage. Any argon detected in them therefore has to have been formed subsequent to this; its amount is a measure of their age. All absolute dates for the Pleistocene after 50,000 BP, for the Pliocene, and for the Miocene quoted in this test have been determined by the potassium/argon method.

Current revised estimates of the geological time scale during the later stages of primate evolution are given in the table below. This differs appreciably from similar tables prepared even ten years ago, more especially as regards the Pliocene-Pleistocene boundary. Potassium/argon dating is gradually providing more established dates for this time, just as radiocarbon dating has permitted a much more accurate determination of events in the late Pleistocene and early Holocene.

References

Carr, D. R., and J. L. Kulp, "Potassium-argon method of geochronometry," *Bull. Geol. Soc. Am.*, **68:** 763, 1957.

Libby, W. F., *Radiocarbon Dating*, Chicago, University of Chicago Press, 1952.

Oakley, K. P. *Frameworks for Dating Fossil Man,* Chicago: Aldine, 1964.

Scheme Showing the Approximate Currently Accepted Dating and Subdivision of the Portion of Geological Time which Covers Anthropoid Evolution

Epoch	*Time of Commencement in Millions of Years* BP	*Period*	*Era*
Holocene (*recent*)	(10–30,000 years BP)	Quaternary	
Pleistocene	4		
Pliocene	12		Cenozoic
Miocene	25		
Oligocene	35	Tertiary	
Eocene	55		
Paleocene	60		
	120	Cretaceous	Mesozoic

Appendix III

HOMINID MODELS

Throughout the account of human evolution in this text attention has been drawn to the still controversial nature of many of the theories presented. By modern scientific standards supporting material evidence is too often fragmentary, statistically significant measurements minimal, and speculation free.

In recent years, however, electronic data-processing techniques have made possible comparisons between extensive series of detailed measurements, which has greatly stimulated quantitative exercises in anthropology and paleontology. Resolution of differences of opinion has been raised from the level of authoritarian pronouncements to verifiable statements of statistical validities. These techniques made possible, for example, positive allocation of the Steinheim skull to the *Homo sapiens* grade. Armed with a radiometrically determined date of approximately 250,000 BP, it can be stated with confidence that at least one individual with cranial characteristics falling within the range of modern man was present in Europe a quarter of a million years ago. Chances are there were many more as further finds may confirm. We need to have similar statistics about these others to provide *population* data. Only when we have physical information as to population ranges and means, and cultural information as to associated remains and artifacts, can we begin to be sure that further chance finds will not completely upset our first conjectures.

Among the most speculative of these conjectures is the kind of flesh which once clothed the bare bones of fossil finds. This is still largely decided from experience, skill, and intuition. Figures III-1 and III-2 illustrate the major musculature of modern man which medical anatomists know in very great detail. From the size and position of the muscle attachment areas

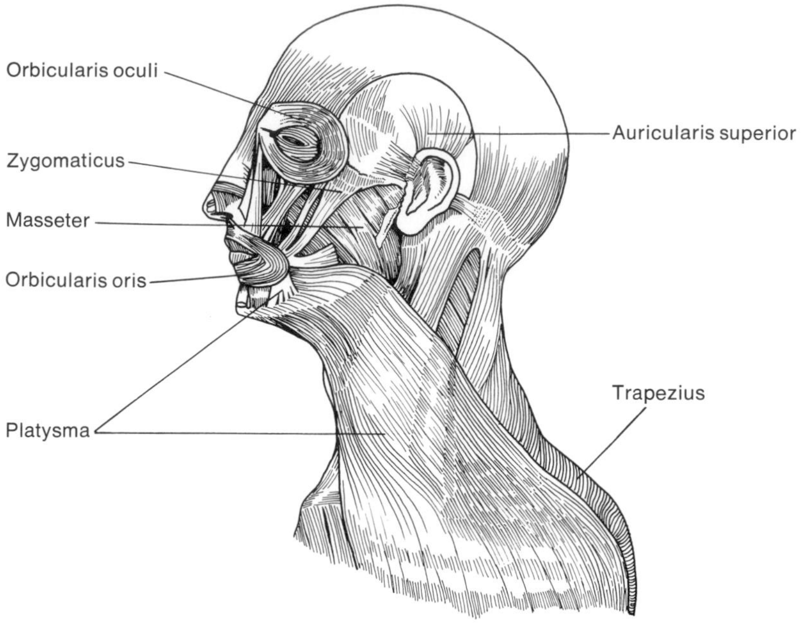

Figure III-1. *The arrangement of muscles in the contemporary human head and neck.* An intimate knowledge of this musculature system enables medical anatomists to build up a reconstruction of the system associated with particular fossil skulls. It is from such skillfully prepared reconstructions that authenticated hominid models and illustrations can be prepared. (Based on J. Buettner-Janusch, 1966.)

on the bones, they can estimate the size and position of the muscles and the relative movement capacities of the anatomical parts they controlled.

It is therefore possible for an anatomist to clothe the cast of a skull or skeleton with clay muscles and to surround them with a simulated skin. The various body parts can be related to one another on a similar basis to provide a postured form. Intelligent guesses can be made, for example, that the skin cover of all tropical hominids was heavily pigmented. Because only short kinky head hair is found in modern tropical African aborigines, African hominid models can be given kinky hair which, like the skin, was just as surely black, as the eyes would be dark. Other traits at least partially environmentally determined can also be inserted, such as wide flared nostrils and a squat nose on a tropical rain forest hominid.

Thus, although hominid models prepared even three decades ago now appear to us incredibly naive, contemporary models, many of which are featured in this text, have a firmer basis for both their scientific and their more conjectural elements. Some conjectural elements, however, we shall never be able to eliminate completely, whatever our technical advances.

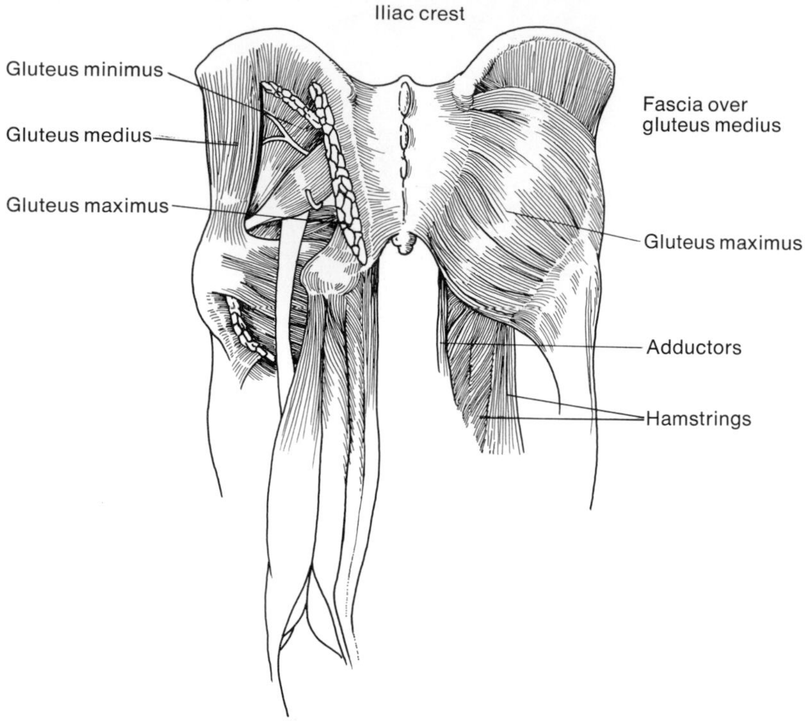

Figure III-2. *The arrangement of muscles in the contemporary human pelvic area.* Drawn from behind. The size and position of these muscles can be assessed by medical anatomists working with fossil hominid material, as in the case of the head and neck muscles illustrated in Figure III-1. This provides information not only as to morphology, but also on posture and gait. (Based on J. Buettner-Janusch, 1966.)

Author Index

(Citations in *italics* are to bibliographical references.)

Author Index

Subject Index

(Citations in **boldface** are to illustrations.)

Subject Index